Symposium on Foods:
The Chemistry and Physiology of Flavors

other Oregon State University Symposia
published by AVI

FOOD ENZYMES—1959 Symposium
edited by Schultz

LIPIDS AND THEIR OXIDATION—1961 Symposium
edited by Schultz, Day and Sinnhuber

PROTEINS AND THEIR REACTIONS—1963 Symposium
edited by Schultz and Anglemier

Symposium on Foods:
The Chemistry and Physiology of Flavors

The fourth in a series of symposia on foods held at Oregon State University

Editor **H. W. SCHULTZ, Ph.D.**

Head, Department of Food Science and Technology
Oregon State University
Corvallis, Oregon

Associate Editors **E. A. DAY, Ph.D.**

Vice President,
International Flavors and Fragrances, Inc.
Formerly Professor of Food Science
and Technology
Oregon State University
Corvallis, Oregon

L. M. LIBBEY, Ph.D.

Assistant Professor of
Food Science and Technology
Oregon State University
Corvallis, Oregon

WESTPORT, CONNECTICUT

THE AVI PUBLISHING COMPANY, INC.

1967

Printed in the United States of America

BY MACK PRINTING COMPANY, EASTON, PENNSYLVANIA

Contributors to this Volume

J. E. AMOORE, Western Utilization Research and Development Division, U.S. Dept. of Agr., Albany, California

R. G. BUTTERY, Western Utilization Research and Development Division, U.S. Dept. of Agr., Albany, California

L. D. CALVIN, Oregon State University, Corvallis, Oregon

J. F. CARSON, Western Utilization Research and Development Division, U.S. Dept. of Agr., Albany, California

J. R. COFFMAN, General Mills, Inc., Minneapolis, Minnesota

E. A. DAY, Oregon State University, Corvallis, Oregon

K. B. DÖVING, Karolinska Institutet, Stockholm, Sweden

ANDREW DRAVNIEKS, Illinois Institute of Technology, Chicago, Illinois

A. I. FARBMAN, Northwestern University, Chicago, Illinois

D. A. FORSS, Commonwealth Scientific and Industrial Research Organization, Highett, Australia

MAURIZIO GIANTURCO, Tenco Division of the Coca-Cola Company, Linden, New Jersey

J. E. HODGE, Northern Utilization Research and Development Division, U.S. Dept. of Agr., Peoria, Illinois

IRWIN HORNSTEIN, Market Quality Research Division, U.S. Dept. of Agr., Beltsville, Maryland

W. G. JENNINGS, University of California, Davis, California

N. R. JONES, Torry Research Station, Aberdeen, Scotland

AKIRA KUNINAKA, Yamasa Shoyu Company, Ltd., Choshi, Japan

R. C. LINDSAY, Oregon State University, Corvallis, Oregon

R. W. MONCRIEFF, The Gables, Chichester, England

O. W. PARKS, Eastern Utilization Research and Development Division, U.S. Dept. of Agr., Washington, D.C.

E. L. PIPPEN, Western Utilization Research and Development Division, U.S. Dept. of Agr., Albany, California

R. SELF, Low Temperature Research Station, Cambridge, England

R. M. SILVERSTEIN, Stanford Research Institute, Menlo Park, California

ROY TERANISHI, Western Utilization Research and Development Division, U.S. Dept. of Agr., Albany, California

A. D. WEBB, University of California, Davis, California

Preface

This is the fourth since 1959 in a series which presents the scientific papers given at the *Symposia on Foods* in the Department of Food Science and Technology at Oregon State University. It is a comprehensive summary and source of reference material on the chemistry and physiology of flavor prepared by twenty-four of the outstanding scientists in the field today. Further, it provides calculated viewpoints regarding the opportunities for future research to remove some deficiencies of our knowledge of flavor.

In the true tradition of a symposium as a forum to present, defend, and discuss scientific data as well as their interpretation and significance, this Symposium on Flavor was lively from the delightful stage-setting, thought-inspiring introduction by R. W. Moncrieff on September 8, 1965, through the concluding summarizing panel discussion three days later. In the tradition of the *Symposia on Foods* initiated in 1959 (Enzymes in Foods) and continued in 1961 (Lipids and Their Oxidation), and in 1963 (Proteins and Their Reactions), there was an effort to build a bridge of helpful communication between those working in one scientific disciplinary area of the broad subject field and those working in another disciplinary area. Specifically, the Symposium brought together the chemists who use objective methods to probe the chemistry of the synthesis and deterioration of flavors, with the scientists and statisticians concerned with the subjective response of a person to a flavor, and lastly with other scientists delving into the microstructure and physiology of the chemical senses.

The character and significance of any symposium is dependent upon the people who participate in it. In this regard the Symposium on Flavor was indeed excellent and deepest gratitude is extended to all who presented papers which are now chapters of this book. We also thank the 250 participants who contributed through their presence and discussion.

Selecting speakers and making and carrying out arrangements for the Symposium were very capably handled by the Department staff under the fine leadership of E. A. Day. Thanks are extended to all concerned, especially to Mrs. Bruce Wyatt for handling many details so well.

We wish to give special recognition with thanks to the Division of

Environmental Engineering and Food Protection, Bureau of State Services, U. S. Public Health Service, for Grant No. EF-00766-01 to cover the direct costs of the Symposium and most of the publication costs. The publisher has foregone the usual profit for a book of this nature and thus has our thanks and the gratitude of those who purchase the book at a much reduced cost and thereby participate in the benefits of the Symposium.

H. W. SCHULTZ
Corvallis, Oregon

December 1966

Contents

Section V.   Origin of Flavor in Foods

Introduction

CHAPTER 1

R. W. Moncrieff | Introduction to the Symposium

INTRODUCTION

I think you would like me to begin by thanking our hosts at Oregon State University for inviting us all to this symposium on foods and for affording those of us who have not previously been to this lovely state an opportunity to see its natural beauties. We shall be given a great deal of new information on flavor by the group of specialists which the Symposium Committee has assembled, and we should have a very happy and rewarding three days in front of us. Additionally, we have the opportunity to live in the University buildings and to enjoy its pleasant and academic atmosphere. For these amenities we are grateful to our hosts.

One thing that should be said at once is that the success of a symposium, of almost any scientific congress, depends not only on the speakers, but very largely on all the participants. If the members contribute forthright questions and engage in vigorous discussion, then that sets the seal on any symposium. We shall no doubt be given reports of experiments that have been carried out and of the findings of the experiments; we shall hear what deductions and inferences are drawn from the experimental data; what new hypotheses are postulated; how the findings may lend support to or cast doubt on existing theories; and perhaps new theories may be put forward. A main function of a symposium such as this is to look carefully at all that is reported and to refine it by critical and constructive discussion. It should be remembered that the viewpoints of the industrialist, the farmer, and the grower may be appreciably different from that of the laboratory scientist; the union of thought of academic scientist, applied scientist, and commercial executives and managers should insure that the greatest benefit is drawn from new knowledge. Exchange of ideas and debate constitute the heart of a symposium.

CONFERENCES AS MILESTONES

The scientific conference is earning widespread recognition as a more and more important part of scientific progress. At first, the time and journey money spent on attending conferences were looked at questioningly. Was anything useful or valuable likely to accrue from this expenditure? It was recognized that many of the scientific papers that would be contributed by university research workers would not mean very much to many of those attending. This difficulty has been mitigated by the effort that is now made by research workers to keep their presentations simple. There are plenty of journals of the learned societies where highly technical and erudite papers can be published; the scientific conference is one place where specialized scientific terminology should be avoided and where the effort should be made to have papers that are understandable not only by specialists, but by all men and women who have had a scientific training. This simplification has made discussion easier and has greatly helped to popularize the scientific conference. Many people consider that the discussions, both those that take place in the conference hall and those that occur informally among participants in the off periods, constitute the single item that has most value in a conference. Today, it is no exaggeration to say that the advance of such a study as olfaction can be measured using conferences as milestones. The 1953 New York Basic Odor Correlation Conference set a new standard in such conferences. Not only was it the first which treated so thoroughly the subject of olfaction, but it purposefully set out to examine the scope of our knowledge of the subject and of the most obvious gaps in it with the intention of encouraging workers to try to fill them in a little.

The next landmark was the 1962 Stockholm Conference, the so-called First International Symposium on Olfaction and Taste, which attracted people from all over the world and at which many fine papers were read. There was no attempt made to survey the field as a whole, nor to take a good look at the biggest gaps in our knowledge and to see if much could be done about them. The very existence of the Stockholm Conference was itself a striking tribute to the value of conferences; it was held in the new WennerGren Center which in 1962 had only recently been completed and which had been built specifically to provide a forum where scientists from all over the world could gather to exchange knowledge and ideas.

Although the Stockholm Conference lacked cohesion, it was a landmark in the study of olfaction and taste. Perhaps we may hope that the present symposium, the fourth at Corvallis but the first that deals specifically with flavor, may become another landmark in the advance of our science. To that end we must take account not only of what is new, but examine the trends and try to survey the territory in which advances will be made in the next few years.

FLAVOR A COMPLEX SENSATION

The study of flavor is one of those subjects in which science has never caught up with everyday experience. Mainly, flavor is composed of taste and odor. Hold the nose or even hold the breath, and flavor vanishes in a second; breathe again and it reappears at once. Of the other qualities that enter into it, texture is probably the most important: smoothness or roughness, particle size, solubility, even a glutinous quality can modify flavor. Less usual modifiers of flavor are the hotness of spices such as ginger, the coolness of menthol. Then there are the metallic, alkaline, and meaty tastes: if we are to accept the orthodox view that there are only four true tastes, sweet, bitter, sour, and salt, then the metallic and alkaline tastes must presumably be accepted as modalities of the common chemical sense. So far as concerns the alkaline taste, Liljestrand and Zotterman (1956) have reported that under the conditions of their experiments alkali had a pronounced stimulating effect on the taste receptors and that it could even induce a sweet taste. The metallic taste seems not to have been well defined, although the lowest concentrations of metal ions that will stimulate it are known reasonably well. The metallic taste is of considerable importance, and more study is needed to fill in our knowledge of it. One way in which the problem could be approached would be to ascertain the proportion of taste-buds which are known to respond to the different "true" tastes that would also respond to metallic taste stimuli. Some early information could be obtained by investigating the responses of papillae (which contain many taste-buds) to the metallic taste and as a follow-up the similar behavior of individual taste-buds themselves.

For the practical purposes the main contributors to flavor are the tens of thousands of odors, and the sweet, sour, salt, and bitter tastes, with the metallic taste cropping up too frequently to be disregarded.

THE FLAVOR STIMULUS

A short review of the main features of the stimulation of the sensation of flavor may be useful as a background against which to view the more recent discoveries that are going to be described to us.

Taste

Those materials that are sapid are all water-soluble. Water-solubility is the first requirement. There is a fair degree of correspondence between the kind of taste that a substance has and its chemical constitution. Practically all acid substances are sour; common salt and similar salts taste salty, although as the constituent atoms get bigger and heavier, a bitter taste develops. Thus potassium bromide is both salty and bitter while the still heavier potassium iodide has a dominating bitter taste. Sweetness is a characteristic of the sugars and is apparently due to their possession of several hydroxyl groups and similarly glycerin is sweet; but lead acetate (sugar of lead) and the salts of beryllium (glucinum) have long been recognized as sweet substances, while saccharin and the cyclamates (Sucaryl sodium and Sucaryl calcium) provide striking evidence that there is no general relation between chemical structure and sweetness. So it is, too, with bitterness; heavy salts, picric acid, and the alkaloids show clearly enough that bitterness is not easily tied to any characteristic structural molecular features. Nevertheless the two most primitive tastes, salt and sour do show a much better correlation with structure than do the later developing sweet and bitter tastes. Furthermore, the metallic taste can be correlated with chemical constitution as well as any of them. The relation of constitution to taste has been discussed in more detail elsewhere (Moncrieff 1951) and the special problems of the metallic taste have been reviewed separately (Moncrieff 1964).

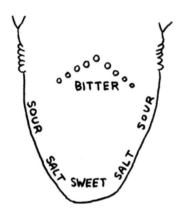

FIG. 1. THOSE AREAS OF THE TONGUE THAT ARE
ESPECIALLY SENSITIVE TO THE FOUR TASTES

The sensitive surfaces on the tongue are the taste-buds which are grouped in papillae. Most papillae appear to be sensitive to more tastes than one, but there is undoubtedly a regional distribution of the four main kinds of taste receptors; the sweet taste is most easily sensed at the tip of the tongue, the bitter at the back, the sour at the edges, and the salt taste both on the tip and at the edges (Fig. 1). When a sapid substance, or its solution, comes in contact with the sensitive area of the tongue, electric pulses pass up various nerves to the cortex of the brain and there stimulate the sensation of taste. The most accessible of these nerves is the *chorda tympani* and it is usually in this that recordings are made of the changes in electric potential in the nerve fiber consequent on the application of some sapid substance to the tongue. Whereas the number of olfactory receptor cells in a mammal is counted in millions, the gustatory cells number only thousands.

Olfaction

The possession of odor depends on volatility; only those substances which are constantly throwing off molecules can possibly be odorous. The thrown-off molecules mingle with the air and are inspired up the nose along with it. At the top and back of the nose there is a patch of a few square centimeters of yellowish skin and this is the sensitive area for olfaction; a small proportion of the inspired air ordinarily passes over this area and if we take a sniff, this proportion is considerably increased. As the odorous air passes over the sensitive area, the odorant molecules are adsorbed by it (Moncrieff 1954, 1955, 1956); all the molecules of the oxygen, nitrogen, argon, and so on in the air and the molecules of the odorant are in a rapid state of motion, traveling at room temperature at a speed approaching that of sound and all are hitting the olfactory sensitive surface. Whereas those of the light gases, oxygen and nitrogen, bounce off the surface almost instantaneously, the heavier molecules of the odorous materials are held for a fraction of a second by the surface and as they are caught and held they give up a little energy. Then perhaps a hundredth of a second later they tear themselves away from the surface and rejoin the main airstream, so depriving the surfaces of energy. The energy changes to which the olfactory epithelium is so subjected stimulate the olfactory cell so that electric pulses pass down the exit nerve, the axon into the olfactory bulb, the frontal extension of the brain. Probably about one hundred million separate nerve fibers pass into the bulb; they are incredibly fine only about 0.1 to 0.2 μ in diameter, smaller than the wavelength of visible light and consequently impossible to see clearly in the optical microscope; they associate into bundles of perhaps 100, but even in the bundles the fibers preserve their autonomy, although there may be some interaction between them. In the olfactory bulb they enter globular structures known as glomeruli where they are condensed into the much smaller number of a few thousand exit fibers because some 25,000 olfactory fibers end in each glomerulus. Then via the mitral cells the pulses pass to the cortex of the brain and stimulate the sense of smell on their arrival there.

Flavor

The synchronous sensation of taste and odor leads to the perception of flavor, and this may be modified by the simultaneous perception of tactile properties in the mouth. In principle, the processes that lead up to flavor perception are simple: the inspiration of molecules of odorous material along with the air, their adsorption on the sensitive olfactory epithelium, the transfer of energy from the odorant molecules to the olfactory cell and nerve, the passage of the electric pulses to the cortex of the brain after integration in the bulb, and the somewhat similar chain of events, but from solution of the sapid substance in water (the saliva) instead of in air that leads to the sensation of taste. Looked at broadly, one can follow the processes with some understanding and say that they are fairly simple.

OLFACTORY PREFERENCES

In one respect, the simplicity of flavor sensation is very evident indeed and that is in the response. Ask a person "Do you like this fruit juice?" "Do you like this meat better than that?" or a dozen other similar questions and the reply will nearly always be instant and sure. The certainty will be just as great if a child answers as if a grown person, even one with special experiences in flavors. Irrespective of how many millions of olfactory cells and thousands of taste-buds and tens of thousands of nerve fibers have been at work to send many thousands of messages to the brain, that wonderful sorting office copes effortlessly with them all and gives the immediate answer "Yes, I like this raspberry flavor" or "This fruit juice is better than that" with complete confidence and superb detachment. Recognition of familiar flavors is immediate and the liking or disliking of them is quite definite and unmistakable. Our anatomical equipment is vastly complex but its over-riding task is to keep us in harmony with our environment. The human brain is the most complex instrument that we know; it has the ability to take almost involuntarily on our part, information from a thousand or a million receptors or feelers, to integrate it all and to come out instantaneously with the report "I like" or "I dislike" or "I prefer." The apparatus is complex, but its conclusions are fast and sure.

Olfactory preferences, and in a large measure these constitute flavor preferences, are sharp and well-defined, but they change quite remarkably as we go through life. The child's preferences are very different from those of the grown person. Added to this, there is the well-known greater liking of children for sweet confections. This preference has its origin in the wider distribution of their taste-buds as was observed by Richter and Campbell (1940); it is responsible for the lower threshold concentration of sugar (0.68 per cent) in children compared with that (1.23 per cent) for adults. No such anatomical advantage on the part of children in respect of the olfactory receptors has been recorded, but

TABLE 1

SOME OF THE ODORANTS USED WITH A NOTE OF THEIR RANKINGS

Odorant	Type of Odor	Average Rank Assigned by The Whole Group of Subjects
Red rose flower, Ena Harkness	Deep rose	1
Heliotrope flower	Cherry pie	15
Rose attar	Powerful rose, but not so fresh as the flower	29
Isoeugenol	Spicy, hint of cloves	43
Amyl acetate	Pear drops	57
Patchouli resin	Bland Eastern odor	71
Benzene hexachloride	Earthy	85
Undecalactone	Nutty, hint of peach	99
Civet 5% in alcohol	Sweet, slightly fecal	113
Ethyl mercaptan 0.5% in water	Foul, alliaceous	127

there are nevertheless well-defined preferences and these probably have their origin in anatomical differences.

In some work which has been carried out at Chichester, based on the arrangement of a number of odorous materials in order of preference, it has been found that children are much less appreciative of flower odors than are adults, that they rate fruity odors much higher than adults do, and that they have a greater dislike for oily smells. A wide range of odorant materials ranging from very pleasant to very unpleasant was used; a few typical members together with the mean placings in order of preference by a group of people which included children and adults is shown in Table 1; this simply indicates the range of odorant materials that was used.

TABLE 2

OLFACTORY REACTIONS TO FLOWER ODORS

| Flower | Average Ranking Out of 132 Odors of the Flower Perfumes By | |
	Whole Group of People	Children
Red rose, Ena Harkness	1	11
Sweet peas	3	10
Rose, New Dawn	4	12
Rose, Emily Gray	5	9
Stock, double 10-week	6	24
Honeysuckle	7	46
Wild rose	8	18
Meadowsweet	12	44
Heliotrope	15	48

TABLE 3

OLFACTORY REACTIONS TO FRUIT ODORS

Fruit or Essence	Average Ranking Out of 132 Odors of the Fruit Odors By	
	Whole Group	Children
Strawberries, fresh	2	1
Raspberry essence	9	2
Strawberry essence	14	3
Banana essence	17	4
Lemon essence	16	7
Amyl acetate	57	29
Allyl caproate	74	34

The much poorer appreciation by the children of flower perfumes is shown in Table 2. Their much greater appreciation of fruit odors is shown in Table 3. The high rating of the raspberry fruit essence was so remarkable that inquiry was made as to its nature of the manufacturers who told us that it was 99 per cent natural material.

In a related series of experiments, ten diverse odorous materials were arranged in order of preference by some 500–600 people. The way in which the liking for the fruity smell of a good strawberry essence changes with age was so determined and can be seen in Fig. 2. The liking for the fruity strawberry odor seems to reach a peak at age 10 or 11 years and thereafter to fall, except that there is a standstill at the time of adolescence.

Other odors were found which varied considerably in the liking that people of different ages, and sometimes of the two sexes, had for them.

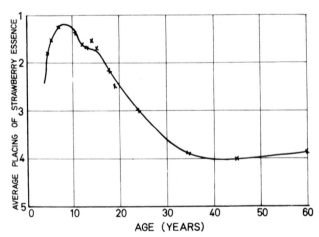

FIG. 2. VARIATION IN PREFERENCE OF STRAWBERRY ODOR WITH AGE OF SUBJECT

But such odors were relatively few in number and most often there was a reasonable uniformity of reaction to them. This uniformity is illustrated for two age groups in Table 4.

TABLE 4

LIKENESS OF SMELL PREFERENCES BY THE MIDDLE AND HIGH AGE GROUPS

	Average Ranking By	
Odorant	15–25 Years Group	Over 25 Years Group
Sweetpeas, flower	3	5
Stock, double 10-week flower	6	7
Sweet orange oil	16	13
Catmint (Nepeta) fresh leaves	21	28
Flowering currant (Ribes) fresh leaves	32	33
Amyl cinnamic aldehyde	79	83
Skatole	98	120

Very often, the degree of liking of an odor or flavor is common to all ages and both sexes, but sometimes, although less often, there are big differences in response. But whatever the response, it comes with facility and certainty; hesitation is almost unknown and the responses are as simple as they possibly could be.

INSTRUMENTAL DETECTION OF ODORS

One feature of the perception of flavor is that the primary stimulus for olfaction, a main part of flavor and very much the main discriminatory part, is itself a simple and well understood process, that of adsorption. When once it was appreciated (Moncrieff 1955) that this was so, the possibility of instrumental detection of odors presented itself. The thermistor proved to be a timely and useful tool for this purpose, and the glass-enclosed type with a room temperature resistance of about 2000 ohms was used. When the tip of such a thermistor was coated with a film, with almost any kind of film, but suitably with a protein or a cellulose ester film, and exposed to air which contained an odorous material, then the odorous material was adsorbed on to the film to which it gave up energy in the form of heat of adsorption, so that the film, and accordingly the thermistor, warmed up slightly and so that the electrical resistance of the thermistor fell by about 60 ohms for each 1°C. rise in temperature.

In practice the arrangement shown in Fig. 3 was used. Air was drawn over the tips of two thermistors of which only one was film-coated. The two thermistors, one film-coated and one uncoated, constituted two arms

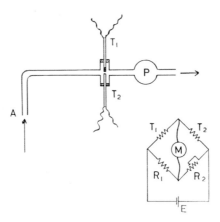

FIG. 3.   ONE FORM OF THE MECHANICAL NOSE

Air is drawn in at A, by the pump P, and it passes around the functional tips of the two thermistors T_1, T_2, of which only T_1 is film-coated to adsorb odorant material.   The function of T_2 is to balance out temperature variations in the air itself.   The leads from T_1 and T_2 are taken to a Wheatstone bridge in which R_1 is a fixed resistor of 2000 ohms, and R_2 a variable resistance of about the same value; its use enables the bridge to be balanced, the zero to be set on the microammeter, M.   The bridge is energized by a 4.5 volt dry battery, E.   In operation, when the air drawn in at A is odorized, there is a needle deflection on the meter, M.

of a Wheatstone bridge; if inodorous air was drawn over them any temperature changes due to the air were balanced out because both thermistors are heated or cooled equally, but if the air that was drawn over them contained an odorant then that was adsorbed on the thermistor that was film-coated, but not on the uncoated thermistor; the former was warmed but not the latter, the bridge was unbalanced and the reading on the galvanometer G, which in practice is suitably a moving-coil microammeter, was a measure of the energy given up by the odorant as it was adsorbed on the film.   The meter deflection is specifically produced by the presence of an odorant material.   If different kinds of film are used, it is found that while all are slightly sensitive to all odorants, some are much more sensitive to certain kinds of odorants.   Here we have a kind of specificity that is similar to what we believe is responsible in our own olfactory equipment for discrimination between one smell and another.   An instrument similar to this just described, but incorporating some refinements of which the chief is humidity control, has been described elsewhere (Moncrieff 1961).   It is convenient to use about six different films, although there is no theoretical reason why more

TABLE 5

METER DEFLECTIONS (MICROAMPERES) DUE TO DRAWING ODORIZED AIR AT 1 LITER/MIN OVER
TWO THERMISTORS (ONE FILM-COATED, ONE UNCOATED)

Odorant	PVC[1] Film	Peanut Protein Film
Empty tube	0	0
Chloroform	82	8
Acetone	48	5
Carbon disulfide	32	8
Ammonium sulfide	2	40
Ammonia (25% wt./wt.)	2	62
Triethylamine	12	13

[1] Polyvinyl chloride.

should not be used, and if six are used a good deal of olfactory discrimination is possible. Some measurements that were made with just two kinds of film: PVC (polyvinyl chloride) and peanut protein are shown in Table 5. The figures in Table 5 illustrate the potentiality of odor discrimination by using a number of different kinds of films.

NEW TOOLS BRING NEW KNOWLEDGE

Some remarkable work has come within the last few years from the chemists of Firmenich et Cie disclosing the chemical entities that make up the flavor of the strawberry and raspberry. The general scheme, first described for raspberries, has been to start with half a ton of fresh fruit, to crush it into a purée and to subject the purée to flash evaporation so that the volatile constituents are carried over in an aqueous distillate, and then to extract and concentrate the aromatic principles that are in the distillate. Great care is taken at every stage to avoid air oxidation or metallic contamination. Carbonyl compounds are isolated as 2,4-dinitrophenylhydrazones. These are separated by chromatography and also the carbonyl compounds are re-formed and identified spectrographically. The alcohol constituents are similarly made into derivatives of dinitrobenzoyl chloride and the derivatives are dissolved and examined chromatographically. So that the flavor constituents from half a ton of fruit are subjected to the refined and delicate analysis made possible by the new tools of chromatography and spectrography. Not surprisingly, many compounds not hitherto known to contribute to the flavor of these fruits are found.

Strawberry Flavor.—A very similar investigation of the aromatic principles of fresh strawberries has been contributed by Winter and Willhalm (1964). These workers identified 35 compounds among the aldehyde, ketone, and ester groups and of these about one-half had not previously been known to be present in the strawberry. The main com-

TABLE 6

VOLATILE FLAVOR CONSTITUENTS OF THE CRUSHED STRAWBERRY (P.P.M.)

More Than 1	0.1–1	0.01–0.1	Less Than 0.01 (Traces Only)
Hexene-2-al (6.35)	Hexanal	Diacetyl	Acrolein
	Hexene-2-ol *trans*	Pentene-2-al	Crotonaldehyde
Acetone (3.0)	Hexanol	*cis* Hexene-3-al	Propanal
Acetaldehyde (1.8)	Methyl butyrate	Heptanone-2	Pentanone-2
	Ethyl butyrate	Methanol	Propyl acetate
Ethanol (1.51)	Methyl caprote	Butanol	
	Ethyl caproate	Pentene-1-ol-3	
	Hexyl acetate	Heptanol-2	
		Ethyl acetate	
		Ethyl propionate	
		Butyl acetate	
		Isopropyl butyrate	
		Ethyl crotonate	
		Heptanone	
		Hexene-2-yl acetate	
		Hexene-2-yl butyrate	
		Hexyl butyrate	
		Isoamyl acetate	

ponents that they identified are shown in Table 6. These volatile constituents obviously constitute a very complex mixture. One has nowadays
to regard the flavor constituents of a fruit as a dynamic system, continuously growing, always synthesizing and esterifying, some large molecules being built up and others simultaneously being degraded The
refined and sensitive analytical methods that are now available will give
such accuracy and detail that we can look for today's strawberries to give
rather different flavor compositions from yesterday's, perhaps even for one
berry to yield a different analysis from another. Those days when we
could think of a fruit flavor as being 2% of one ester, 15% of another and
so on are gone; the flavor changes from day to day, from minute to minute,
and from berry to berry. Perhaps the changes themselves, the esterification and hydrolytic processes, the ring closures and openings and the
oxidation and reduction processes go on in the live fruit even while it is
being crushed in the mouth and perhaps these processes with their
liberation or absorption of energy and with the transient appearance of
a host of unstable intermediates make up the strawberry flavor that we
know. Bite two berries one after another and there will most likely be
a difference in flavor (just as there is in the analysis), due to differences
in ripeness, in size, and to location favorable or otherwise which the berry
occupied on the plant. How easily chemical changes take place is
exemplified by Winter and Willhalm's statement that hexene-2-al, the main
carbonyl constituent of crushed strawberry does not even exist in the
undamaged fruit and neither does diacetyl. Modern analytical methods

are catching up with nature's complexity and are showing that the composition of all living material is constantly changing The delightful fruity smells are the manifestation of a host of complex chemical changes. The more and more sensitive do the analytical techniques become, the more and more complex will the natural flavor systems be found to be. The chemists of Firmenich in 1964 carried out a superb chemical analysis and identified 35 chemical entities and noticed a few more that they could not positively identify. In another 10 or 15 years, they or their successors will double the number and so it will go on. Everything in the animal and vegetable kingdoms grows and changes; if it did not, there would be no such thing as flavor, nor indeed as consciousness. In the future we must look on flavors as dynamic and ever-changing. The true strawberry flavor can live only in the strawberry; he who extracts it from the fruit sees it quickly deteriorate and change; he who attempts to compound it from synthetic materials fails abysmally. Flavor and essence manufacturers do their best and do very well indeed; their best creations are always those that they have extracted from the fruit, and often they hold their flavor remarkably well—indeed surprisingly well. The knowledge and experience that they have accumulated especially in the last 20 years enable them to work wonders·

Bartlett Pears.—The specific flavor character of Bartlett pears appears to be due, as has been shown by Heinz *et al.* (1964), to esters of 2,4-decadienoic acid; aroma intensity of pear essences agrees well with the intensities of their absorptions at 2630–2670 Å. This affords another illustration of the fineness of analysis and of the possibilities of defining the chemical source and even flavor nuances by using the new analytical tools.

NATURAL COMPLEXITY

We can see that flavor is no simple study. The responses of the brain to flavor are simple and well-defined but the natural apparatus and processes responsible for them are complex.

This is in line with our general experience: only superficially is science simple. A perfect example is afforded by Boyle's Law for gases which states that at constant temperature:

$$pv = k$$

Nothing could be simpler, but the simplicity is misleading, because further study shows that the law is only approximate and that divergencies are caused by the volume of the molecules themselves and by the forces of attraction, sometimes of considerable magnitude, which operate between them.

The optimistic belief that underlying all there is a simple organization, reaches its peak in Bondi and Gold's perfect cosmological principle described by Bondi (1960) in his book. This principle avers that apart from local irregularities the universe presents the same aspect from any place at any time and that if sufficiently large samples of the universe are considered they will be similar and that in fact the universe is homogeneous. But how large must these samples be? If they are to be nearly as large as the universe, the principle ceases to have much meaning. Hoyle has pointed out that the fact that the cosmological principle does not apply in detail must gravely weaken confidence in its validity. To the professional mathematician the cosmological principle is a useful simplification device, but to the layman it seems to require a simplicity of universal structure for which there is no supporting evidence.

Abstract thought provides little support for the idea that nature is simple. Samuel Alexander (1922, 1939) who held the chair of philosophy at Manchester in the 'twenties subscribed to a system of Natural Piety which included a reverent acceptance of many of the characteristics of nature that were beyond explanation by us. Alexander went further than we might like to go with him today, but his main theme that nature is so very complex that we cannot hope to understand very much of it, is easy to accept. Every discovery that is made, every scientific advance, exposes in its turn new problems. There can be no end to research and investigation.

THE COMPLEXITY OF FLAVOR PERCEPTION

And so it is with flavor. There is very little that is simple about flavor. The receptors for both odor and taste which looked fairly simple when we had only the optical microscope to examine them with are seen to be infinitely complex under the greater power of the electron microscope. The beautiful electron micrographs that de Lorenzo (1957, 1958, 1960) has published of the olfactory epithelium and the taste-buds of mammals show that the further we can see in terms of magnification of the very small, the more complex is the structure seen to be. The better the tools, the more detail is revealed. Any hope that the new tools, notably the electron microscope, would reveal simple structural units from which the sensitive surfaces are built up has been dispelled.

There is more detail available in electron micrographs than can be assigned functions. It has too, always to be remembered that the histologist's thin slice of tissue, fixed in formaldehyde and stained with silver or osmium, is very different indeed from the original fresh tissue; it has shrunk and probably shrunk unevenly and some of the finer anatomical details, notably the olfactory cilia, may have been completely lost. The changes that take place during the preparation of specimens for the electron microscope are even greater and all that is left for examination is a skeleton. It may be that the time has come when we can say that the enormously high magnification of such preparations of tissue which are inevitably damaged, might come to a stop, and that more effort should be devoted to the preparation of tissue photo-micrographs or better still, micro-cine films of the olfactory and gustatory equipment in the living animal. Magnification would be much less, detail which ordinarily depends on silver staining would be mostly lost, but the yield of information from the living and functioning cells might be much greater. Le Gros Clark (1957) has referred very appreciatively to some remarkable motion pictures of tissue culture preparations of the olfactory epithelium from a human fetus which have been made by Dr. C. M. Pomerat of the University of Texas. This film, together with his own observations with the optical microscope, suggested to Clark that the olfactory hairs are normally splayed out like a daisy in full flower, but when stimulated by odorous material become partly bunched together like the petals of a half-opened bud. In one sense, the use of the fetus that has never inspired air might be bettered; air inspiration is essential for olfaction, but nevertheless the making of the film seems to have been a considerable achievement. This may be one gap in our science that can and should be filled in a little.

The nervous pathways, the nerve fibers that run from the sensitive cells to the brain are no less complex; anatomically the chemical senses are rich in detail, so rich that at present it passes our understanding. Le Gros Clark (1956, 1957) has shown that in the rabbit there are some fifty million olfactory receptors on either side and that apparently each is connected by an independent axon to the olfactory bulb, so that on the order of fifty million separate nerve fibers must pass up from each side of the nose to reach the olfactory bulb, the forward extension of the cerebral hemisphere. Some 25,000 of the olfactory fibers end in each glomerulus which is no more than 0.2 mm. in diameter and here they come into contact with the dendrites of the large mitral cells of the bulb. The mitral cells in their turn give rise to fibers which form the olfactory tract and relay impulses to the cortex. Le Gros Clark, in his survey, concludes by remarking that the sense of smell is still only little understood in anatomical and physiological terms and "this only serves to emphasize how incredibly complex is any problem whose basis is neurological."

OLFACTORY DISCRIMINATION

Somewhere in our anatomical equipment there is built a device that sorts out thousands of different kinds of odors and enables us to distinguish one flavor from another, and to detect even a slight off-flavor. Those who drink cider may be familiar with the fleeting whiff of butanol vapor when a bottle of one variety is opened; those who drink gin emphatically prefer one brand over another although the difference between them seems to be no more than a slight difference in odor. The causes of the difference in response are still undecided. When Adrian (1963) opened the 1962 Stockholm Conference on taste and smell, he discussed the problem of olfactory discrimination; his own work had shown that there were some differences in those areas of the sensitive epithelium that were affected by different kinds of odorants, e.g., fruity and oily, and also that there were some temporal differences and that these differences might enable odors to be sorted out into about five classes. His work (1955) had shown too that some of the mitral cells had a definite specificity of response, one cell requiring a much higher concentration of a certain chemical than another which reacts to a lower concentration and that the particular chemical to which a cell was specially sensitive was different for one cell from another. He suggested that, similarly, the receptor cells might have specific sensitivity to certain chemicals and that there might be 50 different kinds of these. Having said this, Adrian then said that he would stop guessing and let those who had done the work tell us the facts. As it transpired, nobody had very much to add. Le Gros Clark had earlier suggested a number of 500 different kinds of receptor cells, i.e. sensitive to different kinds of smells, but there is no concrete evidence for this figure; it is simply the instinctive feeling of a man immersed in his subject of what is necessary to account for the undoubted fine analytical discriminatory competence of the nose.

Furthermore, why does nature provide a hundred million separate receptors and nerve axons and then group them into lots of 25,000 or so? Why not simply have a few thousand receptors? Such a number, one would think, would be adequate to afford discrimination between different odors. This is a mystery that may take some time to understand.

MANY DISCIPLINES

It does not take long for the scientist who elects to work on flavor to find that he must widen his interests and learn something about disciplines other than his own. Anatomy, physiology, psychology, chemistry, physics, histology, cytology, entomology, botany, and zoology are some of the sciences with which some familiarity must be acquired. Which are most useful? It is hard to say. Another subject that uses many disciplines is that of forestry: when an inquiry was sent to 234 graduates of a School of Forestry, asking them to check if a good knowledge of the various branches of their studies had proved useful in their professional tasks, 110 replies were received and the number of acknowledgments to the usefulness of the different sciences was as follows: botany 84, mathematics 84, entomology 72, geology 62, soils 60, physics 55, zoology 20, bacteriology 7, and chemistry 2. The investigation was carried out by Mason (1944) at Oregon State College as a study in education and guidance. Perhaps today with a greater range and more widespread use of insecticides and with the understanding of some insect sex lures, the chemist might do rather better. But it is at least as true of flavor as of forestry that many disciplines are necessary for its study.

THE PROBLEM OF CONSCIOUS PERCEPTION

One problem that still completely defeats us is why the arrival of messages in the form of electric pulses at the cortex of the brain should evoke consciousness. The final act, the conversion of the integrated electrical messages into a sensation, is still mysterious. Whether the messages relate to olfaction and taste, to flavor, to hearing, vision or touch, this final act is still a mystery—an act going on throughout man's conscious life, in fact making his consciousness and yet, so far an act that is incomprehensible to man. A century ago Thomas Huxley in the terminology of his time said to his listeners, "The thoughts to which I am now giving utterance and your thoughts regarding these are the expression of molecular changes in that matter of life which is the source of our other vital phenomena." As Sherrington (1940) has more recently put it, "The concomitance in time and place between 'the molecular changes' and 'the thoughts' is still all we have correlating the two. Regarded as a paradox it has become more intriguing; regarded as a gap in knowledge more urgent."

A century ago the gap lay between molecules and thoughts, now it lies between electric pulses and thoughts, a century hence it will lie between something else and thoughts; the terminology will be different, but the gap will be the same. At one side of the gap there may be ecstasy. Peaches and pears may bring it to some; a rainbow to others. The joy is the same. As one of our Lakeland poets put it, a long time ago:

> My heart leaps up when I behold
> A rainbow in the sky:
> So was it when my life began;
> So is it now I am a man;
> So be it when I shall grow old,
> Or let me die!
> The Child is father of the Man;
> And I could wish my days to be
> Bound each to each by natural piety.

DISCUSSION

J. R. Coffman.—If you draw air through the artificial nose and this air is laden with a fatty material, will a lipoprotein give you a greater response than a nonlipoprotein on the thermistor coated with a protein and vice versa for other types of aromas?

R. W. Moncrieff.—The specific point you raise as to whether a lipoprotein and another kind of protein would behave differently, I cannot answer from actual experimental findings. I have no doubt from the findings that I have with other films, that they would. If, for example, you use a peanut protein film, you find that it is very responsive, indeed, to polar substances, such as ammonium sulfide and ammonia; very unresponsive, but still responsive, to things like methylene chloride and acetone, and intermediately to compounds like triethylamine. If you use, on the other hand, a film which is made of a nonpolar material such as PVC (polyvinyl chloride), you find exactly the opposite state of affairs. There you have very little response to polar substances, but you have very big responses to acetone and organic solvents. There lies the indication that olfactory discrimination can be reproduced, as indeed it can, by using several films. One other thing, the neurophysiologists seem to say at present that the likelihood is that all our receptor cells are a little sensitive to all odors, but that each receptor cell is specifically sensitive to certain odors. Now, in the aforementioned films you have the same picture. Whatever the film, it is responsive to every smell to some extent, but particularly responsive to certain smells.

L. N. Ferguson.—Do you think there are five different types of taste receptors, or do you think that you get these five qualities by differences in numbers of receptors that are excited?

R. W. Moncrieff.—At present I do not believe anyone really knows. You can only say, well what do the people who are immersed in their work think. When I was at the Stockholm Conference and Lord Adrian gave the opening address and he said, "What about olfactory discrimination?" He said we know there are temporal and spatial differences in excitement and these can divide all odors into perhaps 5 and 6 different classes, but no more. "How," he asked, "do we account for the vast number of different odors?" "What is the discriminatory apparatus?" and he said it was only a guess, that there might be 50 different kinds of receptors specifically sensitive to particular kinds of stimuli. Now another authority, Le Gros Clark who was professor of Anatomy at Oxford, suggested in a lecture, some 8 or 9 years ago now, that he thought there were about 500 different kinds. You see, it varies. I believe that Dr. Amoore has suggested there are 8 different kinds. Zwaardemaker has suggested 8, Henning 8, Bain 8, and so on. Everbody has had a crack at this, but the experimental evidence, as far as it goes, indicates in my view that the number is fairly large. I do not think anybody knows at present.

D. A. Forss.—I was very interested in your comments on olfactory receptors and your like-dislike response. How does the brain distinguish, for instance, between a very mature cheese and rancid milk, where essentially we are smelling the same chemical compounds. In other words, do we have to have a visual picture, perhaps, of whether we like or dislike a smell?

R. W. Moncrieff.—No, I do not think so. I think the olfactory receptors are very competent indeed. Even though rancid milk and cheese have a certain amount of similarity, they are still enormously different and to such a refined and sensitive instrument as the nose, they are poles apart. I do not think there is any doubt about that.

D. A. Forss.—What you are saying is that the pattern is sufficiently different chemically.

R. W. Moncrieff.—Yes. Probably many times more than sufficiently different.

A. Dravnieks.—In your studies on the odor preferences, is there any distinct difference between non-learned observers and groups of people who are quite skilled in distinguishing odors? Do they rate preference differently?

R. W. Moncrieff.—If you ask children, do you like this smell, do you dislike it, do your prefer this smell to that? The answer is just as instant and just as positive as if you asked a grown person, and as if you asked a grown person who is practiced in flavor smelling. We encountered this many times because there was a group of us who were working every day on smell and nearly always the responses were typical. I do not believe learning makes the slightest bit of difference.

H. W. Schultz.—Did those who were in the test see the rose or see the strawberries? This might help Mr. Forss's question. Did they actually see it or were these essences merely on a paper or in a vessel of some kind?

R. W. Moncrieff.—They could see them. In the first part of the research they could see the rose, they could see the strawberries, and so on. One has to remember that many of the things were in bottles and that the contents did not thereby convey very much. It is perfectly true that the rose and the strawberries could be seen and one might say, well that is giving the strawberries an unfair advantage as far as the children are concerned. In the second part of the research when we had these ten odorants, they were in bottles. There was no question then of seeing strawberries. We simply had these six-ounce, wide-neck bottles, each containing 50 ml. of the particular odorant. Of the 600 people who smelled them, probably not more than 20 or 30 had any special knowledge of smell. To the others they were simply liquids. Furthermore, the last point that I would like to make, is that these same ten odorants were offered to a dog, to my own dog, and the most pleasant of the ten odorants to myself and to most of the men, who smelled these ten, was some musk lactone. I offered the various bottles to my dog and he would come and take a sniff and when he came to the musk bottle he not only kept on sniffing, but he licked the neck of the bottle. Now, the most unpleasant of the ten odorants was an oil-soluble chlorophyll. But when I held this bottle containing the oil-soluble chlorophyll to my dog, he backed away. It was just as if he had been hit, and I'm sure that it is just as cruel to offer a bad smell to an animal as it is to hit it. Maybe more cruel.

BIBLIOGRAPHY

ADRIAN, E. D. 1955. Potential oscillations in the olfactory organ. J. Physiol. *128*, 21P–22P.

ADRIAN, E. D. 1963. Opening address. *In* Olfaction and Taste, Y. Zotterman, Editor. Pergamon Press, Oxford.

ALEXANDER, S. 1922. Natural piety. The Hibbert J. *20*, 609–621.

ALEXANDER, S. 1939. Philosophical and Literary Pieces. (Edited by his literary executor) Macmillan, London.

BONDI, H.   1960.   Cosmology.   2nd Edition.   University Press, Cambridge, England.

HEINZ, D. E., PANGBORN, R. M., and JENNINGS, W. G.   1964.   Pear aroma: Relation of instrumental and sensory techniques.   J. Food Science 29, 756–761.

LE GROS CLARK, W.   1956.   Observations on the structure and organization of olfactory receptors in the rabbit.   Yale J. Biol. Med. 29, 83–95.

LE GROS CLARK, W.   1957.   Inquiries into the anatomical basis of olfactory discrimination.   Proc. Roy. Soc.   London Series B 146, 299–319.

LILJESTRAND, G., and ZOTTERMAN, Y.   1956.   The alkaline taste.   Acta Physiol. Scand. 35, 380–389.

DE LORENZO, A. J.   1957.   Electron microscopic observations on the olfactory mucosa and olfactory nerve.   J. Biophys. Biochem. Cytol. 3, 839–850.

DE LORENZO, A. J.   1958.   Electron microscopic observations on the taste buds of the rabbit.   J. Biophys. Biochem. Cytol. 4, 143–150.

DE LORENZO, A. J.   1960.   Electron microscopy of the olfactory and gustatory pathways.   Ann. Otol. Rhin. Laryng. 69, 410–420.

MASON, E. G.   1944.   A Functional Curriculum in Professional Forestry.   Oregon State College, Corvallis, Oreg.

MONCRIEFF, R. W.   1951.   The Chemical Senses.   2nd Edition.   Leonard Hill, London.

MONCRIEFF, R. W.   1954.   The characterization of odours.   J. Physiol. 125, 453–465.

MONCRIEFF, R. W.   1955.   The sorptive properties of the olfactory membrane.   J. Physiol. 130, 543–558.

MONCRIEFF, R. W.   1956.   The sorptive nature of the olfactory stimulus.   Proc. 2nd. Internat. Congr. Surface Activity 321–328.

MONCRIEFF, R. W.   1961.   An instrument for measuring and classifying odors.   J. Appl. Physiol. 16, 742–749.

MONCRIEFF, R. W.   1964.   The metallic taste.   Perf. Ess. Oil Rec. 55, 205–207.

RICHTER, C. P., and CAMPBELL, K. H.   1940.   Sucrose taste thresholds of rats and humans.   Am. J. Physiol. 128, 291–297.

SHERRINGTON, C.   1940.   Man on His Nature.   University Press, Cambridge, England.

WINTER, M., and WILLHALM, B.   1964.   Research on aromas.   On the aroma of fresh strawberries.   Analysis of carbonyl compounds, volatile esters and alcohols (in French).   Helv. Chim. Acta 47, 1215–1227.

Physiological Aspects of Olfaction and Gustation

CHAPTER 2

Albert I. Farbman | # Structure of Chemoreceptors[1,2]

INTRODUCTION

The chemoreceptors concerned with flavor perception are the taste and olfactory organs. These organs are named chemoreceptors because they are endowed with the capacity to respond to relatively low concentrations of chemical stimuli. Their histology was first described in the middle of the nineteenth century; the classical concepts derived from these descriptions had remained relatively unchanged until recently. Within the last decade, the utilization of the electron microscope in anatomy has made available a good deal of new information concerning the detailed histology and cytology of taste and olfactory receptors. It is the purpose of this paper to review some of the recent electron microscopic findings on the structure of these organs and briefly to discuss some of these findings in terms of chemoreceptor function.

TASTE ORGAN

Distribution and Innervation

In the vertebrate, the taste receptors are groups of sensory epithelial cells innervated by sensory nerve endings. One of the first investigators to identify and describe the taste receptor histologically likened its appearance to that of a flower bud (Schwalbe 1868) and the term "taste-bud" has been retained ever since.

Wherever they occur, taste-buds are located on moist body surfaces that are lined with stratified squamous epithelium. In fishes, they are found in the oral cavity and pharynx, the gills, and the epidermis. In amphibians and land dwelling animals, they are found almost exclusively in the oral cavity and pharynx. The major organ of taste is the tongue. Taste-buds are found in the epithelium of the tip, lateral, and dorsal surfaces where they are almost invariably associated with certain papillae. These are the fungiform papillae on the anterior part of the tongue and the foliate and vallate papillae on the posterior part. A few buds may

[1] Part of this work was supported by U. S. Public Health Service General Research Grant #1SO1-FR-05311-04.

[2] ACKNOWLEDGMENT. I wish to express my deep appreciation to Dr. Donald Frisch, New York University Medical Center, for giving me the micrographs of olfactory mucosa and for his helpful comments in the preparation of this manuscript. Many thanks also to Mrs. Karen Packan for technical assistance.

also be found in other areas such as the soft palate, pharynx, and larynx where they are not associated with papillae but are simply embedded in the epithelium of the mucous membrane.

Associated with the distribution of taste-buds in different areas is the fact that their innervation is derived from the sensory portions of three different cranial nerves, namely the facial, glossopharyngeal, and vagus. In fishes, the glossopharyngeal and vagus innervate taste-buds in the gill region whereas the facial innervates buds in the mouth, pharynx, and epidermis. In mammals, a branch of the facial nerve innervates the taste-buds in the anterior part of the tongue and those in the soft palate, whereas the other two cranial nerves supply sensory innervation to all the remaining buds on the posterior part of the tongue, the pharynx, and larynx.

General Histology

The general configuration of taste-buds is remarkably similar in all vertebrate species examined. The bud is usually described as an ovoid structure, about 50 to 80 μ long and 30 to 50 μ wide. It is constituted of 30 to 50 or more elongated, slender cells resting on a basement membrane and tapering apically to end in a taste pore which communicates with the external environment. A subepithelial nerve plexus sends several nerve processes into the taste-bud.

Traditionally, the cell population of the taste-bud was considered to

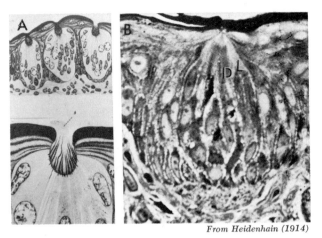

From Heidenhain (1914)

Fig. 4. A. Classical Histological Concept of the Taste Bud. B. Phase Micrograph Showing Differing Densities in Apical Cytoplasm of Taste Bud. Light (L) and Dark (D) Cells are Distinguishable ($\times 880$)

be composed of two cell types, a darkly staining, spindle-shaped sensory (receptor) cell with an oval shaped, dense nucleus, and a lightly staining, elongated, supporting cell with a round, vacuolated nucleus (e.g., Loven 1868; Schwalbe 1868). This traditional concept of two distinct cell types is illustrated in Fig. 4A (Heidenhain 1914). In the upper part of this diagram the shapes and densities of the two nuclear types are illustrated in three taste-buds. This figure may be compared with Fig. 4B, a phase micrograph of an unstained section through a rat taste-bud. In this micrograph, nuclear differences are not obvious in the taste-bud cells, but near the apical pole of the bud, there are differences in the cytoplasmic densities of the cells. These nuclear and cytoplasmic differences were the bases for classification of cells into two types and this distinction is still made by most contemporary textbooks of histology (e.g., Bloom and Fawcett 1962; Copenhaver 1964). However, there is little or no direct anatomical or physiological evidence to warrant the functional labeling of either cell type as either a sensory or supporting cell. The histological analysis of the taste organ is further complicated by reports that intermediate cell types may be found in taste-buds; this would mean that classification of all of the cells in the taste-bud population into two distinct types is not always possible (Heidenhain 1914; Engstrom and Rytzner 1956A and B; Trujillo-Cenoz 1957; Murray and Murray 1960). Supportive evidence for this latter school of thought comes from recent studies demonstrating a turnover of the cell population in taste-buds (Beidler et al. 1960; Beidler 1962, 1963; DeLorenzo 1963). Accordingly, in a system in which cell replacement is continually occurring, it would not be surprising that several intermediate cells may be found.

This difference of opinion is not hopelessly unresolvable if one examines the two sides more closely. The evidence for cell replacement does not answer the question of whether there is continuous replacement of all or only some cells. The possibility exists that there may indeed be two distinct cell types, either one or both of which are short-lived and are continually replaced during the life of the animal. The morphological evidence from recent electron microscope studies strongly suggests that a clear distinction into two cell types can be made. In addition, there is some evidence that cell turnover may occur.

In the following discussion, morphological data will be presented which will demonstrate clearly that there are two cell types in the taste-bud. In addition some of the evidence for cell replacement will be discussed. Most of the data to be described was taken from rat tongue and prepared by ordinary techniques for electron microscopy. The findings made in my laboratory will be compared with findings made by others studying taste-buds from other animals, primarily the rabbit and monkey.

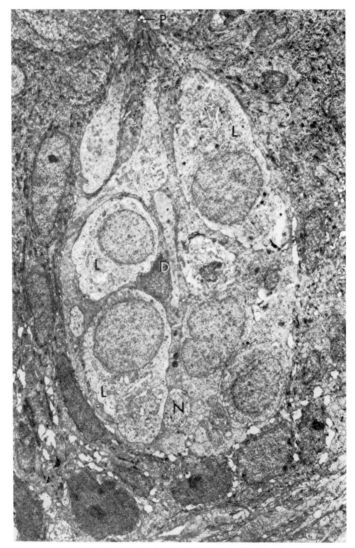

FIG. 5. LOW POWER ELECTRON MICROGRAPH ($\times 2800$) SHOWING THE
TWO CELL TYPES IN THE TASTE BUD, THE LIGHT (L) AND THE DARK
(D)

The bud tapers at its apex where several microvilli project into the
taste pore area (P). (N) Nerve.

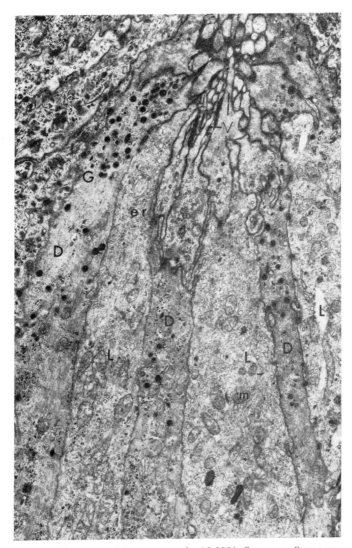

Fig. 6. Electron Micrograph (×10,000) Showing Supranuclear Cytoplasm and Apexes of Taste Bud Cells

Light (L) and dark cells (D) are seen, the latter containing dense
secretory granules (G). The microvilli (V) project from the
apexes of the cells. (er), endoplasmic reticulum; (m) mitochondrion.

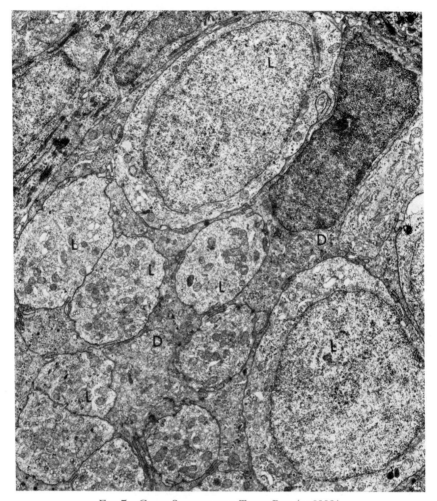

FIG. 7.   CROSS-SECTION OF A TASTE BUD (×6000)

The light cells (L) are round to oval in contour and dark cells (D) seem to fill in the spaces between them.

Electron Microscopy of Taste-Buds

Cell Types.—Examination of the taste-bud with the electron microscope reveals that there are two morphologically distinguishable cell types present, a light cell and a dark cell (Figs. 5–8, 11).   The light cell contains a large, spherical nucleus and a cytoplasm which is characterized by numerous mitochondria, a prominent golgi apparatus, glycogen particles and a rich network of vesicles and vacuoles; these latter elements are all membrane bounded, and, taken together, may be said to constitute an agranular endoplasmic reticulum (Figs. 6, 8, 11). In cross-section (Fig. 7) this cell type has a circular or elliptical, smooth contour, and on this basis alone is easily recognizable.

The dark cell, on the other hand, is characterized by a rather more dense nucleus than that of the light cell (Figs. 5, 7), and a cytoplasm filled with an abundance of delicate filamentous material. The close packing of the filamentous material imparts the density to the cytoplasm which gives the electron microscopic image of a "dark" cell. In the supranuclear area of dark cells from vallate papilla taste-buds, there are several membrane-limited secretory granules containing a very dense core (Figs. 6, 8). The dense core often does not completely fill the area enclosed by the limiting membrane of the granule (Fig. 8). Interestingly enough, identical secretory granules have been described in taste-bud cells from rabbit foliate papillae (DeLorenzo 1963; Nemetschek-Gansler and Ferner 1964), but they are not seen in dark cells of rat fungiform papillae (Farbman 1965A and B). The latter cells, however, characteristically contain large, pleomorphic, dense bodies with ribbon-like lamellae (Farbman 1965A and B). The significance of these cytological differences between apparently homologous cells in the same species is undetermined, although they may reflect functional differences. In addition to secretory granules or dense bodies, the dark cells contain a moderately extensive golgi apparatus, some mitochondria, ribosomes, and a paucity of endoplasmic reticulum. In general, it is fair to state that the total amount of organelles is considerably less in dark cells than in light cells.

In addition to the differences described above between the light and dark cells of the taste-bud, there are differences in the relationships with intraepithelial nerve processes. The dark cell may either envelop the nerve process and form a mesaxon in a manner similar to that of a Schwann cell, or it may share contact of a nerve process with another cell (Fig. 11). The light cell has not been described to completely enclose the periphery of an intraepithelial nerve process.

The striking morphological dissimilarities between light and dark cells favors the interpretation that there are indeed two cell types. Both cells appear to be highly differentiated and there appears to be no convincing evidence suggesting that they are interconvertible. If we attempt to reconcile this interpretation with the experiments demonstrating cell turnover in the taste-bud, one possibility is to assume that the two cell types differentiate independently from their precursors, possibly from a common precursor. A scheme for the cytodifferentiation of the dark cell has been indicated by tracing its development from a stem cell type, the peripheral cell in the taste-bud from rat fungiform papilla (Farbman 1965A and B). The peripheral cell is morphologically undifferentiated, is not in contact with nerve processes, and is located in the area which first shows uptake of injected tritiated thymidine and also shows arrested mitoses in animals injected with colchicine (Beidler *et al.* 1960; DeLorenzo 1963). According to the scheme, the peripheral cell migrates into the central area of the taste-bud, establishes contact with a nerve process, and undergoes some interesting morphological changes. A cluster of vesicles appears in the cytoplasm adjacent to the area contiguous with the nerve process. This has been interpreted to represent a reflection of an interaction between nerve and cell, an interaction which heralds the onset of differentiative changes in the cell. Cells have been seen that are intermediate between the basal cell type and the dark cell. Thus, it is proposed that the sequence of events proceeds from peripheral to basal to dark cell. The sequence of events in the cytodifferentiation of the light cell, however, remains unclear, because it is difficult to find cells that can be categorized as intermediate between light cell and basal cell, or any other cell type. The foregoing discussion leads us only to uncertain and tentative conclusions as to whether all the taste-bud cells are replaced, or only one of the two types. If there is replacement at the suggested rate, i.e. complete turnover in less than seven days (Beidler 1962), there should be morphological evidence of dying or dead cells in the taste-bud. This has been reported by others (DeLorenzo 1960; Nemetschek-Gansler and Ferner 1964) but in my experience dead cells occur extremely rarely, if at all.

If we pause at this juncture to reflect over what has been stated, it seems there is enough data to support the premise stated initially, namely that there are two cell types in the taste-bud. However, the nagging question remains as to whether one, both, or neither of these is the receptor cell. Traditionally, the dark cell type has been considered the sensory cell, but, as stated in a previous paragraph, there is no conclusive evidence for this. It may be that both cell types are receptors, or possibly just the light cell. There is yet another possible alternative, namely that neither cell is the actual receptor but the site of receptor activity is in the intraepithelial nerve ending. This is very unlikely according to calculations made by Beidler (1962) on the basis of his electrophysiological evidence. He points out that the time that would be necessary for taste substances to traverse the distance from the epithelial surface into the taste-bud to the intraepithelial nerve endings is much greater than the experimentally measured time between application of taste stimulus to the tongue surface and recording of the response in the sensory nerve several millimeters away. Further data indicating that

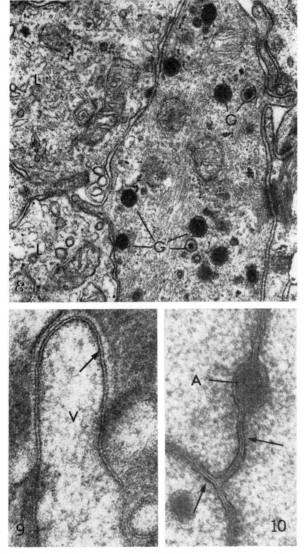

Fig. 8. This Micrograph (×32,000) Illustrates the Dense-cored Secretory Granules (G) of the Dark Cell at Higher Magnification

Parts of two light cells (L) are at the left.

Fig. 9. High Magnification of a Single Microvillus (V) in the Taste Pore

The membrane limiting the villus has three layers (arrow).

Fig. 10. High Magnification (×112,000) of a Junctional Complex

The outer leaflets of adjacent trilaminar membrane are fused so that a 5 layered tight junction is formed (arrows). What appears to be dense material similar to that seen in secretory granules lies in the space between cells (A).

the cells of the taste-bud are the receptors comes from experiments in which microelectrodes were inserted into the cells and quantitative responses to taste substances were measured (Kimura and Beidler 1961; Tateda and Beidler 1964).

Receptor Site

If the cell is assumed to be the receptor, then the most likely part of the cell where the initial encounter between stimulus and receptor occurs would be the part closest to the external environment, i.e. at the taste pore. Histologists traditionally conceived of taste cells ending in hairs which projected into the taste pore (cf. Fig. 4A). However, electron microscopic evidence reveals that the taste-bud cells actually send several small, cytoplasmic projections or microvilli into the taste pore (Figs. 5, 6, 9). These microvilli have been demonstrated in all taste-buds examined to date (DeLorenzo 1958, 1960, 1963; Engstrom and Rytzner 1956A and B; Trujillo-Cenoz 1957, 1961; Murray and Murray 1960; Nemetschek-Gansler and Ferner 1964; Farbman 1965A and B; Gray and Watkins 1965) and the consensus is that they are not distinguished by any special kind of morphology, but are merely membrane-enclosed cytoplasmic projections which, at high magnification, contain a small amount of delicate filamentous material (Fig. 9). The limiting membrane is a continuation of the plasma membrane. It is a 90 Å thick trilaminar structure comprised of an electron translucent line sandwiched between two dense lines, of which the innermost is slightly more dense (Fig. 9). Sometimes these microvilli appear to be dilated and pass out beyond the pore (Gray and Watkins 1965).

What was thought by the older histologists to be taste hairs was probably condensed mucoid material or debris that can usually be found in the oral cavity (Nemetschek-Gansler and Ferner 1964). The dense material found in taste pores with the electron microscope has been related to a secretion product of the dark cell type. Similar material is sometimes found between cells near the pore (Fig. 10). It will be recalled that the dense-cored granules of the dark cell are usually described as secretory granules because of their morphology. In taste-buds of rat fungiform papilla, where these dense granules do not occur, the amorphous material in the taste pore is thought to be debris (Farbman 1965B). In addition to the amorphous material found in taste pores, there are some small, membrane-enclosed vesicular elements, which, from their size and shape appear to be separate and distinct from cellular microvilli, i.e. they may be cell products but are probably not directly connected to cells (Farbman 1965B).

Unfortunately, the resolving power of the electron microscope falls somewhat short of elucidating the specific molecular configuration on the plasma membrane of the microvilli. There is abundant quantitative electrophysiological evidence that such configurations do exist and that the initial event in receptor activity is adsorption of taste substances onto these specific sites (Beidler 1962). It is not known, however, what role, if any, the amorphous or vesicular contents of the taste pore play in mediating the initial event in taste perception.

Although there is some evidence for molecular specificity in the taste response, the degree of cellular specificity for each of the taste modalities is not absolute. Taste physiologists generally conceive of four basic taste modalities, namely salt, sweet, sour and bitter, and some include, as a fifth modality, a specific water taste which is demonstrable in some animals (Liljestrand and Zotterman 1954). However, response specificity to taste stimuli is not demonstrable by electrophysiological methods either in individual receptor cells (Kimura and Beidler 1961; Tateda and Beidler 1964) or in single nerve fibers from taste nerve bundles (Cohen et al. 1955; Pfaffmann 1955; Fishman 1957; Andersen et al. 1963). The explanation usually brought forth for the latter phenomenon is that a single nerve fiber probably innervates several different cells in different taste-buds and it is unlikely that all of these would be absolutely specific to any one taste substance. Since individual receptor cells respond to more than one taste substance we are led to the conclusion stated above, namely that there may be several receptor sites on each cell.

As we have already seen, it is not possible with our present morphological techniques to differentiate between more than two cell types that are likely to be receptors. There is, however, some morphological evidence for a possible contributing factor to the lack of receptor cell specificity. Tight junctions or fusions between the outer lamellae of adjacent trilaminar membranes are formed between taste-bud cells near their distal ends (Fig. 10). This type of membrane complex has been reported in other types of epithelium and is thought to represent a physical barrier against passage of material across epithelia (Sjostrand and Elfvin 1962; Sjostrand 1963; Farquhar and Palade 1963, 1965; Brightman and Palay 1963). In the taste-bud, the tight junction may act as a barrier, but there are other implications because of the function of the bud as a receptor. It has been shown recently in some epithelia where tight junctions occur that the electrical resistance across such junctions is significantly lower than that across areas of the plasma membrane not involved in the junction (Lowenstein et al. 1965). Consequently, there exists a potential pathway through which excitation arising in one taste cell can spread to other cells in the receptor organ, thus rendering it impossible to demonstrate substrate specificity.

Synapses

The final point to be considered in this discussion of the functional anatomy of the taste-bud is the relationship between the receptor cell and the nerve ending, where presumably the response of the receptor is transduced into a nerve impulse. An intelligent appraisal of this area, which can be called a synapse, is at present impossible, because we cannot be entirely certain about the correct identification of the receptor cell. Nevertheless, we can examine the relationships between intraepithelial nerve processes and the various cell types.

There are essentially two ways in which cells and nerve elements are anatomically related in the taste-bud: (a) the cell may completely ensheath the nerve process in a manner analogous to that of a Schwann cell, or (b) the nerve process may lie between cells so that it is in contiguity with two or more cells. As has already been mentioned, only the dark cell has the first type of relationship with intraepithelial nerve processes. In all cases, there is a definite space or synaptic cleft between the cell membrane and the axon membrane. This is significant because it suggests that the type of transmission is more likely to be chemical rather than electrical (Gray and Watkins 1965). The nature of the chemical transmitter remains a subject of controversy. Acetyl choline has been suggested by some experiments (Landgren *et al.* 1954) and ruled out by others (Duncan 1963).

It remains to examine the synapse for characteristic specializations of the contiguous membranes such as are found in nerve-nerve synapses (DeRobertis 1958) or in neuromuscular junctions (Anderson-Cedergren 1959). It has already been mentioned that in basal cell cytoplasm, near the area of contact with nerve processes, there is frequently an accumulation of vesicles oriented toward the nerve process (Farbman 1965A and B). These are not considered to be related to "presynaptic vesicles" because the cell is relatively undifferentiated and thus is not likely to be a receptor cell. In this regard, it is interesting to note that some of the nerve elements contain vesicles which are similar to presynaptic vesicles, but as has been pointed out (DeLorenzo 1963; Gray and Watkins 1965), if this is the true synapse, the vesicles are on the postsynaptic or "wrong" side. DeLorenzo (1963) has suggested an alternate interpretation, namely that these nerve processes with vesicles may not be sensory nerves at all but that they may be efferent nerves, in which case the vesicles would be on the presynaptic side. As further evidence for the presence of efferent nerves, he cites the differences in size of the nerve processes as they appear in sections under the electron microscope (*cf.* Fig. 11). Some are 2 or 3 μ in diameter and contain many mitochondria and vesicles, while others are only about 0.2 μ in diameter and contain

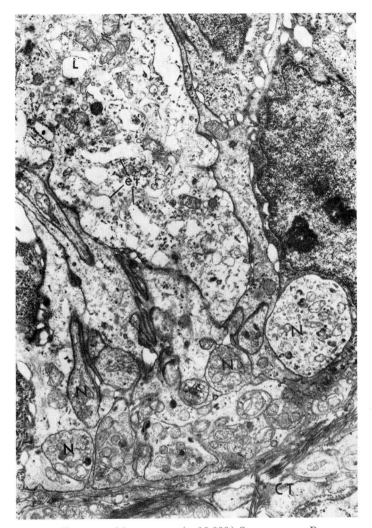

FIG. 11. ELECTRON MICROGRAPH (×10,000) SHOWING THE PROXIMAL
PART OF THE TASTE BUD

Several nerve processes (N) of different sizes are present. (L) light
cell; (CT) connective tissue; (er) endoplasmic reticulum.

few formed elements. However, some nerve elements are seen to expand
from a narrow portion into a wide portion so that classification of nerve
processes into functional groups according to size would only be possible
after reconstruction of a sizeable length of nerve by examination of serial
sections (Farbman 1965B).

Gray and Watkins (1965) describe morphological specialization of the cell membrane at the alleged synaptic site in taste-buds. Their observations reveal tiny "dense projections" along the presynaptic membrane which they interpret to be small coiled or curled filaments that sometimes pierce the presynaptic membrane and possibly serve as conveyors of a transmittor substance across the synapse. The only other description of structures in the vicinity of the cell-nerve junctions are flattened, membranous sacs sometimes seen lying parallel but not attached to what would be the presynaptic membrane, i.e. the plasma membrane of the taste-bud cell (Farbman 1965B). This sac may be found in both light and dark cells. However, it is also found occasionally near areas of the cell membrane where the latter is not in proximity to nerve processes, so its specificity for the synapse remains questionable.

Of major importance in considering the functional synapse in the taste-bud is the turnover of the cell population mentioned above. If the receptor cells are continually being replaced, then synapses are constantly being broken and re-established (Beidler 1963). This complicates considerably any attempt at interpretation of static micrographs of the taste-bud as well as interpretation of short-term electrophysiological studies.

OLFACTORY RECEPTOR

General Features

The olfactory receptor area in amphibians and land dwelling animals is located in the roof of the nasal cavity and may be reflected onto the upper part of the nasal septum and nasal conchae. This area is lined with a so-called olfactory epithelium which in the fresh state is distinguishable by its yellowish color from the pink respiratory epithelium around it. In some vertebrates there is an accessory olfactory receptor area known as the vomeronasal organ (organ of Jacobson). This is located in a small pouch within the bony part of the nasal septum. The vomeronasal organ opens into the nasal cavity but is also connected to the oral cavity by a small canal opening into the hard palate. The morphological characteristics of its epithelium are identical to those of the olfactory mucosa so that this accessory organ will not be considered separately.

The surface of the olfactory epithelium is coated by a layer of mucus produced mostly by the subepithelial Bowman's glands, whose ducts open onto the epithelial surface. Embedded in this mucus layer is a mat of fine hair-like appendages of the olfactory cells. These are called cilia.

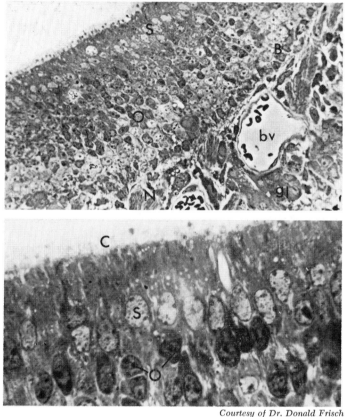

Courtesy of Dr. Donald Frisch

FIG. 12. LOW MAGNIFICATION PHASE MICROGRAPH (×300) OF SECTION THROUGH OLFACTORY MUCOSA

(S) Supporting cell; (O) Olfactory cell; (B) Basal cell; (bv) Blood vessel; (N) Nerve bundle; (gl) Bowman's gland cell.

Courtesy of Dr. Donald Frisch

FIG. 13. HIGH MAGNIFICATION PHASE MICROGRAPH (×1200) SHOWING UPPER PART OF OLFACTORY EPITHELIUM

(S) Supporting cell nucleus; (O) Olfactory cell nucleus; (C) Ciliated border of epithelium.

For orientation purposes, it will be helpful to describe briefly the general histological features of the olfactory mucous membrane before examining the receptor in detail. Figure 12 is a low power phase micrograph of the olfactory mucosa of the mouse. The epithelium is the pseudostratified columnar type. In the apical part of the epithelium, a row of clear nuclei is arranged parallel to the surface. They are seen to better advantage in Fig. 13 which is a higher magnification of the apical half of the olfactory epithelium. These relatively clear nuclei belong to the supporting or sustentacular cells, the tall slender cells reaching from the basement membrane to the epithelial surface. In some animals, supporting cells contain yellowish-brown pigment granules in the supranuclear area of the cytoplasm (Bloom 1954). At the basal side of the epithelium, a row of nuclei similar to those of the supporting cells is seen (Fig. 12). These nuclei belong to the small basal cells which rest on the basement membrane but do not reach more than approximately one quarter the distance toward the epithelial surface.

Between the regular rows of basal and supporting cell nuclei, there are many relatively dense nuclei at various levels in the epithelium (Figs. 12, 13). These are the nuclei of the olfactory cells. Although the olfactory cell nuclei are at different levels in the epithelium, the cytoplasm of these cells reaches the epithelial surface and extends to the basement membrane. This has been demonstrated in teased preparations.

At the epithelial surface, there are very fine projections extending out from the epithelial cells, thus giving the appearance of a striated border on the epithelial surface. These striations represent the surface modifications of the epithelial cells, primarily the long cilia of the olfactory cells and the shorter microvilli of the supporting cells. In fresh preparations, some of the cilia are seen to be motile (Reese 1965).

Beneath the epithelium, in the connective tissue, there are thin-walled blood vessels and several nerve bundles (Fig. 12), both of which are characteristic findings in olfactory mucous membrane. In the lower right corner of Fig. 12, part of one olfactory gland of Bowman can be seen.

In any pseudostratified epithelium the following features are characteristic: (1) all cells rest on the basement membrane; (2) nuclei are not all on the same level; (3) usually not all cells reach the epithelial surface. In such epithelia the cytoplasm of the epithelial cells is extremely narrow and attenuated in some cases. In fact, the perinuclear area is the broadest part of the epithelial cell in all cases and it is usually not possible under ordinary conditions with the light microscope to define the cytoplasmic limits of individual cells. This is particularly true in ordinary histological preparations of olfactory epithelium. Only in certain circumstances can one distinguish cytoplasmic outlines of the epithelial cells. For example, in amphibia the sustentacular cells contain pigmented granules, which render them easily visible. In addition, in histological preparations specially stained to demonstrate olfactory cells, one can distinguish the cytoplasmic outlines of these cells. It is more revealing, therefore, to turn to the electron microscope findings for the fine structural details of this receptor epithelium.

Supporting Cell

The supranuclear cytoplasm of the supporting cell is more or less rod-shaped and 2 to 3 μ in diameter. At the free surface of the epithelium, the plasma membrane of the supporting cell is thrown up into many fine, microvillous processes which project into the mucous coating on the surface (Fig. 14). On the lateral surface of the supporting cell, tight junctions, similar to those described above in the taste-bud have been observed (Frisch 1964; Reese 1965). These membrane complexes may be formed between adjacent supporting cells or between a supporting and an olfactory cell.

In amphibians, the apical cytoplasm of supporting cells contains numerous membrane enclosed secretory granules, and frequently one can see evidence that these granules are released onto the epithelial surface (Bloom 1954; Reese 1965). In mammals, however, the presence of secretory granules is in dispute. It has been reported that in the rabbit

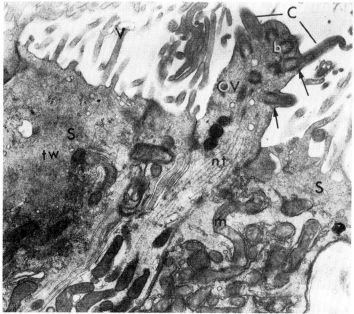

Courtesy of Dr. Donald Frisch

Fig. 14.   Electron Micrograph   ($\times 16,000$)   Showing Olfactory Vesicle (OV) and Upper Borders of two Supporting Cells (S) with Microvilli

The stumps of several cilia (C) are seen. Note, at arrow, the peripheral filaments of the cilia in continuity with the basal body (b). (tw) terminal web; (m) mitochondria; (nt) neurotubules.

olfactory epithelium, supporting cells contain no secretory granules (Gasser 1956; DeLorenzo 1957). On the other hand, small membrane bounded granules have been reported in sustentacular cells of mouse olfactory epithelium (Frisch 1964). These are presumed to be secretory granules, but they do not present nearly so prominent an appearance in the mouse as they do in the amphibian.

A prominent feature of the apical cytoplasm in the mammalian supporting cell is an extensive system of flattened membranous sacs which are often arranged parallel to the longitudinal axis of the cell (DeLorenzo 1957; Frisch 1964). Most of this so-called endoplasmic reticulum is constituted almost entirely of parallel stacks of smooth-surfaced membranes. Often, the smooth membranes are arranged in bizarre forms and they frequently show continuity with other membranous elements in the cytoplasm such as the golgi apparatus or mitochondria (Frisch 1964). In addition to the extensive endoplasmic reticulum, the supporting cell contains a dense concentration of mitochondria near its apex, but often separated from the apex by an area free of membranous organelles (DeLorenzo 1957; Frisch 1964). Because this free area often contains some very delicate, filamentous material, it is sometimes referred to as a terminal web (Fig. 14). In the narrow attenuated proximal cytoplasm of the supporting cell, there are few membranous organelles, but this area often contains free ribosomal particles (Gasser 1956; DeLorenzo 1957).

The cell type described in the preceding paragraphs has traditionally been designated as a supporting cell, but some workers feel that its function goes beyond mere support of other epithelial cells. Gasser (1956) hints at other functions in rabbit supporting cells, but does not say what they might be. The morphology of the supporting cells of the amphibian indicates that the cells have a secretory function and that the product probably makes up part of the mucous coating of the olfactory epithelium. In a recent study, Frisch (1964) suggests that the supporting cell probably modifies the mucous coating of olfactory epithelium both by secretion and absorption because its morphology indicates that it has a transporting function, i.e. it is involved actively and/or passively in the exchange of material across its plasma membrane at the apex.

Basal Cell

There is a paucity of information about the morphology of the basal cell in the published literature. It is a small cell with a spherical nucleus and a rather dense cytoplasm. The cell cytoplasm contains little endoplasmic reticulum, a moderate amount of ribosomes and a few mitochondria (Frisch 1964). The basal cell cytoplasm is disposed in thin processes which are seen to ensheath small bundles of olfactory axons before the axons pass out of the epithelium into the connective tissue (Gasser 1956; Trujillo-Cenoz 1961). It is important to note, however, that their morphology differs significantly from that of the larger supporting cell in the same epithelium, and there seems to be little relation between the two.

Olfactory Cell

The inherent difficulty in the analysis of taste-bud structure, namely the identification of the receptor cell, does not appear to be a problem with the olfactory chemoreceptor. The olfactory cell is a bipolar nerve cell which synapses directly with the cerebrum. Because this peripherally located nerve cell is located within the olfactory receptor area, it has been assumed that it is the receptor cell. Not only does this cell function as a receptor, but by virtue of its direct synaptic connection with the brain, it functions also as the transmitter of information regarding the nature and strength of olfactory stimuli presented to the animal. Moreover, this very unusual cell must have a mechanism for performing the steps intermediate between stimulus reception and impulse transmission, i.e. the translation of specific sensory stimuli into a coded nervous message.

The cell body (perikaryon) of the olfactory cell is located, as has been noted above, in the middle of the olfactory epithelium. From the perikaryon, a cytoplasmic process, conventionally termed the dendrite, passes distally toward the epithelial surface. The dendrite terminates in a slight expansion, the olfactory vesicle, which projects slightly beyond the level of the supporting cell cytoplasm (Fig. 14). The olfactory vesicle bears from 6 to about 16 cilia which project radially into the mucous coating of the epithelium and lie in a plane approximately parallel to the epithelial surface. The number of cilia appears to vary with the species from an average of 6 in the frog (Reese 1965) to an average of 12 or 13 in the rabbit (Le Gros Clark 1957).

Two types of olfactory cilia have been described in the frog, an immotile type, 80 to 200 μ long, and a motile type 25 to 50 μ long (Reese 1965). These are much longer than those reported in olfactory cells of the newt which average 4 μ (Shibuya and Takagi 1964) or those in the rabbit which have been reported to average only 1 to 2 μ (Le Gros Clark 1957).

The olfactory cilium is broader near its base than at its tip (Frisch 1964; Reese 1965). In its proximal part, it is morphologically similar to cilia on other cell types. Examination of this part of the cilium with the electron microscope reveals that it is circular in cross-section, and is bounded by a plasma membrane continuous with that of the dendrite.

It contains nine paired peripheral filaments and two unpaired central filaments, all of which run in its long axis (Fig. 15). This regular arrangement is altered in the narrower, distal part of the cilium by the disappearance of some filaments and sometimes by distortions of the ciliary cytoplasm (Frisch 1964; Reese 1965). Where the cilium joins the olfactory vesicle, the nine pairs of peripheral filaments are continuous with the periphery of the cylindrical basal body in the olfactory vesicle cytoplasm (Fig. 14). The two unpaired central filaments do not, however, pass into the basal body.

The olfactory dendrite is characterized by the presence of neurotubules, about 280 Å in diameter (Fig. 14). Examination of the neurotubules at high magnification with the electron microscope reveals that they are bounded by a trilaminar membrane, 30 to 40 Å in total diameter, and contain a central filament, 90 Å in diameter (Frisch 1964, 1965). Also contained within some dendrites is an accumulation of mitochondria near the olfactory vesicle (DeLorenzo 1957, 1963). Besides the neurotubules and mitochondria, there are few other organelles in the olfactory dendrite. Only an occasional profile of endoplasmic reticulum is present and sometimes a few ribosomes.

Before continuing with the anatomical description, it would be worthwhile to pause and consider whether there is any anatomical basis for the wide range of discriminatory sensitivity possessed by the olfactory organ. It is generally assumed that the receptor sites for odors are located on the cilia, but there is no evidence for a large number of ciliary types, each of which might have a specific sensitivity. Some slight differences in stainability of cilia have been reported (Le Gros Clark 1956) but these are not consistent enough to be evaluated as an expression of an ana-

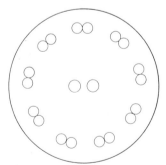

Modified after Fawcett (1961)

FIG. 15.   DIAGRAMMATIC REPRESENTATION OF A CROSS-SECTION THROUGH A TYPICAL CILIUM SHOWING 9 PAIRED PERIPHERAL FILAMENTS AND 2 UNPAIRED CENTRAL FILAMENTS

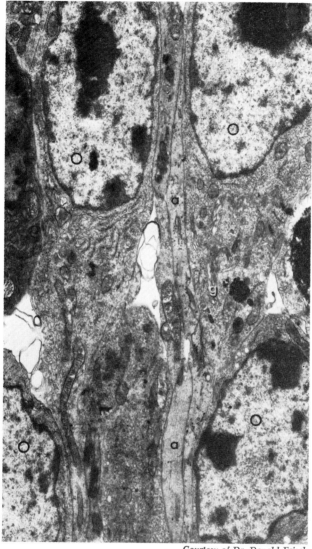

Courtesy of Dr. Donald Frisch

FIG. 16. ELECTRON MICROGRAPH (×7600) SHOWING OLFACTORY PERIKARYA (O) AND ADJACENT AXONS (a)

tomical basis for discrimination. The differences in numbers of mito-chondria (DeLorenzo 1957, 1963) are also insufficient evidence for discriminatory differences among olfactory cells. In a recent review article, Moulton and Tucker (1964) conclude that " . . . the assumptions that functional differences necessarily imply gross morphological differ-ences and vice versa, are false." We can tentatively conclude therefore that although anatomical examination of receptor sites in the olfactory cell has provided a good deal of information, there is no basis for classify-ing receptor cells into different functional categories. In fact, there is reason to believe that this may not be possible with receptor cells. Geste-land *et al.* (1963) have demonstrated in their electrophysiological ex-periments that single receptor units can respond to many different types of stimuli, and have concluded from these experiments that there may be several types of receptor sites on an individual receptor element. It would appear, therefore, that classification may be possible only on the

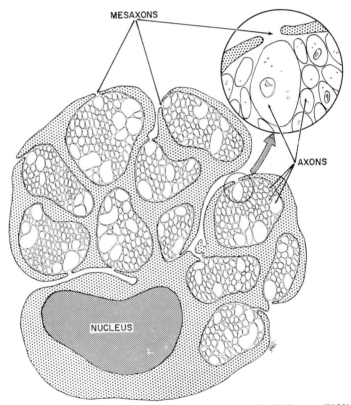

After DeLorenzo (1963)

FIG. 17. DIAGRAMMATIC REPRESENTATION OF THE RELATIONSHIP BE-TWEEN SCHWANN CELLS AND BUNDLES OF OLFACTORY AXONS

basis of receptor site structure (cf. Amoore, Chapter 5, this volume) and that this will be impossible by direct anatomical examination until our methods become sufficiently sophisticated to enable us to visualize the molecular organization of the receptor cell membrane.

The broadest part of the olfactory cell is the perikaryon which contains the cell nucleus and an extensive Golgi apparatus (Fig. 16). In the mouse olfactory perikaryon, a lamellated dense body is frequently seen in proximity to the Golgi apparatus (Frisch 1964). This dense body is identical to that described in dark cells of taste-buds from rat fungiform papillae (Farbman 1965B). It is interesting that this dense body appears in both chemoreceptor organs, but there is no evidence as yet of its function.

From the perikaryon, the cytoplasm of the olfactory cell narrows into a proximal process, the axon, which passes through the basement membrane into the connective tissue. Estimates based on selected micrographs indicate that each olfactory cell has only one axon (Gasser 1956). The axons range in diameter from 0.1 to 0.5 μ, with an average of about 0.2 μ. Several of these tiny axons come together to form small bundles each of which is ensheathed by a basal cell before the axons leave the epithelium. Within the connective tissue, the axon bundles are ensheathed by Schwann cells in a somewhat unusual manner. Most nerve processes outside of the central nervous system are individually enwrapped by Schwann cell cytoplasm so that each individual process is insulated from other tissue elements. The sheet-like Schwann cell proc-

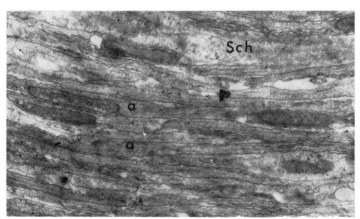

Courtesy of Dr. Donald Frisch

FIG. 18. ELECTRON MICROGRAPH ($\times 14,000$) OF LONGITUDINAL SECTION THROUGH OLFACTORY AXONS (a) IN CONNECTIVE TISSUE

(Sch) Schwann cell cytoplasm.

esses closely approximate the membrane of the nerve process and close over it to form a mesaxon. As is illustrated diagrammatically in Fig. 17, however, several olfactory axons may be wrapped together so that they are not insulated from each other and there may be a ratio of one mesaxon to fifty or more axons, instead of the usual one to one ratio.

The axons contain long rod-like mitochondria, some small vesicles and neurotubules (Fig. 18). Because the axons lie so close to each other there is speculation that impulses passing along an individual axon may affect or be affected by activity in other axons (Gasser 1956; DeLorenzo 1963).

SUMMARY

In the study of any organ, the anatomical and physiological data must be correlated in order to make an intelligent appraisal of the organ's function. In the foregoing account, the morphology of the taste and olfactory organs was discussed in some detail with the emphasis placed on recent electron microscopic studies. It can be seen, that the electron microscope, with its high resolving power, has still not provided us with the answers to some important questions on the structure of chemoreceptors. The answers to such questions very likely await the combined efforts of anatomists, physiologists, and biochemists, in experiments where structure and function are studied together at all levels, from the tissue level to the molecular level.

DISCUSSION

R. W. Moncrieff.—I recently read a paper by DeLorenzo in which he gave some beautiful electron-micrographs of the taste-buds. I believe the purpose of the paper had been to explore the possibility that there might be a correlation between structural features of the taste receptors and their responses to different tastes. DeLorenzo found no such correlation. Would you agree?

A. I. Farbman.—Yes, it would. It agrees not only with the taste-bud, but DeLorenzo has also said the same thing, and so has Dr. Frisch, about the olfactory receptor; namely, that there does not appear to be any morphological difference at all, even with the electron microscope. I think that part of this is explained by this tight junction complex that you see in the taste-bud. In the receptor area of the olfactory cell there are no such tight junctions, i.e., there are tight junctions between cells, but there are no tight junctions between two receptor cells, because at the receptor area there is no contact between receptor cells. There may be contact between cilia. This is a little harder to evaluate, because cilia are all over the place. Your electron microscopic section is just a few hundred angstroms thick, and since the cilium spreads out in all directions, it is very difficult to connect one that is in the periphery with the cell from which it came. So there may be some contact out there. Also, in the olfactory organ you have this very close proximity between nerve elements which might throw the specificity off. You have certain techniques of measuring olfactory and taste responses, which are not perfect, nor is the electron microscope the last word. I think that the anatomists and physiologists are going to have to work together if they are to come up with anything more comprehensive than what we have now.

R. W. Kline.—It occurs to me in hearing this discussion, particularly a comment that you made Dr. Farbman, about the similarity of the membrane of some of these cells to those in the villi of the intestine, that beyond the point of adsorption on these receptor cells, is there actual penetration of these cells, for instance, by sodium choride? Or are the surfaces of the receptor cells in general impenetrable and is the sensation completely kept separate from the external environment, which is the flavor substrate?

A. I. Farbman.—I would suspect that every living cell is permeable to sodium chloride, as well as to water, and to several other things. Now how this will influence the taste response, I do not know. In electrophysiological measurements, the time of stimulation to the time at which a response in the nerve is recorded or in the cell, is too short to propose what you are suggesting, namely, that a taste substrate is absorbed into the cell and somehow changes its make-up so that it initiates a nerve impulse. Beidler has contrived a taste equation which apparently fits his data and he can explain the response of a taste cell, as well as a taste nerve, on the basis of his equation and this is a simple adsorption equation. So that it looks like it is absorption.

A. Dravnieks.—What is the chemical significance of the darker staining on your slides? Is it connected to a certain enzyme system or do certain substances that occur on these spots get stained much darker than others?

A. I. Farbman.—We first fix a piece of tissue in osmic acid. Osmium is a heavy metal and it will be bound onto surfaces of protein molecules and perhaps lipid and polysaccharide molecules, and certainly to most macromolecules to a certain degree. When we see something that is very dense, all that we can say about it is that it has bound more osmic acid than other areas. Now there may be an intrinsic density to this substance that will show up when you just fix a piece of tissue in something that does not contain a heavy metal. This black substance may be an intrinsically dense material, but I am not sure of this. I have not looked at any material that was not fixed in osmium and stained with one or more of the heavy metals such as uranium and lead.

A. Dravnieks.—Would it indicate that some reduction of osmic acid to free metal takes place at some of these spots?

A. I. Farbman.—Yes. It would indicate at least a partial reduction. If the osmic acid, which has a chemical formula of OsO_4, is not reduced, it is soluble. Osmium tetroxide is soluble in water, so unless it is reduced, at least partially to a dioxide or trioxide, or down to the metal itself, it will not be retained by the tissue. So it does indicate that some reduction has taken place. Almost anything will reduce osmium. It is just the degree to which it reduces it that changes the image.

BIBLIOGRAPHY

ANDERSON, H. T., FUNAKOSHI, M., and ZOTTERMAN, Y. 1963. Electrophysiological responses to sugar and their depression by salt. In Olfaction and Taste. Y. Zotterman, (Editor), pp. 177–192. Macmillan Co., New York.

ANDERSON-CEDERGREN, E. 1959. Ultrastructure of motor end plate and sarcoplasmic components of mouse skeletal muscle. J. Ultrastructure Res. Suppl. 1, 1–191.

50   THE CHEMISTRY AND PHYSIOLOGY OF FLAVORS

BEIDLER, L. M. 1962. Taste receptor stimulation. Progress in Biophysics and Biophysical Chemistry 12, 107–151.

BEIDLER, L. M. 1963. Dynamics of Taste Cells. In Olfaction and Taste. Y. Zotterman, (Editor), pp. 133–145. Macmillan Co., New York.

BEIDLER, L. M., NEJAD, M. S., SMALLMAN, R. L., and TATEDA, H. 1960. Rat taste cell proliferation. Fed. Proc. 19, 302.

BLOOM, G. 1954. Studies on the olfactory epithelium of the frog and the toad with the aid of light and electron microscopy. Zeitschr. f. Zellforsch. 41, 89–100.

BLOOM, W., and FAWCETT, D. W. 1962. A Textbook of History. 8th Ed., p. 598. W. B. Saunders, Philadelphia, Pa.

BRIGHTMAN, M. W., and PALAY, S. L. 1963. The fine structure of ependyma in the brain of the rat. J. Cell Biol. 19, 415–439.

COHEN, M., HAGIWARA, S., and ZOTTERMAN, Y. 1955. The response spectrum of taste fibers in cat: a single fiber analysis. Acta Physiol. Scand., 33, 316–332.

COPENHAVER, W. M. 1964. Bailey's Textbook of Histology. Williams and Wilkins Co. Baltimore, Md.

DeLORENZO, A. J. 1957. Electron microscopic observations of the olfactory mucosa and olfactory nerve. J. Biophys. Biochem. Cytol. 3, 839–850.

DeLORENZO, A. J. 1958. Electron microscopic observations on the taste buds of the rabbit. J. Biophysic. and Biochem. Cytol. 4, 143–150.

DeLORENZO, A. J. 1960. Electron microscopy of the olfactory and gustatory pathways. Ann. Otol. Rhinol. Laryngol. 69, 410–420.

DeLORENZO, A. J. 1963. Studies on the ultrastructure and histophysiology of cell membranes, nerve fibers and synaptic junctions in chemoreceptors. In Olfaction and Taste. Y. Zotterman, (Editor), pp. 5–17. Macmillan Co., New York.

DeROBERTIS, E. 1958. Submicroscopic morphology and function of the synapse. Exp. Cell Res., Suppl. 5, 347–369.

DUNCAN, C. J. 1963. Synaptic transmission in taste buds. Nature 203, 875–876.

ENGSTROM, H., and RYTZNER, C. 1956A. The structure of taste buds. Acta Oto-laryngol. 46, 361–367.

ENGSTROM, H., and RYTZNER, C. 1956B. The fine structure of taste buds and taste fibers. Ann. Otol. Rhinol. Laryngol. 65, 361–375.

FARBMAN, A. I. 1965A. Electron microscope study of the developing taste bud in rat fungiform papilla. Devel. Biol. 11, 110–135.

FARBMAN, A. I. 1965B. Fine structure of the taste bud. J. Ultrastructure Res. 12, 328–350.

FARQUHAR, M. G., and PALADE, G. E. 1963. Junctional complexes in various epithelia. J. Cell Biol. 17, 375–412.

FARQUHAR, M. G., and PALADE, G. E. 1965. Cell junctions in amphibian skin. J. Cell Biol. 26, 263–291.

FAWCETT, D. 1961. Cilia and flagella. In The Cell. Vol. II. J. Brachet and A. E. Mirsky, (Editors), pp. 217–297. Academic Press, New York.

FISHMAN, I. Y. 1957. Single fiber gustatory impulses in rat and hamster. J. Cell and Comp. Physiol. 49, 319–334.

FRISCH, D. 1964. An electron microscope study of the nasal mucosa of the mouse. Ph.D. Thesis. New York University.

FRISCH, D. 1965. Ultrastructure of mouse olfactory mucosa. Anat. Rec. 151, 351.

GASSER, H. S. 1956. Olfactory nerve fibers. J. Gen. Physiol. 39, 473–496.

GESTELAND, R. C., LETTVIN, J. Y., PITTS, W. H., and ROJAS, A. 1963. Odor specificities of the frog's olfactory receptors. In Olfaction and Taste. Y. Zotterman, (Editor), pp. 19–34. Macmillan Co., New York.

GRAY, E. G., and WATKINS, K. C. 1965. Electron microscopy of taste buds of the rat. Zeitschr. f. Zellforsch. 66, 583–595.

HEIDENHAIN, M. 1914. The sensory fields and taste buds of the foliate papillae of the rabbit. Arch. f. Mikr. Anat. (in German) 85, 365–479.

KIMURA, K., and BEIDLER, L. M. 1961. Microelectrode study of taste receptors of rat and hamster. J. Cell and Comp. Physiol. 58, 131–140.

LANDGREN, S., LILIJESTRAND, G., and ZOTTERMAN, Y. 1954. Chemical transmission in taste fiber endings. Acta Physiol. Scand. 30, 105–114.

LILJESTRAND, G., and ZOTTERMAN, Y. 1954. The water taste in mammals. Acta Physiol. Scand. 32, 291–303.

LE GROS CLARK, W. E. 1956. Observations on the structure and organization of olfactory receptors in the rabbit. Yale J. Biol. Med. 29, 83–95.

LE GROS CLARK, W. 1957. Inquiries into the anatomical basis of olfactory discrimination. Proc. Roy. Soc. London (Series B) 146, 299–319.

LOVEN, C. 1868. Contributions to the knowledge of the structure of the tastebuds of the tongue (in German). Arch. f. Mikr. Anat. 4, 96–110.

LOWENSTEIN, W. R., SOCOLAR, S. J., HIGASHINO, S., KANNO, Y., and DAVIDSON, N. 1965. Intercellular communication: renal, urinary bladder, sensory and salivary gland cells. Science 149, 295–298.

MOULTON, D. G., and TUCKER, D. 1964. Electrophysiology of the olfactory system. Ann. N. Y. Acad. Sci. 116, 360–428.

MURRAY, R. G., and MURRAY, A. 1960. The fine structure of the taste buds of Rhesus and Cynomalgus monkeys. Anat. Rec. 138, 211–233.

NEMETSCHEK-GANSLER, H., and FERNER, H. 1964. The ultra-structure of the taste buds (in German). Zeitschr. f. Zellforsch. 63, 155–178.

PFAFFMANN, C. 1955. Gustatory nerve impulses in rat, cat and rabbit. J. Neurophysiol. 18, 429–440.

REESE, T. S. 1965. Olfactory cilia in the frog. J. Cell Biol. 25, 209–230.

SCHWALBE, G. 1868. The taste organs of mammals and of man (in German). Arch. f. Mikr. Anat. 4, 154–187.

SHIBUYA, T., and TAKAGI, S. F. 1964. Electrical response and growth of olfactory epithelium of the newt in water and on land. J. Gen. Physiol. 47, 71–82.

SJOSTRAND, F. S. 1963. The ultrastructure of the plasma membrane of columnar epithelium cells of the mouse intestine. J. Ultrastructure Res. 8, 517–541.

SJOSTRAND, F. S., and ELFVIN, L. G. 1962. The layered asymmetric structure of the plasma membrane in the exocrine pancreas cells of the cat. J. Ultrastructure Res. 7, 505–534.

TATEDA, H., and BEIDLER, L. M. 1964. The receptor potential of the taste cell of the rat. J. Gen. Physiol. 47, 479–486.

TRUJILLO-CENOZ, O. 1957. Electron microscope study of the rabbit gustatory bud. Zeitschr. f. Zellforsch. 46, 272–280.

TRUJILLO-CENOZ, O. 1961. Electron microscope observations on chemo- and mechano-receptor cells of fishes. Zeitschr. f. Zellforsch. 54, 654–676.

CHAPTER 3

Kjell B. Doving | Problems in the Physiology of Olfaction

INTRODUCTION

Most animals rely on different systems of sensory detectors, to perform essential life processes such as feeding and reproduction. The ability to distinguish between a large number of different chemical substances in the outside milieu developed early in the course of animal evolution. Primitive olfactory systems developed first in marine animals and are found in animals of today in a variety of morphological forms. Though the antennae of the Arthropods and the olfactory pit of the fish may seem very different, they serve the same function, and at the microscopic level the receptors look very similar. The nervous elements within the sensory system are organized along the same lines in different phyla and the similarities between animals of the same phylum is still greater. The olfactory elements of primitive fish are thus organized in a fashion similar to that in mammals. The remarkable structural conformity of the olfactory system throughout the vertebrate phylum is of great interest to the comparative neurologist and useful to the physiologist.

In humans the olfactory sense is believed to have lost its importance in reproduction and nutrition and the popular view that the olfactory sense is of use mainly in hedonistic activities may seem correct when we consider how dependent we are upon auditory and visual senses. In spite of the growing interest in olfaction and the increased number of publications in this field, our knowledge of the function of the olfactory system and its influence on our behavior is rather scarce and fragmentary. Studies on the physiological basis of olfaction have been greatly hampered by the small dimensions of the olfactory receptors and by the biochemical composition of the receptor membranes. Until recently it has been difficult to obtain pure materials for use in olfactory experiments. Research in olfactory discrimination has also been delayed by the lack of any definite theories. In spite of these drawbacks our knowledge has increased in the recent years, as shown by the quantity of reviews and books on olfaction. Beets (1964) gives an extensive review of work on the stimulating processes and their relation to odor structure. Most aspects of the functions of the olfactory system have been treated by Ottoson (1963A, B). There have been a few reviews of the electrophysiology of the olfactory system (Antonelli 1962; Moulton and Tucker 1964; Benjamin et al. 1965). Several monographs have also been published (Moncrieff

1951; Le Magnen 1961; Wright 1964), together with various proceedings of odor symposia (Zotterman 1963; Le Magnen 1965).

ANATOMY

At the beginning of this century the anatomists Golgi and Ramón y Cajal established a histological method which has proved extremely useful. They applied a silver impregnation technique to histological brain sections which made it possible to trace a single neuron from the dendrites along the axon to the opposite end. Most of our knowledge about the organization of the olfactory system is based upon their technique. The drawings in Fig. 21 and 22 are reconstructions of histological preparations to which the technique has been applied.

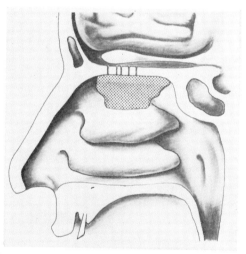

Fig. 19.   Sagittal Section of the Human Nasal Cavity,
Olfactory Epithelium Stippled

The olfactory system in man is outlined in Fig. 19. The sensory epithelium (stippled) lines the walls and roof of the nasal cleft and covers an area of about 2.5 sq. cm. on each side. From the olfactory epithelium, the olfactory nerves pass through holes in the cribriform plate to the olfactory bulb. The olfactory tracts connect the bulbs with the rest of the brain (see also Figs. 21 and 22). There are two extensive reviews on the literature of the anatomy of the olfactory system (Ariëns Kappers *et al.* 1936; Allison 1953).

Olfactory Nerve

Each olfactory receptor conveys information via its thin axon to the olfactory bulb. The diameters of these unmyelinated fibers are about 0.2 μ as resolved by the electron microscope (Gasser 1956; de Lorenzo 1957). These axons are situated in close proximity to each other, and a unique property of these fibers is that several hundred of them are encased in one common satellite cell (see Fig. 20). The size of the olfactory nerve fibers is best illustrated by the number of axons per unit area in electron micrograph cross-sections. Gasser (1956) found a mean value of 10 fibers per sq. μ, in the pig. From the pictures of other authors it is possible to estimate a number of 25 fibers per sq. μ (Andres 1965; de Lorenzo 1957). The number is obviously dependent upon the amount of glia in the sections. In the olfactory nerve of fish (burbot) the mean number of olfactory axons excluding glia has been estimated to be 36 fibers per sq. μ (Gemne 1964).

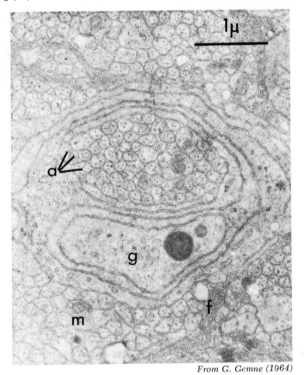

From G. Gemne (1964)

FIG. 20. TRANSVERSE SECTION OF THE OLFACTORY NERVE OF BURBOT

(a) Axons; (m) Mitochondrion; (f) Glial Filaments; (g) Glia Cell.

Olfactory Bulb

The first processing of the information coming from the receptors occurs in the olfactory bulb. Here the receptor axons end in glomeruli
where they make synaptic contact with the dendrites of second order neurons. The glomeruli are spherical structures about 0.2 mm. in diameter
making up an outer layer in the bulb as demonstrated in Fig. 21. The
secondary neurons of mammals are of three kinds: short axon periglomerular cells, small tufted cells situated in the external plexiform layer, and
larger mitral cells making a distinct layer inside the former. In the core

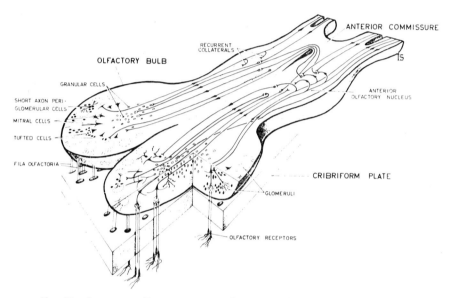

FIG. 21. SCHEMATIC DIAGRAM OF THE OLFACTORY PATHWAYS IN MAMMALS

of the olfactory bulb there are small granular cells with processes directed to the external plexiform layer. In mammals the tufted and mitral
cells send one primary dendrite to the glomeruli, and have several secondary dendrites which end in the external plexiform layer. In the lower
vertebrates the secondary neurons have several dendrites going to different glomeruli (van Gehuchten and Martin 1891; Holmgren 1920; Hanström 1928; Allison 1953). The structural conformity of the olfactory
system is shown in Fig. 22. The olfactory receptors in both arthropods
and vertebrates are bipolar cells making synaptic contact with a relatively
small number of the secondary neurons in the typical glomerular structures.

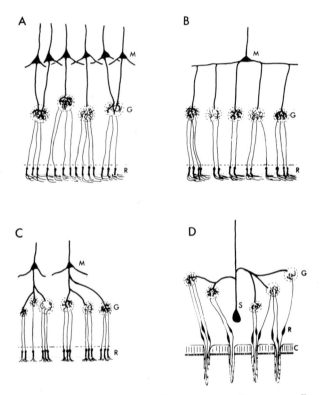

Fig. 22. The Relationship Between the Olfactory Receptors (R), and the Mitral Cells (M) and Secondary Neurons (S) in Different Animals

(A) Mammal; (B) Bird; (C) Fish; (D) Arthropod. (G) Glomeruli; (c) Cuticle.

A most conspicuous fact about the anatomy of the olfactory system is the convergence of a large number of receptors upon the neurons which transfer information to the brain. The number of receptors is very large compared to the number of secondary neurons within the olfactory bulb. In the rabbit the numbers of receptors, glomeruli, and mitral cells have been estimated to be 5×10^7, 1900 and 48,000 respectively (Allison and Warwick 1949). Each glomerulus receives input from about 25,000 receptors and since each mitral neuron has only one primary dendrite, transmits information to about 24 mitral cells. Hence, there is an enormous convergence of receptors upon the mitral cells, averaging 1000 to 1.

Recent electron microscopic studies have demonstrated complex synaptic formations within the olfactory bulb (Hirata 1964; Andres 1965; Rall *et al.* 1966). The synapses in the glomeruli are polarized for nervous transmission from the receptor axons to dendrites of the secondary neurons. In the outer plexiform layer there are dendro-dendritic synapses of different kinds indicating synaptic interaction between the secondary dendrites of the secondary neurons as well as between the dendrites of the secondary neurons and the granular cell processes. Rall *et al.* (1966) proposed that the processes of the granular cells are excited via the mitral cell dendrites, and that the mitral cells may be inhibited by granular cell processes. These dendro-dendritic synapses may be responsible for the large proportion of inhibited units in the olfactory bulb in response to odor stimuli.

The Olfactory Tract

The olfactory bulb is connected to the brain by a fiber tract. In most mammals this is rather short and difficult to discern from other brain structures, but it may be long and easily accessible in some vertebrates, as in man and some fish orders. Each fiber tract is divided into a lateral and a medial bundle, the medial one being called the anterior limb of the anterior commissure in higher vertebrates. In the rabbit both the anterior limb of the anterior commissure and the lateral olfactory tract contain afferent and efferent fibers (Powell and Cowan 1963). In the guinea pig the lateral olfactory tract has been said not to contain any efferent fibers (Lohman 1963). The medial olfactory tract in some fishes contains a large number of unmyelinated fibers with a conduction velocity slightly higher than that of the olfactory nerve fibers (Döving and Gemne 1965). Unmyelinated fibers have also been shown in the human olfactory tract (Liss 1956). These findings indicate that unmyelinated fibers may be more common in the olfactory tract than previously realized.

The long olfactory stalks of some bony fishes (Döving and Gemne 1965) offer a convenient preparation for studying the connections in the telencephalon between those neurons of second or higher order which take part in the olfactory system. The tracts in these fishes may be considered as forward extensions of the forebrain. Electron microscopic investigation of the olfactory tract synapses show (Gemne, in preparation) that in the medial olfactory tract there are frequent conventional synapses with presynaptic clustering of vesicles and the typical specialization of the adjacent part of the postsynaptic membrane. Neuronal processes with numerous neurotubules can be found to cross obliquely the bundles of parallel-running myelinated and unmyelinated fibers and also to approach regions with particularly frequent synapses. Convergence of several fibers making synaptic contacts with one neuron is frequently observed.

The Olfactory Brain

The neurons of the olfactory bulbs are connected directly or indirectly to different brain centers which together are called the "rhinencephalon" or the olfactory brain. An excellent review of this topic is made by Pribram and Kruger (1954). The rhinencephalic areas are divided into three systems based upon their connections to the olfactory bulb. The first system has direct connections with the olfactory bulb and includes the olfactory tubercle, area of diagonal band, prepyriform cortex, and corticomedial nuclei of the amygdaloid complex. The second system has direct connections with the first one but none with the bulb. This in-

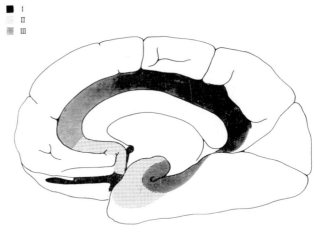

From Pribram and Kruger (1954)

FIG. 23. DIAGRAM OF THE HIGHER BRAIN CENTERS CONNECTED
TO THE OLFACTORY SYSTEM

Olfactory bulb and tract in black: (I) First system; (II) Second system; (III) Third system (see text).

cludes the subcallosal and frontotemporal cortex, and septal nuclei and basolateral nuclei of the amygdaloid complex. The areas which have direct connections with the second system and none with the olfactory bulb or the first system are called the third system and include Ammon's formation and the entorhinal, retrosplenial, and cingulate cortex. The different systems are outlined in Fig. 23.

The effect of electrical stimulation of the olfactory brain areas results in respiratory, vascular, and gross motor changes (for reviews see Kaada 1951, and Gastaut 1952). It should be emphasized that the areas mentioned are not limited to olfactory function. Lesions in the amygdala effect food intake, temperature regulation, and sleeping cycles. Furthermore, lesions in the second system affect emotional behavior. It has been suggested that the amygdaloid complex and Ammon's formation are concerned in both gustatory and olfactory function; this is supported by the occurrence of "uncinate" seizures in man which include both taste and smell sensations.

Efferent Connections to the Olfactory Bulb

In recent years, there has been a growing interest in the central regulation of sensory systems. These centrifugal effects may be exerted on the receptor organs or on the neurons leading to the central nervous system.

In the olfactory system the efferent fibers do not reach the olfactory receptors. Evidence has been presented (Cragg 1962; Powell and Cowan 1963) that some of the efferents end near the glomerular layer of the bulb while most of them end in the granular cell layer (Ramón y Cajal 1911; Powell and Cowan 1963). These findings are supported by electrophysiological evidence showing that the short-axon periglomerular cells are not influenced by stimulation of the lateral olfactory tract. In mammals the efferent neurons presumably have their cell bodies in the anterior olfactory nucleus and olfactory tubercle (Powell and Cowan 1963; Lohman 1963; Ramón y Cajal 1911), exerting their influence upon the secondary neurons (mitral and tufted cells) via the granular cells (Shepherd 1963A, B). The anterior olfactory nucleus is in many species situated close to the olfactory bulb. This fact has not been taken into account in many electrophysiological and anatomical studies involving ablation of the olfactory bulb (von Baumgarten et al. 1962; Green et al. 1962). Ramón y Cajal (1911) proposed that the axons of the tufted cells made up an important pathway between the olfactory bulbs (Allison 1953), constituting a direct interbulbar connection without involving any synapses. This statement has been disputed by several authors (see van Gehuchten 1903; Lohman 1963; Valverde 1965). Recent studies have indicated that the tufted cell axons do not leave the olfactory bulb, and may be considered as short axon periglomerular cells which have migrated inward rather than mitral cells which have migrated outward (Valverde 1965). In fish, the interbulbar connection seems to be mediated via synapses in the telencephalon (Döving and Gemne 1966). The interbulbar connection in mammals may take another route involving the efferent neurons in the anterior olfactory nucleus (Lohman 1963) or possibly the neurons from the olfactory tubercle running in the lateral olfactory tract (Powell and Cowan 1963). The two bulbs may act via these several connections as a functional unit. The efferent neurons involved in the interbulbar pathways may also be influenced by other parts of the central nervous system.

FUNCTIONAL ASPECTS

The large number of technical difficulties involved in studying the physiology of olfaction often leads the student of smell to choose the most convenient animals for his experiments and the larger proportion of the experiments have been made on lower vertebrates such as the frog. This might seem awkward since many people may think that what one learns about olfaction in frogs is not valid for humans. However, comparative neuroanatomy tells us that the elements making up the olfactory system and their general organization are very similar within the vertebrate phylum, so that the differences between frog and man are probably not very great as far as the primary olfactory system and its physiology are concerned.

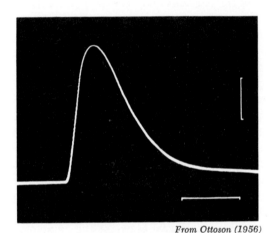

From Ottoson (1956)

Fig. 24.   Response of the Olfactory Epithelium of Frog
to Stimulation with Butanol (EOG)

Upward deflection indicated negativity of the recording electrode.   Vertical bar 1 mV.   Time bar 2 sec.

Primary Processes

When the olfactory epithelium is stimulated with a short blow (one second) of odorous air, the epithelium responds with a slow change in electric potential. Shortly after the molecules hit the epithelium (0.3 sec.) there is a swift negative phase which reaches a maximum and returns to the original baseline several seconds after the end of stimulation (Fig. 24). This monophasic negative change in potential of the receptor epithelium was first described and analyzed by Ottoson (1956, 1958) and was called by him the electro-olfactogram (EOG). Interestingly

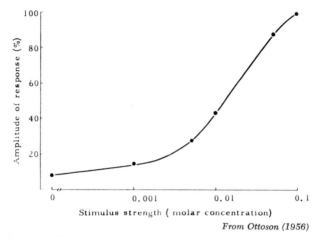

From Ottoson (1956)

FIG. 25.   RELATIONSHIP BETWEEN STIMULUS STRENGTH (BU-
TANOL) AND AMPLITUDE OF THE EOG

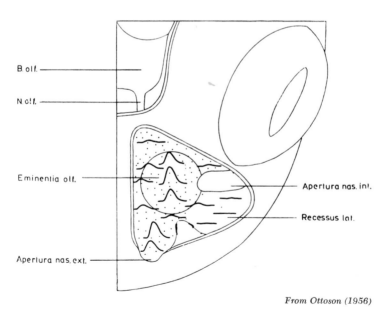

From Ottoson (1956)

FIG. 26.   DISTRIBUTION OF THE EOG IN THE NASAL CAVITY OF FROG
Dotted area indicates olfactory epithelium.

enough, this receptor potential was predicted by Behnke at a symposium of the New York Academy of Sciences in 1953 (Behnke 1954).

The electro-olfactogram is a mass response from all the receptors of the epithelium the amplitude of which is dependent upon the stimulus strength (Fig. 25). The concentration range to which the receptors respond covers about two orders of magnitude. This potential change can be recorded only from the receptor epithelium. Fig. 26 shows the distribution of the EOG in the nasal cavity of the frog. The EOG was obtained from the sensory epithelium, whereas no response was elicited from the respiratory epithelium. For stimuli of equal strength the amplitude of the EOG is highest when the recording electrode is just touching the surface of the epithelium and diminishes as the electrode is pushed into the receptor layer (Fig. 27) (Ottoson 1956; Byzov and Flerova 1964). When the epithelium is covered with a thin film of plastic the EOG does not appear (Ottoson 1956).

It is likely that the potential change originates in the receptor cilia. The receptor potential induced by the stimulus is presumably spread electronically toward the axon where the nerve impulses are initiated. But so far only indirect evidence for this has been presented. The influence of drugs upon the receptor potential has been investigated by several authors (Ottoson 1956; Grundfest and Sigg 1959). The results of these studies show that the EOG is affected in a way characteristic for receptor potentials of other sense organs.

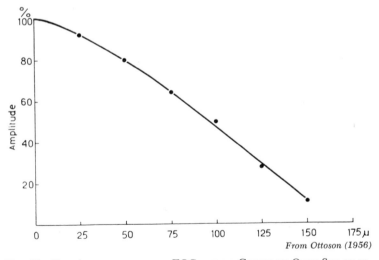

From Ottoson (1956)

Fig. 27. The Amplitude of the EOG with a Constant Odor Stimulus, Recorded with a Microelectrode at Different Depths in the Receptor Layer

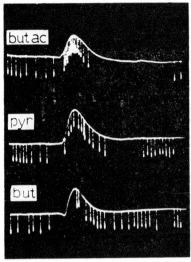

From Gesteland et al. (1963)

FIG. 28.   MICROELECTRODE RECORDING OF IMPULSE ACTIVITY
FROM A SINGLE RECEPTOR STIMULATED WITH BUTYRIC ACID,
PYRIDINE, AND *n*-BUTANOL

A few successful attempts to record the nervous activity of single receptors have been made.   Fig. 28 shows how the activity of one unit
is modified when the epithelium is stimulated with butyric acid, pyridine,
and *n*-butanol.   Butyric acid activates the unit, while it is hardly affected
by pyridine.   This figure also shows that the receptors are spontaneously
active in the absence of overt stimulation and indicates that *n*-butanol
inhibits this activity.   Out of the total number of units sampled 40%
were excited by the 25 stimuli used (Gesteland *et al.* 1963).

Like the olfactory epithelium of vertebrates, the insect antennae respond with a slow monophasic change in potential when stimulated with
an odorous stream of air (for a review see Schneider 1963A).   From these
antennae it is also possible to record spike activity of single receptor
units.   The receptors of the carrion beetle (*Necrophorus*) show in most
cases no spontaneous activity, but are vigorously activated by the odor
of decayed flesh (Boeckh 1962).   The elicited activity may be inhibited
by an additional stimulus as shown in Fig. 29.   As mentioned above, the
olfactory nerve of the vertebrates is composed of receptor cell axons of
about 0.2 μ in diameter.   The small diameter of the fibers as well as
their homogeneity is reflected in the compound action potential of this
nerve, which consists of a single component conducted at a maximum
velocity of about 0.2 m./sec. (Garten 1903; Fox *et al.* 1944; Gasser 1956;

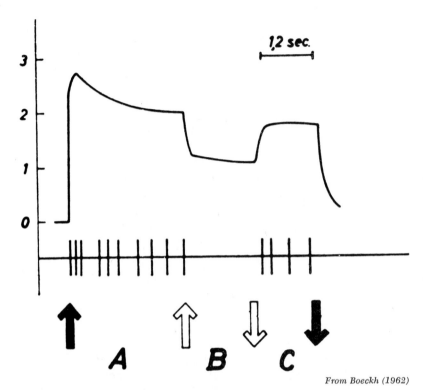

From Boeckh (1962)

Fig. 29. The Responses of Insect Antenna of *Necrophorus Humator* to Simultaneous Stimulation of Decayed Flesh (A and C) and Cyclohep-tanone (B), Showing Inhibition of Receptor Activity (Lower Trace) and a Coincidence of Positive Dip in the Slow Potential Change

Ottoson 1959C; Tucker 1963). In many animals the slow rate of conduction is compensated for by a short distance to the olfactory bulb. In most fishes, however, the olfactory nerve is very long.

The peculiar and unique arrangement of the olfactory nerve fibers with their close proximity to each other has raised doubts about their functional individuality, i.e. that there might be ephaptic transmission between these axons. For the preservation of information it seems to be important that the receptor units do not act in unison. Gasser (1955) discussed this problem at some length for other unmyelinated fibers and concluded that the axons act independently. His conclusions were partly based upon anatomical reconstructions which showed that an axon frequently passed from one bundle to another. Gesteland *et al.* (1963) recorded the nervous impulses of several receptor units simultaneously, but did not report any unit activity which was dependent on the activity of other units. This argues against the possibility of one receptor unit affecting its neighbor ephaptically. It can further be argued that the long duration of the action potential and its slow rate of conduction are unfavorable for ephaptic transmission. The relatively high threshold of these fibers to electrical shocks also make it improbable that the axons are affected by each other. The extracellular space of about 200 Å thickness seems adequate to carry the axon currents without influencing the neighboring axons (Kuffler and Potter 1964).

Secondary Processes

The olfactory bulb exhibits persistent electrical activity in the absence of direct (overt) stimulation of the olfactory mucosa. This was first demonstrated by Gerard and Younge (1937) who showed that continuous activity is maintained in the absence of afferent inflow, i.e. after transection of the olfactory nerve. The intrinsic activity either persists unchanged or becomes enhanced when the bulb is isolated from the rest of the brain by sectioning the olfactory tract. When the olfactory epithelium is stimulated with a short puff of odorized air, an electrode on the sur-

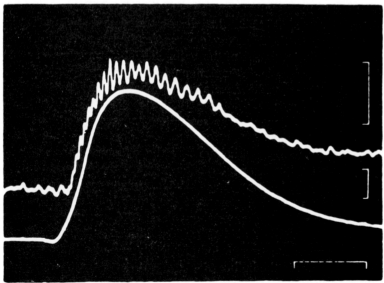

From Ottoson (1959 B)

Fig. 30. Relationship Between the Frog's EOG (Lower Trace) and the Gross Activity Recorded at the Surface of the Olfactory Bulb (Upper Trace)

Stimulus 0.1 M butanol. Time bar 1 sec. Vertical bars 1 mV.

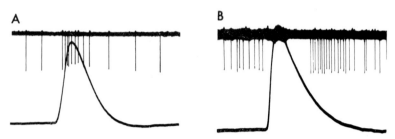

FIG. 31. SIMULTANEOUS RECORDING OF EOG (LOWER TRACE) AND DISCHARGE
OF A SINGLE BULBAR UNIT, STIMULUS BUTANOL

(A) Excitatory Type of Response; (B) Inhibitory Type of Response.

face of the bulb records a slow sustained potential upon which is superimposed oscillatory waves. Experimental evidence suggests that the
slow potential is developed in the dendritic network of the secondary
neurons, while the oscillatory waves most probably arise from synchronous firing of the bulbar neurons. The bulbar activity is shown recorded
simultaneously with the EOG in Fig. 30. The time courses of the two
slow potentials are very similar and their amplitudes have almost identical relations to the stimulus strength (Ottoson 1959A, B).

Adrian (1950, 1953, 1956) first demonstrated that the application of
odorous stimuli to the olfactory mucosa resulted in a discharge of impulses from the deep layers of the bulb. There is a regular spontaneous
discharge of impulses, and stimulation with odors increases the firing rate
(Fig. 31A). The recordings were most probably done from the secondary neurons. Recent studies (Mancia et al. 1962A; Döving 1964) have
shown that most frequently the secondary neurons are not excited but
inhibited as shown in the record of Fig. 31B. Comparative studies of the
nervous activity in the epithelium and the olfactory bulb suggest that
this inhibition is a result of interaction between the neurons of the bulb
even though some inhibiting effects have been shown at the receptor level.
Only ten per cent of the neurons in the frog's bulb remain unaffected
(Döving 1964) while in the periphery about 60% are unaffected by odor
stimulation (Gesteland et al. 1963). The difference in behavior may be
due to the convergence mentioned previously and also to interaction between the neurons in the bulb.

Central Regulative Mechanism

The efferents to the olfactory bulb can be divided into two groups,
those mediating impulses from higher brain centers such as the reticular
formation, and those taking part in the interbulbar connections. De-

pending on the anatomical arrangement of the nervous pathways, a given efferent neuron may be involved in both of these pathways (see Fig. 21).

The existence of a functional linkage between the two bulbs has been repeatedly documented in different vertebrates (Kerr and Hagbarth 1955; Kerr 1960; Walsh 1959; Mancia *et al.* 1962B; Callens 1965; Döving and Gemne 1966). Mancia *et al.* (1962B) showed that the activity from a single mitral cell in the bulb is excited by stimulation of the sensory epithelium on one side, but inhibited when the contralateral side was stimulated with the same odor.

In general, electrical stimulation of one bulb tends to suppress the spontaneous or induced activity of the other (Kerr and Hagbarth 1955; Kerr 1960). Stimulation of the anterior commissure at a low frequency excites the olfactory bulb while shocks applied at high frequency inhibit the activity (Kerr 1960; Callens 1965). Stimulation of the lateral olfactory tract induces single spikes in the mitral cells (Phillips *et al.* 1963; Shepherd 1963A, B) followed by a suppressed excitability. The units in the granular cell layer respond with bursts of impulses to olfactory tract volleys (Shepherd 1963B), and to stimulation of the contralateral olfactory bulb and prepyriform cortex (Callens 1965). In fish the interbulbar connection is most probably mediated via synapses in the telencephalon, and single efferent neurons may be excited by stimulation of both the ipsilateral and contralateral tracts (Döving and Gemne 1966). In this way some efferents take part in a feedback loop between the bulb and the telencephalon. The possible existence of such a loop has been pointed out by several anatomists (Ramón y Cajal 1911; Allison 1953; Powell and Cowan 1963).

The bulbar activity of mammals is influenced by the reticular formation (Hernández-Peón *et al.* 1960; Mancia *et al.* 1962B). The latter authors showed that single bulbar units could be both excited and inhibited by electrical stimulation of the reticular formation and frequently the type of response changed from excitatory to inhibitory upon such stimulation. The function in olfactory discrimination of the efferent system including its participation in these feedback loops is still unknown.

Olfactory Brain

There have been several experiments in which the behavior of the animals was studied following excision or stimulation of neural structures. Studies on olfactory discrimination in rats have been made by Swann (1934, 1935), who trained rats in an experimental maze and found that excision of the olfactory bulb or section of the intermediate olfactory stria impaired discrimination. However, section of the medial and lateral olfactory stria, and lesions of the septal region, prepyriform cortex, amygda-loid complex, and Ammon's formation did not affect the discriminatory performance. Furthermore it has been demonstrated that large lesions involving up to 85% of the cortex have failed to interfere with the olfac-tory behavior of the rat. Similar experiments (Brown et al. 1963; Lashley and Sperry 1943) have also demonstrated that in the performance of ol-factory discrimination only the olfactory bulb seems to be of significance.

An interesting finding in fish is that the unmyelinated fibers of the ol-factory tract terminate on the neurosecretory cells of the preoptic nucleus (Sheldon 1912; Holmgren 1920; Kandel 1964). A similar connection may be present in higher vertebrates as indicated by poliomyelitis virus trac-ings made by Bodian (1950). According to his findings, the olfactory system is directly connected by means of this pathway to the hormone-secreting pituitary gland. Experimental evidence for a connection be-tween the olfactory system and the pituitary gland has been given by several other authors (Nováková and Dlouhá 1960; Miline 1955, 1957; Powell et al. 1963). Nováková and Dlouhá (1960) observed a condition similar to diabetes insipidus in rats 20 days after ablation of the olfactory bulbs, and suggested that the removal of the olfactory bulb caused fiber degeneration reaching to the nuclei of the hypothalamus. Miline (1955, 1957) found morphological changes in the hypothalamus after the ani-mals had been exposed to certain strong odors.

OLFACTORY THRESHOLD

For a long time there has been interest in the minimum concentration of odorous material that can evoke a sensation. Threshold concentrations are known for a large number of substances (Passy 1892; Backman 1917; Henning 1924; Komuro 1921; Zwaardemaker 1921; Moncrieff 1951; Stui-ver 1958; Schneider 1966) and may be as low as 10^6 molecules per cc.

TABLE 7

THRESHOLD CONCENTRATIONS OF DIFFERENT ODOROUS SUBSTANCES OBTAINED WITH NORMAL INSPIRATION[1]

Odor threshold concentration in molecules/cc.

Allyl mercaptan	6×10^7
Secondary butyl mercaptan	1×10^8
Isopropyl mercaptan	1×10^8
Isobutyl mercaptan	4×10^8
Tertiary butyl mercaptan	6×10^8
Thiophenol	8×10^8
Ethyl mercaptan	1×10^9
1,3-Xylen-4-ol	2×10^{12}
m-Xylene	2×10^{12}
Acetone	6×10^{13}

[1] From Stuiver (1958).

with normal breathing.   The values vary according to the method of testing, viz., whether the subject sniffs, inspires normally, or has the gas blown
into his nose.   Typical examples are given in Table 7.

The low concentrations necessary to evoke a sensation have quite naturally led to speculation about the minimum number of molecules required to stimulate a single olfactory receptor.   For the potent mercaptan substances this number has been calculated to be less than ten per
receptor (Stuiver 1958).   The same author concluded that at least 40
receptors must be activated simultaneously before a sensation is perceived.   The male silk moth (*Bombyx mori*) is especially sensitive to the
sexual attractant bombycol (for a review see Karlson and Butenandt 1959;
Schneider 1963A, B, 1966).   The male moths have a large pair of antennae with many receptors all of which are sensitive to bombycol
(Schneider 1962).

Human olfactory acuity is generally believed to be inferior to that of
dogs and other mammals with well developed olfactory epithelium.   Recent psychophysical experiments have shown that the threshold concentration detected by dogs (Moulton *et al.* 1960; Becker *et al.* 1957, 1962)
and rats (Moulton and Eayrs 1960; Goff 1961) is about one hundred
times lower than in man.   The threshold concentrations for the odor trail
substance in fire ants have been estimated to be about 10^{15} molecules per
cc. (Wilson and Bossert 1963), which is considerably higher than the
threshold for the sex attractant in the silk moth, which is about 10^7 molecules per cc. (Schneider 1966).   Phenol has been demonstrated to be per-

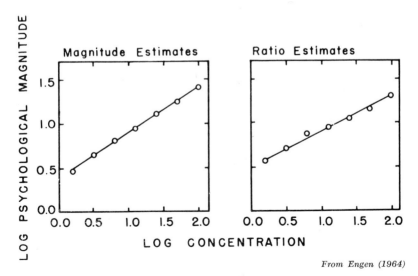

From Engen (1964)

Fig. 32.   Psychological Magnitude Estimates of Amyl Acetate

ceived by fish at a concentration of about 10^{13} molecules per cc. (Hasler and Wisby 1949; Marcström 1959) which again is lower than the threshold for man. Bull (1937) estimated the threshold concentrations for detection of salinity changes in fish to be about 0.03–0.3% depending upon the rate of change. What sense organ is involved in this astonishing performance is not known. A review of the chemoreception in fish is given by Teichmann (1962).

Psychophysical scaling of odor intensity has been shown to be an exponential function, at least for some substances (Fig. 32) (Engen and Lindström 1962; Engen 1961, 1964). The typical exponent for the stimulus response relationship was found to be low compared with other sensory systems (Stevens 1957; Reese and Stevens 1960).

Variations in Olfactory Threshold

The olfactory sensitivity varies from time to time for the same subject. These variations may be due to changes in the function of the olfactory epithelium, or may depend upon changes in the central nervous system. Recent observations by Schneider and Wolf (1960) indicate that factors which interfere with the sensory epithelium are responsible for these changes in olfactory threshold. They found a close relationship between olfactory threshold and swelling, shrinkage, and color of the olfactory mucosa. Both shrunken and swollen epithelia were associated with decreased olfactory sensitivity.

The olfactory and taste thresholds may be reduced in certain patients with cystic fibrosis (Henkin and Powell 1962; Henkin and Kopin 1964), but the cause of these disorders is not well understood.

It is well known that there is a correlation between sexual function and olfaction. Systemic administration of estrogenic hormones produces a swelling of the nasal mucosa (Mortimer et al. 1936A, B, C). It seems likely that the changes in olfactory sensitivity which have been observed during pregnancy might be explained as hormonal effects upon the nasal mucosa. Schneider et al. (1958) found that in hypogonadal women the olfactory threshold decreased with estrogen and increased with androgen administration. Hammer (1951) found that the olfactory threshold of pregnant women was lowest just before and after giving birth.

The olfactory threshold has been shown by Le Magnen (1952) to fluctuate with the menstrual cycle. For the substance exaltolide, a macrocyclic musk, the threshold decreases after menstruation, reaching a minimum about the time of ovulation. Just after ovulation the threshold rises to the normal value. Köster (1965) found a small but significant decrease in olfactory threshold for meta-xylenes about the time of ovulation. For other substances the olfactory sensitivity did not alter during the men-

TABLE 8

MAGNITUDE ESTIMATE OF A MACROCYCLIC MUSK (EXALTOLIDE) AMONG MEN, WOMEN, BOYS AND
GIRLS[1]

Intensity Scale	Men, No.	Women, No.	Boys, No.	Girls, No.
Odorless or very weak	18	4	15	10
Weak	5	3	6	14
Strong	2	11	1	0
Very strong	0	7	0	1

[1] From Le Magnen (1948A).

strual cycle (Le Magnen 1952; Köster 1965). These differences may be odor specific, and the musky odor of exaltolide has been associated with the sexual character of this odor. In a recent study, Cluzel (1964) showed that removal of the ovaries or menopause in women resulted in a loss of sensitivity to exaltolide. Other authors found a rise in threshold for citral during menstruation, but no dip in threshold at the time of ovulation (Schneider and Wolf 1955). Le Magnen (1948A, 1950) found that women perceived exaltolide as a much stronger odor than did men, boys and girls (Table 8).

Guild (1956) found diurnal variations in olfactory threshold which may be related to food intake. Hammer (1951) demonstrated the same diurnal variations for taste and flicker-fusion threshold and concluded that food intake was not the only factor responsible for the changes in threshold.

No significant rise in olfactory threshold after food intake was observed by Furchtgott and Friedman (1960). However, Berg et al. (1963) showed that the olfactory *acuity* was increased after food intake.

It is a common observation in medical clinics that some patients treated with penicillin acquire a lower olfactory threshold to this substance which is normally practically odorless. Le Magnen (1948C) has demonstrated that the threshold for amyl salicylate, eucalyptol, camphor, and ether decreased markedly one to eight days after injection of the substances in normal subjects. The decreased threshold was maintained for about 30 days, and then returned to the original value. An additional injection during the sensitive period caused an immediate increase in threshold. The results of these experiments led Le Magnen to suggest a similarity between olfactory and immunological processes.

ADAPTATION

It is a common experience that the perception of a constant odor stimulation diminishes with time. Experimental results support the view that the olfactory organ slowly adapts both to continuous and repetitive stim-

From Ottoson (1956)

Fig. 33. Recording from the Olfactory Epithelium of the Frog Showing Response to Continuous Stimulation with a Flow of Odorized Air

Stimulus butanol, stimulus time 15 sec. Vertical bar 0.5 mV.

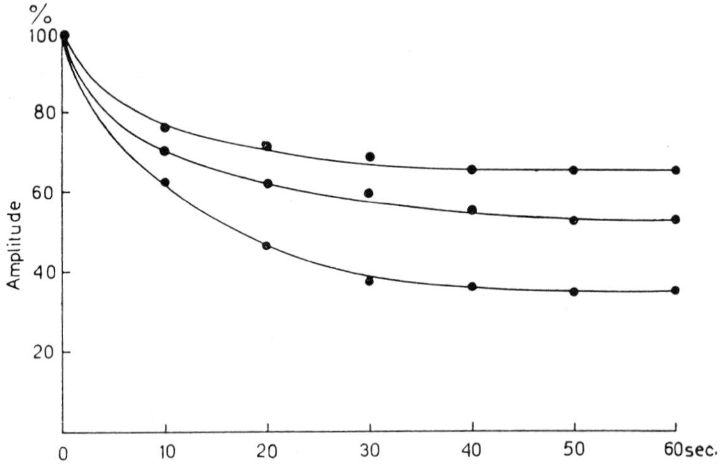

From Ottoson (1956)

Fig. 34. Decrease in Amplitude of EOG to Repeated Stimulations
of the Epithelium

Ordinate, amplitude in per cent of initial response. Upper curve, .001 M;
middle curve, .01 M; lower curve, .1 M butanol. Stimulus interval 10 sec.

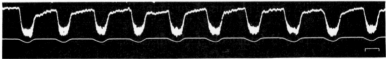

From Ottoson (1959 A)

Fig. 35. Responses from the Olfactory Bulb of the Rabbit to Repeated
Stimulation with Butanol Odorized Air (Upper Trace). Lower Trace
Indicates Stimulation

Time bar 0.5 sec.

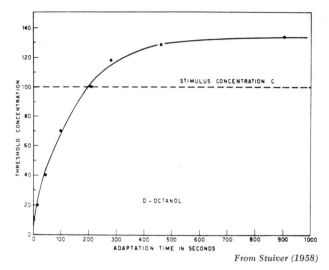

From Stuiver (1958)

FIG. 36. THE INCREASE IN HUMAN OLFACTORY THRESHOLD
DURING CONTINUOUS STIMULATION WITH *d*-OCTANOL AT 100
TIMES THRESHOLD CONCENTRATION

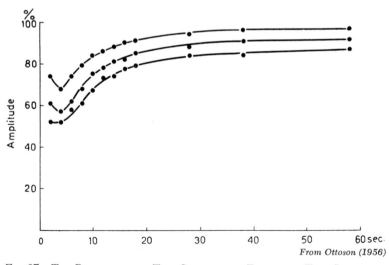

From Ottoson (1956)

FIG. 37. THE RECOVERY OF A TEST STIMULUS AT DIFFERENT TIME INTERVALS
AFTER THE CONDITIONING STIMULUS

Ordinate: Amplitude of EOG in per cent of conditioning response. Stimuli butanol; upper curve, 0.001 M; middle curve 0.01 M; lower curve, 0.1 M.

ulation (Adrian 1950, 1956; Ottoson 1956). The record in Fig. 33 shows how the EOG reaches a maximum at the beginning of the stimulus and is maintained at a nearly steady level during the stimulation. With repetitive stimulation using short puffs of odorous air the amplitude of the frog EOG decreases as shown in Fig. 34. The decrease is more rapid with higher concentrations. The time course of these effects is not consistent with the rate of adaptation occurring in human perception. The bulbar activity in the rabbit is hardly affected by repetitive stimulation

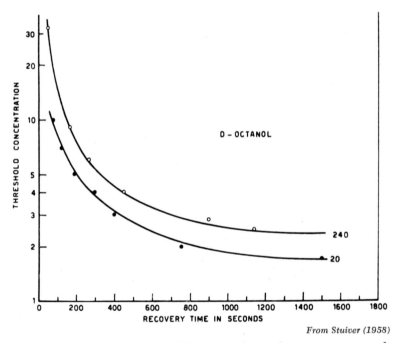

From Stuiver (1958)

Fig. 38. Recovery to Normal Threshold After Stimulation with *d*-Octanol at 120 Times Normal Threshold Concentration for 240 and 20 Sec.

at intermediate stimulus strengths (Fig. 35). In human subjects the threshold rises during stimulation in the way demonstrated in Fig. 36. The threshold rises above the stimulation concentration about three min. after onset of stimulation.

After a stimulus has been applied to the olfactory system its excitability is reduced and slowly recovers to the original level. The time course of the recovery has been studied on the sensory epithelium of the frog and is demonstrated in Fig. 37. Two stimulations of the same strength were applied at different intervals, as seen there is a rapid increase in the amplitude of the second response with intervals of 5 to 20 sec. The slow recovery of the olfactory epithelium is illustrated by the fact that after 1 min. the amplitude of the second response is about 20% of the first one for 0.1 M butanol. The recovery of the human olfactory threshold after adaptation was studied by Stuiver (1958) and two of his experiments with d-octanol are shown in Fig. 38.

Stuiver (1958) measured the duration of the state of increased threshold after a masking stimulus. The technique allowed him to apply mono- and birhinal stimulation. He showed that the duration of reduced sensitivity was longer with increasing stimulus strength and longer for bilateral than for unilateral stimulation. Exposure of only one side of the nose to a stimulus 70 times greater than threshold resulted in about the same reduc-

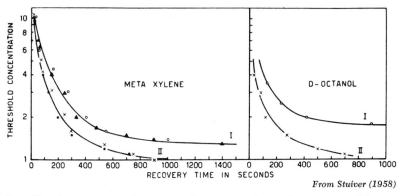

From Stuiver (1958)

FIG. 39. RECOVERY OF OLFACTORY THRESHOLD AFTER IPSILATERAL (I) AND CONTRALATERAL (II) STIMULATION

m-Nylene injected for 80 sec. at a concentration 70 times normal threshold
d-octanol injected for 100 sec. at a concentration 50 times threshold.

tion of sensitivity on both sides, but the sensitivity of the nonstimulated side recovered to a normal level much more rapidly than the stimulated side (Fig. 39).

The results of both electrophysiological and psychophysical experiments in humans indicate that the adaptation process takes place at higher levels than the olfactory bulb. The efferent system has not been studied very much, but it might also play a role in the adaptation process. The probability that adaptation takes place at a higher level makes it more easily accessible for input from other brain areas and might explain why perfumers can perceive an odor longer than an untrained person.

OLFACTORY INFLUENCE UPON
BEHAVIOR AND BODY FUNCTION

The influence of the olfactory system on behavior and body function has been studied by comparatively few authors. Recent experiments have demonstrated that food intake is markedly varied by food flavoring, and the activity of the reproductive system may be altered by olfactory cues.

An outstanding protective behavior pattern has been developed in carp. These fish have specialized "club" cells in their skin, the contents of which are released when the skin is ruptured, for example when the fish is caught by a predator. The substances from these cells in the skin creates a so-called "fright reaction" in the other fish: the school breaks up and each individual seeks a hiding place on the bottom where it remains motionless (von Frisch 1941). The reaction is mediated via the olfactory system and is absent when the olfactory epithelium or the olfactory tracts are destroyed. Comparative studies have demonstrated that the alarm substances of one species may to a certain extent evoke reactions in individuals of another species. These substances are thus not entirely specific for a given species and are most probably chemically related (Schutz 1956; Pfeiffer 1962). In spite of the relatively simple bioassay involved in the identification of the alarm substances, the chemical composition of the substances themselves is not known. Homing salmon are frightened by water in which humans have rinsed their hands, the active substance in this case probably being a polypeptide containing L-serine (Idler *et al.* 1956, 1961; Alderdice *et al.* 1954).

Reproduction

A dramatic influence exerted by the olfactory system upon reproductive function has recently been demonstrated in mice (Bruce 1959, 1962A, B, 1963A, B; Bruce and Parkes 1961; Parkes and Bruce 1961; Parkes 1962A, B, 1963). Newly mated female mice fail to become pregnant if they are subsequently exposed to different males during the preimplantation period. The pregnancy block is most probably caused by a failure in the production of pituitary luteotropic hormone (prolactin) which in normal cases is involved in the preparation of the uterine wall for implantation of the fertilized egg. These effects are strongest in the case of males from other strains but the presence of strange males from the same strain would in some cases also induce the pregnancy block. The experiments indicate that the pregnancy block is caused by some odor from the males which influences the endocrine system via the olfactory bulb. Van der Lee and Boot (1955, 1956) showed that housing female mice together induced a prolongation of the estrus cycle by introduction of pseudopregnancies. When a male was placed in the cage most of the females went into estrus after three or four days (Whitten 1956A, 1957, 1959). The pregnancy block and these other social effects on reproduction in mice, do not occur in females after ablation of the olfactory bulbs (Bruce and Parrot 1960; van der Lee and Boot 1956; Whitten 1956B).

The hypothalamus, which is involved in the olfactory bulb pituitary chain, has connections with both the second and third olfactory systems (see Pribram and Kruger 1954). A direct connection between the olfactory bulb and hypothalamic areas is indicated by the experiments of Bodian (1950). The olfactory connections to the hypothalamus have recently been stressed by Powell et al. (1963). In fish a large number of unmyelinated fibers of the olfactory tract terminate on the neurosecretory cells of the preoptic nucleus, whose axons enter the pituitary gland (Sheldon 1912; Holmgren 1920; Kandel 1964; Döving and Gemne 1965). An analogous innervation may remain in the higher vertebrates and may have escaped detection because of the poor staining ability of such thin fibers. Their slow rate of conduction may have led physiologists to regard this pathway as a multisynaptic rather than a direct one.

The results of the experiments made by Bruce (see above) indicate that each male mouse has a particular odor which is recognized by the female. We do not know what particular odors are involved, but presumably the different odors originate from skin glands. Such scent glands are known in a variety of animals, the best known being the civet cat and the musk ox (see Schaffer 1940). In insects the odors secreted may have a physiological effect on other individuals and such substances are called pheromones (cf. Karlson and Butenandt 1959; Wilson 1963, 1965). They may also be used in territory marking (Tinbergen 1951; Thorpe 1956).

Male rats select females in estrus more frequently than those in anestrus, as shown in T-maze experiments by Le Magnen (1951A, B). This preference was induced by olfactory cues, and was not present in immature or castrated males. Carr and Caul (1962) and Carr et al. (1962) found that there was no difference between normal and castrated males in their ability to distinguish between the odors of females in estrus and anetrus. These results indicate that the hormonal state of the male rats affected their behavior response to the female odors rather than their ability to distinguish the odors. Moncrieff (1966) has recently shown that odor preference in humans changed markedly around the age of puberty.

Olfactory Conditioning

There are many animals which rely on their olfactory sense when migrating or seeking the specific places to carry out their reproductive activities (Scheer 1939; Shapovalov 1940). The predatory wasp Nemeritis normally lays its eggs in the larvae of the flour-moth *Ephistia* (Thorpe and Jones 1937; Thorpe 1938). The female wasp selects the larvae by olfactory cues. Experimental rearing of the wasps in wax-moth larvae or exposure of the newly hatched wasps to the odor of these larvae caused a temporary preference for these larvae. A similar but longer lasting impregnation of olfactory preferences occurs in salmon. The salmon fry return to the actual place where they grew up and started their migration, irrespective of the birthplace (Hasler and Wisby 1951; Wisby and Hasler 1954; Hasler 1960; Donaldson and Allen 1957).

Nutrition

As mentioned in the introductory remarks, many animals rely upon the olfactory sense when seeking food. It has also been shown that the sense of smell is important for the selection of an adequate diet and for the regulation of food intake.

The influence of the sense of smell on the amount of food eaten has long been recognized, but experimental evidence has appeared only recently. The most interesting experiments in this field have been made by Le Magnen (1953, 1956A, B, C, 1959). He has shown that rats offered four different flavored diets eat a regular amount of each diet, after an adaptation time of about one month. The total amount of food eaten was greater, however, when a mixture of all four flavors was given than when a separate flavor was given at each meal. In another series of experiments Le Magnen showed that rats which were used to nonodorized meals showed a reduced food intake when the food was flavored. However, the normal consumption was soon re-established. When the rats had adapted, they were again given the nonodorized food and the food intake increased by some 50%. The increased consumption of the nonodorized food was maintained for about three days, and then gradually decreased.

Olfaction also plays an important role in the selection of an adequate diet. This was first shown by Harris *et al.* (1931) when testing the selection of food in rats depleted of vitamin B. These rats mostly chose the adequate diet when offered a choice of food with or without vitamin B. When the vitamin was offered in a highly concentrated form, the rats could not make this choice. Rats which were not depleted of vitamin B showed no preference until they started to suffer from vitamin deficiency, but then began to make the correct choice. When the number of feeding places offered at each meal was large, the rats were unable to make the correct choice. The typical behavior of the rats making the diet choice was first to sniff at both of the offered diets before eating and then to eat the diet containing the vitamin. Similar experiments have been made by Scott and Quint (1946) and Scott and Verney (1947). This type of behavior might be explained in terms of recent studies showing that physiological situations may occur, either innately or developed through insufficiencies, which give rise to appetite behavior (Lorenz 1950; Tinbergen 1951; Thorpe 1956). It has been proposed that such situations are developed by hormonal changes affecting the central nervous system. The appetite behavior is characterized by a random seeking of food which continues until the drive ceases, i.e. until the appetite is fulfilled. It is well known that the hypothalamus is intimately involved in the appetite behavior patterns (cf. Andersson et al. 1958; Brobeck 1957; Mayer 1952).

TECHNICAL APPLICATIONS

The great acuity of the sense of smell is utilized in daily life such as in finding leakages in the gas tubing, recognizing sour milk, etc. The nearly unmatched ability of the olfactory sense to detect impurities and unwanted substances may be useful in problems of water supply (Hasler and Wisby 1949; Henderson and Pickering 1963; Baker 1963) and air pollution (Gruber et al. 1960).

Gas-liquid chromatography has been of much help in analyzing the constituents of foods and beverages, especially the substances which make up their smell and taste, i.e. their "flavor." Although one may know all the constituents of a product, the blend is very hard to imitate, mostly because one does not know the degree of flavor given by each of the substances. To overcome these difficulties, a new method was developed by Ottoson and von Sydow (1964). The method consists principally of testing the separated substances from a gas-chromatograph directly on biological material. When the indicator records a peak, the outflow is allowed to reach the olfactory receptor epithelium. The area of the chromatogram peak is compared to the corresponding amplitude of the evoked electro-olfactogram. The relation between the concentration of the constituent in the food and its stimulating efficiency might yield information which can help food scientists to imitate the natural product.

A similar way of applying gas chromatography has been developed by Fuller et al. (1964). Instead of using frog olfactory epithelium, they let trained perfumers act as detectors of the gas stream leaving the gas chromatograph. Besides demonstrating the perfumers' professional ability, they also showed that the human nose could detect substances at concentrations which were not detected by the thermal conductivity cell of the apparatus (e.g. methyl heptyl carbonate).

Promising development of instruments for detection of air-borne chemicals has been made in recent years (Moncrieff 1961; Tanyolaç 1965). These devices are based on different absorption coefficients of chemicals on different surfaces, in imitation of the olfactory epithelium.

DISCRIMINATORY MECHANISMS AND ODOR SIMILARITY

The human nose can distinguish a large number of substances. An untrained person can classify about 2000 different odors, and a perfumer or trained chemist about five times that number. This remarkable performance is achieved by a receptor organ about five square centimeters in area containing millions of receptors. It is generally believed that the differentiation takes place at the level of the receptor epithelium, and Adrian (1953, 1956) suggested three possible mechanisms by which the olfactory organ could distinguish the odors: (1) by the existence of different types of receptors with selective sensitivity to different odors; (2) by a spatial distribution of the odors in the receptor epithelium; and (3) by a temporal pattern of excitation. The second hypothesis was advanced on the basis of the observation that different parts of the olfactory bulb exhibited different thresholds to a given odor. Thus the anterior part was shown to have a lower threshold to water-soluble substances than the posterior part, which was more sensitive to lipid-soluble substances (Adrian 1950; Mozell and Pfaffman 1954). The olfactory epithelium of both man and frog is a small sheet situated in a comparatively simple tubular system, where gas-chromatographic-like effects can hardly be assumed to occur, yet these animals perform an adequate discrimination of odors. The different threshold of the different parts of the olfactory bulb may also be explained if one assumes that an uneven distribution of receptor types in the sensory epithelium is projected on to the olfactory bulb. That there is such a projection was demonstrated by Le Gros Clark (1950).

An interesting method for evaluating the degree of similarity between different odor substances which may lead to an identification of the different olfactory receptors was developed by Le Magnen (1948C). The method is based upon the property of the olfactory system to become insensitive to an odor after prolonged stimulation. Le Magnen used different adapting and testing stimuli and showed that, for example, when a subject had adapted, to benzonitrile after a standardized time, he developed insensitivity to benzaldehyde in low concentrations, and described high concentrations as safrole. Adaptation to nitro-musks caused no difference in the threshold of macrocyclic musks, and vice versa. Although two different substances give similar subjective olfactory impressions, these experiments show that they do not necessarily create identical responses in the elements of the olfactory organ. The "cross-adaptation" method has been used by several authors (Cheesman and Mayne 1953; Cheesman and Townsend 1956; Moncrieff 1956; Engen 1963). Cheesman and Mayne (1953) and Cheesman and Townsend (1956) allowed subjects to sniff a certain concentration of one odor, and then the threshold for perceiving the same or another odor was judged under standardized

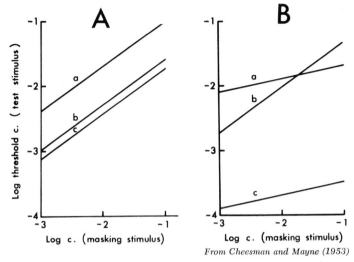

From Cheesman and Mayne (1953)

Fig. 40.   A.   Relationship Between Masking and Test Stimulus
Concentration for Homogeneous Pairs

(a) Isopropanol; (b) Dioxane; (c) Cyclopentanone.

B.   Relationship Between Masking and Test Stimulus
for Heterogeneous Pairs

(a) Masking stimulus cyclopentanone, test stimulus isopropanol; (b)
Masking stimulus cyclopentanone, test stimulus dioxane; (c) Masking
stimulus isopropanol, test stimulus cyclopentanone.

conditions.   These authors showed that the threshold concentration of the
test stimulus was a linear function of the masking stimulus concentration
when plotted on a double logarithmic scale (Fig. 40).   The slopes of the
lines are about 0.7 when the test odor is the same as the masking odor.
The slope varies for different combinations of two odor substances, but is
not dependent on which of them is the masking odor.

The first electrophysiological evidence for the existence of receptor types
of different sensitivity was obtained by Ottoson (1956) who observed the
receptor potential (EOG) in frogs during selective fatigue.   As shown in
Fig. 41 the amplitude of the receptor potential decreased more for butanol
than for amyl acetate after the epithelium had been repetitively stimulated with butanol.

The time-course of the EOG is different for different odors (Fig. 42);
amyl acetate gives a response with a fast rising phase and a rapid decline;
(Ottoson 1956, 1958) other odors give a slow rise and a still slower de-
scending phase.   The different time courses of the receptor potential are

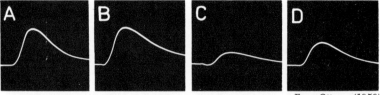

From Ottoson (1956)

FIG. 41. THE EOG OF THE SENSORY EPITHELIUM OF THE FROG TO STIMULA-
TION WITH AMYL ACETATE (A AND D) AND BUTANOL (B AND C)

Records A and B obtained before, C and D after the olfactory epithelium was
repeatedly stimulated with butanol.

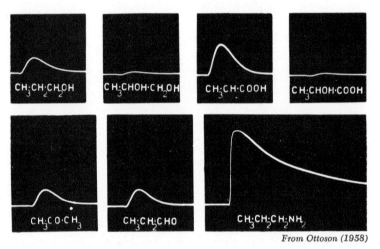

From Ottoson (1958)

FIG. 42. THE OLFACTORY EPITHELIUM RESPONSES TO PROPANOL, PRO-
PYLENE GLYCOL, PROPIONIC ACID, LACTIC ACID, ACETONE, PROPANAL, AND
PROPYLAMINE

reflected in the slow responses obtained from the olfactory bulb. As
Ottoson (1963A) has pointed out, the differences in time course of the excitatory processes for various odors are not necessarily associated with
discriminatory mechanisms.

More direct evidence for the presence of different receptor types was
obtained by Gesteland *et al.* (1963). Using different odor stimuli they
found receptor types with different patterns of response. Some odors excited the units as previously described while other units were inhibited.
Differences in sensitivity have also been demonstrated in the receptors of
the antennae of various insects (for a review, see Schneider 1963B).

Adrian (1951, 1953) first recorded activity from single units in the olfactory bulb in the rabbit and demonstrated that different units, probably

mitral cells, had different thresholds to odors. Further studies have shown that the same bulbar unit may be excited or inhibited by different odor stimuli (Mancia et al. 1962B; Döving 1964).

By observing a relatively large number of units for a given set of odors, the data can be analyzed to yield information about the discriminatory properties of the olfactory system (Döving 1965). The method applied is the chi-square test for independence between any two odors, categorizing the response in excited and inhibited types. Table 9 gives the num-

TABLE 9

THE DISTRIBUTION OF EXCITED AND INHIBITED BULBAR UNITS ELICITED BY STIMULATION OF THE OLFACTORY EPITHELIUM WITH CITRAL AND GERANIOL[1]

		Citral		
		+	−	Total
Geraniol	+	12	11	23
	−	6	37	43
	Total	18	48	66

[1] From Döving (1965).

ber of units of the frog olfactory bulb found to be excited or inhibited by citral and geraniol. The chi-square value on the basis of this data was calculated by Yates' formula and found to be 9.19, which indicates that the two odors are not independent at a significance level of one per cent. The chi-square values tell the degree of similarity between any two odors. High values indicate that the two odors have more similar olfactory properties. In the case of citral and geraniol, this does seem reasonable, since these compounds are an aldehyde and alcohol of the same substance. The different odor pairs obtained with five odors are ranked according to the chi-square values in Table 10. These values tell us that citral, ger-

TABLE 10

THE CHI-SQUARE VALUES BETWEEN PAIRS OF THE ODORS CITRAL, COUMARIN, GERANIO L L-MENTHOL AND SALICYLALDEHYDE[1]

Pair of Odors	Chi-square Values
Citral-geraniol	9.193
Citral-L-menthol	4.928
Geraniol-L-menthol	3.755
Coumarin-salicylaldehyde	2.238
Citral-salicylaldehyde	2.116
Geraniol-salicylaldehyde	1.412
L-menthol-salicylaldehyde	0.220
Coumarin-geraniol	0.049
Citral-coumarin	0.032
Coumarin-L-menthol	0.031

[1] From Döving (1965).

aniol, and menthol are fairly similar in olfactory properties, and indicate that the odors are treated in the same manner by the frog's olfactory system. Two odors with similar olfactory properties will influence the elements of the olfactory system in a similar way and the chi-square value will be high. When the two odors have different olfactory properties, the chi-square values will be low. The possibility exists that odors could have just the opposite influence on the olfactory elements with an associated high chi-square value, but no such odors have been found yet. The discriminatory power of the olfactory system can be described as its ability to give independent responses to different odors. The chi-square value can be taken as a measurement of this ability. This method should also be applicable to the study of insect olfactory systems. Comparative studies of the different organs would give valuable information about the stimulating properties of the odors and the functional properties of the olfactory receptors.

When a series of homologous alcohols were tested in the frog, the chi-square values given in Table 11 were obtained (Döving 1966). These

TABLE 11

THE CHI-SQUARE VALUES BETWEEN PAIRS OF ALCOHOLS (FIRST COLUMN)[1] AND PSYCHOPHYSICAL SIMILARITY ESTIMATES BETWEEN THE SAME SUBSTANCES (SECOND COLUMN)[2]

Pair of Odors	Chi-square Values	Similarity Estimates
Propanol-butanol	46.88	77
Propanol-pentanol	5.77	35
Propanol-hexanol	2.46	46
Propanol-heptanol	1.62	37
Propanol-octanol	0.19	24
Butanol-pentanol	17.06	47
Butanol-hexanol	7.00	45
Butanol-heptanol	3.86	36
Butanol-octanol	1.98	35
Pentanol-hexanol	29.82	53
Pentanol-heptanol	17.88	53
Pentanol-octanol	7.39	44
Hexanol-heptanol	57.97	51
Hexanol-octanol	27.66	58
Heptanol-octanol	47.15	81

[1] Döving (1966).
[2] Engen (1963).

results demonstrate that the neighboring substances have more similar olfactory properties than those more widely separated in chain length. Furthermore, the results show that the similarity in olfactory properties between a pair of adjacent alcohols increases with the number of carbon atoms in the chain (e.g., more similarity between pentanol and hexanol than between propanol and butanol).

The same aliphatic alcohols as those used above have been applied by Engen (1962) in psychophysical similarity estimates. These estimates were made by subjects judging the degree of similarity between pairs of odors on a scale from zero (no similarity) to 100 (identical). The values given for the alcohols are based upon about ten judgments, and the scattering of the data is comparatively large. The mean similarity values are given in Table 11 together with the chi-square values. The rank-correlation coefficient between the values from these two methods is significant at the 0.1% level. The good correlation between the electrophysiological and the psychophysical data is surprising, in view of the species difference. It is comforting, however, since it indicates that the integrative processing is similar in the two species. This finding is in line with the morphological similarity in organization demonstrated by comparative neuroanatomists.

DISCUSSION

Lois Sather.—What method do you use in presenting your odor stimuli to human subjects?

K. B. Döving.—I did not do the experiment, but they have been applied in different methods. In the latest experiment, the subjects were allowed to sniff odors from a flask.

A. I. Farbman.—There are two questions I would like to ask. First, do you think that the electro-olfactogram is a generator potential?

K. B. Döving.—Yes, by all evidence it is the generator potential.

A. I. Farbman.—Then, how do you account for the fact that the amplitude of the potential diminishes drastically when you push your electrode through the epithelium? Also, does it diminish when you blot the mucus at the surface of the epithelium?

K. B. Döving.—Well, if you assume that the receptor potential is generated at the receptor cilia, it seems fairly obvious that it must be decreasing when going through. If you have a receptor surface, the amplitude of the potential would naturally, by physical laws, decrease when you go deeper into the epithelium.

A. I. Farbman.—The second question is, do you think the olfactory mucosa is innervated by the trigeminal nerve or by some other nerve that might influence its electrical response?

K. B. Döving.—It is innervated by the trigeminal nerves. Whether it influences its electrical activity or not, is not known.

A. I. Farbman.—What makes you certain that it is innervated by the trigeminal nerve?

K. B. Döving.—I have made recordings from the trigeminal nerves, but these are sensory trigeminal nerves and not efferents. They are insensitive to the chemical stimuli used, but they are sensitive to mechanical stimulation as touch receptors.

D. A. Fellers.—I would like to ask about the immunological sensitivity which you mentioned earlier. Do you build up this sensitivity by just smelling these compounds or do they have to be injected?

K. B. Döving.—In the experiments mentioned they have been injected.
D. A. Fellers.—I was wondering if this might be related to the development of expert taste panels? In other words, an expert taster would build up a sensitivity due to constantly smelling this particular odor?
K. B. Döving.—That is an important question.

BIBLIOGRAPHY

ADRIAN, E. D. 1950. The electrical activity of the mammalian olfactory bulb. EEG Clin. Neurophysiol. 2, 377–388.
ADRIAN, E. D. 1951. Olfactory discrimination. L'année Psychol. 50, 107–113.
ADRIAN, E. D. 1953. Sensory messages and sensation. The response of the olfactory organ to different smells. Acta Physiol. Scand. 29, 5–14.
ADRIAN, E. D. 1956. The action of the mammalian olfactory organ. J. Laryng. 70, 1–14.
ALDERDICE, D. F., BRETT, J. R., IDLER, D. R., and FAGERLUND, U. 1954. Further observations on olfactory perception in migrating adult coho and spring salmon: properties of the repellent in mammalian skin. Fish. Res. Board Can. 98, 10–12.
ALLISON, A. C. 1953. The morphology of the olfactory system in the vertebrates. Biol. Rev. 28, 195–244.
ALLISON, A. C., and WARWICK, R. T. T. 1949. Quantitative observations on the olfactory system of the rabbit. Brain. 72, 186–197.
ANDERSSON, B., JEWELL, P. A., and LARSSON, P. 1958. An appraisal of the effects of diencephalic stimulation of conscious animals in terms of normal behaviour. In Ciba Foundation Symposium on the Neurological Basis of Behaviour, pp. 76–89 London.
ANDRES, K. H. 1965. Fine structure of the rat olfactory bulb with special regard to the synaptic connection (in German). Z. Zellforsch. 65, 530–561.
ANTONELLI, A. R. 1962. Bibliographic review of electrophysiological research on the olfactory system. I. Electrical activity of the olfactory receptors and the olfactory bulbs. Minerva Otorinolaring. 12, 592–598.
ARIËNS KAPPERS, C. V., HUBER, G. C., and CROSBY, E. C. 1936. The Comparative Anatomy of the Nervous System of Vertebrates, Including Man. Macmillan, New York.
BACKMAN, E. L. 1917. Experimental investigation of olfactory physiology (in Swedish). Uppsala Läk. Fören. Förh. 22, 319–464.
BAKER, R. A. 1963. Odor testing laboratory. J. Water Poll. Control Fed. 35, 1396–1402.
VON BAUMGARTEN, R., GREEN, J. D., and MANCIA, M. 1962. Recurrent inhibition in the olfactory bulb. II. Effects of antidromic stimulation of commissural fibers. J. Neurophysiol. 25, 489–500.
BECKER, R. T., KING, J. E., and MARKEE, J. E. 1962. Studies on olfactory discrimination in dogs. II. Discriminatory behaviour in a free environment. J. Comp. Physiol. Psychol. 55, 773–780.
BECKER, F., MARKER, J. E., and KING, J. E. 1957. Studies on olfactory acuity in dogs. I. Discriminatory behaviour in problem box situations. Brit. J. Animal Behaviour 5, 94–103.
BEETS, M. G. J. 1964. A molecular approach to olfaction. Molecular Pharmacology. E. J. Ariëns (Editor), Academic Press. 2, 3–51.

BEHNKE, A. R. 1954. Basic odor research correlation: Introduction. Ann. N. Y. Acad. Sci. *58*, 15–21.

BENJAMIN, R. M., HALPERN, B. P., MOULTON, D. G., and MOZELL, M. M. 1965. The chemical senses. Ann. Rev. Psychol. *16*, 381–416.

BERG, H. W., PANGBORN, R. M., ROESSLER, E. B., and WEBB, A. D. 1963. Influence of hunger on olfactory acuity. Nature *197*, 108.

BODIAN, D. 1950. The non-olfactory character of the hippocampus, as shown by experiments with poliomyelitis virus. Anat. Rec. *106*, 178.

BOECKH, J. 1962. Electrophysiological investigations on single odor receptors of the antenna of the carrion beetle (*Necrophorus, Coleoptera*) (in German). Z. Vergl. Physiol. *46*, 212–248.

BROBECK, J. R. 1957. Neural control of hunger appetite and satiety. Yale J. Biol. Med. *29*, 565.

BROWN, T. S., ROSVOLD, H. E., and MISHKIN, M. 1963. Olfactory discrimination after temporal lobe lesions in monkeys. J. Comp. Physiol. Psychol. *56*, 190–195.

BRUCE, H. M. 1959. An exteroceptive block to pregnancy in the mouse. Nature *184*, 105.

BRUCE, H. M. 1962A. The importance of the environment on the establishment of pregnancy in the mouse. Animal Behaviour *10*, 3–4.

BBUCE, H. M. 1962B. Continued suppression of pituitary luteotropic activity and fertility in the female mouse. J. Reprod. Fertil. *4*, 313–318.

BRUCE, H. M. 1963A. A comparison of olfactory stimulation and nutritional stress as pregnancy-blocking agents in mice. J. Reprod. Fertil. *6*, 221–227.

BRUCE, H. M. 1963B. Olfactory block to pregnancy among grouped mice. J. Reprod. Fertil. *6*, 451–460.

BRUCE, H. M., and PARKES, A. S. 1961. An olfactory block to implantation in mice. J. Reprod. Fertil. *2*, 195–196.

BRUCE, H. M., and PARROTT, D. M. V. 1960. Role of olfactory sense in pregnancy block by strange males. Science *131*, 1526.

BULL, H. O. 1937. Studies on conditioned responses in fishes. Part VIII. Discrimination of salinity changes by marine teleosts. Report of the Dove Marine Laboratory (Third Series No. 5), 1–35.

BYZOV, A. L., and FLEROVA, G. I. 1964. Electrophysiological research on the olfactory epithelium of the frog. Biofizika. *9*, 217–225.

CALLENS, M. 1965. Peripheral and central regulatory mechanisms of the excitability in the olfactory system. *Thesis*. Brussels 1–132.

CARR, W. J., and CAUL, W. F. 1962. The effect of castration in rats upon the discrimination of sex odors. Animal Behaviour *10*, 20–27.

CARR, W. J., SOLBERG, B., and PFAFFMAN, C. 1962. The olfactory threshold for estrous female urine in normal and castrated male rats. J. Comp. Physiol. Psychol. *55*, 415–417.

CHEESMAN, G. H., and MAYNE, S. 1953. The influence of adaptation on absolute threshold measurements for olfactory stimuli. Quart. J. Exptl. Psychol. *5*, 22–30.

CHEESMAN, G. H., and TOWNSEND, M. J. 1956. Further experiments on the olfactory thresholds of pure chemical substances, using the "sniff-bottle method." Quart. J. Exptl. Psychol. *8*, 8–14.

CLUZEL, J. C. J. 1964. Contribution of the olfactometer to the studies of some endocrine syndromes (in French). *Thesis*. Marseille.

CRAGG, B. G. 1962. Centrifugal fibers of the retina and olfactory bulb, and composition of the supraoptic commissures in the rabbit. Exptl. Neurol. 5, 406–427.

DONALDSON, L. R., and ALLEN, G. H. 1957. Return of silver salmon Oncorhynchus kisutch (Walbaum) to the point of release. Trans. Am. Fish. Soc. 87, 13–22.

DÖVING, K. B. 1964. Studies of the relation between the frog's electro-olfactogram (EOG) and single unit activity in the olfactory bulb. Acta Physiol. Scand. 60, 150–163.

DÖVING, K. B. 1965. Studies on the responses of bulbar neurons of frog to different odor stimuli. Rev. Laryng. (Bordeaux). 86, 845–854.

DÖVING, K. B. 1966. An electrophysiological study of odour similarities of homologous compounds. J. Physiol. In Press.

DÖVING, K. B., and GEMNE, G. 1965. Electrophysiological and histological properties of the olfactory tract of the burbot. J. Neurophysiol. 28, 139–153.

DÖVING, K. B., and GEMNE, G. 1966. An electrophysiological study of the efferent olfactory system in the burbot. J. Neurophysiol. In Press.

ENGEN, T. 1961. Direct scaling of odor intensity. Psychol. Lab. Univ. Stockholm. Rep. 106, 1–13.

ENGEN, T. 1962. The psychological similarity of the odors of aliphatic alcohols. Psychol. Lab. Univ. Stockholm. Rep. 127, 1–10.

ENGEN, T. 1963. Cross-adaptation to the aliphatic alcohols. Amer. J. Psychol. 76, 96–102.

ENGEN, T. 1964. Psychophysical scaling of odor intensity and quality. Ann. N. Y. Acad. Sci. 116, 504–516.

ENGEN, T., and LINDSTRÖM, C. O. 1962. Psychophysical scales of the odor intensity of amyl acetate. Psychol. Lab. Univ. Stockholm, Rep. 114.

FOX, C. A., MCKINLEY, W. A., and MAGOUN, H. W. 1944. An oscillographic study of the olfactory system of cats. J. Neurophysiol. 7, 1–16.

VON FRISCH, K. 1941. Concerning an alarm substance of fish skin and its biological importance (in German). Z. Vergl. Physiol. 29, 46–145.

FULLER, G. H., STELTENKAMP, R., and TISSERAND, G. A. 1964. The gas chromatograph with human sensor: Perfumer Model. Ann. N.Y. Acad. Sci. 116, 711–725.

FURCHTGOTT, E., and FRIEDMAN, M. P. 1960. The effects of hunger on taste and odor RLs. J. Comp. Physiol. Psychol. 53, 576–587.

GARTEN, S. 1903. Physiology of autonomic nerves (in German). Gustav Fischer. Jena.

GASSER, H. S. 1955. Properties of dorsal root unmedullated fibers on the two sides of the ganglion. J. Gen. Physiol. 38, 709–728.

GASSER, H. S. 1956. Olfactory nerve fibers. J. Gen. Physiol. 39, 473–496.

GASTAUT, H. 1952. Correlations between the vegetative nervous system and the connecting pathways in the rhinencephalon (in French). J. Physiol. et Path. Gen. 44, 431.

VAN GEHUCHTEN, A. 1903. Contribution to the study of olfactory processes (in French). Le Nevraxe 6, 193–200.

VAN GEHUCHTEN, A., and MARTIN, I. 1891. The olfactory bulb in several mammals (in French). La Cellule. 7, 205–237.

GEMNE, G. 1964. Personal communication.

GERARD, R., and YOUNGE, J. Z. 1937. Electrical activity of central nervous system in frog. Proc. Roy. Soc. B. 122, 343–352.

GESTELAND, R. C., LETTVIN, J. Y., PITTS, W. H., and ROJAS, A. 1963. Odor specificities of the frog's olfactory receptors. *In* Proc. First Intern. Symp. Olfaction and Taste. Y. Zotterman (Editor). 1963. *1*, 19–34. Pergamon Press.

GOFF, W. R. 1961. Measurement of absolute olfactory sensitivity in rats. Am. J. Psychol. *74*, 384–393.

GREEN, J. D., MANCIA, M., and VON BAUMGARTEN, R. 1962. Recurrent inhibition in the olfactory bulb. 1. Effects of antidromic stimulation of the lateral olfactory tract. J. Neurophysiol. *25*, 467–488.

GRUBER, C. W., JUTZE, G. A., and HUEY, N. A. 1960. Odour determination techniques for air pollution control. J. Air Pollution Control Assoc. *10*, 327.

GRUNDFEST, H., and SIGG, E. B. 1959. Pharmacologic differences of similarly electrogenic neuraxial sites of the bullfrog. Am. J. Physiol. *197*, 539–543.

GUILD, A. A. 1956. Olfactory acuity in normal and obese human subjects: diurnal variations and the effects of d-amphetamine sulphate. J. Laryng. *70*, 408–414.

HAMMER, F. J. 1951. The relation of odour, taste and flicker-fusion thresholds to food intake. J. Comp. Physiol. Psychol. *44*, 403–411.

HANSTRÖM, B. 1928. Comparative anatomy of the nervous systems in invertebrate animals with consideration of its function (in German). Springer. Berlin.

HARRIS, L. J., CLAY, J., HARGREAVES, F. J., and WARD, A. 1931. Appetite and choice of diet. The ability of the vitamin B deficient rat to discriminate between diets containing and lacking the vitamin. Proc. Roy. Soc., Ser. B. *113*, 161–190.

HASLER, A. D. 1960. Homing orientation in migrating fishes. Ergebn. Biol. *23*, 94–115.

HASLER, A. D., and WISBY, W. J. 1949. Use of fish for the olfactory assay of pollutants (phenols) in water. Trans. Am. Fish. Soc. *79*, 64–70.

HASLER, A. D., and WISBY, W. J. 1951. Discrimination of stream odors by fishes and its relation to parent stream behavior. Am. Naturalist. *85*, 223–238.

HENDERSON, C., and PICKERING, Q. H. 1963. Use of fish in the detection of contaminants in water supplies. J. Am. Water Works Assoc. *55*, 715–720.

HENKIN, R. I., and KOPIN, I. J. 1964. Abnormalities of taste and smell thresholds in familial dysautonomia: Improvement with methacholine. Life Sci. *3*, 1319–1325.

HENKIN, R. I., and POWELL, G. F. 1962. Increased sensitivity of taste and smell in cystic fibrosis. Science *138*, 1107.

HENNING, H. 1924. Odor (in German). Leipzig.

HERNÁNDEZ-PEÓN, R., LAVÉN, A., ALCOCER-CUARÓN, C., and MARCELIN, J. P. 1960. Electrical activity of the olfactory bulb during wakefulness and sleep. EEG Clin. Neurophysiol. *12*, 41–58.

HIRATA, Y. 1964. Some observations on the fine structure of the synapses in the olfactory bulb of the mouse, with particular reference to the atypical synaptic configurations. Arch. Histol. Jap. *24*, 293–302.

HOLMGREN, N. 1920. The anatomy and histology of the fore- and midbrain of the bony fishes (in German). Acta Zool. (Stockholm) *1*, 137–315.

IDLER, D. R., FAGERLUND, U., and MAYOH, H. 1956. Olfactory perception in migrating salmon. I. L-serine, a salmon repellent in mammalian skin. J. Gen. Physiol. *39*, 889–892.

IDLER, D. R., McBRIDE, J. R., JONAS, R. E. E., and TOMLINSON, N. 1961. Olfactory perception in migrating salmon. II. Studies on a laboratory bioassay for homestream water and mammalian repellent. Can. J. Biochem. Physiol. 39, 1575–1584.

KAADA, B. R. 1951. Somato-motor, autonomic and electrocorticographic responses to electrical stimulation of "rhinencephalic" and other structures in primates, cat and dog. Acta Physiol. Scand. 24, Suppl. 83, 1–285.

KANDEL, E. R. 1964. Electrical properties of hypothalamic neuroendocrine cells. J. Gen. Physiol. 47, 691–717.

KARLSON, P., and Butenandt, A. 1959. Pheromones (ectohormones) in insects. Ann. Rev. Entomol. 4, 39–58.

KERR, D. I. B. 1960. Properties of the olfactory efferent system. Aust. J. Exptl. Biol. Med. Sci. 38, 29–36.

KERR, D. I. B., and HAGBARTH, K.-E. 1955. An investigation of olfactory centrifugal fiber system. J. Neurophysiol. 18, 362–374.

KOMURO, K. 1921. Odor threshold in an enclosure absolutely odor free (camera inodorata) (in French). Arch. Neurol. Physiol. 6, 20–58.

KÖSTER, E. P. 1965. Olfactory sensitivity and the menstrual cycle. Intern. Rhinol. 3, 57–64.

KUFFLER, S. W., and POTTER, D. D. 1964. Glia in the leech central nervous system: physiological properties and neuron-glia relationship. J. Neurophysiol. 27, 290–320.

LASHLEY, K. S., and SPERRY, R. W. 1943. Olfactory discrimination after destruction of the anterior thalamic nuclei. Am. J. Physiol. 139, 446–450.

VAN DER LEE, S., and BOOT, L. M. 1955. Spontaneous pseudopregnancy in mice. Acta Physiol. Pharmacol. Neerl. 4, 442–444.

VAN DER LEE, S., and BOOT, L. M. 1956. Spontaneous pseudopregnancy in mice II. Acta Physiol. Pharmacol. Neerl. 5, 213–215.

LE GROS CLARK, W. E. 1950. Projection of the olfactory epithelium on to the olfactory bulb: a correction. Nature 165, 452–543.

LE MAGNEN, J. 1948A. A case of olfactory sensitivity being present as a feminine secondary sexual character (in French). Compt. rend. 226, 694–695.

LE MAGNEN, J. 1948B. Analysis of complex odors and homologs by fatigue (in French). Compt. rend. 226, 753–754.

LE MAGNEN, J. 1948C. A study of dynamic factors in olfactory stimulation (in French). Ann. Psychol. 77–89.

LE MAGNEN, J. 1950. New information on the exaltolide phenomenon (in French). Compt. rend. 230, 1103–1105.

LE MAGNEN, J. 1951A. A method for the determination of the response of an animal to biological odors of the male and female (in French). Compt. rend. Soc. Biol. Paris 145, 851–853.

LE MAGNEN, J. 1951B. Variations with sexual state in the response of males to the odor of females and the response of females to the odor of males (in French). Compt. rend. Soc. Biol. Paris 145, 857–860.

LE MAGNEN, J. 1952. Olfacto-sexual phenomena in man (in French). Arch. Sci. Physiol. France 6, 125–167.

LE MAGNEN, J. 1953. Olfaction. Olfactive functioning and its intervention in psychophysiological regulations (in French). J. Physiol. (Paris) 45, 285–326.

LE MAGNEN, J. 1956A. Overeating induced in the white rat by alteration of the mechanism of peripheral satiety (in French). Compt. rend. Soc. Biol. Paris 50, 32–34.

LE MAGNEN, J. 1956B. The role of odor added to the diet in the short-term quantitative regulation of food intake in the white rat (in French). Compt. rend. Soc. Biol. Paris 50, 136–139.

LE MAGNEN, J. 1956C. The role of olfacto-gustatory stimulation on the mechanism and regulation of food intake (in French). Ann. Nutrit. Alim. 10, 153–188.

LE MAGNEN, J. 1959. The role of olfacto-gustatory stimuli on the regulation of feeding behavior in the mammal (in French). J. Psychol. 2, 137–160.

LE MAGNEN, J. 1961. Odors and perfumes. Presses Universitaires de France.

LE MAGNEN, J. 1965. Fourth Mediterranean Symposium on Olfaction (in French). Rev. Laryng. Bordeaux. 86, 821–1008.

LISS, L. 1956. The histology of the human olfactory bulb and the extra-cerebral part of the tract. Ann. Otol. Rhinol. Laryngol. 65, 680–691.

LOHMAN, A. H. M. 1963. The anterior olfactory lobe of the guinea pig. Acta Anatomica. 53, Suppl. 49, 1–109.

LORENZ, K. 1950. The comparative method in studying innate behaviour patterns. Soc. Expt. Biol. Symp. on Physiological Mechanisms in Animal Behaviour (Cambridge) 4, 221–268.

DE LORENZO, A. J. 1957. Electron microscopic observation of the olfactory mucosa and olfactory nerve. J. Biophys. Biochem. Cytol. 3, 839–850.

MANCIA, M., VON BAUMGARTEN, R., and GREEN, J. D. 1962A. Response patterns of olfactory bulb neurons. Arch. Ital. Biol. 100, 449–462.

MANCIA, M., GREEN, J. D., and VON BAUMGARTEN, R. 1962B. Reticular control of single neurons in the olfactory bulb. Arch. Ital. Biol. 100, 463–475.

MARCSTRÖM, A. 1959. Reaction thresholds of roaches (Leuciscus rutilus L.) to some aromatic substances. Arkiv för Zoologi. 12, Ser. 2, 335–338.

MAYER, J. 1952. The glucostatic theory of food intake and the problem of obesity. Bull. New Engl. Med. Center 14, 43.

MILINE, R. 1955. Contribution to the study of the role of the hypothalamus in the adaptation syndrome (in French). Rec. Méd. Soc. Sci. Répub. Pop. Monténégro 6, 227–241.

MILINE, R. 1957. Olfactory influence on the hypothalamus (in French). Compt. rend. Assoc. Anat. 95, 572–578.

MONCRIEFF, R. W. 1951. The Chemical Senses. Leonard Hill, London.

MONCRIEFF, R. W. 1956. Olfactory adaptation and odour likeness. J. Physiol. 133, 301–316.

MONCRIEFF, R. W. 1961. An instrument for measuring and classifying odors. J. Appl. Physiol. 16, 742.

MONCRIEFF, R. W. 1966. Changes in olfactory preferences with age. Rev. Laryng. (Bordeaux). 86, 895–904.

MORTIMER, H., WRIGHT, R. P., BACKMAN, C., and COLLIP, J. B. 1936A. Effect of oestrogenic hormone administration upon nasal mucous membrane of the monkey (Macaca mulatta). Proc. Soc. Exp. Biol., N.Y. 34, 535–538.

MORTIMER, H., WRIGHT, R. P., and COLLIP, J. B. 1936B. The effect of the administration of oestrogenic hormones on the nasal mucosa of the monkey (Macaca mulatta). Can. Med. Assoc. J. 35, 503–513.

MORTIMER, H., WRIGHT, R. P., and COLLIP, J. B. 1936C. The effect of oestrogenic hormones on the nasal mucosa; their role in the nasosexual relationship and their significance in clinical rhinology. Can. Med. Assoc. J. 35,
615–621.

MOULTON, D. G., ASHTON, E. H., and EAYRS, J. T. 1960. Studies in olfactory
acuity. 4. Relative detectability of n-aliphatic acids by the dog. Animal
Behaviour 8, 117–128.

MOULTON, D. G., and EAYRS, J. T. 1960. Studies in olfactory acuity II. Relative detectability of n-aliphatic alcohols by the rat. Quart. J. Exptl. Psychol.
12, 99–109.

MOULTON, D. G., and TUCKER, D. 1964. Electrophysiology of the olfactory
system. Ann. N.Y. Acad. Sci. 116, 380–428.

MOZELL, M. M., and PFAFFMANN, C. 1954. The afferent neural processes in
odor perception. Ann. N.Y. Acad. Science. 58, 96–108.

NOVÁKOVÁ, V., and DLOUHÁ, H. 1960. Effect of severing the olfactory bulbs
on the intake and excretion of water in the rat. Nature 186, 638–639.

OTTOSON, D. 1956. Analysis of the electrical activity of the olfactory epithelium. Acta Physiol. Scand. 35, Suppl. 122, 1–83.

OTTOSON, D. 1958. Studies on the relationship between olfactory stimulating
effectiveness and physico-chemical properties of odorous compounds. Acta
Physiol. Scand. 43, 167–181.

OTTOSON, D. 1959A. Studies on slow potentials in the rabbit's olfactory bulb
and nasal mucosa. Acta Physiol. Scand. 47, 136–148.

OTTOSON, D. 1959B. Comparison of slow potentials evoked in the frog's nasal
mucosa and olfactory bulb by natural stimulation. Acta Physiol. Scand. 47,
149–159.

OTTOSON, D. 1959C. Olfactory bulb potentials induced by electrical stimulation of the nasal mucosa in the frog. Acta Physiol. Scand. 47, 160–172.

OTTOSON, D. 1963A. Some aspects of the function of the olfactory system.
Pharmacol. Rev. 15, 1–42.

OTTOSON, D. 1963B. Generation and transmission of signals in the olfactory
system. In Proc. First Intern. Symp. Olfaction and Taste. Y. Zotterman
(Editor). 1, 35–44, Pergamon Press.

OTTOSON, D., and VON SYDOW, E. 1964. Electrophysiological measurements
of the odour of single components of a mixture separated in a gas chromatograph. Life Sci. 3, 1111–1115.

PARKES, A. S. 1962A. Olfactory stimuli in mammalian reproduction. J.
Endocrinol. 9, 238–239.

PARKES, A. S. 1962B. Pregnancy block in female mice placed in boxes soiled
by males. J. Reprod. Fertil. 4, 303–308.

PARKES, A. S. 1963. Olfactory and gustatory discrimination in man and
animals. Proc. Roy. Soc. Med. 56, 47–51.

PARKES, A. S., and BRUCE, H. M. 1961. Olfactory stimuli in mammalian reproduction. Science 134, 1049–1054.

PASSY, M. J. 1892. The odor of a series of alcohols (in French). Compt. rend.
Soc. Biol. Paris 44, 447–455.

PFEIFFER, W. 1962. The fright reaction of fish. Biol. Rev. 37, 495–511.

PHILLIPS, C. G., POWELL, T. P. S., and SHEPHERD, G. M. 1963. Responses of
mitral cells to stimulation of the lateral olfactory tract in the rabbit. J.
Physiol. London 168, 65–88.

POWELL, T. P. S., and COWAN, W. M. 1963. Centrifugal fibres in the lateral olfactory tract. Nature *199*, 1296–1297.

POWELL, T. P. S., COWAN, W. M., and RAISMAN, G. 1963. Olfactory relationships of the diencephalon. Nature *199*, 710–712.

PRIBRAM, K. H., and KRUGER, L. 1954. Functions of the "olfactory brain." Ann. N. Y. Acad. Sci. *58*, 109–138.

RALL, W., SHEPHERD, G. M., REESE, T. S., and BRIGHTMAN, M. W. 1966. Dendro-dendritic synaptic pathway for inhibition in the olfactory bulb. Exptl. Neurol. *14*, 44–56.

RAMÓN Y CAJAL, S. 1911. Histology of the Nervous System of Man and the Vertebrates (in French). Paris. *2*.

REESE, T. S., and STEVENS, S. S. 1960. Subjective intensity of coffee odor. Am. J. Psychol. *73*, 424–428.

SCHAFFER, J. 1940. The Epidermal Gland Organs of the Mammals (in German). Urban und Schwartzenberg, Wien and Berlin.

SCHEER, B. T. 1939. Homing instinct in salmon. Quart. Rev. Biol. *14*, 408–430.

SCHNEIDER, D. 1962. Electrophysiological investigation on the olfactory specificity of sexual attracting substances in different species of moths. J. Insect Physiol. *8*, 15–30.

SCHNEIDER, D. 1963A. Electrophysiological investigation of insect olfaction. Proc. First Intern. Symp. Olfaction and Taste. Y. Zotterman (Editor). 85–103, Pergamon Press.

SCHNEIDER, D. 1963B. Comparative receptor physiology demonstrated by the olfactory organs of insects. (in German). Jahrbuch 1963 der Max-Planck-Gesellschaft zur Förderung der Wissenschaften. 150–177.

SCHNEIDER, D. 1966. Chemical sense communication in insects. Soc. Exptl. Biol. Symp. *20*. In press.

SCHNEIDER, R. A., and WOLF, S. 1955. Olfactory perception threshold for citral utilizing a new type of olfactorium. J. Appl. Physiol. *8*, 337–342.

SCHNEIDER, R. A., and WOLF, S. 1960. Relation of olfactory acuity to nasal membrane function. J. Appl. Physiol. *15*, 914–920.

SCHNEIDER, R. A., COSTILOE, J. P., HOWARD, R. P., and WOLF, S. 1958. Olfactory perception thresholds in hypogonadal women. Changes accompanying administration of androgen and oestrogen. J. Clin. Endocrin. *18*, 379–390.

SCHNEIDER, R. A., COSTILOE, J. P., VEGA, A., and WOLF, S. 1963. Olfactory threshold technique with nitrogen dilution of *n*-butane and gas chromatography. J. Appl. Physiol. *18*, 414–417.

SCHUTZ, F. 1956. Comparative investigations on the alarm reaction in fish and its distribution (in German). Z. Vergl. Physiol. *38*, 84–135.

SCOTT, E. M., and QUINT, E. 1946. Self selection of diet. J. Nutr. *32*, 113–119.

SCOTT, E. M., and VERNEY, E. L. 1947. Self selection of diet. VI. The nature of appetites for B vitamins. J. Nutr. *34*, 471–480.

SHAPOVALOV, L. 1940. The homing instinct in trout and salmon. Proc. Sixth Pacific Sci. Cong. of the Pacific Sci. Assoc. *3*, 317–322.

SHELDON, R. E. 1912. The olfactory tracts and centers in teleosts. J. Comp. Neurol. *22*, 177–339.

SHEPHERD, G. M. 1963A. Responses of mitral cells to olfactory nerve volleys in the rabbit. J. Physiol. London. *168*, 89–100.

SHEPHERD, G. M. 1963B. Neuronal systems controlling mitral cell excitability. J. Physiol. London. *168*, 101–117.

STEVENS, S. S. 1957. On the psychophysical law. Psychol. Rev. *64*, 153–181.

STUIVER, M. 1958. Biophysics of the sense of smell. *Thesis.* Groningen University.

SWANN, H. G. 1934. The function of the brain in olfaction. J. Comp. Neurol. *59*, 175–201.

SWANN, H. G. 1935. The function of the brain in olfaction. Am. J. Physiol. *111*, 257–262.

TANYOLAÇ, N. N. 1965. Electro-odorcell for odor measurement. Intern. Rhinol. *3*, 129–134.

TEICHMANN, H. 1962. Chemoreception in the fishes (in German). Ergebn. Biol. *25*, 177–205.

THORPE, W. H. 1938. Further experiments on olfactory conditioning in a parasitic insect. The nature of the conditioning process. Proc. Roy. Soc. B *126*, 370–397.

THORPE, W. H. 1956. Learning and Instinct in Animals. Harvard Univ. Press, Cambridge, Mass.

THORPE, W. H., and JONES, F. G. W. 1937. Olfactory conditioning and its relation to the problem of host selection. Proc. Roy. Soc. B *124*, 56–81.

TINBERGEN, N. 1951. The Study of Instinct. Clarendon Press, Oxford.

TUCKER, D. 1963. Physical variables in the olfactory stimulation process. J. Gen. Physiol. *46*, 453–490.

VALVERDE, F. 1965. Studies on the Piriform Lobe. Harvard Univ. Press, Cambridge, Mass.

WALSH, R. R. 1959. Olfactory bulb potentials evoked by electrical stimulation of the contralateral bulb. Am. J. Physiol. *196*, 327–329.

WHITTEN, W. K. 1956A. Modification of oestrus cycle of the mouse by external stimuli associated with the male. J. Endocrinol. *13*, 399–404.

WHITTEN, W. K. 1956B. The effect of removal of the olfactory bulbs on the gonads of mice. J. Endocrinol. *14*, 160–163.

WHITTEN, W. K. 1957. Effect of exteroceptive factors on the oestrus cycle of mice. Nature *180*, 1436.

WHITTEN, W. K. 1959. Occurrence of anoestrus in mice caged in groups. J. Endocrinol. *18*, 102–107.

WILSON, E. O. 1963. The social biology of ants. Ann. Rev. Entomol. *8*, 345–368.

WILSON, E. O. 1965. Chemical communication in the social insects. Science *149*, 1064–1070.

WILSON, E. O., and BOSSERT, W. H. 1963. Chemical communication in animals. Recent Progr. in Hormone Res. *19*, 672–710.

WISBY, W. J., and HASLER, A. D. 1954. Effect of olfactory occlusion on migrating silver salmon (*O. kisutch*). J. Fish. Res. Board Can. *11*, 472–478.

WRIGHT, W. H. 1964. The Science of Smell. Allen and Unwin, London.

ZOTTERMAN, Y. 1963. Proc. First Intern. Symp. Olfaction and Taste. Pergamon Press.

ZWAARDEMAKER, H. 1921. Odor and chemical phenomena (in French). Arch. Néerl. Physiol. *6*, 336–354.

CHAPTER 4

Andrew Dravnieks | # Theories of Olfaction[1]

INTRODUCTION

The objective of an olfaction theory is to explain how the chemoreceptors in the nose differentiate odorivectors and odorivector mixtures. At
present, all researchers seem to agree that to produce an olfactory[2] sensation the odorivector molecules must physically reach the chemoreceptors
or at least an intermediate biochemical system while the receptor observes
some change in this system. In the latter case the burden of olfactory
discrimination is on the intermediate system.

The objectives of the olfaction theories can be subdivided further.
They must outline: (a) how odorivector molecules cause electrical
changes in the chemoreceptor neurons; (b) why different odorivectors
produce different response patterns from the assembly of chemoreceptors;
(c) what properties of odorivectors and their mixtures determine their
olfactory thresholds, quality, and intensity; and (d) how odors could be
classified and precisely described.

None of these questions can be answered within the framework of any
single discipline. Physiology, biochemistry, physical chemistry, and perception psychology become closely intermeshed. For the flavor chemist,
the progress toward the last two objectives is perhaps more immediately
significant than that toward the first two. The flavor chemist and many
others concerned with odors and aromas can add a fifth objective: to
arrive at devices that can measure odors objectively without use of olfactory panels.

Thus, a review of olfaction theories necessarily must include a discussion of all five objectives with emphasis on those more directly important
to flavor chemistry.

MECHANISMS AT THE CHEMORECEPTOR ASSEMBLY LEVEL

The final act in the sequence of olfactory sensing is the propagation of
a neural pulse along the nerve fiber from the chemoreceptor toward the
higher neural network. The pulse is a complex event that is accompanied by a collapse of the electrical potential which normally exists across
the sheath or membrane of the neuron. The potential is of the order of

[1] Based in part on work supported by the National Institutes of Health Grant
5-R01-NB05310-02 (Neurological Diseases and Blindness).
[2] The term "olfactory" in this chapter includes olfactory and trigeminal sensations.

0.07 volt, but since the membrane wall is only a few molecules thick, the electrical field in the membrane may exceed 10^5 volt $\cdot$ cm.$^{-1}$. The collapse is accompanied also by an ion exchange between the inside of the neuron and the surrounding phase. After collapse, the wall heals, and after a definite time interval, the neuron is ready to transmit another pulse. The pulse intensity does not change; all information is coded through spacing of the pulses in time.

The chemoreceptory function is presumed to reside on the end sections of the olfactory (or trigeminal) neurons facing the nasal cavity. The question is, then: How does the arrival or the residence of the odorivector molecule there influence the frequency of the neural pulses?

Some researchers have proposed that the energy from a combination, e.g., adsorption or oxidation, of the odorivector with the chemoreceptor or with an intermediate system is the direct cause of the neural impulse. Ruzicka (1957) has suggested enzymatic consumption. Rosano and Scheps (1964) worked with nitrochromic acid as an oxidizer model. Moncrieff (1961), Friedman et al. (1964), Wilkens and Hartman (1964), and Berton (1960) have studied possible physiochemical or electrochemical analogs for the olfactory process based, at least in part, on heats of adsorption, sorption, or electrochemical conversion. Beck (1964) has proposed that an energy exchange occurs between the adsorbed odorivector and the bulk phase of the chemoreceptor. Calculations by Davies and Taylor (1957) and Dravnieks (1964) indicate that for many odorivectors at threshold concentrations the number of the odorivector molecules reaching the chemoreceptors is much too small to produce enough energy or enough adsorption potential change. Hence the sorption or reaction energy *per se* is an unlikely source of the neural impulse.

Other theories propose that the energy for production of a neural impulse is supplied from an independent source and that the odorivector merely triggers the release of this energy. Davies' (1953, 1962, 1965) and Davies' and Taylor's (1954, 1955, 1957) theory comes closest to the concepts of neuroelectrophysiology. He proposes that the odorivector adsorbs across the interface between the thin lipid membrane, which is a part of the cylindrical wall of the neuron, and the surrounding aqueous phase. The molecule orients with its hydrophilic end toward the aqueous phase. The adsorption is a dynamic process with a relatively low free energy of adsorption, 1 to 8 kcal/mole.

Now and then, and more often if the adsorption is weaker, an odorivector molecule desorbs into the aqueous phase, leaving a defect. The defect may close by coalescence of the membrane matrix. However, the healing is not instantaneous, and ions have an opportunity to adsorb into the defect. When this occurs, the membrane potential collapses through puncturing of the membrane matrix by ions. Davies' mechanism elegantly leads into the customarily accepted concepts on processes by which the neuron pulses propagate. The energy comes from the collapse of the electrical field that initially existed across the membrane wall; the odorivector simply triggered a release of this energy. The wall potential then repairs by the usual membrane processes, which are known only in general terms. The important factors in odorivector differentiation through the Davies mechanism are discussed in the section on the odorivector properties.

A similar but less elaborate membrane puncturing theory has been proposed by Mullins (1955). He suggested that the odorivectors that dissolve in the neuron membrane disorder it and cause the collapse of the cell wall potential. In essence, his theory is similar to that of Davies. However, Davies considers the membrane/aqueous phase interface rather than the membrane matrix as the seat of the olfactory discriminative processes. More recently (1965) he introduced kinetic factors: desorption rates and coalescence rate of the membrane surface. Mullins (1955) did not invoke kinetic effects.

Other energy-triggering theories that explain the primary olfaction act are less developed and perhaps should be classified as speculative hypotheses.

Pigment theories form one subgroup. Briggs and Duncan (1961, 1962A, B) have commented that the olfactory receptor mechanism can be similar to the visual receptor mechanism, since the tissues are embryologically related. As a possibility, they suggested that the odorivector can cause an isomerization and a change in the carotene-protein complex; however, the presence of carotenes in olfactory areas of mammals is disputed by Moulton (1962), with rebuttals by Briggs and Duncan (1962A). Wright et al. (1956; Wright 1957, 1964) propose that olfactory pigment molecules excited by some metabolic process can couple with the odorivector molecule when vibrational frequencies match and can induce a de-excitation accompanied by loss of the polarity that characterized the excited state. The nature of the olfactory pigment, if such exists, is not known. Since interpretations of the biological mechanisms on the basis of change-transfer complexes are rapidly gaining acceptance (Isenberg and Szent-Györgyi 1958, 1959; Kareman 1954; Pullman and Pullman 1961), Wright is touching fertile ground. So far, the formulation of his mechanism is vague, and attempts to link it to the vibrational theory of odorivectors may encounter difficulties because correlations between the vibrational spectra and odor of the odorivectors are still elusive.

Another group of hypotheses consider enzyme mechanisms on the basis that biochemical processes are principally enzymatic and that various enzymes have been found in the olfactory tissues (Bourne 1948; Baradi and Bourne 1951A, B; Philippot and Gerbetzoff 1956, 1958; Briggs and Duncan 1961, 1962B; Bronshtein 1960, 1962). Mechanisms in which the odorivector is changed by the enzyme are unlikely; the stability and reactivity of the odorivectors can be so different that it is highly improbable for enzymes to cope with the recognition of the odorivectors. Mechanisms in which an odorivector interferes with an enzymatic energetic process, as suggested by Kistiakowski (1950), Alexander (1951), and Thompson (1957), appear more plausible; the "lock and key" concept used to visualize the selectivity of the enzyme process can be easily adapted to explain how an odorivector molecule can get in the way of a match between the "lock" and "key." Arguments against the enzymatic theory even in this form are based on the knowledge that the enzymatic reactions are sensitive to pH changes, while electrophysiological studies by Tucker (1963) indicate that the olfactory response to odorivectors is relatively insensitive to changes in ionic strength and pH. It is almost sure that metabolic enzymatic processes do serve to supply energy for the operation of the olfactory sensing mechanism, but whether they provide for olfactory discrimination is questionable.

Among assorted "triggering" hypotheses is a suggestion by Dravnieks (1962) based on Athestaedt's (1960) compilation of evidence that ferroelectric[3] and piezoelectric structures occur in tissues. Before a transition to a ferroelectric form, the sensor lattice possesses strain energy. When a transition is triggered, e.g., by the odorivector nucleating the transition, this energy is released and causes an appearance of electrically charged layers of opposite signs on the opposite ends of the lattice.

A third type of mechanism, different in principle from the reaction energy and the triggering mechanisms, is possible. The chemoreceptor could behave as a passive entity and merely change in some characteristic when the odorivector interacts with the receptor. The source of energy may then be the neuron impulses themselves that originate through an independent mechanism elsewhere in the neuron. For example, Dravnieks (1964) proposed that the receptor could operate as a nonlinear circuit element. Nonlinear elements, e.g., double layers, intermodulate electrical frequencies by respacing the energy waves in the time axis; such a mechanism would be phenomenologically similar to the transmission of information through neurons.

In summary, many theories on the generation of the neural signal by odorivector-chemoreceptor interactions have been proposed. The most comprehensive theory and one which easily blends with the common bio-

---

[3] Ferroelectric substances exhibit high dielectric constants in some range of temperatures because of certain molecular configurations in the lattice.

chemical concepts is that of Davies, according to which the polarized neuron cell wall supplies the energy while the odorivectors trigger the release of this energy. Even Davies' theory is supported thus far only by circumstantial evidence.

MECHANISMS AT THE CHEMORECEPTOR ASSEMBLY LEVEL

Little is known about the formation of an olfactory pattern or "image" from the response of the millions of olfactory neurons, each of which presumably communicates with at least one chemoreceptor unit. The simplest concept that nonphysiologists have most frequently preferred is that several types of chemoreceptors exist; neurons are equipped each with one of these types; an odorivector can stimulate either one or more of the receptor types, and the odorivectors differ in their ability to stimulate different types. This concept leads to the belief that certain odorivectors can be found, each of which stimulates almost exclusively one type of the receptor and each represents one primary odor. A nonprimary or complex odorivector or a mixture, such as food aroma, could then be represented in terms of the degree of stimulation of a yet unknown number of the types of receptors. This concept so far has eluded a definite confirmation. Reasonable evidence that a single chemical can stimulate only one receptor type exists primarily in chemosensing by insects, in which receptors specializing on detection of sex attractants have been found (Schneider 1963).

Electrophysiological experiments on higher animals indicate that specificities of the receptor-equipped olfactory neurons are broad and diffuse. Gesteland *et al.* (1963) and Gesteland (1964) concluded that gradations exist in specificities of neurons, perhaps because of differences in the relative population of several types of chemoreceptor sites on the neuron. These gradations are possibly continuous. The response of many neurons, each not very specific, results in a composite olfactory pattern when processed at a higher neural level. It is also possible that odor discrimination is assisted by the spatial distribution of chemoreceptor sites in the neuron or of neurons in the olfactory area. Adrian (1950, 1953) has suggested that spatial and temporal patterns of the olfactory stimulation integrate into an olfactory image in the same manner that the responses of optical sensors combine to form a visual image.

Findings by Beidler (1963) on the life cycle and dynamics of taste-buds and the presence of several gustatory types of sensors in the same bud lead to some speculation, by analogy that olfactory receptor sites similarly may have a limited life length and continuously re-form.

Further discussion on odor types and their number requires consideration of odorivector properties and is given later.

RELATIONS BETWEEN ODOR PARAMETERS
AND PROPERTIES OF ODORIVECTORS

An understanding of the olfaction mechanisms at the chemoreceptor and at the receptor-assembly levels would be tremendously helpful in discovering which properties of the odorivectors account for their odors, thresholds, and odor intensities. However, the relations between the objectively measurable characteristics of the odorivectors and their odor parameters can be studied directly even without a reference to mechanism. Relations discovered independently of the mechanism or with some hypothesis as a guide can, in turn, assist in formulating the olfaction mechanisms. At the same time, discovering such relations is the first step toward measuring odors and flavors by objective methods.

The measurable or the calculable molecular properties that have been considered by odor researchers as candidates for the odor-relevant factors range from simple molecular characteristics, e.g., molecular cross-section, to more complex, e.g., molecular shapes or spectra. Realization that interaction with chemosensors probably depends on several molecular characteristics presents odor researchers with further choices. Some attempt to combine selected molecular parameters, e.g., shape and chemical functionality, in the hope that certain combinations correlate with odor qualities or threshold levels. Others select bulk properties, e.g., mole volumes or vapor pressures. Here the underlying thought is that an easily measurable bulk property represents a complicated function of the molecular parameters, hopefully combined so as to give the right balance for correlations with odor.

Molecular characteristics, their combinations, and the bulk parameters resulting from these describe an odorivector *per se* without a reference to the chemosensor matrix. Still other groups of odor theories consider parameters that describe behavior of the odorivector with respect to some other tangible system, hopefully an analog of the chemosensor, e.g., a selected interface. Again, in principle the interactions with the matrix of the analog system can be derived from the molecular parameters of the odorivector and the system. More realistically, some composite function of the interactions, e.g., adsorption energy, is measured. Each of the analogs represents a set of several types of interactions, although their nature and the degree of participation for every odorivector/analog combination can be estimated only. Dravnieks (1965A) has pointed out that there is no real conflict between the approaches based on the molecular characteristics, bulk properties, or properties described in terms of interaction with another physicochemical system. The last approach is the most comprehensive; the first two attend to interrelated aspects, many of which are important in determining the interactions.

VIBRATIONAL THEORY

Dyson (1937, 1938, 1954), Wright (1954, 1957, 1964), Wright and Serenius (1954), Wright et al. (1956), and Wright and Michels (1964) have searched for correlations between infrared or Raman spectra and odor quality. Since these spectra describe vibrational energy levels in the molecule, this concept has been termed the vibrational theory of odors. In its present form, the theory does not claim that the vibrations are the cause of odor but merely that they may correlate with odor. The region of the spectrum that has received recent attention is, in wave numbers, below 700 cm.$^{-1}$. In this region, the vibrations are not characteristic of stretching definite intramolecular bonds. Vibrations of chains and flexing or twisting of bonds, especially between groups of atoms in the molecule, become the principal sources of energy levels represented by the low-frequency absorption spectra. Hence perhaps the best way to look at the correlations that might arise from the vibrational theory is to consider that the low-frequency spectra describe indirectly the size, shape, and flexibility of the odorivector molecule.

The success of the vibrational theory in correlating the spectra and odor has been limited. Wright and Michels (1964) statistically analyzed the similarity of odors in a group of 50 chemicals with respect to nine dissimilar odorants among them, extracted statistical factors, and tested again statistically if similarities in Raman spectra below 700 cm.$^{-1}$ were found within groups of odorivectors selected by their factor loadings. They concluded that correlations exist between their factors and Raman spectra. Analysis of correlations by inspection appears less favorable. Wright (1965) had communicated that little likeness exists among the low-frequency spectra of the camphoraceous odorants, and that the macrocyclic musks differ from other musks. Thus, findings by Wright and Serenius (1954) that almond-like odorivectors, despite different chemical structures, have similar Raman spectra are not paralleled in other odor classes. Also, since the spectrum per se is not the cause of odor, it is perfectly possible that for a series of compounds similarity in spectra can correlate with the similarity in odor, while other compounds can have similar spectra but different odors. The frequency of instances in which spectra are similar but odors differ has not been explored.

As a whole, the vibrational theory presents a simple approach for describing complex molecular characteristics, including shape if extended to the microwave region. At the same time it probably suffers from inclusion of many irrelevant spectral features. Its future significance depends on isolation of the pertinent factors.

MOLECULAR SIZE AND SHAPE THEORIES

The molecular size can be measured by the molecular weight, average molecular diameter, cross-section, or mole volume. The substances that exhibit odors can have molecular weights up to 300 when no heavier elements are involved, and up to 400 to 500 if the molecule contains heavy halogen atoms. The range of mole volumes is somewhat less since the heavy halogen atoms increase the density as well as the molecular weight. Although the direct relevance of size is the ability to fit or fill some limited space or area, the indirect effects of size are probably more important. They include such important factors as vapor pressures and solubilities.

The simplest description of molecular shape is the degree of fit into various postulated containers; this was done by Amoore in his earlier theory (1952, 1962, 1964). In his modified theory, Amoore (1965) compared likeness of shape as well as size with reference to selected molecules. Other approaches to the description of shape consider only certain features of the shape, as in Beets' (1957, 1961, 1962) comparisons of similarities in the arrangement of functional groups on the molecule. Dravnieks (1956A, C) has suggested that since in capturing by a chemoreceptor the molecule surrenders its rotational freedom, the three principal rotational momenta of the molecule may be pertinent parameters for the description of shape as well as size.

The existence of some relations between the olfactory properties of odorivectors and the sizes and shapes of the molecules of individual compounds is acceptable on the basis of experimental evidence, especially Amoore's work, which is the subject of his own paper in this symposium. A theory based exclusively on the parameters of size and shape is clearly insufficient and consequently all theories resort to additional parameters. Amoore considered nucleophilic and electrophilic characteristics as the principal parameters for some smaller molecules, regardless of their shapes.

In his work on synthesis of complex odors from simpler odorivectors assumed to represent primary classes, Johnston (1965B) concluded that probably the nucleophilic or electrophilic characteristics superimpose over the steric classes.

Earlier, Beets (1957) advanced his profile functional group theory. He postulated that a molecule orients with its strongest and most exposed functional group toward a receptor, and then the similarity in the erected profile of the oriented molecule leads to similarity in odor. Thus, in Beets' theory, some functional groups merely contribute to the shape and size, irrespective of their chemistry, while others on the same molecule through their specific properties determine the orientation to be used in the profile comparison. Beets' theory explained some effects of structure on the similarities or dissimilarities of odors, but a broader theory of odors did not develop.

Beck (1964) attempted to correlate odor thresholds with the dynamic molecular sizes, which, in his concept, are areas swept on the surface by a planarly rotating adsorbed molecule. In addition to shape and size, he also had to consider functionality, since for alcohols and aliphatic acids the axis of rotation was at the polar group rather than in the center of gravity.

The theories of odor quality and thresholds based solely on molecular size and shape have not been adequate and usually have been modified by introduction of some interaction parameter.

INTERMOLECULAR INTERACTION THEORIES

This class of theories on relations between odor parameters and tangible properties of the odorivectors is the most promising and can stand on its own or assist other, e.g., stereochemical, theories. Vapor pressure, solubility, and other bulk characteristics are results of the molecular interactions and hence belong to the same class.

Since interactions have to be probed in reference to systems of some liquid or solid substances (interactions in the gas phase are low), there is a wide choice of values for describing the strength of the interactions. The system can be a membrane, an interface, an enzyme system, etc.

In Mullins' theory (1955) only the simplest intermolecular interactions are implicitly considered. His theory utilizes the concepts of one class of nonideal solutions termed regular. In analogy to a narcosis theory, he assumes that the neuron membrane must dissolve the odorivector and that membranes differ in this respect. Some odorivectors dissolve better in a certain membrane. Then this membrane is a partially selective sensor for these odorivectors. For the nonideal solutions, when the concentration of the odorivector in air is n_a molecules/cc., the mole fraction of vapor in solution is:

$$x = \frac{1}{\gamma} \cdot \frac{n_a}{n_0} \tag{1}$$

Here γ is the activity coefficient of the odorivector in the membrane; n_0 is the concentration of the odorivector in air when in equilibrium with the pure odorivector at nose temperature. The n_a/n_0 at threshold is denoted A_0 and is equivalent to the relative vapor pressure of the odorivector at threshold. If it is assumed that a certain mole fraction level has to be reached to disarrange the membrane, the relative threshold, A_0, will be lower for odorivectors with smaller γ.

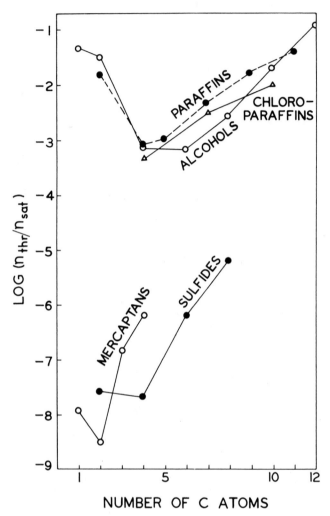

FIG. 43. VARIATION IN A_o WITH NUMBER OF CARBON ATOMS IN SEVERAL SERIES OF NONBRANCHED CHAIN HOMOLOGS

Values of A_0 versus the number of carbon atoms for several homolog series are plotted in Fig. 43. Data are from Mullins (1955) and Katz and Talbert (1930). The values go through a minimum at 2 to 5 carbon atoms and are much lower for the two series containing sulfur atoms. Since the differences in the vapor pressures of the odorivectors are accounted for by the use of A_0, this term is a measure of the comparative strength of the interaction of the odorivector with the membrane relative to interaction of the odorivector with its own molecules in a condensed state (Dravnieks 1964).

The solution theory utilized by Mullins gives values of γ equal to or in excess of unity. They arise if the so-called solubility parameters of the cohesive energy densities of the odorivector and membrane differ. The solubility parameter

$$\delta_2 = \left(\frac{\Delta E}{V_2}\right)^{1/2}$$

measures the strength of the intermolecular interactions if these originate primarily from London dispersion forces. Here ΔE is the energy of vaporization and V_2 the molar volume. The activity coefficient of the odorivector, γ_2, should then relate to the solubility parameters approximately through (Hildebrand and Scott 1962):[4]

$$\gamma_2 = \exp\left[V_2(\delta_1 - \delta_2)^2\right] \qquad (2)$$

Here δ_1 and δ_2 are the solubility parameters of the membrane and odorivector, respectively; whenever $\delta_1 = \delta_2$, γ_2 is 1. When $\delta_1 > \delta_2$ or $\delta_2 < \delta_1$ the activity coefficient always exceeds unity. Then a larger A_0 is necessary to reach the same mole fraction of the odorivector in the membrane, if the disarranging power per odorivector molecule remains the same. Therefore, in Mullins' theory membranes with a given δ_1 are more easily disarranged by odorivectors with $\delta_2 = \delta_1$. Odorivectors with $\delta_2 \neq \delta_1$ are sensed by the same membrane to a lesser extent, (higher A_0), and an assembly of chemoreceptors with different δ_1 will provide a differentiation between the odorivectors with different δ_2.

Mullins' approach allows some selectivity and would explain the minimum in A_0 (Fig. 43, p. 104), except for the fact that the matching low δ_1 for the membrane requires a low molecular-weight matrix. This approach does not allow for the large differences in A_0 for small molecules with different functional groups, since it does not consider selectivity based on $\gamma < 1$, which is possible when specific interactions occur. Thus, although Mullins' theory is a significant advance in the concepts, it is self-limited because characteristics other than δ are not included.

Dravnieks (1965C) has pointed out that Mullins' theory can be broadened if specific interactions based on the electron donor-acceptor complexes (Mulliken 1952; Briegleb 1961; Andrews and Keefer 1964) are considered. Molecules with oxygen, sulfur, or nitrogen atoms and hydrocarbons with double bonds, including aromatics, can act as electron don-

---

[4] Since the solution of the odorivector in the membrane is dilute, the term for the volume fraction of the solvent (membrane) is unity and is not shown explicitly in Equation 2.

ors with respect to molecules that tend to accept electrons, e.g., halogens, some acid anhydrides, sulfur dioxide, and those double-bond hydrocarbons, including aromatics, which have electronegative substituents such as halogens and nitro and cyano groups. Electron transfer is frequently only partial and results in a weak bond with an energy of a few kcal per mol. Hydrogen bonding with shift of a H toward another molecule is a subcase in which the other molecule acts as an electron donor toward the hydrogen atom. The ability to form acceptor-donor complexes is greatly influenced by substitutions and steric hindrances.

Equation 2 can be stated in another form:

$$(\Delta \overline{F}_E)_r = RT \ln \gamma_2 = V_2(\delta_1 - \delta_2)^2 \tag{3}$$

Here $(\Delta \overline{F}_E)_r$ is the excess partial free energy of solution of the odorivector in the membrane if the solution is regular, and only the London dispersion forces are important (excess is over that of an ideal solution). The general expression for the excess free energy of solution is:

$$\Delta \overline{F}_E = RT \ln \gamma_2 \tag{4}$$

Specific interactions produce an excess free energy increment, $(\Delta \overline{F}_E)_{sp}$, that is negative. Then

$$\Delta \overline{F}_E = (\Delta \overline{F}_E)_r + (\Delta \overline{F}_E)_{sp} = RT \ln \gamma_2 \tag{5}$$

Specific interactions reduce the value of γ_2 and, if strong enough, can make $\Delta \overline{F}_E$ negative and $\gamma_2 < 1$. Suppose that the membrane has electron acceptor properties. Those odorivectors that can act as good donors toward the membrane will build up to the same mole fraction in the membrane at a lower A_0 than the odorivectors that are poorer donors. This mechanism can account for large differences in A_0 for odorivectors with similar mole volumes and solubility parameters but with different chemical characteristics.

Values are available for the strength of complexes of several odorivectors with iodine, which is a strong electron acceptor. Fig. 44 indicates that the odorivectors that form strong complexes, as evidenced by larger absolute values of the heats of formation, have lower relative thresholds. Thus, indications exist that electron donor or acceptor characteristics of the odorivector molecules are significant factors in their olfactory threshold. It must be kept in mind that the donor-acceptor interactions depend on the type of donor and acceptor, hence correlation quality can vary, depending on the selected model of the chemoreceptor.

Other interaction theories utilize more tangible chemosensor analogs with or without an olfaction mechanism as a supporting hypothesis.

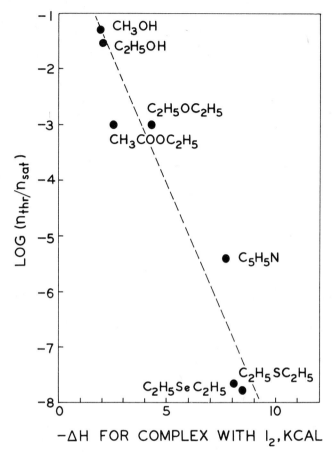

Fig. 44.   Variation of A_o with the Electron Donor
Strength of Several Odorivectors

Davies' theory (Davies 1962, 1965; Davies and Taylor 1957) is based
on the mechanism of neuron membrane puncturing already discussed.
He considers the membrane/aqueous phase interface as the interaction
source. This is a very significant advance, as compared with Mullins'
theory. At the interface one end of the odorivector molecule interacts
with the presumably lipid phase and the other, hydrophilic end, with the
aqueous phase.

A physical analog of this interface is an interface between water and a
light hydrocarbon (petroleum ether). The measure of the strength of
interactions is the free energy of adsorption, $\Delta F_{0/w}$, of the odorivector at
this interface. This energy accounts in an indirect way for the shape,

size, functional groups, and their positions and distribution on the odorivector molecule. In a sense, it is a thermodynamic form of the profile
functional group concept. Compared with Mullins' theory and its expansion proposed by Dravnieks, Davies' theory has an additional degree of
definition, since the opposite ends of the odorivector molecules interact
with different phases. Even an electron donor-acceptor complex concept
is partially built into the Davies theory; through its oxygen atom a water
molecule can act as an electron donor, or through its hydrogen atom it can
enter hydrogen bonding with electron donors.

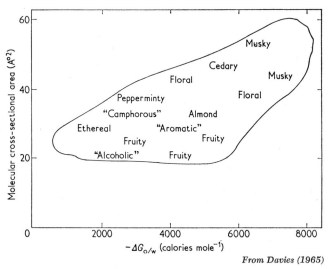

From Davies (1965)

FIG. 45. A DAVIES (1965) PLOT FOR CORRELATIONS BETWEEN
ODOR QUALITY AND PROPERTIES OF THE ODORIVECTOR

Davies' (1965) theory of correlations between the odor quality and
odorivector properties is summarized by his plot in Fig. 45. The two
parameters are the molecular cross-section and the $\Delta F_{o/w}$ term defined
above. Similar odors fall in certain areas of the field. Since the data
used to measure the odor quality are not described in detail, the quality
of correlation is difficult to estimate without further work. Note also that
pungent, putrid, or other unpleasant odors are not represented. Thus,
attractive as it is, the plot must await further confirmation and much additional study. Quantitative odor measurements demonstrated by Schutz
(1964) and used by Amoore in his more recent work should give more
exact odor descriptions. Perhaps additional parameters, e.g., electron
donor or acceptor strength, must be introduced as a third coordinate.

Davies' threshold theory (1962) is a precursor of his plot in Fig. 45, and an analysis of its mathematical form (Dravnieks 1965A), indicates that principally it relates the molecular cross-section to the threshold, with $\Delta F_{0/w}$ only as a modifying factor. Hence it basically recognizes the significance of the molecular size as most other threshold theories do. The threshold data used in Davies' work are in part old and questionable. For instance, values for alcohols are in considerable disagreement with Mullins' 1955 data.

The intermolecular interaction theories appear to be a very promising approach for discovering correlations between odor parameters and odorivector properties.

INTERACTIONS WITH EMPIRICAL SYSTEMS

The realization that intermolecular interactions responsible for adsorption or solution may correlate with odor parameters has prompted several studies with empirical analogs of chemoreceptors.

Moncrieff (1957) proposed that the strength of sorption of the odorivector at or in a selected set of substances can characterize an odor. The technique utilized measurement of breakthrough times of the odorivector's odor through adsorbent or absorbent columns. Four of the substances were adsorbents (carbons, silica gel, alumina, and fuller's earth), and one was an absorbent (vegetable fat). In his experiment the breakthrough time depends on the rate of airflow, surface area of the adsorbent or volume of the absorbent, as compared with the free air volume in the column, concentration of the odorivector in air, and the olfactory threshold for the odorivector. Thus, the values obtained are arbitrary and depend on sorbents with ill-defined properties. The relative degree of interaction with several condensed phases cannot be compared in more basic terms. However, the technique seems to be exceedingly promising and is discussed later.

Schutz (1965) attempted in 1961 to find correlations between the odor parameters and interactions of the odorivectors with water, albumin, brain homogenate (which represents in part the nerve tissue), and wool, considered as an analog of the cholinesterase-inhibiting property. The interactions were studied in terms of retention times in gas-chromatographic columns of these materials. Stronger interaction and lower vapor pressures result in larger retention volumes. Correlation between the retention times and olfactory characteristics were poor.

More complex interactions with systems in which kinetic processes occur also have been studied. Davies and Taylor (1954) have found that olfactory thresholds correlate with the ability of the odorivectors to accelerate hemolysis of the red blood cell wall membranes by saponin.

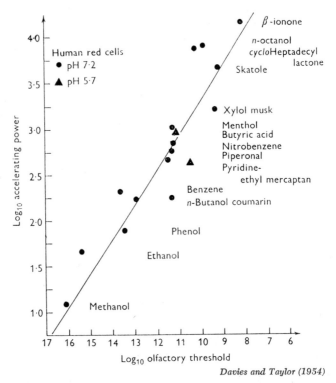

Davies and Taylor (1954)

FIG. 46. CORRELATION BETWEEN OLFACTORY THRESHOLD OF
ODORIVECTORS AND THEIR ABILITY TO ACCELERATE HEMOLYSIS

Their data are reproduced in Fig. 46. The question on the correlations with the odorivector properties is then replaced by another: which properties correlate with the ability to accelerate hemolysis? The finding, however, led to the development of the Davies' (1965) theory already discussed. Schutz (1965) has searched for correlations between the ability to change the activity of acetylcholinesterase and odor threshold, suprathreshold intensity, and the rate of adaptation. From the above odor characteristics, only weak correlations with the rate of adaptation were observed.

In the same class of interactions with empirical systems are the studies in which the electrical effects at immersed electrodes (Rosano and Scheps 1964; Wilkens and Hartman 1964; Berton 1960) or at an air/condensed phase interface are studied (Friedman *et al.* 1964; Tanyolac 1965; Dravnieks 1965B). These studies produce estimates that emphasize certain aspects of interactions, e.g., oxidizability, orientation after adsorption, etc. Their merits can be assessed only through further research.

Thus far studies of interactions with empirical systems, hopefully relevant analogs of some part of the chemoreceptor system, have not yielded significant results. However, it is basically sound and, with some assistance from theory and better olfactory data, should be successful in the future.

CLASSIFICATION AND DESCRIPTION OF ODORS

The ultimate classification of odors will be possible only after the olfaction theories at the chemoreceptor and receptor assembly level mature. At present, only a crude assessment of the thinking is possible.

The efforts of Wright and Michels (1964), Schutz (1964), Johnston (1965A), and Amoore (1965) indicate that odors can be reasonably and reproducibly described by comparison with a set of selected reference odorivectors. The number of the reference odorivectors is usually 7 to 9. Whether a larger number or another selection can result in a better description has not been established. Some, e.g., Johnston, believe that a larger number of categories may be necessary. Hainer et al. (1952) estimated that, since skilled persons can discriminate approximately 10,-000 odors, at least 14 different sensors, each responding on a "yes" or "no" basis, would be needed to code odors. In general, the consensus seems to be that a reasonable number of reference odors, perhaps nine of any kind, if they do not resemble each other too much, can be used to describe odors.

Several questions arise. Are these primary odors? Are there odorivectors, which represent the primary odors in pure or almost pure form? The trend at present seems to be away from the concept of primary odors from which all other odors can be composed. The main reason is the difficulties encountered in attempts to match the odor sensation produced by some substances or their mixtures by a proper mixture from a set of "primaries"—vectors of primary odors. Mullins (1955), Cheesman (1960), and Koester (1965), by studies of changes of the threshold of one odorivector when olfactory fatigue was induced by another, found cases of considerable as well as negligible cross-adaptation. The cross-adaptation at higher intensities should be more pertinent to odor synthesis but has received little attention. Electrophysiologists, who usually work with relatively high odorivector concentrations, find little differentiation in response. Gesteland (1964) and Jones and Woskow (1964) have shown that the subjective intensity of binary mixtures of odorivectors is neither additive nor an average.

These bits of information seem to hint that a certain, as yet unknown, number of odorivectors can be found for which the cross-adaptation, when close to the threshold, is at a minimum. These could then be considered as the most dissimilar and come closest to the definition of primaries. The meaning would be that either at the chemoreceptor or higher levels olfactory pathways exist that permit detection of each of the primaries with a minimum interference from the others. These could then be termed "threshold primaries." At higher concentrations, one of the threshold primaries will interfere with the perception of the other primaries to an olfactorily significant but different extent. Odorivectors that have significant influence on the thresholds of several threshold primaries will interfere in a more complex manner and could be termed "multiclass threshold

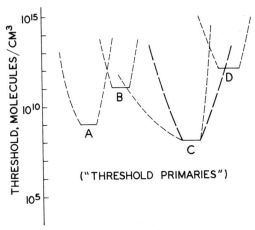

FIG. 47. HYPOTHETICAL MUTUAL INTRUSION OF "THRESHOLD PRIMARIES" INTO OLFACTORY PATHWAYS

odorivectors." The intrusion of threshold primaries and multiclass odorivectors into olfactory reception and perception paths of other primaries and nonprimaries results in complex olfactory patterns or images. A hypothetical situation for four threshold primaries is shown in Fig. 47. For olfactory pathway C, two odorivectors with the same threshold influence B and D in different manner when present at higher concentrations. However, that does not mean that sufficient intrusion can be achieved by any threshold primary. For instance, musks of several chemical families may utilize the same olfactory path at low concentrations, as indicated by the work of Johnston and Sandoval (1962). At higher concentrations, intrusion into olfactory paths of another odor class can be different for different musks, so that a synthesis of some complex odors with a musky note would be impossible by using one musk threshold primary but possible if another musk primary or even a multiclass threshold odorivector were used. Mullins', Cheesman's, and Koester's work does not seem to indicate that pure threshold primaries exist. An odorivector always, at least slightly, influences the thresholds of other odorivectors. Much more data needs to be accumulated to bring more clarity into this area.

OBJECTIVE MEASUREMENTS OF ODOR QUALITY

The measurement of odor quality by instruments is still in the embryonic stage and is hampered by several unresolved questions. One question involves the existence, number, and nature of primary odors; another, the laws governing change of the odor of the same odorivector with change of concentration; and third, the laws through which a complex odor image results when several odorivectors are presented to the nose simultaneously. Some progress in these areas is being made in various research groups, and data gradually accumulate that answer at least parts of the above questions. Many aspects will have to be answered first through panel studies, by perception physiologists, and electrophysiologists.

First, instruments need a process that can give similar readings for substances with similar odors. The above review of correlations between the properties of the odorivectors and their odor shows that the most promising of the approaches is the study of intermolecular interactions with respect to selected bulk or interface phases.

The approaches advanced by Moncrieff and Schutz are particularly appealing, despite their initial primitive form and perhaps unfortunate selection of the chemoreceptor phase analogs. The best presently available technique for the evaluation of the intermolecular interactions is gas chromatography. The retention volumes of two odorivectors, A and B, relate as their partition coefficients, K_a and K_b, and these are described by the equation of the form:

$$K = \text{constant} \cdot \frac{1}{\gamma_2} \cdot \frac{1}{\rho_2{}^\circ}$$

where γ_2 is the activity coefficient of the odorivector in the stationary phase, and $\rho_2{}^\circ$ is the vapor pressure of the odorivector in the pure state at the column temperature. From γ_2, the excess free energy of solution can be obtained.

$$\Delta \bar{F}_E = RT \ln \gamma_2 \quad (cf. \text{ Equation 5})$$

and this serves as a measure of the intermolecular interactions.

Moncrieff's (1957) work is particularly interesting in the selection of the detector, the human nose. In essence, his technique is a frontal analysis gas chromatography. In the characterization of odors of single odorivectors, the nose detector automatically accounts for the olfactory threshold, while the delay time describes the intermolecular interactions with the column material. For more exact studies, the advantage of the nose detector is offset by its lesser reliability, and the modern detectors may serve better.

With better insight into the significance of the specific types of the intermolecular interaction, better choices of the stationary phases can be made. Thus, the techniques of gas chromatography used for resolution of flavors into their chemical components seem to be destined to meet the odor sciences at still another juncture.

CONCLUSIONS

Theories of olfaction deal (1) with mechanisms by which odorivectors produce responses in chemoreceptors, (2) with correlations between the odor parameters (quality, threshold, intensity) and tangible properties of the odorivectors, (3) with the questions of complex odors, and (4) with odor classifications. Davies' olfaction theory appears to be the most satisfactory of the theories proposed thus far and is based on the thermodynamics of the odorivector interaction with the biomembrane aqueous phase interface, kinetic properties of the membrane, and the conventional concept of the neuron signal propagation. However, his theory awaits further experimental confirmation.

Correlations of odor parameters with sizes and shapes of odorivector molecules appear to hold to some extent. As generally recognized, these correlations need amendments to account for the more specific effects caused by functional groups. There are indications that electron donor-acceptor complexing may be one of the additional parameters. Intermolecular interactions between the odorivector and selected organic liquids are probably the most promising properties to be correlated with the odor parameters.

The question of the odor classifications and the nature of complex odors is probably best understood through a concept of threshold primaries; however, these require much more investigation. Differentiation through intermolecular interactions should lead to a better classification of odors and hopefully to objective olfactometry. This principle, first demonstrated by Moncrieff, should grow in usefulness as the relative significance of various interactions becomes better known so that pertinent analog matrices can be selected.

DISCUSSION

K. B. Döving.—First of all, I would like to ask what is an odorivector and what is a sensor?

A. Dravnieks.—An odor vector is a molecule which when it comes to the nose gives an impression of odor. It is the carrier of the odor. The sensor is what the molecule interacts with to initiate a signal. I did not make a distinction between olfactory and trigeminal sensing mechanisms. I think it is difficult to distinguish at this stage of development.

R. Self.—I would like to ask Dr. Dravnieks his opinion of the Davies' theory, specifically about the plot from the 1965 paper. Can you suggest any other dimension which might be useful to measure to enlarge upon this classification? For instance, in the 20 Å cross-sectional area, you have the alcohols on the chart. Also, at this place you would have every other homologous series—how do we differentiate between these homologous series at this level?

A. Dravnieks.—Well, Davies' paper does not really give enough data on which his graph is based. I feel that there is a third dimension due on the graph and this third dimension may be the electron-donor-acceptor type of interaction. Certainly there is nothing wrong with the Davies' theory—I like it very much, but it may need additional dimensions.

R. Self.—Yes, we thought maybe either something psychological such as likes and dislikes or maybe something more physical such as polarity may give us a third dimension here.

A. Dravnieks.—Polarity does not seem to have much relation. It seems that when you look at the tables of olfactory thresholds, for instance, you can find highly polar substances at both ends. So I would feel that it is primarily the molecular size and shape, and certain functional groups. Functional groups can act either by polarity in the way it is understood in gas chromatography, such as partitioning in a polar phase, or else it may be understood as a functional group which acts as a donor or acceptor of electrons and is different from hydrocarbons.

BIBLIOGRAPHY

ADRIAN, E. D. 1950. The electrical activity of the mammalian olfactory bulb. Electroenceph. Clin. Neurophysiol. *2*, 377–388.

ADRIAN, E. D. 1953. Sensory messages and sensation. The response of the olfactory organ to different smells. Acta Physiol. Scan. *29*, 5–14.

ALEXANDER, J. 1951. The catalyst theory of olfaction. Proc. Sci. Sect. Toilet Goods Assoc. No. *16*, 1–8.

AMOORE, J. E. 1952. The stereochemical specificities of human olfactory receptors. Perf. Ess. Oil Record. *43*, 321–323.

AMOORE, J. E. 1962. The stereochemical theory of olfaction, I, II. Proc. Sci. Sect. Toilet Goods Assoc., Spec. Suppl. to No. 37, 1–12; 13–23.

AMOORE, J. E. 1964. Current status of the steric theory of odor. Ann. N.Y. Acad. Sci. *116*, 457–476.

AMOORE, J. E. 1965. Psychophysics of odor. Presented at Symp. on Quant. Biol., Sensory Receptors, June, 1965. Cold Spring Harbor, New York. In press.

ANDREWS, L. J., and KEEFER, R. M. 1964. Molecular Complexes in Organic Chemistry. Holden-Day, Inc., San Francisco, Calif.

ATHESTAEDT, H. 1960. Ferroelectric and piezoelectric properties of organisms. Naturwissensch. 47 (19), 455.

BARADI, A. F., and BOURNE, G. H. 1951A. Theories of taste and odors. Science 113, 660–661.

BARADI, A. F., and BOURNE, G. H. 1951B. Localization of gustatory and olfactory enzymes in the rabbit, and the problems of taste and smell. Nature 168, 977–979.

BECK, L. H. 1964. A quantitative theory of the olfactory threshold based upon the amount of the sense cell covered by an adsorbed film. Ann. N.Y. Acad. Sci. 116, 448–456.

BEETS, M. G. J. 1957. Structure and odor. In Molecular Structure and Organoleptic Quality, 54–90. Soc. Chem. Ind. Monograph No. 1, London.

BEETS, M. G. J. 1961. Odor and molecular constitution. Am. Perfumer Arom. 76, No. 6, 54–63.

BEETS, M. G. J. 1962. Some aspects of odor problems. Perf. Cosm. Savons 5, No. 4, 1–10.

BEIDLER, L. M. 1963. Dynamics of taste cells. In Olfaction and Taste, 113–145, Y. Zotterman, (Editor). Macmillan Co., New York.

BERTON, A. 1960. Galvanic cells with two identical electrodes as detectors of vapors, liquids, and solids in air. Compt. rend. 250, 126–127.

BOURNE, G. H. 1948. Alkaline phosphatase in taste buds and nasal mucosa. Nature 161, 445 –446.

BRIEGLEB, G. 1961. Electron Donor-Acceptor Complexes. Springer Verlag, Berlin.

BRIGGS, M. H., and DUNCAN, R. B. 1961. Odour receptors. Nature 191, 1310–1311.

BRIGGS, M. H., and DUNCAN, R. B. 1962A. Pigment and the olfactory mechanism. Nature 195, 1313–1314.

BRIGGS, M. H., and DUNCAN, R. B. 1962B. Odor receptors. Arch. Otolaryngol. 67, 116–117.

BRONSHTEIN, A. A. 1960. Cytochemical and histochemical studies of the olfactory organs in mammals. Tsytologia 2, 194–200.

BRONSHTEIN, A. A. 1962. Distribution of nucleic acids, proteins, and certain of their functional groups in olfactory cells of some vertebrates. Tsytologia 4, 418–426.

CHEESMAN, G. H. 1960. Odour and chemical constitution—a new approach. Proc. Roy. Australian Chem. Inst., 70–73.

DAVIES, J. T. 1953. Olfactory stimulation. Some ideas and possible model systems. Intern. Perfumer 3, 17–22.

DAVIES, J. T. 1962. The mechanism of olfaction. Symp. Soc. Exp. Biol. 16, 170–179.

DAVIES, J. T. 1965. A theory of the quality of odors. J. Theor. Biol. 8, 1–7.

DAVIES, J. T., and TAYLOR, F. H. 1954. A model system for the olfactory membrane. Nature 174, 693–694.

DAVIES, J. T., and TAYLOR, F. H. 1955. Olfactory thresholds: a test of a new theory. Perf. Ess. Oil Record 46, No. 1, 15–18.

DAVIES, J. T., and TAYLOR, F. H. 1957. Molecular shape, size, and adsorption in olfaction. Proc. 2nd Intern. Congress Surface Activity 4, 329–339.

DRAVNIEKS, A. 1962. Possible mechanism of olfaction. Nature 194, 245–247.

DRAVNIEKS, A. 1964. Physiochemical basis of olfaction. Ann. N.Y. Acad. Sci. 116, 429–439.

DRAVNIEKS, A. 1965A. Chemoreceptor description through molecular parameters of odorivectors. Presented at 2nd Intern. Conf. on Olfaction and Taste, Sept. 11–13, Tokyo, Japan.

DRAVNIEKS, A. 1965B. Contact potentials in detection of airborne vapors. In Surface Effects in Detection, pp. 103–122, J. I. Bregman and A. Dravnieks, (Editors). Spartan Book Co., Washington, D.C.

DRAVNIEKS, A. 1965C. Current status of odor theories. Flavor Symposium, Am. Chem. Soc. Detroit, April 6, 1965. In press.

DYSON, G. M. 1937. Raman effect and the concept of odour. Perf. Ess. Oil Record 28, 13–19.

DYSON, G. M. 1938. The scientific basis of odour. Chem. Ind. (London) 16, 647–651.

DYSON, G. M. 1954. Odour and chemical constitution. Nature 173, 831.

FRIEDMAN, H. H., MACKAY, D. A., and ROSANO, H. L. 1964. Odor measurement possibilities via energy changes in cephalin monolayers. Ann. N.Y. Acad. Sci. 116, 602–607.

GESTELAND, R. C. 1964. Initial events of the electro-olfactogram. Ann. N.Y. Acad. Sci. 116, 440–447.

GESTELAND, R. C., LETTVIN, J. Y., PITTS, W. H., and ROJAS, A. 1963. Odor specificities of the frog's olfactory receptors. In Olfaction and Taste, pp. 17–19, Y. Zotterman, (Editor). The Macmillan Co., New York.

HAINER, R. M., EMSILE, A. G., and JACOBSON, A. 1952. An information theory of olfaction. Ann. N.Y. Acad. Sci. 58, 158–173.

HILDEBRAND, J. H., and SCOTT, R. L. 1962. Regular Solutions. Prentice-Hall, Englewood Cliffs, N.J.

ISENBERG, I., and SZENT-GYÖRGYI, A. 1958. On the absorption of heterocyclic donors and acceptors. Proc. Nat. Acad. Sci. 44, 857–862.

ISENBERG, I., and SZENT-GYÖRGYI, A. 1959. On charge-transfer complexes between substances of biochemical interest. Proc. Nat. Acad. Sci. 45, 1229–1231.

JOHNSTON, J. W. 1965A. Experiments on the specificities of human olfaction. In Surface Effects in Detection, pp. 29–52, J. I. Bregman and A. Dravnieks, (Editors). Spartan Books, Washington, D.C.

JOHNSTON, J. W. 1965B. Private Communication.

JOHNSTON, J. W., and SANDOVAL, A. 1962. The validity of muskiness as a primary odor. Proc. Sci. Sect. Toilet Goods Assoc., Spec. Suppl. to No. 7, 34–45.

JONES, F. N., and WOSKOW, M. H. 1964. On the intensity of odor mixtures. Ann. N.Y. Acad. Sci. 116, 484–494.

KATZ, S. H., and TALBERT, E. J. 1930. Intensities of odors and irritating effects of warning agents for inflammable and poisonous gases. U.S. Bureau of Mines Tech. Paper 480.

KAREMAN, G. 1954. Electronic aspects of quantum biology. Ann. N.Y. Acad. Sci. 96, 1029–1055.

KISTIAKOWSKI, G. B. 1950. On the theory of odors. Science 112, 154–155.

KOESTER, E. D. 1965. Private communication.

MONCRIEFF, R. W. 1955. Classification and identification of odorants. Food 24, 154–157.

MONCRIEFF, R. W. 1957. The sorptive nature of the olfactory stimulus. Proc. 2nd Intern. Congr. Surface Activity 4, 321–328.

MONCRIEFF, R. W. 1961. An instrument for measuring and classifying odors. J. Appl. Physiol. 16, 742–749.

MOULTON, D. G. 1962. Pigment and olfactory mechanism. Nature 195, 1312–1313.

MULLIKEN, R. S. 1952. Molecular compounds and their spectra. J. Am. Chem. Soc. 74, 811–824.

MULLINS, L. J. 1955. Olfaction. Ann. N.Y. Acad. Sci. 62, 249–276.

PHILIPPOT, E., and GERBETZOFF, M. A. 1956. New studies of lipids of olfactory mucosa. J. Physiol. Paris 48, 683–684.

PHILIPPOT, E., and GERBETZOFF, M. A. 1958. First results of analysis of olfactory pigment. J. Physiol. Paris 50, 451–452.

PULLMAN, B., and PULLMAN, A. 1961. Quantum Biochemistry. Interscience Publishers, New York.

ROSANO, H. L., and SCHEPS, S. Q. 1964. Adsorption-induced electrode potentials in relation to olfaction. Ann. N.Y. Acad. Sci. 116, 590–601.

RUZICKA, L. 1957. Fundamentals of odour chemistry: A summary. In Molecular Structure and Organoleptic Quality, 116–124. Soc. Chem. Industry Monograph No. 1, London.

SCHNEIDER, D. 1963. Electrophysiological investigation of insect olfaction. In Olfaction and Taste, pp. 85–103, Y. Zotterman, (Editor). Macmillan Co., New York.

SCHUTZ, H. G. 1964. A matching-standards method for characterizing odor dimensions. Ann. N.Y. Acad. Sci. 116, 517–526.

SCHUTZ, H. G. 1965. Communication on work conducted in 1961.

TANYOLAÇ, N. 1965. The Electro-Odocell for odor measurement and surface effects. In Surface Effects in Detection, pp. 89–102, J. I. Bregman and A. Dravnieks, (Editors). Spartan Book Co., Washington, D.C.

THOMPSON, H. W. 1957. Some comments on the theories of smell. In Molecular Structure and Organoleptic Quality, pp. 103–115. Soc. Chem. Ind. Monograph No. 1, London.

TUCKER, D. 1963. Olfactory, vomeronasal, and trigeminal receptor responses to odorants. In Olfaction and Taste, pp. 45–69, Y. Zotterman, (Editor). The Macmillan Co., New York.

WILKINS, W. F., and HARTMAN, J. D. 1964. An electronic analog for the olfactory processes. Ann. N.Y. Acad. Sci. 116, 608–620.

WRIGHT, R. H. 1954. Odour and molecular vibration I. Quantum and thermodynamic considerations. J. Appl. Chem. (London) 4, 611–615.

WRIGHT, R. H. 1957. Odor and molecular vibration. In Molecular Structure and Organoleptic Quality, pp. 91–102. Soc. Chem. Ind. Monograph No. 1, London.

WRIGHT, R. H. 1964. Odor and molecular vibration: the far infrared spectra of some perfume chemicals. Ann. N.Y. Acad. Sci. 116, 552–558.

WRIGHT, R. H. 1965. Private Communication.

WRIGHT, R. H., and MICHELS, K. M. 1964. Evaluation of far infrared relations to odor by a standard similarity method. Ann. N.Y. Acad. Sci. 116, 535–551.

WRIGHT, R. H., REID, C., and EVANS, H. G. V. 1956. Odor and molecular vibration III. A new theory of olfactory stimulation. Chem. Ind. (London) 37, 973–977.

WRIGHT, R. H., and SERENIUS, R. S. E. 1954. Odour and molecular vibration: Raman spectra of substances with the nitrobenzene odour. J. Appl. Chem. 4, 615–621.

CHAPTER 5

J. E. Amoore | **Stereochemical Theory of Olfaction**

INTRODUCTION

The flavor of a food is a complex attribute depending upon numerous physical and chemical properties of the foodstuff and perceived through many sensory systems. One most important component of flavor is unquestionably the sensation of smell, caused by volatile constituents of the food entering through the nostrils or the nasopharynx. Progress in the separation and identification of the chemical compounds present in food volatiles has accelerated tremendously in the last ten years, thanks largely to the advent of gas chromatography and allied physicochemical instrumentation. Many hundreds of compounds may be found in the vapors of a single food. However, in this realm physiology and psychology have lagged behind the dramatic advances of physical chemistry. The result is lopsided growth. Great quantities of excellent chemical data have accumulated, without any obvious prospect of an early physiological interpretation. This chapter outlines the beginnings of what may become a comparable advance in psychophysics, with the promise of restoring the balance between chemical analysis and organoleptic appraisal.

We urgently need better understanding of how chemical constitution is related to odor sensation. Theories abound, but few have the support of appreciable experimental evidence. One which is currently the subject of intensive research is the "Stereochemical Theory of Olfaction." Based on an idea which may be traced to Lucretius (Latham 1951), the theory has evolved rapidly in recent years, but is still a long way from perfect. Fundamentally the theory is that the different qualities of odor sensations—flowery, musky, rancid, etc.—are determined by the shapes and sizes of the molecules concerned. The concept is beautifully simple, but its investigation, confirmation, and application has been a complicated proceeding in which numerous shifts of viewpoint and methodology have been necessary.

The recent development of the stereochemical theory of olfaction may be outlined as follows. Timmermans (1938) and Pauling (1946) pointed out that a camphoraceous odor was generally associated with spherical molecules. Moncrieff (1951) suggested that odorous molecules were adsorbed on superficial receptor sites at the olfactory nerve endings. The present author (Amoore 1952) contributed the definite proposal of seven

119

primary odors, together with detailed specifications of the shapes and dimensions of receptor sockets corresponding with each class of odor. Although based on the classical "lock and key" concept (Fischer 1894), long accepted in enzymology, immunology, and pharmacology, the rejuvenated stereochemical theory was almost universally ignored. It was rescued from obscurity by the diligent labors of Dr. James W. Johnston Jr. of Georgetown University, who amassed considerable independent support for the theory (Johnston 1960; Johnston and Parks 1960; Johnston and Sandoval 1960). This encouraged the present author to publish in full the evidence on which the stereochemical theory of olfaction was based (Amoore 1962A, B).

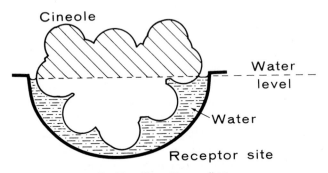

FIG. 48. THE "SITE-FITTING" METHOD

Front view (elevation) of the molecular model of 1,8-cineole fitting into the cavity of the "camphoraceous" receptor site (modeled in clear plastic). The cavity is filled with water to a datum point 1 mm. below the rim. From the volume of water required, and knowing the site volume and molecule volume, the degree of complementarity between the molecule and the site is estimated.

The reader who requires a succinct general introduction to the stereochemical theory of odor may refer to the semi-popular summary prepared by Amoore, Johnston, and Rubin (1964). The article illustrates the simple concept of seven primary odors, each represented by a distinctive receptor socket into which odorant molecules fit. It reflects the status of the theory at that time. This account may well be adequate for the nonspecialist but subsequent research has demanded important refinements. The site-fitting concept especially required modification to include total molecular shape, and the number of primary odors may have to be increased substantially. These modifications are taken up in this paper and in other cited publications.

During the last two years the stereochemical theory has been intensively investigated at the Western Regional Research Laboratory of the U.S. Dept. Agr. at Albany, California. Improved experimental methods have been developed for measurement of molecular shape (Amoore 1964) and of odor quality (Amoore and Venstrom 1966). These methods were systematically applied to 40 odorous compounds (Amoore 1965). It was found that the classical "site-fitting" concept (Fig. 48) was rather

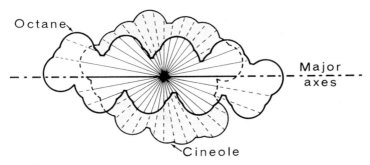

FIG. 49. THE "SHADOW-MATCHING" METHOD

Top silhouette photograph of the elongated molecule of *n*-octane superimposed on that of 1,8-cineole (the globular camphoraceous standard). The centers of gravity and main axes of the silhouettes are coaligned. The differences in the lengths (i.e., the overlap) of the corresponding radii (broken lines) measure the difference in molecular size and shape between these two compounds.

inadequate because it assesses only one-half of the molecule. It was found preferable to take all aspects of the molecular surface into consideration, as is done in the new "shadow-matching" method (Fig. 49). Highly significant correlations were consistently obtained between the odor qualities and the molecular sizes and shapes. The survey has recently been extended to a total of 107 compounds. The results have still more strengthened the foundations of the stereochemical theory of olfaction (Amoore and Venstrom 1965).

EXPERIMENTAL PROOF OF THE STEREOCHEMICAL THEORY

In the earlier version of the theory, the evidence was largely qualitative and intuitive (Amoore 1952, 1962A, B). That is, odor descriptions were taken from the literature of organic chemistry, and overall molecular sizes were estimated from pantograph tracings of molecular outlines. To render the whole investigation more quantitative and objective, methods have recently been developed for systematic assessment of odor quality and of molecular shape. As absolute measurements of odor quality remain inaccessible, we made use of relative measurements throughout, comparing the unknowns with arbitrary standards of reference. For this purpose five compounds were chosen as representatives of the first five odor classes of the theory—ethereal, camphoraceous, musky, floral, and minty (Table 12).

TABLE 12

ODOR STANDARD SOLUTIONS
THE COMPOUNDS WERE DISSOLVED IN TRIPLE-DISTILLED WATER

Standard Odor	Representative Compound	Concentration (P.P.M.)
Ethereal	1,2-Dichloroethane	800
Camphoraceous	1,8-Cineole	10
Musky	15-Hydroxypentadecanoic acid lactone	1
Floral	d,l,β-Phenylethylmethylethyl carbinol	300
Minty	d,l-Menthone	6
Pungent	Formic acid	50,000
Putrid	Dimethyl disulfide	0.1

Organoleptic Measurements

The assessments of odor quality were made by a panel of 29 judges (13 men and 16 women). The procedure is reported in detail elsewhere (Amoore and Venstrom 1966). Because the stereochemical theory primarily sets out to explain odor quality, not intensity, it was decided to equalize as far as possible the intensities of the odors. (A successful theoretical interpretation of odor intensity or odor threshold, the theory of Davies (1962), will be discussed below.) The concentrations of the standard and unknown odorants were adjusted until the panel of judges as a whole rated them of equal intensity. For this purpose a one ppm solution of 15-hydroxy-pentadecanoic acid lactone was adopted as the standard of intensity.

The judges were supplied with a set of seven stoppered flasks containing the standard odorant solutions. Each unknown odorant was presented in a similar flask. The judge compared the unknown with each standard, sniff by sniff, and rated the degree of similarity of odor on a scale from 0 to 8 (Table 13). Each compound was presented twice to the panel (on different days), and an average value for the whole panel was obtained for the similarity of the unknown odor to each standard. This procedure is called an "odor dimension analysis."

The comprehensive data serve to measure the odor of each unknown in terms of its similarity to the chosen standards. The originator of this "matching standards" method (Schutz 1964) intended it to provide a rea-

TABLE 13

SCALE OF SIMILARITY FOR ODOR JUDGMENTS

Similarity	Rating
Extremely similar	8
	7
Very similar	6
	5
Moderately similar	4
	3
Slightly similar	2
	1
Not similar	0

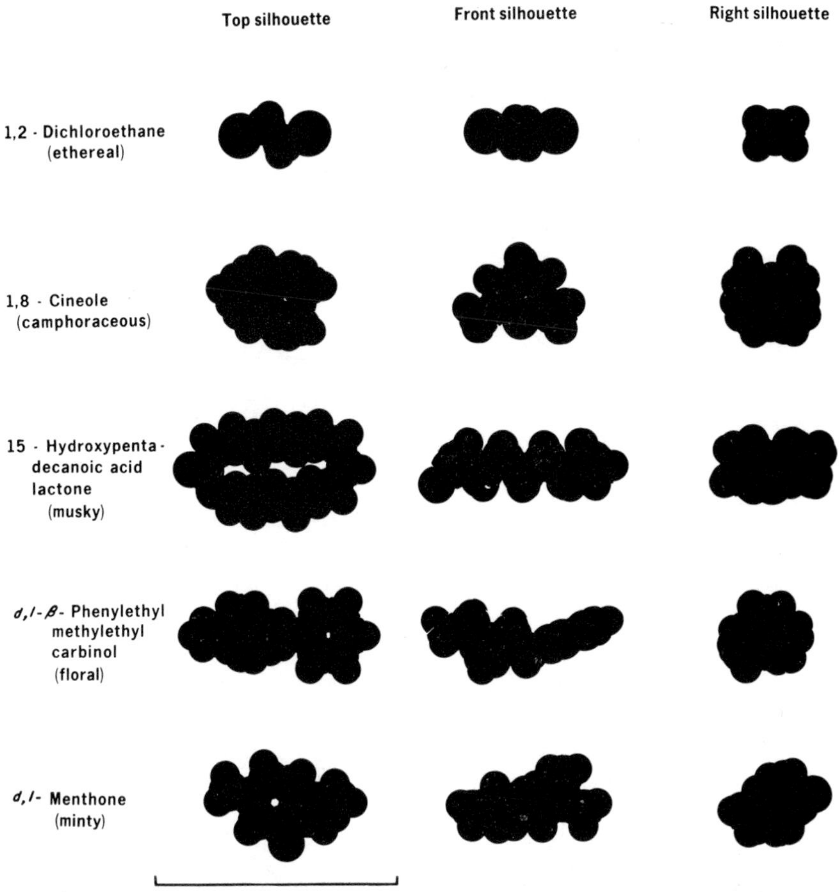

FIG. 50. MOLECULAR MODEL SILHOUETTES OF THE FIVE STANDARD ODORANTS
The scale marker shows 15 Å.

sonably objective description of the unknown odor and it does so. In the present context, the numbers serve the even more useful purpose of providing the raw data on odor similarity which can serve to test the stereochemical theory, or any other theory of odor quality. All that is needed is to measure that molecular property (in this case size and shape) which hypothetically determines odor quality, and then to examine the two sets of data by graphical or statistical tests of correlation.

Stereochemical Measurements

Indirect methods of visualizing the sizes and shapes of volatile molecules are necessary. One method is to construct molecular models from

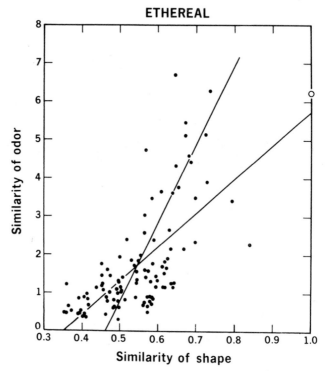

FIG. 51. ORGANOLEPTIC ANALYSES COMPARED WITH STEREO-CHEMICAL ASSESSMENTS BY THE SHADOW-MATCHING METHOD: GRAPH OF THE "ETHEREAL" DATA

The open circle represents the ethereal standard odorant itself, 1,2-dichloroethane. The other points show for each of the 106 "unknown" odorants the correlation between the similarity of odor quality to the standard and the similarity of molecular shape to the standard. The calculated regression lines are shown.

sets of scale atomic units. The necessary dimensions and configurational rules are well established in physical chemistry. The molecular models were photographed in silhouette (Amoore 1964) from three directions mutually at right-angles to record the "top," "front," and "right" silhouettes of the molecule. Fig. 50 shows the silhouettes of the five standard compounds employed in this survey. Their distinctive molecular shapes become apparent in the three views. Thus the ethereal standard is a small, rod-shaped molecule, the camphoraceous standard is a larger sphere, and the musky standard is a still larger disk. The floral and minty standards are of intermediate size, but differ in shape; the former is rather kite-shaped and the latter wedge-shaped.

The following method was designed to take account of both size and shape (Amoore 1965). The photographs were all taken according to a convention which kept the major axes of the molecules co-aligned. Hence

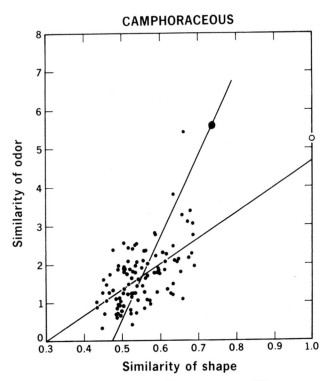

CAMPHORACEOUS

Similarity of odor

Similarity of shape

FIG. 52. GRAPH OF THE "CAMPHORACEOUS" DATA

The standard odorant is 1,8-cineole (open circle). The unknown odorants are the same in all five graphs. The shadow matching method is used throughout.

corresponding silhouettes for an unknown and a standard molecule could be superimposed (Fig. 49) with the center of gravity of each silhouette as a datum point. Radii were drawn every 10° of arc from the center of gravity to the periphery. The difference in length between the corresponding radii of the two compounds is a measure of the difference in molecular size and shape. The overall average difference in molecular radius ($\bar{\Delta}$) was found for all three silhouettes (ignoring sign). However, the panel measurements of odor quality were in terms of similarity, not difference; so the molecular measurements were put into reciprocal form, actually $1/(\bar{\Delta} + 1)$, before plotting the graphs.

Correlations Between Molecular Shape and Odor

These experiments have been completed on 107 compounds up to the present. Full numerical data are reported elsewhere (Amoore and Venstrom 1965). The data are divided into five sets of 107 measurements,

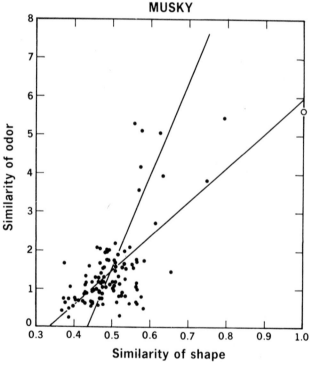

Fig. 53. Graph of the "Musky" Data

The standard odorant is 15-hydroxypentadecanoic acid lactone.

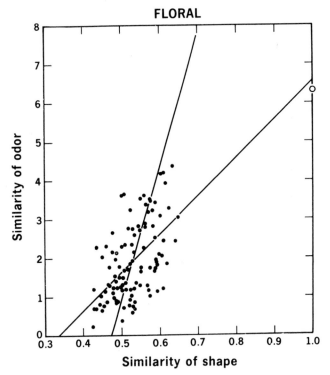

FIG. 54.   GRAPH OF THE "FLORAL" DATA

The standard is d,l-β-phenylethylmethylethyl carbinol.

one set for each of the five standard odorants.   The results are conveniently displayed in the form of five graphs (Figs. 51–55) which show for each standard odor the plot of odor similarity against shape similarity. Each point signifies a separate compound, and represents the result of about 160 measurements (ca. 50 of odor and 108 of shape).   Although the individual points are quite scattered, the general agreement between molecular shape and odor is obvious.   To confirm this intuitive appraisal, the coordinates of each point on each graph (omitting the standard) were put through a computer for a complete straight-line regression analysis by the method of least squares.   The lines obtained are plotted on the graphs.   There are two lines because there is no basis for deciding whether the molecular shape (shallower line) or the odor similarity (steeper line) should be regarded as the independent variable.

The correlation coefficients (r) ranged between 0.52 for the minty graph and 0.66 for the ethereal graph (0.00 would mean no correlation

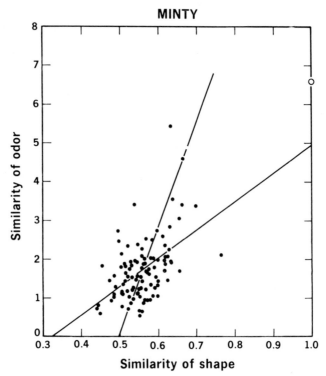

FIG. 55. GRAPH OF THE "MINTY" DATA

The standard is *d,l*-menthone

at all and 1.00 would indicate a perfect linear correlation). The statistical certainty of the existence of a real correlation between molecular shape and odor depends on the number of compounds (N) surveyed. The standard odorant itself is omitted from the statistical analysis of each graph, which reduces N from 107 to 106. For $N = 106$ and $r = 0.52$, the probability (P) of the observed distribution of points being merely a random result is less than 10^{-9}, or one in a billion. Considering that this value of P was achieved or bettered for all five graphs attempted, the odds are astronomical that a strong correlation does exist between molecular size and shape and odor quality.

The significance of the correlation is collective, in that it applies to a large number of compounds drawn from a wide variety of chemical classes. Many familiar odorants were surveyed, and so were a few rather unusual compounds. Among these was the spherically symmetrical hydrocarbon adamantane, only recently obtainable readily by chemical synthesis; the rare steroid Δ^{16}-androsten-3α-ol, so scarce that even the discoverers had expended their stock, but a 4-mg. sample was finally obtained from a medical reference collection; and the newly discovered isopropylcarborane, whose molecular structure containing an icosahedron of "hexavalent" boron and carbon atoms is so bizarre that no commercial molecular models could represent it (Fein *et al.* 1963). Familiar or strange, the compounds all fitted into the stereochemical theory of olfaction.

POINTS OF CLARIFICATION

Straightforward presentation of the theory has left a number of matters in need of further detailed explanation. Some of these are amplifications of bald experimental results presented elsewhere (Amoore and Venstrom 1965), or modifications of views presented in earlier papers.

Transduction Mechanism

The stereochemical theory is based on the psychophysical hypothesis that somehow the olfactory nerves can distinguish molecular sizes and shapes. No assumption need be made as to exactly how the shapes are registered by the nerve endings, nor as to the mechanism of transduction whereby the presence of an odorant molecule gives rise to a nervous impulse. Incidentally, these are virtually unsolved problems for all the senses, not just olfaction, but more progress has been made toward a solution for some of the other senses, particularly vision. The uncertainty does not prevent us from making extremely valuable use of the psychophysical principle that the molecular shape is related to odor. After all, tricolor printing, color photography, and color television were all developed from the psychophysical principle that the wavelength of light determines color sensation without exact knowledge of how a quantum depolarizes an axon.

Site-Fitting Method

The classical lock and key concept has just about run its course as regards olfactory theory. It is too inflexible in application, and cannot account for the total 3-dimensional shape of the molecule (Amoore 1965). It has been superceded as an experimental method by the shadow-matching procedure. The latter too will probably have to make way in due course for more sophisticated measurements of molecular shape. The human mind creeps up on Nature's truth by a series of guesses (sometimes called scientific method).

Molecular Cooperation

Some difficulty was found (Amoore 1962B) with a few compounds that were reported to have a particular odor, but did not appear large enough to satisfy the appropriate receptor site. In such cases it was assumed that pairs of molecules would associate together, for instance through hydrogen bonding, and that the combined pair of molecules would fill the site. Two such examples are salicylaldehyde and phenylacetic acid, noted as respectively a delicate floral and a civet-like (musk-type odor) in Moncrieff's book (1951). These two examples have now been put through our odor dimension analysis procedure, with the gratifying result that the corresponding floral and musky scores were not high (0.85 and 1.98). The molecular shape data for the single molecules correlated reasonably well with the revised odor similarities. There was no necessity to postulate molecular cooperation in explaining the odor qualities of these, or any other of the 107 compounds surveyed so far.

Molecular Contortion

A disadvantage of the site-fitting concept was that it was often necessary to distort the configuration of a molecular model to fit a particular site. For example, to fit 1-pentyl acetate into the camphoraceous receptor site required 120° rotation at three bonds in the main chain: $C_1—C_2$, $C_2—C_3$ and $C_3—C_4$. The chances of obtaining just such a restrained configuration are small both energetically and statistically. In the new shadow-matching method, the molecular model is photographed in a single, most probable configuration and a standard orientation. This configuration is used exclusively in the measurements of the present stereochemical survey. In an earlier paper (Amoore 1962B) some rather forced configurations were employed (e.g., stearaldehyde fitting into the ethereal site). Special configurations should not be postulated without a thorough examination of the molecular energetics and "rotational isomerism."

Complex Odors

Earlier papers of this series asserted that there are but seven "primary odors" and that all other odors are complex, made up of differing proportions of the primary sensations in various permutations. Today, the postulate that there are odor primaries still holds good in principle, but the number may be more than seven. Current experiments and thinking, in this and other laboratories, suggest that some of the original "primary odors" may have to be split into subgroups of two or more, and that certain presumptive "complex odors" may turn out to represent primaries in their own right. Also other odors not yet named in this series of papers may correspond with new true primaries.

This anticipated multiplication of primaries does not affect the principle that it should be possible to reconstitute a complex odor from its presumed primary constituents using the stereochemical theory as a guide

(Johnston 1963, 1965). Many useful shades of color have been created by mixing pigments without knowledge of the spectral sensitivity curves of the retinal cones. The expected refinement in our knowledge of the true identities of the primaries will lend greater precision to experiments in odor-mixing. Like the classical site-fitting concept, the 7-primary-odor hypothesis has served its alloted span. It provided the means of marshalling the chaotic disarray of olfactory information into sufficient order to perceive the underlying stereochemical principle. Now that the whole problem is amenable to detailed and systematic investigation, we have to be prepared to relinquish a concept attractive in its simplicity, but unable to reflect the full complexity of Nature.

Electroactive Groups

The steric theory of odor applies only to molecules which are reasonably neutral in electronic status. If strongly electrophilic or nucleophilic groups are present, particularly in a small molecule, their effect overrides any considerations of molecular shape, and the steric correlations fail. Hence instead of the expected odor (usually ethereal) the odor is pungent or putrid. Thus formic acid and dimethyl disulfide (the last two of the seven odor standards) registered negligible ethereal scores of 0.41 and 0.29, although their molecular sizes and shapes would predict ethereal scores of about 3 and 4 respectively. Such compounds lie outside the present compass of the stereochemical theory, because no system has yet been developed for assessing electrophilic or nucleophilic character in the context of odor analysis.

Literature Odor Descriptions

Text books and "handbooks" of organic chemistry and perfumers' catalogs contain numerous valuable descriptions of the odors of chemicals. Such indeed were the indispensable sources for the original stereochemical theory. They have the shortcomings that they represent usually the judgment of a single observer or at best a very few, and they describe samples of unknown purity. Regarding the latter criticism, it should be pointed out that no professional chemist relishes the thought of being the author of physical data (melting point, boiling point, specific gravity, etc.) later to be proved incorrect on account of impurities. The first sample prepared of a new compound stands a good deal better chance of being pure than many a subsequent preparation by other scientists or manufacturers, at least until somebody makes a very special effort by advanced methods to establish quantitative limits for impurities.

The method of odor analysis by a large panel of judges used in this investigation compensates for individual idiosyncrasies and bias. It also has the great advantage of producing quantitative and comparative data for every compound examined. However the present method of running the odor dimension analyses uses a "vocabulary" of only seven words (classes of odor), whereas the conventional verbal odor description can draw on the whole language. Hence descriptions in the literature of substances we have analyzed, though superseded for the purposes of the present study, still have a great deal of untapped information to convey, particularly in respect to shades and nuances of odor.

Exceptions

There are certain odor descriptions in the literature which appear to be unbalanced, in that a minor aspect of the odor has been given undue prominence in the accepted description. Such examples appear to be exceptions to the stereochemical theory. Hydrogen cyanide generally has been recorded as almond-like. The odor panel method however showed it to have a predominantly pungent odor (Amoore and Venstrom 1966). The same paper assigned hexamethylethane to the camphoraceous class although it had been called pungent before. In an earlier section of the present paper the apparent exceptions salicylaldehyde and phenylacetic acid were resolved. To these one might add methyl cyclopropyl ketone, described in Beilstein as strongly camphoraceous. The molecule seemed too little to smell camphoraceous, instead it should smell more ethereal. Indeed, when tested on the panel, the camphoraceous score of 1.42 was far outweighed by the ethereal component of 3.77. This result agrees better with Perkin's (1885) statement that the compound is an oil "of powerful odor, recalling somewhat that of camphor." The panel of judges provides an effective method of settling such discrepancies. So far, "the exceptions prove the rule."

LIMITATIONS OF THE THEORY

The stereochemical theory, in its present stage of development, is subject to certain quantitative reservations. Perhaps future research will reduce or even eliminate them, but they remain obstinately with us now, and restrict the immediate usefulness of the theory.

Scatter on the Graphs

As indicated by the rather modest correlation coefficients of about 0.6, the graphs (Figs. 51–55) fall a good deal short of the ideal straight line expected by a physicist or chemist who has all his independent variables isolated or at least under strict experimental control. But to persons versed in the difficulties of studying a phenomenon as ephemeral as an odor by an instrument as capricious as a human being, it may be surprising that the correlations are as good as they are.

There is a general scatter of the experimental points in a roughly elliptical contour, seen most clearly in the camphoraceous and floral graphs (Figs. 52 and 54). A few individual points are very wild, particularly in the ethereal graph (Fig. 51). An unexpectedly low odor dimension-analysis score may well suggest that the sample employed contained odorous impurity. The origins of the scatter undoubtedly include both experimental error and theoretical over-simplification. The error presumably arises in both the odor analyses and the steric assessments. It will demand great attention to detail to eliminate the various sources of error from the investigation.

Odor Qualities Not Distinguished

The restricted "vocabulary" of the present odor quality analysis method is probably responsible for certain quite distinguishable odorants coming out with almost identical scores. An example is provided by four compounds whose odor dimension analyses are virtually the same, considering the known standard error of about ±0.5 unit in the mean odor analysis scores (Amoore and Venstrom 1966). These are benzaldehyde, isoquinoline, limonene, and 1-pentyl acetate. Their odors might be loosely grouped as fruity, but they are readily distinguishable by their respective almond, aniseed, lemon, and banana notes. Evidently, the quantitative results introduced with the panel method cannot compensate for the loss of descriptive vocabulary imposed by seven odor categories. Introduction of more standard odorants for special purposes could improve the situation.

The Amyl Acetates

Isomeric Molecules Not Resolved.—Conversely a group of closely related chemicals may not vary in odor with shape as the stereochemical theory predicts. For example, we have studied the family of "amyl acetate" isomers, kindly made available in highly refined and isomerically pure forms by Dr. Roy Teranishi and his colleagues in this laboratory (Teranishi *et al.* 1966). The detailed olfactory and stereochemical measurements are reported elsewhere (Amoore and Venstrom 1965). The eight structural isomers of amyl acetate, or 1-pentyl acetate as it is systematically named are as follows: 1-pentyl acetate; *d,l*-2-pentyl acetate; 3-pentyl acetate; *d,l*-2-methyl-1-butyl acetate; 3-methyl-1-butyl acetate; 2-methyl-2-butyl acetate; *d,l*-3-methyl-2-butyl acetate and 2,2-dimethyl-propyl acetate. Their alicyclic relative, cyclopentyl acetate, was also included, though it is not strictly an isomer, lacking two hydrogen atoms.

In addition four metameric isomers of 1-pentyl acetate were examined: methyl *n*-hexanoate; ethyl *n*-pentanoate; *n*-propyl *n*-butyrate and *n*-butyl propionate. The *n*-hexyl formate was too unstable for study. Unfortunately the hexanoate, pentanoate, and butyrate esters, though pure by instrumental analysis, exhibited by-odors reminiscent of the free aliphatic acids. When submitted to the odor panel, these three esters earned unreasonably high pungent and putrid scores of between 1 and 3. Accordingly they were omitted from the survey, pending further investigation of their homogeneity.

Figure 56 shows the results from the eight isomeric pentyl acetates, plus cyclopentyl acetate and *n*-butyl propionate (ten compounds in all). The same points are of course included in the main 107-compound graphs (Figs. 51–55) but have been replotted separately in Fig. 56 for clarity. The rank-order correlation coefficients (Spearman's ρ) are also entered on each graph. For ten compounds, positive significant correlation at the five per cent level requires a value for ρ of at least $+0.56$. This value was achieved on the camphoraceous graph alone; the other four graphs showed nil or negative significant correlation. The reason is not far to seek, when the graphs of Fig. 56 are compared with the corresponding graphs of Figs. 51–55. The ten isomers are so similar that they cover only a small fraction of the range of molecular shapes and odor qualities. Furthermore, the fraction that the ten do cover is probably much the same as the standard errors of the measurements themselves.

There is some consolation in reflecting that these ten compounds contain the same atoms and the same functional group and exhibit bewilderingly similar physical, chemical, and spectroscopic properties. According to most other theories of odor, the isomers should smell identical. In fact they are to varying degrees distinguishable to the nose. The stereochemical theory appears to have the best potentiality, as yet unrealized, of resolving their odors. The challenge is however severe; two of the isomers are so alike that they run the gauntlet of 500 feet of gas chromatographic capillary and emerge unseparated.

Statistical vs. Individual Predictions

The correlations between shape and odor so far hold good only for a reasonably large group of compounds taken as a whole. For a minimum correlation coefficient of 0.5, as has been achieved in this survey, significance at the five per cent level can only be expected if at least 15 compounds are examined, and they must represent a fairly wide variety of molecular sizes and shapes. The theory in its present form is statistical rather than particular in its application. It could probably be vindicated at the 0.1% level with any group of 40 or more nonelectroactive odorants.

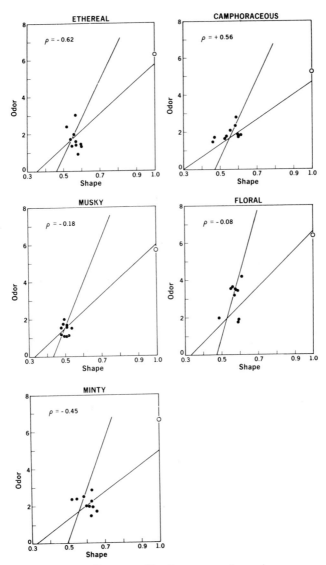

FIG. 56. THE DATA FOR TEN ISOMERS OF AMYL ACETATE

These compounds are included in Figs. 51–55, from which the regression lines are taken. Evidently the amyl acetates are too similar to each other to be resolved by the present stereochemical theory.

However, the theory in its present degree of refinement cannot generally be used to predict the odor of a single compound. It would be unrealistic to attempt to read off from the graphs (Fig. 51–55) the odor similarity scores corresponding with a single particular molecular shape. The spread of points up and down any given ordinate is too great. Only if a fair-sized group of substances were to be tested, for instance in a program of organic syntheses, could one be reasonably certain of achieving a particular odor.

Nevertheless, in one type of special case predictions of the odor of a single compound would be on firmer ground. Variations only by isosteric replacement of atoms or groups preserves the shape of the molecule almost intact and should result in the retention of an extremely similar odor quality. One such example is provided by the pair hexamethylethane and hexachloroethane, which have nearly identical odors (Amoore and Venstrom 1966).

ALTERNATIVE THEORIES OF ODOR

At the last count (Moncrieff 1951) there were at least 24 more or less distinct "theories of odor," and the rate at which new ones appear has not fallen off appreciably since then. They may be roughly divided into two classes, the corpuscular and the radiative. In the former class, which includes the stereochemical theory, odor is considered to be associated with some structural aspect of part or all of the molecule, regarded as a particle. The latter class connects odor with the vibrational properties of part or all of the molecule and in its more extreme forms extends to actual propagated radiation. However, among all the various theories of odor, only two appear to have sufficient experimental detail to merit consideration as serious alternatives to the stereochemical theory.

Wright's Vibrational Theory

It is postulated in this theory of odor that the characteristic odor quality of a compound is connected with particular vibrational frequencies of segments of the molecule, or even of the total molecule (Wright 1954, 1957, 1964A). The frequencies may be conveniently detected and measured by infrared or Raman spectroscopy. Wright's papers offer considerable evidence for recurring frequency distributions among compounds belonging to the same odor class, such as almond or musk.

Recently, an independent investigator (a namesake of the originator of the theory) has conducted a systematic experimental test of the vibrational theory (Wright and Michels 1964). This investigation has many parallels with the survey of the stereochemical theory outlined in the present paper. Nine compounds were chosen as odor standards, and 50 unknown compounds were rated for similarity on a scale of 0 to 6 by 84 judges. A complete table was presented of the similarity ratings for the 50 unknown compounds against the nine standards. Next the Raman spectra of the same compounds were examined, and the similarities among the compounds were quantitatively assessed in terms of the sum of the spectral intensities occurring within particular wave-number intervals. The intervals were 150 cm.$^{-1}$ and covered the range of 176 to 625 cm.$^{-1}$. Regrettably no actual tables of similarities in Raman spectra are published.

When the similarities in odor were compared with the similarities in Raman spectra for the 50 compounds, the result was disappointing. There was no correlation between the spectra and the odors ($P > 0.5$). Wright and Michels then converted their table of odor similarity ratings into a 50 $\times$ 50 correlation matrix, which was factor analyzed by a computer program. Eight factors emerged, to which odor names were assigned. When the computer-isolated odor factor loadings were used (instead of the original odor similarity ratings from the panel of judges), then significant correlations were found with the Raman spectra (P ca. 0.01).

This evaluation by Wright and Michels of Wright's theory does provide some support for the vibrational theory. However, the correlation was not apparent until the odor similarity data were factor analyzed by computer. Even then the probability level reached in the final correlation fell short of that achieved by the stereochemical theory in a comparable survey without factor analysis.

Davies' Adsorption Theory

The other detailed theory of odor is that due to Davies (Davies and Taylor 1954, 1959; Davies 1962). This theory primarily offers to explain odor intensity or threshold, rather than quality. It postulates a connection between the olfactory threshold concentration of a compound and a function containing two variables; molecular cross-sectional area and the coefficient of adsorption of the compound at an oil/water interface. The theory successfully predicts the olfactory threshold for various compounds over a wide range of intrinsic intensities (Davies 1962). This adsorption theory appears to be an important contribution toward the understanding of olfactory thresholds.

Davies has recently tried extending his theory to embrace odor quality as well as intensity (Davies 1965). He has plotted for a number of compounds the molecular cross-sectional area as a function of the energy of desorption of the molecule from the lipid-water interface into water. It transpired that certain regions on the resulting graph were associated with particular classes of odor. The segregation was incomplete, but it was clear enough to suggest that there is some sort of connection between the variables studied. However, as regards odor quality, Davies' adsorption theory has not yet been investigated with the thoroughness applied to Wright's vibrational theory or Amoore's stereochemical theory.

When it comes to prediction, both Wright's method and Davies' method require an actual sample of the chemical to be available (for measurements of the infrared spectrum and the adsorption coefficient) before any prediction of odor quality is possible. In the stereochemical theory, only a molecular model need be constructed.

Assessment of Theories Now Possible

There is little doubt that all three theories are reflecting some relationship between odor quality on the one hand, and molecular shape, vibration, or adsorption on the other. The question as to which is the most realistic description could best be settled by an organized comparison of the three theories by means of a common set of odorous compounds. The methods for conducting such a test are fully available for the stereochemical theory (Amoore 1965) and for the vibrational theory (Wright and Michels 1964). The same type of odor similarity data could test the adsorption theory if there were a method for assessing the similarities of molecular area and adsorption coefficient.

An agreed set of test compounds should cover a wide spectrum of odor types. Some, or all, of the test compounds would be used as standards of comparison, for measuring the similarity of odor quality and the similarity of molecular shape, infrared spectra, and oil/water adsorption. In the first instance the data would best be displayed graphically to show for each standard the correlation between the experimentally measured odor quality and the chosen molecular parameter. The correlation coefficient would appear to be as fair a yardstick as any for comparing the relative success of the alternative theories. Later a factor analysis of the original data could be used to see if the correlations can be improved.

The correlation coefficients would measure the relative merits of the Amoore stereochemical theory, the Wright vibrational theory, and the Davies adsorption theory. The results would indicate which is the most reliable guide for odor and flavor research.

CRITICISMS OF THE STEREOCHEMICAL THEORY

A number of investigators and reviewers have pointed out inadequacies in the present-day stereochemical theory of odor. Two of the criticisms are especially important and must certainly be considered in the subsequent development of the theory.

Electrophysiology and Receptor Specificity

In the first classification of odors, it was natural to think in terms of a limited number of "primary odors" (Amoore 1952). It was further tempting to believe that a distinct type of olfactory nerve ending would sense each primary odor, analogous to the retinal cones of color vision (Amoore 1964). The experimental study of this question has proved a very challenging problem in electrophysiology, and has only recently been solved (Gesteland et al. 1963). Electrical impulses are detected in a single olfactory receptor cell by means of a microelectrode. The earliest results, from the olfactory epithelium of the frog, suggested that the receptors might belong to a small number of classes, about eight, and that the different receptors responded fairly selectively.

However, further experiments in which many more receptors were examined with a greater variety of odorants led to a more realistic assessment (Gesteland et al. 1965). No two cells gave identical responses to a given set of odorants; conversely no two odorants produced identical responses in a given group of cells. This result indicates that the simple concept of specific primary receptor cells probably does not apply to vertebrate olfaction. It may however apply for certain specialized pheromone receptors in insects, according to Schneider et al. (1964).

The outcome is disheartening for odor research in general because it suggests that the electrophysiological approach, initially so promising, is not likely to identify the true primary components of the olfactory discriminating system. For the stereochemical theory in particular, the single-receptor studies force abandonment of the clear-cut idea of a few types of olfactory receptor cell, each bearing a single specific kind of receptor site. A compromise which recurs in the writings of Gesteland and his collaborators is to imagine that each receptor cell bears several different types of receptor sites and that the selection and proportion of the various sites differs from cell to cell. Such a model would account for most of the electrophysiological observations.

Partial Anosmia and the Number of Primaries

In his delightful book, "The Science of Smell," Wright (1964B) tackled the problem of the number of primary odors. For example, the existing stereochemical theory lumps all the musk odors together, considering them to stimulate a single primary odor sensation. Detailed olfactometric experiments by Johnston and Sandoval (1962) supported the view that musk is a primary. Nevertheless Guillot (1948) noted that rare individual persons lack the ability to perceive the odor of one of the chemical families of musks but have no difficulty smelling members of two other families of musks. Such persons are said to be "partially anosmic." The results were confirmed by Le Magnen (1948) on normal observers by the method of selective olfactory fatigue. Tiring the nose by continued sniffing of one type of musk fatigued the ability to perceive other members of the same family of musks, but did not affect the perception of the different families. The implication is very strong that the musk sensation is itself multiple, and is composed of at least three fundamentals.

Records of about a dozen types of partial anosmia have found their way into the literature, and Guillot (1948) maintains very plausibly that these must represent the start of a list of the true fundamental or primary odors. The actual number is an open question. Their identification and specification constitute possibly the most urgent single problem in olfaction research.

PROPOSED REFINEMENTS OF THE THEORY

Further development of the theory is expected to progress along two lines.

Experimental Modifications

Certain detailed improvements in experimental technique would very likely increase the correlation coefficient observed (Amoore 1965). The test compounds should all be purified. The judges should be selected for olfactory skill. A threshold method utilizing cross-adaptation could be employed for measuring the similarity between odorants. Flying spot scanner or computer simulation techniques might be used to improve the assessments of molecular shape. Factor analysis of the raw data might reveal detailed correlations at present obscure. Methods are needed for assessing the molecular electronic status, which is of paramount importance to pungent and putrid odors, but probably also plays some part in modifying the smell of most other odorants. Consideration should be given to the position and affinity of polar-associative and hydrogen-bonding groups in the molecule.

Identification of Primary Odors

Right alongside such detailed improvements, a fundamental attack on the question of primaries is necessary. The most promising approach would seem to be a search for persons exhibiting partial anosmia, i.e. people with a generally normal olfactory sense, but lacking the ability to perceive one particular compound or a small group of similar compounds. One such case has recently come to the author's attention, of partial anosmia to the rancid-smelling compound isobutyric acid. This appears to be a particularly favorable example for systematic experimental study. Primary odors discovered by examining partial anosmias should be confirmed on normal subjects by the method of cross-adaptation of odors.

As each primary odor is confidently identified, and there could be scores of them, a representative pure compound should be chosen and included as a standard odorant in future organoleptic and stereochemical surveys. In practice the stereochemical theory may well turn out to lose the "attractive simplicity" of its original seven primaries. Fundamental ideas are often simple in principle, but in practical application become extremely complex. A Fourth of July rocket is admirably simple but a large ballistic missile is not.

RELEVENCE OF THE THEORY TO FLAVOR RESEARCH

The stereochemical theory has been presented above as a problem in pure research. How useful can it be in applied research on flavor?

If one is considering a single isolated compound, such as eugenol or vanillin, the theory is not very helpful at present because it lacks the necessary exactitude. However, the volatiles of most foodstuffs contain dozens or even hundreds of compounds, so that the sum of the separate assessments on each compound could be statistically meaningful. For example application of the theory has contributed to the understanding of a food odor in study of volatiles from brined cucumber fermentations by Aurand et al. (1965). That investigation used the earliest, intuitive form of the theory (Amoore 1952), before methods were developed for the quantitative assessment of odor qualities of single chemicals or whole foodstuffs by the matching standards method (Schutz 1964; Amoore and Venstrom 1966).

Assessment of the full organoleptic impact of the volatiles of a given foodstuff could perhaps include the following stages. First, one starts with the analysis of an aqueous extract of the food by gas-liquid chromatography and associated physical methods, to identify the compounds present and to estimate their concentrations in the extract. This has of course been done qualitatively for numerous foods, but quantitative analyses are harder to find. One simplifying feature is that many of the same compounds crop up in a variety of foods, so that the total number in all foods of compounds that will require organoleptic and stereochemical assay is not quite so prodigious as might at first be feared.

Secondly, one should determine the odor threshold concentrations of all the compounds observed. This tedious task has rarely been undertaken; a fine example is the continuing study of hop oil constituents by Guadagni, Buttery, and Harris (1966). The relative quantitative contributions of each volatile constituent to the overall aroma can then be estimated, using as an approximation the rule of additivity of subthreshold concentrations (Guadagni *et al.* 1963). Even compounds present in the food at less than their individual threshold concentration can apparently contribute to the total aroma. One complication in this procedure, however, is that the threshold concentration of a dissolved compound can be greatly altered by the nature of the solvent, particularly whether it be in an oily or aqueous phase (Patton 1964). A further difficulty is that suprathreshold intensities for different compounds do not necessarily vary in the same way with concentration. With the standard odorants used in the present work the matching intensities were far from a constant multiple of the threshold concentrations (Amoore and Venstrom 1966).

Finally each compound should be submitted to organoleptic analysis by a large group of judges, using the matching standards method to measure the similarities of odor to each of the chosen standards (Amoore and Venstrom 1966). A check on the overall accuracy of the investigation is provided by the consideration that the sum of the odor constituents should equal the whole. That is, a sum should be taken of the contributions by each odorant to each odor class (as indicated by the odor dimension analyses), and properly weighted according to the measured concentration of each odorant in the food extract (from the gas chromatographic analysis), and according to its threshold (by paired comparison) and according to its matching intensity (by the ranking method). The sums for each odor class should agree closely with the odor dimension analysis obtained on the whole food extract (itself tested at its matching concentration).

This extensive schedule of experiments would appear to be the minimum that could possibly be called a complete chemical and organoleptic analysis of a food aroma. Note that the gas-chromatographic analysis, already a technically challenging and time-consuming operation, represents merely the first battle of an extended campaign.

The organoleptic information obtained would be the necessary basis for a number of important applications in food technology. First and foremost, it could reinforce quality control. It may be a helpful practice to estimate a single indicator substance (e.g., *n*-hexanal in potato granules) as a check on quality, but it would inspire more confidence if one really knew that the chosen compound was the key substance in the flavor (Boggs *et al.* 1964). Second, it would help in trouble-shooting. Off-flavors developing in storage could be quantitatively apportioned to the desirable compounds that are disappearing or to the undesirable ones that are forming. Third, it could assist in product improvement. If manufacturers knew which compounds were most important for the best flavor (and the nicest are often the most delicate) they could adjust processing conditions to preserve these compounds intact through to the consumer. Fourth, it might serve as a guide in plant and animal breeding. If the geneticist knew what compound or class of compounds were responsible for the most sought-after flavor, and which caused the most rejection, he could study his chromosome maps with more insight.

The above scheme of organoleptic assessment of a foodstuff could perhaps be conducted empirically without reference to the stereochemical theory of odor but that would be a myopic expedient. For maximum accuracy in the organoleptic assessment, the standards of odor employed should correspond with the true primary odors. For a fundamental understanding of why each compound contributes the odor it does and what are the limiting molecular sizes and shapes involved, one should refer to the stereochemical theory. When trace components of an "aromagram" are identified spectroscopically but are not available in sufficient quantity or purity for organoleptic analysis, the theory could be useful. These inaccessible constituents could be assessed stereochemically from molecular models to estimate their probable odor contributions pending confirmation by chemical synthesis.

CONCLUSIONS

The present situation in food flavor research may be appraised as follows. The problem is very complex. Nevertheless the experimental methods for its analysis are available. The theoretical principles that underlie it are understood. All that is needed is the manpower to solve it.

Flavor research is today just about where genetics research was ten years ago, and where cancer research may be ten years hence. Flavor research has just had a first glimpse of its Rosetta stone, the "olfactory code."

ACKNOWLEDGMENT

The author is most grateful to Dr. Horace K. Burr for his continued interest in this work, for much helpful discussion, and last but not least, for very kindly agreeing to present this paper at the Symposium on Foods, during the author's absence at the International Symposium on Olfaction and Taste.

DISCUSSION

A. D. Webb.—Referring to the earlier theory about stereochemistry, I wonder if it has been possible, using molecular models, to build satisfactory models of these various receptor shapes? Ones that would be composed of say proteinaceous or mucus-type constituents and ones that would be stable when they were not filled?

H. K. Burr.—Of course, in developing his theory, Dr. Amoore deduced what he thought would be the most likely shapes for these receptor sites and defined them in terms of dimensions. He has made these with transparent plastic material on an appropriate scale and can fit molecular models into them. I'm not sure whether you were speaking of receptor sites on the angstrom plane or the centimeter plane.

A. D. Webb.—I'm speaking about what exists in the human being, I realize you can make models out of plastic that fit perfectly, but presumably what we are after here is a site that exists within the nose somewhere that these molecules which have these various shapes can fit into. Unless we can visualize a shape built of true molecules within the nose that has this shape and maintains it, we cannot select these various molecules according to their differing shapes.

H. K. Burr.—I should note that Amoore has now modified the idea of these specific receptor sites and one reason was the following: For the camphoraceous site he postulated a basin-shaped depression 9 Å long, 7 Å across, and 4 Å deep, and he conceived the molecules as fitting into it. But he found that there were some molecules that when fitted into the site, fitted equally well, without extending outside and these did not smell camphoraceous, and so he had to elaborate his theory and he now thinks that this site has got to have a cover, and if the cover does not fit well with the molecule in the site, then that molecule cannot be said to fit. In other words, he had to recognize the overall shape of the molecule, not merely the part that would fit down into the site. So he no longer concerns himself with the actual sites and makes no assumptions as to what goes in when the molecule comes down against the epithelium.

T. G. Keppler.—I can tell you of another substance which has a very striking ability to be smelled by one person and not at all by another. It is methional, you can smell it at 1 ppb and it has a very nasty smell. Others can have a room full of it and not notice it. I would like to tell you that we were busy testing the Amoore theory and we synthesized many of the normal aldehydes, both saturated and unsaturated. It has worried us that the aldehyde data does not fit Amoore's theory. But I will go home now, much more satisfied.

M. E. Mason.—Do any of the three theories which you just got through discussing, or which Dr. Dravnieks has spent considerable time on, explain the differences in odor between the d- and l- and the syn and anti forms of compounds? Do any of these theories approach an explanation of these differences?

A. Dravnieks.—I do not believe there is any evidence in the literature that there is a striking difference between the stereoisomers. It has usually been traced down to impurities and when pure compounds are taken and more careful work is done, less differences have been found between stereoisomers. Unless there is some new recent evidence, this is the point where the knowledge of stereoisomers rested a couple of years ago.

T. G. Keppler.—Cis and trans isomers and positional isomers exhibit differences in flavor and in flavor threshold values. If you have, say the C_7 aldehyde, and you have a double bond in the 4 position, the trans form is a hundredfold different in threshold value and it has a different type of flavor than the cis form.

I. Hornstein.—It seems to me that cis and trans isomers are one thing, and d- and l-isomers are another. In one case you really would have a difference in shape and electronic distribution and in the other you would not. The chances are that *d*- and *l*-isomers would probably show no differences, while *cis* and *trans* isomers would.

A. Dravnieks.—I want to make the same point. For instance the differences in threshold of *cis* and *trans* 2-butene is about one hundredfold and the only difference between the properties which I could find in the literature is that the *trans* form complexes with silver. This is used in gas chromatography. I guess the *trans* complex can form easily if other molecules can get at the double bond and it cannot do so if hindered. So I think for *cis* and *trans* isomers, it is well established. But for stereoisomers it is questionable.

J. E. Amore (in Proof).—In reply to M. E. Mason I would point out that most biochemical reactions are stereo-specific, on account of the asymmetry of the enzymes themselves, so that if and when a difference in the odors of optical antipodes can be proved, one need only postulate an asymmetrical receptor site (like the old "minty" site) to explain the difference.

BIBLIOGRAPHY

AMOORE, J. E. 1952. The stereochemical specificities of human olfactory receptors. Perfum. Ess. Oil Rec. *43*, 321–323; 330.

AMOORE, J. E. 1962A. The stereochemical theory of olfaction. 1. Identification of the seven primary odors. Proc. Sci. Sect. Toilet Goods Assoc. Supplement to No. 37, 1–12.

AMOORE, J. E. 1962B. The stereochemical theory of olfaction. 2. Elucidation of the stereochemical properties of the olfactory receptor sites. Proc. Sci. Sect. Toilet Goods Assoc. Supplement to No. 37, 13–23.

AMOORE, J. E. 1964. Current status of the steric theory of odor. Ann. N. Y. Acad. Sci. *116*, 457–476.

AMOORE, J. E. 1965. Psychophysics of odor. Cold Spring Harbor Symposia Quant. Biol. *30* 623–637.

AMOORE, J. E., JOHNSTON, J. W., and RUBIN, M. 1964. The stereochemical theory of odor. Sci. Am., *210*, No. 2, 42–49.

AMOORE, J. E., and VENSTROM, D. 1965. Correlations between stereochemical assessments and organoleptic analyses of odorous compounds. *In* Olfaction and Taste, Vol. 2, T. Hayashi, (Editor). Macmillan Co., New York.

AMOORE, J. E., and VENSTROM, D. 1966. Sensory analysis of odor qualities in terms of the stereochemical theory. J. Food Sci. *31*, 118–128.

AURAND, L. W., SINGLETON, J. A., BELL, T. A., and ETCHELLS, J. L. 1965. Identification of volatile constituents from pure-culture fermentations of brined cucumbers. J. Food Sci. *30*, 288–295.

BOGGS, M. M., BUTTERY, R. G., VENSTROM, D. W., and BELOTE, M. L. 1964. Relation of hexanal in vapor above stored potato granules to subjective flavor estimates. J. Food Sci. *29*, 487–489.

DAVIES, J. T. 1962. The mechanism of olfaction. Symposia Soc. Exptl. Biol. *16*, 170–179.

DAVIES, J. T. 1965. A theory of the quality of odours. J. Theoret. Biol. *8*, 1–7.

DAVIES, J. T., and TAYLOR, F. H. 1954. A model system for the olfactory membrane. Nature *174*, 693–694.

DAVIES, J. T., and TAYLOR, F. H. 1959. The role of adsorption and molecular morphology in olfaction: The calculation of olfactory thresholds. Biol. Bull. *117*, 222–238.

FEIN, M. M., BOBINSKI, J., MAYES, N., SCHWARTZ, N. N., and COHEN, M. S. 1963. Carboranes. I. The preparation and chemistry of 1-isopropenyl-carborane and its derivatives (a new family of stable clovoboranes). Inorg. Chem. 2, 1111–1115.

FISCHER, E. 1894. Influence of configuration on the action of enzymes (in German). Ber. deut. chem. Ges. 27, 2985–2993.

GESTELAND, R. C., LETTVIN, J. Y., and PITTS, W. H. 1965. Chemical transmission in the nose of the frog. J. Physiol. 181, 525–559.

GESTELAND, R. C., LETTVIN, J. Y., PITTS, W. H., and ROJAS, A. 1963. Odor specificities of the frog's olfactory receptors. In Olfaction and Taste, pp. 19–34, Y. Zotterman, (Editor). Macmillan Co., New York.

GUADAGNI, D. G., BUTTERY, R. G., and HARRIS, J. 1966. Odor intensities of hop oil constituents. J. Sci. Food Agr. 17, 142–144.

GUADAGNI, D. G., BUTTERY, R. G., OKANO, S., and BURR, H. K. 1963. Additive effect of sub-threshold concentrations of some organic compounds associated with food aromas. Nature 200, 1288–1289.

GUILLOT, M. 1948. Partial anosmias and fundamental odors (in French). Compt. Rend. 226, 1307–1309.

JOHNSTON, J. W. 1960. Current problems in olfaction. Georgetown Med. Bull. 13, 112–117.

JOHNSTON, J. W. 1963. An application of the steric odor theory. Georgetown Med. Bull. 17, 40–42.

JOHNSTON, J. W. 1965. Experiments on the specificities of human olfaction. In Surface Effects in Detection, 29–52. J. I. Bregman and A. Dravnieks, (Editors). Spartan Books, Washington, D.C.

JOHNSTON, J. W., and PARKS, A. B. 1960. Odor-intensity and the stereochemical theory of olfaction. Proc. Sci. Sect. Toilet Goods Assoc. No. 34, 4–7.

JOHNSTON, J. W., and SANDOVAL, A. 1960. Organoleptic quality and the stereochemical theory of olfaction. Proc. Sci. Sect. Toilet Goods Assoc. No. 33, 3–9.

JOHNSTON, J. W., and SANDOVAL, A. 1962. The stereochemical theory of olfaction. 3. The validity of muskiness as a primary odor. Proc. Sci. Sect. Toilet Goods Assoc. Supplement to No. 37, 34–45.

LATHÁM, R. E. 1951. Lucretius on the Nature of the Universe (translation), Books II and IV. Penguin Books Ltd., Harmondsworth, England.

LE MAGNEN, J. 1948. Analysis of complex and homologous odors by fatigue (in French). Compt. rend. 226, 753–754.

MONCRIEFF, R. W. 1951. The Chemical Senses. 2nd Ed. Leonard Hill Ltd., London,

PATTON, S. 1964. Flavor thresholds of volatile fatty acids. J. Food Sci. 29, 679–680.

PAULING, L. 1946. Analogies between antibodies and simpler chemical substances. Chem. Eng. News 24, 1064–1065.

PERKIN, W. H. 1885. On the synthetical formation of closed carbon-chains. J. Chem. Soc. 47, 801–855.

SCHNEIDER, D., LACHER, V., and KAISSLING, K.-E. 1964. The mode of reaction and the reaction spectrum of olfactory cells in Antherea pernyi (in German). Z. Vergleich. Physiol. 48, 632–662.

SCHULTZ, H. G. 1964. A matching-standards method for characterizing odor qualities. Ann. N. Y. Acad. Sci. 116, 517–526.

TERANISHI, R., et al. 1966. Gas chromatography, infrared, proton magnetic resonance, mass spectral and threshold analyses of all the pentyl acetates. J. Agr. Food Chem. 14, 253–262.

TIMMERMANS, J. 1938. A new mesomorphic state. The organic plastic crystals (in French). J. Chim. Phys. 35, 331–344.

WRIGHT, R. H. 1954. Odour and molecular vibration. I. Quantum and thermodynamic considerations. J. Appl. Chem. (London) 4, 611–615.

WRIGHT, R. H. 1957. Odour and molecular vibration. In Molecular Structure and Organoleptic Quality, 91–102. Monograph No. 1. Society of Chemical Industry, London, England.

WRIGHT, R. H. 1964A. Odour and molecular vibration: The far infrared spectra of some perfume chemicals. Ann. N. Y. Acad. Sci. 116, 552–558.

WRIGHT, R. H. 1964B. The Science of Smell. George Allen and Unwin, Ltd., London.

WRIGHT, R. HUEY, and MICHELS, K. M. 1964. Evaluation of far infrared relations to odor by a standards similarity method. Ann. N. Y. Acad. Sci. 116, 535–551.

Advances in
Analytical Methodology

CHAPTER 6

Lyle D. Calvin | Statistical Methods

INTRODUCTION

The use of modern statistical methods has been prevalent in the foods research field for many years. Many examples are found both in the foods research papers (IFT Committee on Sensory Evaluation 1964) and also in examples in statistical texts (Fisher 1935; Snedecor 1946; Ostle 1954; Li 1964). An excellent chapter on "Statistical Methods in Foods Research" by Ostle and Tischer (1954) was published in *Advances in Food Research*.

Most of the modern statistical techniques are well known to foods research workers and are presented in many books and articles. There are, however, certain areas and subjects not well understood or confusing and it is to these subjects that I would like to address our attention today. Unfortunately, or perhaps fortunately, no method is intended to solve all problems. Some computational methods are well understood and often available in computer programs, although the methods may be used for purposes not originally intended. Because of this, certain confusion and controversy has risen over many of them. Most of the confusion can be eliminated by a clearer understanding of what these methods are intended to do and some understanding of the conditions under which they may be used.

In discussing these methods, it will be necessary to include both theoretical and practical considerations. In the application of statistical methods, theory and practice are inseparable and must be discussed together. In fact, nearly all the important advances in statistical methodology in the modern era have been made because of practical problems raised. Without this attention to application statistical theory would not be where it is today.

STATISTICAL INFERENCE

Statistical methods are concerned with the collection and treatment of multiple observations. These observations are subject to an error component which may arise from many sources, among them environmental variation, material variation, or measurement error. By appropriate procedures an attempt is made to reduce the effect of the errors in interpreting the data. Since some error variation is nearly always present, statistical analysis frequently involves the estimation or measurement of the

151

error component so as to separate it from the effects of interest. To do this, multiple observations must be made. Quoting from Bartlett (1965) in a recent paper, "The statistical approach cannot by nature deal with the unique sample—it must contemplate statistical variation."

These multiple observations are considered to be a sample from some defined population. This population may represent actual observations on people, strawberries, or animals, but they may also be potential populations which would be obtained if a particular treatment were successful. Because of this, we are most often working with populations which are considered to be infinite or at least very large. This is not a necessary restriction since methods are also available of working with finite populations as well. Most problems of inference, however, involve a hypothetical infinite population.

In statistical analysis we are largely concerned with the problem of inductive inference, or reasoning from the sample to the population. If this inference problem is to be adequately handled it is necessary that certain assumptions be satisfied in drawing the sample so that it can adequately represent the population. No practical methods are available for ascertaining if a particular sample adequately represents the population. It therefore falls to the method of sampling for this insurance. It is for this particular reason that the statistical method is concerned not only with the analysis but also with the collection of the data themselves.

Even with a particular method of data collection or experimental design, the techniques of analysis may differ from one research worker or one statistician to another. Considerable discussion and debate is sometimes centered around these minor technical differences. The important point, however, is that the conclusions from all these analyses are usually very nearly the same. Some methods are slightly more efficient than others and some methods may extract more of the information than others, but most of the standard methods are fairly efficient, and competent research workers using different statistical methods seldom differ appreciably in the conclusions drawn from the data.

Statistical analysis has often been considered to fall into two categories, estimation and testing. Because of the analysis of variance procedures developed initially by Fisher (1925) there has been a tendency to put a heavy emphasis on testing, whereas estimation is most often the objective of the research worker. The analysis of variance and the resulting tests of significance are unquestionably of value; however they usually provide only an intermediate step in the analysis. The problem of interest is more often to estimate the effect of a particular treatment, or the size of the difference between two treatments, or the quantitative relationship between two variables. In such cases the statistics of interest are statistics such as means and standard errors or fiducial intervals. These same statistics are also the ones used in making tests of significance. In fact, a fiducial interval statement always includes a significance statement, but the converse is not true. The ease with which tests of significance can be made should not overshadow the statistical inference problem of estimation.

Of interest in the past few years, although little has yet entered into the foods literature, is the method of inverse probability based upon Bayes theorem (Savage *et al.* 1962). Under this type of inference the reasoning is also from observed events to the hypothesis which may explain them. One may also consider that it is an attempt to utilize prior probabilities based on degree of belief in the hypothesis prior to conducting studies to obtain new data. If these prior probabilities can be determined to the satisfaction of the researcher, the Bayes procedure is an excellent way of taking advantage of such additional information. In many scientific investigations, however, little or no concensus can be obtained concerning these prior beliefs, and the attempt has been made to make the methods self-sufficient. In any case, there is a need for a method which will evaluate the results of an independent experiment.

One class of problems in which the Bayes approach would appear appropriate is in decision making. In this case, some action must be taken based upon all the information available, and the personal prior beliefs of the person making the decision should be included. It matters not that others may have other prior beliefs; the person making the decision is responsible and therefore his prior beliefs, which probably are subjective, are quite appropriate. In the scientific research area, however, such a method would appear of importance only if a method is available for determining the generalized prior beliefs of a large number of people. In general, generalized prior beliefs are not readily available.

DATA COLLECTION

Recognizing that statistical inference involves a concept of sampling from a population, it is apparent that the method of collecting data becomes important in the analysis and interpretation of the observations. Although serendipity unquestionably has its place in science, most discoveries and advances are made by means of orderly investigations. Where variation is small compared to effects being observed, these investigations may take the form of trials or tests conducted individually or sequentially. Biological material, however, generally has sufficient variation that well designed experiments and surveys are necessary in order to draw unbiased conclusions efficiently. Nearly 40 years ago, R. A. Fisher (1926) laid down the basic principles of sound experimental design in his paper on "The Arrangement of Field Trials." These principles were expanded in his book (Fisher 1935) on the "Design of Experiments" and have drawn wide acceptance ever since.

These basic principles consist of replication, randomization, and blocking of experimental units. The principle of combining treatments in a factorial arrangement was also advocated to provide a broader basis for inference and this is sometimes listed as a fourth basic principle. It is worthwhile to review these principles briefly to examine the basis for them. Most research workers are aware of and use these principles, but the reasons are not always clearly understood.

Replication serves three purposes—to increase precision, to estimate experimental error, and to provide a broader coverage of the population. The precision of the estimate of a treatment mean is related directly to the square root of the number of replications. By increasing the number of replications the precision is correspondingly increased. Another method of increasing precision might be to enlarge the size of experimental units without increasing the number of replications. Empirical results have shown that increasing the number of replications increases precision faster than increasing the size of experimental units.

Another reason for replication is the estimation of experimental error. Without replication an estimate of experimental error must rest upon assumptions that are often rather questionable. In general, this is not desirable and replication has proved to be by far the most satisfactory basis of estimating experimental error.

The broader coverage which can be obtained with increased replication is sometimes of considerable importance. Small experimental units can be spread widely over the population to include a wide range such as may be necessary when using animals or field plots. By covering the population more widely, or by covering larger populations, a broader basis for inference is provided. Increased replication may provide only added observations within a narrow population, but may more effectively be used to broaden the population by taking observations sampled from other parts of the overall population. Examples of this are samples taken from additional fields, locations, animals, or judges.

Randomization is used to estimate experimental error and to objectivize the collection of the data. Under randomization theory an estimate of the experimental error is available. Without randomization no satisfactory theory has yet been developed by which to estimate experimental error. In experiments in which the error is known to be small or negligible compared to the effects of interest, randomization may be unnecessary. It is still very useful in cases of this type to insure that a proper degree of objectivity has been used in collecting the data. Each of us is subject to biases in the selection or allocation of units to treatments and randomization is a method whereby our personal biases can be eliminated.

Blocking of experimental units, such as with the randomized block design (in which all treatments in the experiment are placed within a common block and each block contains all treatments) yields a considerable increase in precision. The reduction in the experimental error may be large, if the research worker has been able to make the blocking effective in the sense of putting homogeneous experimental units within each block. This is equivalent to allocating the experimental material in such a way that the differences among the block means is as large as possible.

These basic principles, together with the elegance afforded by the associated analysis of variance, brought wide acceptance to their use in formulating sound experimental designs. Although the principles are well accepted a considerable amount of ingenuity is provided by foods research workers and statisticians in formulating experimental designs to answer specific objectives. The art of formulating efficient designs requires an intelligent use of these principles. The literature is full of special designs for special objectives. It remains for each investigator to consider carefully whether he should use one of the common designs or devise another for his special purposes, always using the basic principles stipulated above.

DATA ANALYSIS

The statistical analysis of data is related to the method of data collection but can be discussed independently. Many methods have been developed for the statistical analysis of data, and as might be expected, certain questions have arisen concerning the validity or appropriateness of some of them. I should like to discuss a few of the methods around which there has developed some confusion or lack of understanding.

Analysis of Variance with Two Sources of Random Variation.—In tests of flavor evaluation the common experimental designs recognize sources of variation due to both judges and materials. Under the analysis of variance for such designs, there is no single source of variation which is an appropriate error term to test for the significance of treatments. The analysis of variance would include, as sources of variation of interest, treatments, judge by treatment interaction, material by treatment interaction, and judge by material by treatment interaction. The test of significance of treatments has been discussed by Cochran (1951) and Anderson and Bancroft (1952). An appropriate F test is the ratio of the treatment mean square plus the three factor interaction to the sum of the 2 two-factor interactions. The degrees of freedom are somewhat modified and may have to be calculated according to formulas given by the references to make a rigorous test. This is a rather easy test statistic to calculate but the computation of the degrees of freedom is somewhat complicated and time consuming. It has been found from a large number of flavor evaluations conducted at Oregon State University that an F test, which is nearly equivalent to the one given by Cochran, is the ratio of the treatment mean square to the judge by treatment interaction. This usually gives about the same F value as the more complicated expression and is easier to compute. Although this has proved a satisfactory test at Oregon State University it cannot at this time be recommended universally until it has been tested further for other materials and judges. For a quick and easy test it is worthy of consideration, and I should like to suggest it to you.

Multiple Comparison of Treatment Means.—Although it has been recognized for a number of years among research workers that there are some deficiencies in the use of the LSD (least significance difference) there has been no consensus on what to use in its place. Suggested methods have included Duncan's multiple range test and multiple comparison methods by Scheffé and Tukey (Federer 1955). Although I do not wish to look at the calculating procedures for each of these methods I should like to consider certain differences among them.

One difference is in the manner of designating the error rates. The LSD is on a per comparison basis, i.e. on the expected number of comparisons falsely declared significant divided by the total number of comparisons made. Duncan's procedure modifies this somewhat so that the significance level is based upon the number of means being compared. It is a difficult concept to keep in mind and any procedure suffers from a serious defect when the research worker is not able to fully comprehend what is meant by the test. The Scheffé and Tukey methods express the error rates on a per experiment basis, i.e. on the expected number of experiments with at least one comparison falsely declared significant divided by the number of experiments. This is a much more stringent error rate; however, the significance levels can be placed where the research worker wishes them, somewhat offsetting the stringent error rate. The concept is more difficult for most research workers to grasp, and until more experience leads them to an intuitive "feel" for such error rates, the per experiment basis will be confusing.

Another major difference between these methods is the difference in time at which the hypotheses to be tested are formulated. The use of the LSD requires that the hypothesis be formulated before the treatment means are known, whereas in the other methods the comparisons may be stipulated after examining the treatment means. This difference is reflected by the manner of expressing the error rates. This would appear to give a definite advantage to the newer methods rather than the LSD. However, it is quickly found that there is a price which must be paid. Treatment differences will be judged "significant" with the LSD with smaller differences than with any of the other tests, except when comparing only two treatments. If one is able to designate the hypotheses to be tested prior to examining the treatment means, then the LSD is a more powerful test than the other methods. If, however, differences of interest become apparent after looking at the treatment means then the other methods provide a basis for making a test.

Stepwise Multiple Regression.—With the advent of high-speed computing, programs such as stepwise multiple regression are becoming very common. These programs have many admirable qualities. However, some of them do occasionally get misused. The stepwise multiple regression program is one that is misused probably as often as any other. Because so many of the programs have considerable flexibility they are widely used, however, and can often contribute to a better understanding of a set of data.

In stepwise multiple regression the dependent variable is regressed first against the independent variable which shows the highest simple correlation with it. In the second step the dependent variable, adjusted for regression on the first independent variable, is used as a new dependent variable and this regressed against the independent variable in the remaining set which shows the highest correlation with the adjusted dependent variable. This stepwise feature can be continued until all independent variables are included in the equation or stopped at a designated point in this progression of steps. It does not necessarily give the regression equation with the highest multiple correlation for a given number of independent variables. For example, in some programs, a dependent variable may be regressed against variables 1, 3, and 5 out of 10 independent variables with the first three steps in stepwise regression; whereas 1, 5, and 8 might be the three variables which together show the highest correlation in predicting the dependent variable.

The stepwise multiple regression approach is commonly used to determine the variables to include in a prediction equation. Instead of including all the independent variables, the equation used is often that at which the standard error of estimate no longer decreases or at which additional variables are no longer termed "significant" by the t test. Although well known by statisticians, research workers are not always aware of the fact that the probability levels in these tests of significance have no meaning as such, because they are based on the supposition that the model has been prespecified. The given probability level is appropriate for testing the significance of the regression coefficient if the particular equation has already been specified and not for the equation using the selected variables from the total set of independent variables.

The residual regression error under stepwise multiple regression is not the same as prediction error. The error of prediction is often larger and sometimes very much larger than the residual regression error would lead one to assume. Some attempts have been made to estimate prediction error from the same set of data used to estimate the regression model, however the most reliable method and the only method acceptable to most people at this time is to use an independent set of data to estimate the error. This can be done by obtaining a new set of data, or in cases when a large amount of data is available originally, by dividing the original set into two subsets, one to obtain a model or regression equation and the second to estimate the error.

The stepwise multiple regression method, however, is quite useful in obtaining evidence for variables to include in a predictive or descriptive model. One should certainly not rely entirely upon the empirical model or equation obtained from the stepwise regression program; however, it is quite useful in obtaining evidence as to the variables which may be included in an equation based upon both logic and empirical evidence. One defect in the stepwise regression program is that certain variables may be relegated to a rather late stage or later step because of their higher correlation with prior variables included, when often it would be more logical to include the latter variable. One method of getting around this with high-speed computers is to use a regression program in which all possible combinations of the variables are examined. Several programs do this and some recent work by Mallows (1965) has provided some possible methods which appear to be more efficient than those which have been used in the past. Methods of searching for groups of variables to include in a prediction model will continue in an attempt to do what many people now attempt to use a stepwise regression model for, i.e. to obtain a prediction model empirically.

Estimation of Regression Coefficients.—One of the uses of multiple regression is in obtaining estimates of the constants or regression coefficients. It is sometimes very confusing to find that although the multiple correlation coefficient is very high and significant, none of the individual partial regression coefficients are significant. This is caused by high correlation among the independent variables such that the regression coefficients are actually very poorly estimated. Even independent estimates of the constants from independent sets of data may show wide fluctuation while the multiple correlation coefficient remains high in each set. If the independent variables tend to vary together this is to be expected and large amounts of data are necessary to obtain regression coefficients with high precision. Klein (1962) presents a discussion of this problem in his recent book.

Graphical Methods.—Certainly one of the earliest methods of looking at data for the purpose of drawing inferences about comparisons and relationships was the use of graphs and charts. With the advent of strong analysis tools and quick computing methods, graphical methods have largely been pushed aside, except for the presentation of results. The fact that graphing data in more than three dimensions is extremly difficult may also have had some influence. Progress in computers has been rapid enough however, that many graphical displays can now be presented quickly and easily. Promise for additional advances appear certain in the near future. Since no very satisfactory analytical methods have been devised to replace the graphical presentation of data, without assuming some underlying form of the relationship among variables, it is important that full advantage be taken of all forms of analysis including graphical displays. It is unlikely that important advances in our statistical analytical procedures will enable us in the very near future to dispense with visual displays. Studies of new ways of looking at data graphically are being made and results such as those of Watson (1964) on smooth regression analysis will help us to graph and interpret data more efficiently. The point is also emphasized that the interpretation of data still remains with the research worker and statistical methods are merely tools to aid him in this task.

BIBLIOGRAPHY

ANDERSON, R. L., and BANCROFT, T. A. 1952. Statistical Theory in Research. McGraw-Hill Book Co., New York.

BARTLETT, M. S. 1965. R. A. Fisher and the last fifty years of statistical methodology. J. Am. Stat. Assoc. 60, 395–409.

COCHRAN, W. G. 1951. Testing a linear relation among variances. Biometrics 7, 17–32.

FEDERER, W. T. 1955. Experimental Design. Macmillan Co., New York.

FISHER, R. A. 1925. Statistical Methods for Research Workers. Oliver and Boyd, Edinburgh.

FISHER, R. A. 1926. The arrangement of field experiments. Ministry Agr. 33, 503–513.

FISHER, R. A. 1935. The Design of Experiments. Oliver and Boyd, London.

IFT COMMITTEE ON SENSORY EVALUATION. 1964. Sensory testing guide for panel evaluation of foods and beverages. Food Technol. 18, 25–31.

KLEIN, L. R. 1962. An Introduction to Econometrics. Prentice-Hall, Englewood Cliffs, N.J.

LI, J. C. R. 1964. Statistical Inference. Vol. I. Edwards Brothers, Ann Arbor, Mich.

MALLOWS, C. L. 1965. Some approaches to regression problems. Gordon Research Conference, Statistics in Chemistry and Chemical Engineering, New Hampton, N.J., July 12–16, 1965.

OSTLE, B.   1954.   Statistics in Research.   Iowa State College Press, Ames, Iowa.

OSTLE, B., and TISCHER, R. G.   1954.   Statistical methods in food research.   *In* Advances in Food Research 5, 161–259.   Academic Press, New York.

SAVAGE, L. J., *et al.*   1962.   The Foundations of Statistical Inference. Methuen, London.

SNEDECOR, G. W.   1946.   Statistical Methods.   4th Edition.   Iowa State College Press, Ames, Iowa.

WATSON, G. S.   1964.   Smooth regression analysis.   Sankhya *26*, 359–372.

CHAPTER 7

Roy Teranishi,
R. E. Lundin,
and J. R. Scherer

Analytical Technique

INTRODUCTION

Aroma research requires teamwork. It requires a group consisting of chemical engineers to concentrate large quantities of raw material to essences and "absolute" oils, organic chemists (well versed in micro, analytical, and natural products chemistry) to separate and purify the constituents of the essences and oils, and physical chemists to obtain and study the physical properties of the minute quantities of the pure material isolated. Furthermore, after the chemical structure is established, then the organoleptic properties of the compound must be determined. In every phase of such research, analyses are extremely important.

The fundamental steps in any analyses are separation, detection, and, then, identification. Extreme demands are made in aroma research analyses: we must know the minute details of chemical structure of the constituents of appallingly complex mixtures which are available only in very small quantities. Spectroscopic purity is difficult enough to attain, but for valid conclusions, the material must be organoleptically pure if we are to assign odor characteristics to any compound or chemical structure. Therefore, the investigator engaged in aroma chemistry often finds that even the ultimate methods available for separation, detection, and identification are not good enough. However, some remarkable advances have been made recently, and we are able to obtain information in cases which were very, very difficult to study previously. I wish to discuss some of these developments in analytical techniques which are helpful to the aroma chemist.

GAS CHROMATOGRAPHY

Gas chromatography (GC) is only in its second decade, but it is one of the very powerful methods useful in aroma analyses. It can be used for the separation and detection of volatiles directly from fresh and processed foods, for the fractionation of oils isolated from foods, and for the purification of the constituents for physical, chemical, and organoleptic properties. It has the resolution to separate epimers and a limit of detection of less than fractions of nanograms. It can be used for an indication of purity of a sample or of the complexity and range of molecular weight in a mixture. In spite of its usefulness and versatility, however, we must always remember that GC is a method useful predominantly for separation and detection, and its use for identification purposes is very limited. For assignment of chemical structure with a good degree of certainty, we must rely on chemical and physical properties.

Separation and Detection

Since even the theoretical limit of the GC flame ionization detector is not comparable to the olfactory senses with respect to some compounds (Weurman 1963), we must certainly try to utilize the maximum sensitivity possible with such detectors. A hypothetical GC peak is shown in Fig. 57, in which signal, noise, and drift are illustrated. A second GC peak, superimposed on the first, shows approximately the same area, i.e. same amount of sample, but without noise and drift and with a reduced bandwidth. Obviously, the latter peak is the more desirable one because it permits a lower limit of detection.

Some of the variables which must be considered to maximize the signal and to minimize the noise and drift have been discussed (Teranishi *et al.* 1963A, 1964). Although they are still very crude in comparison with the olfactory sense, GC instruments can be made with a very low limit of detection. Practical applications have been made in surveying products to follow autoxidation of potato granules (Buttery 1961), storage of fruits and vegetables (Buttery and Teranishi 1961; Teranishi and Buttery 1962; Teranishi *et al.* 1962), ripening of bananas (McCarthy *et al.* 1963, etc.

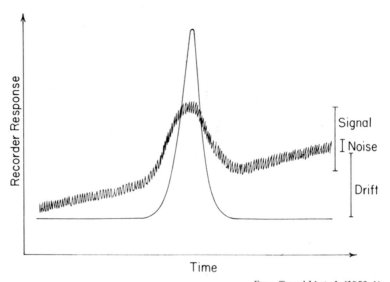

From *Teranishi* et al. *(1963 A)*

Fig. 57. Hypothetical Gas Chromatographic Peaks Illustrating Signal, Noise and Drift

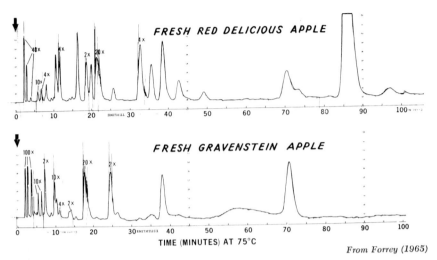

From Forrey (1965)

FIG. 58. DIRECT VAPOR ANALYSES BY GAS CHROMATOGRAPHY OF RED DELICIOUS AND GRAVENSTEIN APPLE VOLATILES

Recorder response is plotted on the vertical axis and time on the horizontal axis.

An example of the usefulness of direct vapor sampling is shown in Fig. 58. Differences in concentration of various volatile constituents are clearly discernible in the comparison of the two varieties of apples; i.e. the volatile constituents are separated and detected. The problem of identifying the chemical structure of the material represented by the peaks now confronts us. Retention times can give some indication of possible compounds. However, great care must be exercised in the assignment of chemical structure solely on the basis of retention data, especially with direct vapor analyses in which considerable amounts of water vapor is injected with the sample. Fig. 59 shows how much retention time of oxygenated compounds can change with or without water vapor in the carrier gas. Obviously, wrong assignments will be made if retention times of known compounds, pure and dry, are compared with those in a mixture with considerable water vapor. Thus, not only is the adsorption, manifested in "tailing" reduced, but also, retention data are more reliable if water vapor is introduced continuously in the carrier gas.

Separation and Isolation

Each recording of a GC separation confronts us with the problem of identifying the compound, or compounds, represented by each peak. Although retention time data may be sufficient for identification of familiar, known compounds, we usually use various other supplementary meth-

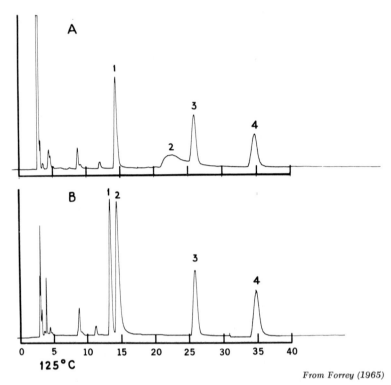

From Forrey (1965)

FIG. 59. GAS CHROMATOGRAM ILLUSTRATING THE EFFECT OF WATER IN THE
CARRIER GAS ON THE RETENTION TIME OF OXYGENATED COMPOUNDS

(A) Without water vapor in the carrier gas; (B) With water vapor in the
carrier gas

ods to obtain chemical and physical properties. If large amounts of easily
separable material are available from preparative GC, general techniques,
such as those presented in the comprehensive work by Bentley (1963)
are applicable. However, as is usually the case in aroma research, if very
closely related compounds are being separated, only small amounts of
material will be available for analysis, and special techniques must be
employed. Only milligram and sub-milligram quantities of material can
be purified with high resolution packed and open tubular columns (Teranishi and Mon 1964).

Column Resolution and Capacity.—Dal Nogare and Juvet (1962) point
out the relationships of relative volatilities, partition coefficients, temperature, and ratio of gas to liquid volumes, to the necessary number of theoretical plates for complete resolution. From such calculations and from
our observations, we can see that for resolution of closely related com-

pounds, columns with over 100,000 theoretical plates and with different stationary liquids are necessary.

There is no doubt that, at the present time, the column with the most resolution is the small-bore open tubular column introduced by Golay (1958). However, other than for mass spectrometry, such columns have capacities much too small for preparation of samples for usual analytical purposes. Scott (1958) has made high resolution packed columns, but these, too, were of low capacity. A practical column for preparation of samples for analytical purposes is one which has milligram or more capacity, 100,000 theoretical plates for 90 to 95% resolution, 15 to 25 p.s.i. pressure drop, and time of elution of C_{15} compounds of less than an hour at 200°C. The obvious goal is to make a column similar to a 200 ft., 0.01 in. I.D., open tubular column coated with various stationary liquids, but with milligram capacity.

In order to increase the capacity of the open tubular column, larger bores have been investigated (Ettre *et al.* 1963; Jentzsch and Hovermann 1963; Quiram 1963; Schwartz *et al.* 1963; Zlatkis and Kaufman 1959; and Teranishi and Mon 1964). Table 14 summarizes the relationship of column diameter with efficiency and capacity. Obviously, the values for the theoretical plates are approximate averages, for it is well known that for any given column under given conditions, varying theoretical plate values are obtained with different compounds (Lipsky *et al.* 1959; Teranishi and Mon 1964) because of the different partition coefficients. It can readily be seen from the figures in Table 14 that it is not practical to use open

TABLE 14

COLUMN EFFICIENCIES AND CAPACITIES[1]

Inside Diameter (In.)	Theoretical Plates Per Ft.	Ft. Per 100,000 Theoretical Plates	Capacity (μg.)
0.01	500	200	1
0.02	250	400	10
0.03	100	1,000	100
0.10	10^2	$10,000^2$	1000^2

[1] From Teranishi and Mon (1964).
[2] Estimated.

tubular columns of 0.10 in. I.D. It is true that the estimated sample size is in the range desired, but the columns would have to be about two miles long to obtain 100,000 theoretical plates, and the time of elution of even unabsorbed material would be about ten hours. Also, the 100,000 theoretical plates are not as valuable with the 0.10 in. I.D. column; i.e. more theoretical plates are needed for comparable resolution achieved with the 0.01 in. I.D. column (Dal Nogare and Juvet 1962). Therefore, a good compromise is the 1000 ft., 0.03 in. I.D. column, and we have used this column for several years to prepare pure samples for analytical purposes (Teranishi and Mon 1964).

Trapping.—Trapping of fractions from conventional packed columns for subsequent analyses, especially for infrared, is quite common. Various methods have been summarized in the GC review by Juvet and Dal Nogare (1964): centrifugal, electrostatic, thermal gradient, total eluent, and simple condensation. Without use of some device, the percentage trapped of high boiling material is very low because of aerosol formation. Because most traps are designed for large preparative work, they are usually too large for routine work with milligram quantities.

Probably the most practical and most used trap for 1 to 10 mg is the simple glass capillary melting point tubing inserted in the GC outlet. Trapped samples in such tubing can be sealed for storage by fusing both ends with a small torch. Centrifugation of the condensed material to one sealed end permits the use of a microsyringe for further manipulation (Hoffmann and Silveira 1964). Teflon tubing with glass collectors can be used for multiple collections (Teranishi et al. 1965).

If the material is too volatile to be condensed in a short Teflon tube, a longer piece can be inserted into the GC outlet, and the effluent gases can be bubbled through a small amount of cooled carbon tetrachloride. This method is convenient for proton magnetic resonance and infrared analyses. For mass spectral analyses, a total effluent trap should be used for high-volatility compounds (Dal Nogare and Juvet 1962; Swoboda 1963; Hornstein and Crowe 1965).

CHEMICAL METHODS

The identification of the components cannot be accomplished with any reasonable certainty by relying on retention data alone especially if the mixture is heterofunctional. Only if the functionality is established can retention data be analyzed.

A simple, rapid, and general method for functional group classification has been developed by Walsh and Merritt (1960). This method can be used with any conventional gas chromatograph equipped with thermal conductivity detectors, or any other nondestructive detectors. The effluent is divided into equal streams, and each of these is allowed to bubble through a vial containing an appropriate reagent. Nine functional groups have been studied: alcohols, aldehydes, ketones, esters, unsaturated aliphatic and aromatic hydrocarbons, amines, alkyl halides, sulfur compounds, and nitriles.

Direct coupling of GC with thin-layer chromatography (GC-TLC) offers new possibilities in qualitative analyses (Casu and Cavallotti 1962;

Janak 1963; Kaiser 1964; Nano *et al.* 1965). Kaiser (1964) has shown that the GC-TLC method is useful in analyzing high boiling polar substances and for further purification for ultraviolet, infrared, proton magnetic resonance, and mass spectral analyses.

INFRARED SPECTROSCOPY

It is well known that infrared (IR) spectra can be used for *finger-printing* organic molecules. The research worker today has access to many catalogued IR spectra in various commercially available files, and a convenient index to these files is published by the American Society for Testing and Materials (Anon. 1962, 1963).

Infrared spectroscopy provides one of the best means of establishing the functional groups which are present in a molecule. The wealth of information known about the absorption frequencies of molecular functional groups, i.e. group frequencies, allows one to sort logically through collections of spectra to find features similar to those found in the spectrum of the unknown. Recognition of the group frequencies in a spectrum often narrows the number of possible structures to a few whose spectra may be quickly located with an empirical-formula file index. If a compound has never been previously measured, group frequency interpretations can often give an insight to the molecular structure. Several good books have been written on the subject of group frequencies (Colthup *et al.* 1964; Potts 1964; Nakanishi 1962; Bellamy 1958; Jones and Sandorfy 1956).

Relatively inexpensive, commercially available, "bench type," double beam IR spectrophotometers are adequate for most simple organic structure identifications; however, instruments with high resolution, fast response, and scale expansion should be used, whenever possible, for extracting the maximum amount of information from a spectrum. Instruments which can be coupled directly to GC units have been recently introduced. These obtain the gas phase spectrum of each fraction as it emerges from the chromatograph. The poor resolution of these instruments leads to a loss of spectral detail which may be useful for complete structural characterization. However, the spectral presentation in seconds rather than in minutes makes these instruments attractive for qualitative determination of group functionality.

Most of the samples separated by GC by the aroma chemist are liquids at room temperature. Fortunately, most GC purified samples are soluble in carbon tetrachloride and carbon disulfide, and these solvents can be conveniently used as diluents and carriers for manipulating GC trapped samples. About 1 to 5 μl. of solution can be transferred by means of microsyringes with short, fixed needles without serious loss of sample, with

0.05 to 0.1 μl. adhering to the walls of the needle. Use of microcells for IR is not new (Jones and Sandorfy 1956), and a variety of such cells are commercially available which are adequate for most analyses. However, the volume needed to fill the microcells can be decreased by diminishing the volume of the filling tubes (Chrenko 1964), and usable spectra can be obtained easily with 0.1 to 0.5 μl. of GC purified material.

Another aid in manipulation is the use of KBr crystals as a carrier. The GC eluent can be condensed directly onto the crystals, or the condensed material can be transferred to the crystals with some volatile solvent and then the solvent evaporated. The KBr crystals can then be pressed to form a clear pellet, which can be easily handled and placed in the IR beam. Thus, IR spectra can be obtained for identification purposes with amounts difficult to handle without the use of any carrier, but care should be taken in comparing IR spectra of compounds in KBr pellets with pure liquids or solution spectra because of possible band shifts with the material in KBr.

An example of an IR solution spectrum obtained with 30 μg. of linalool is shown in Fig. 60. This spectrum was obtained with a high resolution instrument with scale expansion, mirror beam condensers, and microcells. It can be readily seen that even with one-tenth the amount used, the OH stretching (3612 cm.$^{-1}$), the CH stretching (2975 and 2930 cm.$^{-1}$), the antisymmetric CH_3 deformation (1448 cm.$^{-1}$), the methyl umbrella deformation (1375 cm.$^{-1}$), the out-of-plane vinyl twisting (993 cm.$^{-1}$), and the CH_2 vinyl wagging (922 cm.$^{-1}$) modes would be clearly discernible.

MASS SPECTROMETRY

Mass spectrometry (MS) has not been used very much by the organic chemist for the study of chemical structure, in spite of the fact that excellent instruments have been commercially available for years. However, this situation is changing rapidly, and the number of research organizations equipped with these instruments is increasing rapidly, even though the mass spectrometer is expensive. At present there are a number of excellent discussions of theory and applications in the study of the structure of molecules varying from simple aliphatic compounds to amino acids and peptides, alkaloids, steroids, and triterpenes (Stewart 1960; Biemann 1962; Biemann 1963; Budzikiewicz *et al.* 1964A, 1964B; McLafferty 1963; McDowell 1963; Elliot 1963).

Mass spectrometry is the most sensitive of the analytical methods used in combination with GC. This sensitivity, in addition to the fact that compounds purified by GC have enough vapor pressure to be easily analyzed by MS, makes MS very compatible with GC. Two basic methods of sample introduction are used for obtaining MS analyses from GC sep-

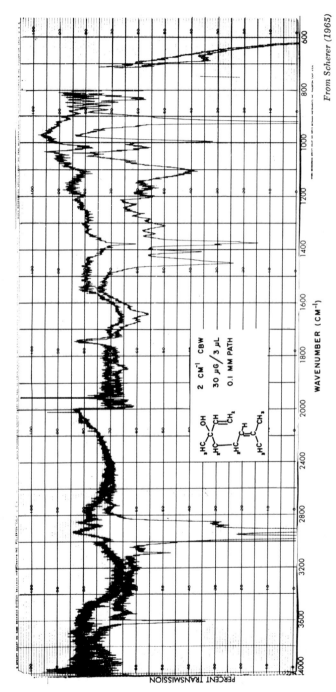

FIG. 60. INFRARED SPECTRUM OF 30 μg. OF LINALOOL

From Scherer (1965)

arated samples, batch and continuous. In the batch method, the fraction is collected so that the sample can be leisurely analyzed. In the continuous method, the effluent from the gas chromatograph is introduced directly into the mass spectrometer (GC-MS). Both methods have their advantages, and various modifications of both are used according to the nature of the material to be analyzed.

Batch Sampling

The batch sample introduction techniques have been discussed in detail by Biemann (1962). No special techniques are needed to handle the GC purified samples because so little material is needed.

There is no doubt that a better quality spectrum can be obtained if ample time is available for an analysis; therefore, if at all possible, it is preferable to collect the GC fractions for subsequent analyses. Moreover, GC-MS combination ties up both instruments and personnel, and each unit can be used more efficiently if operated independently. However, there are situations in which it is desirable to monitor the effluents from a gas chromatographic column directly with a mass spectrometer.

Continuous Sampling

Continuous sampling of column effluents with a mass spectrometer eliminates manipulation losses, contamination, and decomposition often encountered when sub-milligram quantities are first collected, then manually transferred to analytical instruments. Considerable attention has been given to this GC-MS combination recently (Gohlke 1959; McFadden et al. 1963; McFadden and Teranishi 1963; McFadden and Day 1964; Day and Libbey 1964; Day and Anderson 1965; Fagerson 1965; Ryhage 1964; Watson and Biemann 1964, 1965).

The GC-MS combination is particularly useful in analyzing complicated mixtures, available only in small amounts, that can be fractionated satisfactorily only with the high resolution, low capacity, small-bore open tubular columns. An example is the analysis of strawberry oil (Teranishi et al. 1963B; McFadden et al. 1965) shown in Fig. 61. Another good example is the analysis of hop oil by Buttery (cf. Chapter 18, this volume). Even if ample starting material is available with such mixtures, the collection and storing of hundreds of samples for batch introduction would be quite a task.

In addition to problems inherent to both instruments, the combination of the gas chromatograph and the mass spectrometer presents still a further one of connecting the two with a minimum of memory effects, loss of resolution of the separation accomplished by the GC column, and cat-

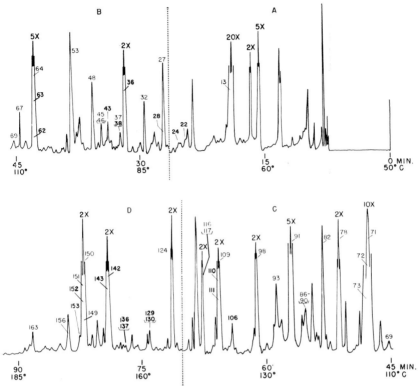

From McFadden et al. (1965)

FIG. 61. TEMPERATURE-PROGRAMMED GAS CHROMATOGRAPHY OF STRAWBERRY OIL FROM THE GAS CHROMATOGRAPHIC-MASS SPECTRAL (GC-MS) ANALYSIS OF STRAWBERRY VOLATILES

alytic or thermal decomposition after the effluents emerge from the column.

Watson and Biemann (1965) have modified and improved the pressure reduction system so that it not only provides a pressure drop but also concentrates the sample 50-fold or more in the gas stream entering the spectrometer. This system utilizes the preferential effusion of helium, the carrier gas, through a fritted glass tube for the enrichment of the sample.

Ryhage (1964) has accomplished sample concentration by using a Becker-type molecular separator (Becker 1961). In this separator, the gas stream of heavier molecules passes straight through two holes of small diameter which are close together, while the helium gas diffuses to the sides and is pumped away by an auxiliary vacuum pump.

Care must be taken to make certain that the connecting system is heated properly, especially in the analyses of high molecular weight compounds.

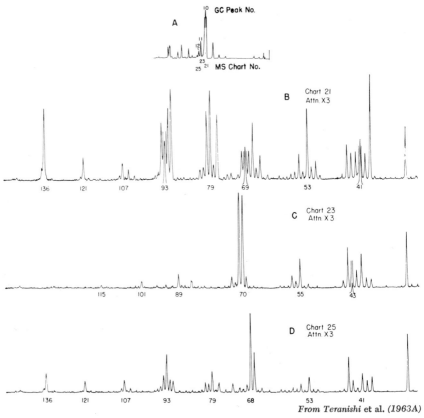

From Teranishi et al. (1963A)

FIG. 62. TIME-OF-FLIGHT MASS SPECTRA SHOWING THE CORRELATION OF SPECTRA TO GC PEAKS

Failure to do so will lead to the loss of the resolution or separation of components accomplished by the GC column. With proper heating, compounds such as oxygenated sesquiterpenes (Schultz *et al.* 1964), or even as large as alkaloids and steroids (Watson and Biemann 1965) can be analyzed by GC-MS.

In order to correlate MS spectra to GC peaks it is important to have a record of the chromatographic separation in a GC-MS run. In the simple case in which most of the effluent from a packed column is passed to a GC detector and only a small part is diverted to the mass spectrometer, the chromatograph is operated in the usual manner, and the usual chromatogram is obtained. If the total effluent is taken, either from a small-bore open tubular or from a packed column through a pressure reduction and sample concentrator system, then some total ion beam monitor must be used because the GC detector cannot be easily incorporated in such a system. With some mass spectrometers, the intensity of a single mass ion may be recorded (Selke *et al.* 1961). However, this method has the disadvantage that it is not quantitative; and in some cases, a compound may have virtually no ions at the selected mass.

When an effluent is observed as a GC-MS chromatogram peak or with an oscilloscope, or both, its complete mass spectrum is recorded on a high-speed oscillograph, magnetic tape, or photographic plate. The spectra are numbered, and these numbers are written on the GC-MS chromatogram precisely at the time the MS pattern is recorded. In this manner, the mass spectra can be correlated with the material represented by the GC peaks, as shown in Fig. 62. Also, these mass spectral charts show how cleanly the material is swept out to give good mass spectra, uncontaminated with previous material, even though the preceding material was present in greater quantity (Teranishi *et al.* 1963A).

Although some high-plate-value packed columns have been made, no packed column has the resolution possible with the 0.01 in. I.D. open tubular columns. Even with these open tubular columns, it is still necessary to find the best suited stationary liquid and temperature program for a given mixture. Because of the complexity of the mixtures encountered, even under the optimum conditions, mass spectral analyses often show the presence of two or more components in the material represented by one GC peak (McFadden *et al.* 1965).

The application of the GC-MS combination is a major advance in the analyses of the volatiles contributing to the aroma of foods. A large number of compounds can be easily identified with a good degree of certainty with sub-microgram quantities. Unknown compounds or mixtures are indicated to guide subsequent work. Thus, the GC-MS method promises to yield a wealth of information very difficult or impossible to obtain previously in aroma research.

PROTON MAGNETIC RESONANCE

Nuclear magnetic resonance (NMR) has proved over the last few years to be a very valuable tool for the elucidation of the details of organic structures. A number of excellent books and review articles are now available dealing with theoretical aspects (Pople *et al.* 1959), instrumentation (NMR-EPR staff, Varian Associates, 1960), and applications to organic chemistry (Jackman 1959; Bhacca and Williams 1964; Conroy 1960; Strothers 1963; and Foster 1964).

Although other magnetic nuclei can be studied, this discussion will be concerned exclusively with proton magnetic resonance (pmr). The techniques discussed here with respect to pmr can be applied directly to fluorine and phosphorus studies, but with a reduction in sensitivity.

The major problem involved in the application of pmr to the analysis of GC effluents is that of sensitivity. Of the spectrometric techniques, pmr is undoubtedly the least sensitive. Until very recently, the minimum sample size was of the order of 10 mg. or more. Thus, only packed column GC was practical when pmr analyses were desired, and even then, several collections were often necessary. Recent developments in pmr instrumentation have dramatically improved this situation. A practical microcell and several complex electronic devices which improve the signal-to-noise ratio have become available. The minimum sample size is now of the order of 10 to 100 μg. The combination of these two advancements with the large-bore open tubular columns has, for the first time, made pmr a really significant analytical tool for the gas chromatographer engaged in aroma research.

The first truly practical pmr microcell became commercially available in 1964. This microcell consists of a 50-μl. bubble blown at the end of a heavy wall Pyrex glass capillary tubing. A solid rod is fused onto the tubing below the bubble and cut to a length such that the bubble is located at the center of the receiver coil in the probe of the pmr spectrometer when the tube is positioned in the air spinner in the usual way. The performance of these tubes is exceedingly variable in respect to the resolution that can be achieved. The best of them will yield resolution only slightly less than that obtainable with the standard, large-bore cylindrical tubes. Others will yield such poor resolution that they must be discarded. Also, any solid material (such as dust, filter paper fibers, undissolved sample, etc.) can seriously degrade the resolution, much more so than observed with standard tubes. A 50 or 100 μl. gas tight syringe with a special 26-gage (0.004 in. I.D.) 8 in. fixed needle is most convenient for filling, emptying, and cleaning the microcells.

Signal enhancement by time averaging many spectral scans is, at the present time, the most powerful means available for improving the signal-to-noise ratio of magnetic resonance spectra. The technique is based on the principal that noise, being a random process, adds only in quadrature,

TABLE 15

SAMPLE-SIZE[1] FOR PMR SPECTRA
(In μg.)

	Varian Instruments		
	A-60	HR-60	HR-100
Standard sample tube	4000	1000	700
Microcell			
Single scan	1000	250	170
500 scans	45	8	5

[1] MW ca. 150.

while signals, if they are made to be coherent, add linearly in intensity. Thus, if a spectrum is swept many times in a reproducible fashion, there is a considerable tendency for positive and negative noise components to cancel while signal components add. The ratio of signal-to-noise increases, to the first approximation, as the square root of the number of scans (Klein and Barton 1963).

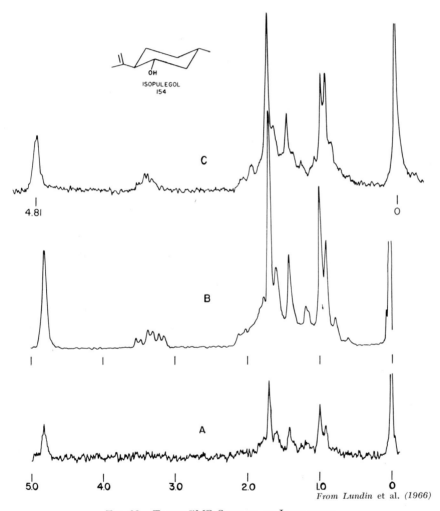

From Lundin et al. *(1966)*

FIG. 63. THREE PMR SPECTRA OF ISOPULEGOL

(A) Single scan of 0.8 mg. in a microcell, 60 Mcps instrument. (B) Same sample in the same instrument, but after 210 scans. (C) Single scan of the sample using a 100 Mcps high resolution instrument.

A number of electronic devices are now available which perform the summing for time averaging. While differing in detail, they all consist of a small computer-type memory in which the signals from the spectrometer are stored as the spectrum is repetitively scanned, and from which the final spectrum is played out on a normal chart.

Table 15 summarizes the sample size requirements with various techniques for compounds with molecular weight of about 150. It can be seen that considerable progress has been made in lowering the sample size requirements in comparison with the single scan with the standard sample tube.

Fig. 63 shows three pmr spectra of isopulegol. Spectrum A is a single scan of 0.8 mg. in a microcell, 60 Mcps analytical spectrometer. Spectrum B is the same sample in the same instrument but after 210 scans. Spectrum C is a single scan of the sample with a 100 Mcps high resolution spectrometer. Samples as small as 50 μg. are now sufficient for usable pmr spectra from analytical type spectrometers (Lundin *et al.* 1966).

DISCUSSION

W. F. Wilkens.—What are some of the difficulties that might be encountered in the hook-up of the GLC and mass spectrometer?

R. Teranishi.—One of the very obvious ones is, that if the hook-up is not warm enough, adsorption will occur along the line and cause tailing. As a result the mass spectral pattern will be smeared by the tailing of fractions into other peaks. As long as the capillary column is in a vacuum, one can maintain the connections at about 100°C. and can still get compounds like the sesquiterpenes and oxygenated sesquiterpenes through. If there are any cold spots in the connection to the mass spectrometer, one can have a 100,000 theoretical plate column and still smear everything. The hook-up distance between the GLC and MS should be as short as possible to decrease the time required for the sample to leave the GLC column to the moment it enters the high vacuum of the ionization chamber. Biemann and others have used all glass systems for their work with such things as alkaloids and steroids, which may decompose if there is any metal present.

M. E. Mason.—Can you take spectra on the front and trailing edges of peaks where the separation is poor and get spectra from which you can make positive identifications with a great deal of confidence?

R. Teranishi.—Dr. McFadden has been able to look at peaks that have no suggestion of impurities and has found them to be in fact mixtures. If one happens to have a mixture like an alcohol with a hydrocarbon, where the mass spectral patterns are considerably different, one can determine with some degree of certainty, what the components are.

R. Self.—Dr. Teranishi, could you tell me the diameter of your capillary column which is most suitable for use with the mass spectrometer?

R. Teranishi.—What we have done is to compromise on a 200 ft. × 0.01 in. I. D. column. The pressure drop on this is about 20 to 25 lb. to achieve optimum linear velocity. Now we can take this 200 ft. × 0.01 in. column with a gage pressure of 25 lb. and go into a hydrogen flame detector with a linear velocity of 15 cm. per sec.; when we connect this column to the mass spectrometer putting the exit end of the column at the pressure of the ionization chamber and the auxiliary roughing pump, we will get a drop of about 15 lb. We are then operating at around 10 lb. per sq. in. If one goes much lower than 8 to 10 lb. per sq. in. on the 0.01 in I.D. column, there are difficulties with the stream splitter. It can be done, but reproducibility is a problem; you may get injection of a very large sample one time and much less another time. So we have chosen the 200 ft. × 0.01 in. I.D. column. If we are going to do mass spec capillary analyses, we take that column and try various stationary phases and check out what seems to be the most suitable. We have recently done some work on the 0.02 in. I.D. column which is an exceedingly nice column. With 500 ft. you have about the same pressure drop as with the 200 ft. × 0.01 in. I.D. column, so you can connect this directly into the mass spectrometer vacuum, but with the 0.02 in. I.D. column you do not need to do any stream splitting. If you recall, its capacity is about 10 μg per large peak, so that now you can take the entire material as long as you have somebody that is quite adept and never injects too much sample. Especially if you have a complex mixture, you can put in enough material and not overload the column. And now the dynamic range is increased by a factor of 10, and the 0.02 in. column has even more resolution than the 200 ft. × 0.01 in. So these are the two columns that we have hooked up and used. The 0.03 in. I.D. column is even better in terms of dynamic range. You can take a look at the bigger peaks and still go as low and come up an order of magnitude more. But this is beginning to present us with some problems. With the 0.03 in. column one cannot do a simple needle valve hook-up to auxiliary pumps. One must now use a Biemann or Ryhage type of molecular separator, as, if I remember correctly, the 0.03 in. column will have a carrier gas flow of about 15 to 20 cc. per min. This is just too much to ask an auxiliary pump to remove, so one should use a molecular separator on this. We are right in the process of making a setup like this.

R. Self.—You did not use a molecular separator with the 0.02 in. I.D. column?

R. Teranishi.—No, we did not.

E. A. Day.—One comment and then a question. A word of caution in regard to collecting from TLC plates where you see several spots from a single GLC peak. We have encountered problems of decomposition on TLC plates which one should be aware of. The question is where you are adding water to your carrier gas, how do you handle this problem in collecting for IR and other operations of this type?

R. Teranishi.—This technique can be used only with vapor analyses. For IR collection, and for all the other techniques, including MS work, this makes the use of packed columns difficult. I think if you go to high resolution, low percentage columns, you cannot really achieve the same characteristics of your stationary phase with capillary and packed columns. Too much gas-solid adsorption takes place and we cannot do anything about it. We just suffer.

M. Gianturco.—You have worked on the combination of the GC and MS for some time now and, I am sure, with a variety of flavors. This is a bit of a nasty question and I do not know the answer. Would you tell me, in your present experience, what your current batting average is for the firm identification by MS alone?

R. Teranishi.—Can I pass this one on, too? I think for smaller molecules where the number of isomers possible is small, that firm identification starts by having the MS and GC retention time of your unknown. Then somehow getting a hold of the compound, whether you buy it or can synthesize it, and having the MS and GC retention times agree. We feel that this is good enough for identification. You can check out a large number of compounds this way as long as you have normal compounds. By normal compound, I mean straight chains, but the moment you start getting isomers, how do you know that the methyl group is alpha or beta? How do you know whether the hydroxyl is up or down? This becomes a problem, and the GC-MS is a tremendous tool and you can obtain much information from it. You can identify a large number of compounds with this technique or at least determine which ones are interesting, and go on from there. I think, however, that it is very dangerous to say that you are going to see all and tell all. Everything in the book is at your disposal but it still is not enough at times. I know I did not answer the question, but I do not know. Dr. Day, do you want to make a comment?

E. A. Day.—Again it depends upon the complexity of the mixture of compounds you have. By using proper trapping techniques to build up your concentration and so forth, you may be able to identify, say 50% of the compounds and that may be a conservative estimate.

BIBLIOGRAPHY

Anon. 1962 and 1963. Molecular Formula List of Compounds, Names and References to Published Infrared Spectra. Special Technical Publication No. 331 and 331A. American Society for Testing and Materials, Philadelphia, Pa.

Bhacca, N. S., and Williams, D. H. 1964. Applications of NMR Spectroscopy in Organic Chemistry. Illustrations from the Steroid Field. Holden-Day, Inc., San Francisco, Calif.

Becker, E. W. 1961. Separation of Isotopes. G. Newnes, Ltd., London.

Bellamy, L. J. 1958. Infrared Spectra of Complex Molecules, John Wiley and Sons, New York.

Bentley, K. W., (Editor). 1963. Elucidation of Structures by Physical and Chemical Methods (Technique of Organic Chemistry, Vol. XI, A. Weissberger, Editor), Part I, Interscience, New York-London.

Biemann, K. 1962. Mass Spectrometry, Organic Chemical Applications, McGraw-Hill Book Co., New York.

Biemann, K. 1963. Applications of mass spectrometry, In Elucidation of Structures by Physical and Chemical Methods, K. W. Bentley, (Editor), (Technique of Organic Chemistry, Vol. XI, A. Weissberger, (Editor), Part I, Interscience, New York-London.

Budzikiewicz, H., Djerassi, C., and Williams, D. H. 1964A. Interpretation of Mass Spectra of Organic Compounds. Holden-Day, Inc., San Francisco, Calif.

Budzikiewicz, H., Djerassi, C., and Williams, D. H. 1964B. Structure Elucidation of Natural Products by Mass Spectrometry, Vol. I and II, Holden-Day, Inc., San Francisco, Calif.

Buttery, R. G. 1961. Autoxidation of potato granules. Part II. Formation of carbonyls and hydrocarbons. J. Agr. Food Chem. 9, 248–252.

Buttery, R. G., and Teranishi, R. 1961. Gas-liquid chromatography of aroma of vegetables and fruit. Direct injection of aqueous vapors. Anal. Chem. 33, 1439–1441.

CASU, B., and CAVALLOTTI, L. 1962. A simple device for qualitative functional group analysis of gas chromatography effluents. Anal. Chem. 34, 1514–1516.

CHRENKO, R. M. 1964. Infrared microcell. Anal. Chem. 36, 1883–1885.

COLTHUP, N. B., DALY, L. H., and WIBERLY, S. E. 1964. Introduction to Infrared and Raman Spectroscopy. Academic Press, New York-London.

CONROY, H. 1960. Nuclear magnetic resonance in organic structural elucidation. In Advances in Organic Chemistry; Methods and Results. Vol. II. R. A. Raphael, E. C. Taylor, and H. Wynberg (Editors). Interscience, New York-London.

DAL NOGARE, S., and JUVET, R. S., JR. 1962. Gas-Liquid Chromatography. Theory and Practice. Interscience, New York-London.

DAY, E. A., and ANDERSON, D. F. 1965. Gas chromatographic and mass spectral identification of neutral components of the aroma fraction of blue cheese. J. Agr. Food Chem. 13, 2–4.

DAY, E. A., and LIBBEY, L. M. 1964. Cheddar cheese flavor: gas chromatographic and mass spectral analyses of the neutral components of the aroma fraction. J. Food Sci. 29, 583–589.

ELLIOT, R. M. (Editor). 1963. Advances in Mass Spectrometry. Pergamon Press, London.

ETTRE, L. S., CIEPLINSKI, E. W., and AVERILL, W. 1963. Application of open tubular (Golay) column with larger diameter. J. Gas Chromatog. 1, No. 2, 7–16.

FAGERSON, I. R. 1965. Private communication. Univ. of Massachusetts Amherst, Mass.

FORREY, R. R. 1965. Private communication. U.S. Dept. Agr., WURDD, Albany, Calif.

FOSTER, H. 1964. Magnetic resonance spectrometry. Anal. Chem. 36, 266R–278R.

GOHLKE, R. C. 1959. Time-of-flight mass spectrometry and gas-liquid partition chromatography. Anal. Chem. 31, 535–541.

GOLAY, M. J. E. 1958. Theory of chromatography in open and coated tubular columns with round and rectangular cross-sections. In Gas Chromatography, 1958, D. H. Desty (Editor), Butterworths, London.

HOFFMANN, R. L., and SILVEIRA, A., JR. 1964. A simple collection tube for gas chromatography. J. Gas Chromatog. 2, 107.

HORNSTEIN, I., and CROWE, P. 1965. Trapping of gas chromatographic effluents using carbon dioxide as a carrier gas. Anal. Chem. 37, 170–171.

JACKMAN, L. M. 1959. Applications of Nuclear Magnetic Resonance Spectroscopy in Organic Chemistry. Pergamon Press, New York-London.

JANAK, J. 1963. Gas chromatography as a sampling procedure for thin-layer or paper chromatography. J. Gas Chromatog. 1, No. 10, 20–23.

JENTZSCH, D., and HOVERMANN, W. 1963. The application of Golay columns of larger diameter. J. Chromatog. 11, 440–451.

JONES, R. N., and SANDORFY, C. 1956. The application of infrared and Raman spectrometry to the elucidation of molecular structure. In Chemical Applications of Spectroscopy, (Technique of Organic Chemistry, Vol. IX, A. Weissberger, Editor), Interscience, New York-London.

JUVET, R. S., and DAL NOGARE, S. 1964. Gas chromatography. Anal. Chem. 36, 36R–51R.

KAISER, R. 1964. Direct and automatic coupling of thin-layer chromatography to gas chromatography. Z. Anal. Chemie. *205*, 284–298.

KLEIN, M. P., and BARTON, G. W., JR. 1963. Enhancement of signal-to-noise ratio by continuous averaging application to magnetic resonance. Rev. of Sci. Instruments *34*, 754–759.

LIPSKY, S. R., LANDOWN, R. A., and LOVELOCK, J. E. 1959. Separation of lipids by gas-liquid chromatography. Anal. Chem. *31*, 852–856.

LUNDIN, R. E., ELSKEN, R. H., FLATH, R. A., HENDERSON, N., MON, T. R., and TERANISHI, R. 1966. Time averaged proton magnetic resonance analysis of micro samples from large-bore open tube gas chromatographs. Anal. Chem. 38, 291–293.

McCARTHY, A. I., PALMER, J. K., SHAW, C. P., and ANDERSON, E. E. 1963. Correlation of gas chromatographic data with flavor profiles of fresh banana fruit. J. Food Sci. *28*, 379–384.

McDOWELL, C. A. (Editor). 1963. Mass Spectrometry. McGraw-Hill Book Co., New York.

McFADDEN, W. H., and TERANISHI, R. 1963. Fast-scan mass spectrometry with capillary gas-liquid chromatography in investigation of fruit volatiles. Nature *200*, 329–330.

McFADDEN, W. H., TERANISHI, R., BLACK, D. R., and DAY, J. C. 1963. Use of capillary gas chromatography with a time-of-flight mass spectrometer. J. Food Sci. *28*, 316–319.

McFADDEN, W. H., and DAY, E. A. 1964. Scan rate considerations in combined gas chromatography and mass spectrometry. Anal. Chem. *36*, 2362–2363.

McFADDEN, W. H., TERANISHI, R., CORSE, J., BLACK, D. R., and MON, T. R. 1965. Volatiles from strawberries. II. Combined mass spectrometry and gas chromatography on complex mixtures. J. Chromatog. *18*, 10–19.

McLAFFERTY, F. W. 1963. Mass Spectral Correlations. American Chemical Society, Washington, D.C.

NAKANISHI, K. 1962. Infrared Absorption Spectroscopy-Practical. Holden-Day, San Francisco, Calif.

NANO, G. M., SANCIN, P., and MARTELLI, A. 1965. An improved method for collecting and identifying small gas chromatographic fractions by TLC. J. Gas Chromatog. *3*, 85–86.

NMR-EPR STAFF, VARIAN ASSOCIATES. 1960. NMR and EPR Spectroscopy. Pergamon Press, New York.

POPLE, J. A., SCHNEIDER, W. G., and BERNSTEIN, H. J. 1959. High-Resolution Nuclear Magnetic Resonance. McGraw-Hill Book Co., New York-London.

POTTS, W. J. 1964. Chemical Spectroscopy. Vol. I and II. John Wiley and Sons, New York.

QUIRAM, E. R. 1963. Applications of wide-diameter open tubular column gas-liquid chromatography. Anal. Chem. *35*, 593–595.

RYHAGE, R. 1964. Use of a mass spectrometer as a detector and analyzer for effluents emerging from high temperature gas-liquid chromatography columns. Anal. Chem. *36*, 759–764.

SCHERER, J. R. 1965. Private communication. U.S. Dept. Agr., WURDD, Albany, Calif.

SCHULTZ, T. H., TERANISHI, R., McFADDEN, W. H., KILPATRICK, P. W., and CORSE, J. 1964. Volatiles from oranges. II. Constituents of the juice identified by mass spectra. J. Food Sci. *29*, 790–795.

SCHWARTZ, R. D., BRASSEAUX, D. J., and SHOEMAKE, G. R. 1963. Capillary column gas-liquid chromatography with thermal conductivity detectors. J. Gas Chromatog. *1*, No. 1, 32–33.

SCOTT, R. P. W. 1958. The construction of high-efficiency columns for the separation of hydrocarbons. *In* Gas Chromatography, 1958. D. H. Desty (Editor), Butterworths, London.

SELKE, E., SCHOLFIELD, C. R., EVANS, C. D., and DUTTON, H. J. 1961. Mass spectrometry and lipid research. J. Am. Oil Chemists' Soc. *38*, 614–615.

STEWART, D. W. 1960. Mass spectrometry. *In* Physical Methods of Organic Chemistry (Technique of Organic Chemistry, A. Weissberger, Editor), 3rd ed., Part IV, Interscience, New York-London.

STROTHERS, J. B. 1963. Application of nuclear magnetic resonance spectroscopy. *In* Elucidation of Structures by Physical and Chemical Methods, Part I, K. W. Bentley (Editor), (Technique of Organic Chemistry, Vol. XI, A. Weissberger, Editor), Interscience, New York-London.

SWOBODA, P. A. T. 1963. Total trapping of chromatographic effluents in argon carrier gas. Nature *199*, 31–32.

TERANISHI, R., and BUTTERY, R. G. 1962. Aromagrams—Direct vapor analyses with gas chromatography. *In* Fourth Report, Sci. Technol. Comm., Int. Fed. Fruit Juice Producers. Juris-Verlag, Zurich.

TERANISHI, R., BUTTERY, R. G., and LUNDIN, R. E. 1962. Gas Chromatography. Direct vapor analyses of food products with programmed temperature control of dual columns with dual flame ionization detectors. Anal. Chem. *34*, 1033–1034.

TERANISHI, R., BUTTERY, R. G., LUNDIN, R. E., McFADDEN, W. H., and MON, T. R. 1963A. Role of gas chromatography in aroma research. Am. Soc. of Brewing Chemists' Proc., 52–57.

TERANISHI, R., CORSE, J. W., McFADDEN, W. H., BLACK, D. R., and MORGAN, A. I., JR. 1963B. Volatiles from strawberries. I. Mass spectral identification of the more volatile components. J. Food Sci. *28*, 478–483.

TERANISHI, R., BUTTERY, R. G., and MON, T. R. 1964. Direct vapor analyses with gas chromatography. Ann. N.Y. Acad. Sci. *116*, 583–589.

TERANISHI, R., and MON, T. R. 1964. Large-bore capillary and low-pressure-drop packed columns. Anal. Chem. *36*, 1490–1492.

TERANISHI, R., FLATH, R. A., MON, T. R., and STEVENS, K. L. 1965. Collection of gas chromatographically purified samples. J. Gas Chromatog. *3*, 206–207.

WALSH, J. T., and MERRITT, C., JR. 1960. Qualitative functional group analysis of gas chromatographic effluents. Anal. Chem. *32*, 1378–1381.

WATSON, J. T., and BIEMANN, K. 1964. High resolution mass spectra of compounds emerging from a gas chromatograph. Anal. Chem. *36*, 1135–1137.

WATSON, J. T., and BIEMANN, K. 1965. Direct recording of high resolution mass spectra of gas chromatographic effluents. Anal. Chem. *37*, 844–851.

WEURMAN, C. 1963. Recent developments in food odour research methods. *In* Recent Advances in Food Science, J. M. Leitch and D. N. Rhodes, (Editors), Vol. 3, 137–150. Butterworths, London.

ZLATKIS, A., and KAUFMAN, H. R. 1959. Use of coated tubing as columns for gas chromatography. Nature *184*, 2010.

Flavor of Foods

CHAPTER 8

J. Robert Coffman | **Bread Flavor**

INTRODUCTION

Freshly baked bread has aroma and flavor that are subtle, yet very attractive to most individuals. Unfortunately, these appealing characteristics disappear rather quickly, so that from the flavor and aroma standpoints, the shelf life of bread is short in duration.

Food flavors are associated with the presence of certain chemical compounds, and bread appears to be no exception. For this reason, numerous workers have undertaken research concerning the fundamental chemistry of bread flavor and aroma. Armed with such information, it should then be possible to improve, enhance, and extend the shelf life of bread with good flavor and aroma characteristics.

It is the purpose of this presentation to review some of the phases of the research on bread flavor and aroma and to update the record of the work which has been done in this area. Several excellent and comprehensive reviews of bread flavor research have been published. The authors in chronological order are Otterbacher (1959), Wiseblatt (1961A, B), Johnson (1963), Collyer (1964), and De Figueiredo (1964).

The present summary of bread flavor research is concerned primarily with white bread as we know it in the United States. Considerable research on the dark bread flavor has been described by many European workers. Their findings and excellent work have been thoroughly reviewed by Collyer (1964).

HISTORICAL BACKGROUND

For many years knowledge of the chemical flavor entities in bread was lacking. An early step to lessen this scarcity of information was carried out by Backe (1910) who described the isolation of maltol and isomaltol from bread. The relationship of these substances to bread flavor remained unknown until Hodge and Moser (1961) incorporated both substances into baked products. Taste panel results indicated that the flavor of yeast rolls was intensified by the addition of maltol. Although the organoleptic tests did not lead to firm conclusions, maltol and isomaltol may play some role in the flavor of bread.

In 1935, Visser'T Hooft and De Leeuw demonstrated that acetoin (acetyl methyl carbinol) was present in bread. These workers believed that acetoin did not enhance bread flavor directly. It was their view that diacetyl was one of the important flavor factors in bread and that this was produced by the slow oxidation of acetoin.

Further literature reports concerning specific chemical compounds associated with bread were practically nonexistent until 1953. Prior to that time, however, Baker and Mize (1939) carried out an extensive study designed to understand the essential factors which contribute to the formation of bread flavor and aroma. The findings of Baker and Mize (1939) demonstrated that two conditions were essential to produce bread flavor and aroma.

One of these conditions was the production of fermentation reaction products in the dough. The other factor was the formation of crust during baking. Bread produced with little or no fermentation or crust did not possess normal bread flavor and aroma.

The important observations by these early workers have actually served as focal points for many subsequent research efforts concerning the fundamental chemistry of bread flavor and aroma.

RECENT STUDIES

Intense research on bread flavor and aroma has been underway only during the past 12 years. This recent effort received its impetus from the work of Baker et al. (1953) who described their observations concerning the chemical composition of the vapors evolved during the baking of bread. The aqueous condensate, resulting from the oven gases was analyzed primarily by colorimetric analysis for a variety of chemical compounds or classes of compounds. While their study did not solve the problem of the composition of bread flavor and aroma, it did serve as one of the factors which stimulated further research work by others.

In addition to the above described research, at least two other factors contributed greatly to the desire and ability to learn more about the fundamental chemistry of bread flavor and aroma. One of these factors was the development of the continuous mix bread process. This was described by Orchard (1953) and was the result of the efforts of a group of workers led by John Baker. In this process, a separate fermentation brew, known as a pre-ferment, is prepared. The pre-ferment is added to flour and other dough ingredients and the whole dough mass is mixed for approximately two minutes. The dough is then extruded into a pan and allowed to undergo proofing for approximately 40 minutes before baking. In the conventional bread process the yeast and dough are in contact for approximately four hours prior to the final baking step. Thus, the fermentation time is considerably shorter for the continuous bread than it is for the conventional bread.

While there exists a difference of opinion concerning the comparative flavor and aroma of the continuous mix and conventional bread, many people believe that continuous mix bread has less flavor than conventional bread. This controversy served to focus attention on research concerning the chemical composition of pre-ferments and doughs. Differences between the two fermentation conditions and their influence upon bread flavor have not been defined.

Another important factor which has had a major influence upon flavor research has been the development of highly sensitive instruments capable of resolving and identifying the components of extremely complex mixtures available in very small amounts. A combination of instrumental techniques such as gas-liquid chromatography, infrared spectroscopy, mass spectrometry, and nuclear magnetic resonance have greatly aided in advancing our knowledge concerning the chemical composition of food flavors.

Subsequent to 1953, the research on bread flavor has been concerned with various aspects of bread production, i.e., pre-ferments, doughs, bread, and the volatiles given off during baking. The various efforts have led to the isolation and identification of approximately 70 substances. These substances are summarized in Tables 16 through 20.

TABLE 16

ALCOHOLS ASSOCIATED WITH WHITE BREAD

	Source		
Alcohols	Brew	Bread	Oven Vapors
Ethanol	Identified by numerous investigators		
n-Propanol	Smith and Coffman (1960)	Wick et al. (1964)	
Isobutanol	Smith and Coffman (1960)		
	Miller et al. (1961)	Wick et al. (1964)	
Isoamyl alcohol	Smith and Coffman (1960)	Baker et al. (1953)	Baker et al. (1953)
		Wick et al. (1964)	
d-Amyl alcohol		Wick et al. (1964)	
2-Phenyl ethanol	Smith and Coffman (1960)		
Levo 2,3-butanediol	Smith and Coffman (1960)		
Meso 2,3-butanediol	Smith and Coffman (1960)		

PRE-FERMENTS

The research effort concerning the chemical composition of pre-ferments has been extensive. Considerable attention has been given to carbonyl components of the pre-ferment because there is a general belief that such substances contribute to a degree to bread flavor and aroma. Many of these substances are present in very small amounts, but they have been concentrated by precipitating them as their 2,4-

TABLE 17

ACIDS ASSOCIATED WITH WHITE BREAD

Acids	Brew	Dough	Bread	Oven Vapors
			Source	
Formic	Hunter et al. (1961)		Wick et al. (1964)	Pence (1952) Baker et al. (1953)
Acetic	Hunter et al. (1961) Johnson (1925) Johnson and Miller (1961)	Johnson (1925) Wiseblatt (1960B)	Pence and Kohler (1961) Wiseblatt (1960B) Wiseblatt and Kohn (1960)	Wiseblatt (1960B) Pence (1952)
Propionic	Hunter et al. (1961)	Wiseblatt (1960B)	Kohn et al. (1961) Pence and Kohler (1961) Wiseblatt and Kohn (1960)	
Butyric	Hunter et al. (1961) Johnson and Miller (1957)	Wiseblatt (1960B)	Wiseblatt (1960 A, B) Pence and Kohler (1961)	
Isobutyric	Hunter et al. (1961)		Pence and Kohler (1961)	
Valeric	Hunter et al. (1961)	Wiseblatt (1960B)	Pence and Kohler (1961)	
Isovaleric	Hunter et al. (1961)		Pence and Kohler (1961) Wiseblatt (1960 A, B)	
Caproic	Hunter et al. (1961)	Wiseblatt (1960B)	Pence and Kohler (1961)	
Isocaproic	Hunter et al. (1961)		Pence and Kohler (1961)	
Heptanoic	Hunter et al. (1961)		Pence and Kohler (1961)	
Octanoic	Hunter et al. (1961)		Pence and Kohler (1961)	
Nonanoic	Hunter et al. (1961)		Pence and Kohler (1961)	
Capric	Hunter et al. (1961)		Pence and Kohler (1961)	
Lauric	Hunter et al. (1961)		Pence and Kohler (1961)	
Myristic	Hunter et al. (1961)			
Palmitic	Hunter et al. (1961)			
Lactic	Johnson et al. (1958) Johnson (1925) McLaren (1954)	Johnson (1925)	Wiseblatt (1957)	
Crotonic	Hunter et al. (1961)		Wiseblatt (1957)	
Pyruvic	Cole et al. (1962)		Wiseblatt (1957)	
Hydrocinnamic			Wiseblatt (1957)	
Benzilic			Wiseblatt (1957)	
Itaconic			Wiseblatt (1957)	
Levulinic				

dinitrophenylhydrazones. These derivatives have been resolved and identified by a variety of chromatographic methods.

In addition to the aldehydes and ketones in pre-ferments, other substances such as acids, alcohols, and esters have also been studied. Johnson *et al.* (1958) demonstrated the presence of acetic, lactic, and one unknown acid in a pre-ferment. The only ester reported was ethyl acetate. Their studies were designed primarily to show how the components of the brew changed with length of fermentation time.

Hunter *et al.* (1961) used gas chromatography to investigate the volatile organic acids obtained from a brew by methylene chloride extraction. They observed the presence of at least 45 acids and identified 17 of the mono carboxylic type. These acids are listed in Table 17.

Cole *et al.* (1962) studied the effect of processing variations upon the total alcohol, carbonyl, and organic acid contents of pre-ferments.

Smith and Coffman (1960) used gas-liquid chromatography to resolve and isolate many volatile substances from a pre-ferment. Yeast-free pre-ferment was distilled under reduced pressure so as to separate volatile and nonvolatile components. Identification of the isolated substances was made chiefly by infrared spectroscopy. A total of 15 substances were identified. These compounds consisted of various alcohols, carbonyls and esters as shown in Tables 16, 17, 18, 19, and 20. The mixture of levo and meso 2,3-butanediols in the nonvolatile fraction, accounted for 85% of the concentrate weight after accounting for the residual ethanol and solvent. These diols may possibly be a source of acetoin and diacetyl which may be involved in bread flavor.

TABLE 18

ESTERS ASSOCIATED WITH WHITE BREAD

	Source		
Ester	Brew	Bread	Oven Vapors
Ethyl formate	Smith and Coffman (1960)		
Ethyl acetate	Smith and Coffman (1960) Johnson *et al.* (1958)	Wick *et al.* (1964)	Baker *et al.* (1953)
Ethyl pyruvate		Wiseblatt (1957) Ng *et al.* (1960) Wiseblatt (1960B)	
Ethyl lactate	Smith and Coffman (1960)	Wiseblatt (1956)	
Ethyl levulinate		Wiseblatt (1957) Wiseblatt (1960B)	
Ethyl succinate		Wiseblatt (1956)	
Ethyl hydrocinnamate		Wiseblatt (1956)	
Ethyl itaconate		Wiseblatt (1956)	
1,3-propane-diol mono-acetate	Smith and Coffman (1960)		
Gamma butyrolactone	Smith and Coffman (1960)		

TABLE 19

ALDEHYDES ASSOCIATED WITH WHITE BREAD

Aldehyde	Brew	Dough	Bread	Oven Vapors
			Source	
Formaldehyde	Linko et al. (1962B), Miller et al. (1961)		Linko et al. (1962A), Ng et al. (1960)	Baker et al. (1953), Ng et al. (1960), Wiseblatt (1960A)
Acetaldehyde	Linko et al. (1962B), Smith and Coffman (1960), Miller et al. (1961)	Kohn et al. (1961)	Linko et al. (1962A), Ng et al. (1960), Wiseblatt (1957), Wiseblatt (1960B), Kohn et al. (1961), Linko et al. (1962A)	
Propionaldehyde	Linko et al. (1962B), Miller et al. (1961)			
n-Butanal	Linko et al. (1962B), Miller et al. (1961)	Kohn et al. (1961)	Linko et al. (1962A), Rothe and Thomas (1963), Linko et al. (1962A)	Ng et al. (1960)
Isobutanaldehyde	Linko et al. (1962B), Miller et al. (1961)			
n-Valeraldehyde	Linko et al. (1962B), Miller et al. (1961)			Ng et al. (1960)
Isovaleral	Linko et al. (1962B), Miller et al. (1961)	Kohn et al. (1961)	Linko et al. (1962A), Rothe and Thomas (1963), Linko et al. (1962A)	Kohn et al. (1961)
2-Methylbutanal	Miller et al. (1961)		Linko et al. (1962A), Ng et al. (1960)	
n-Hexanal	Linko et al. (1962B)	Kohn et al. (1961)	Linko et al. (1962A)	
2-Ethylhexanal			Ng et al. (1960), Wiseblatt (1960B), Kohn et al. (1961), Wiseblatt (1960B)	
Crotonaldehyde		Kohn et al. (1961)		
Benzaldehyde		Kohn et al. (1961)	Baker et al. (1953), Kohn et al. (1961), Wick et al. (1964), Baker et al. (1953), Linko et al. (1962A), Kohn et al. (1961)	Baker et al. (1953)
Pyruvaldehyde				
Furfural			Ng et al. (1960), Wiseblatt (1957), Wiseblatt (1960B), Linko et al. (1962A)	Baker et al. (1953)
Hydroxymethyl furfural				
2-Butanal			Kohn et al. (1961)	

Miller *et al.* (1961) concentrated the carbonyl compounds present in a pre-ferment by precipitating the 2,4-dinitrophenylhydrazones. These derivatives were analyzed by gas-liquid, column, and paper chromatography. Two ketones and eight aldehydes were identified. These compounds are presented in Tables 19 and 20. Further studies on both the qualitative and quantitative nature of the pre-ferment carbonyls were made by Linko *et al.* (1962A). A combination of gas-liquid and paper chromatography was used to identify the 2,4-dinitrophenyl-hydrazones. Ultraviolet spectroscopy was used to obtain the quantitative data. In this study, propionaldehyde and *n*-hexaldehyde were identified for the first time.

BREAD AND DOUGHS

Attempts to understand the nature of the chemistry of bread flavor and aroma have involved the soluble and volatile components of doughs and breads.

Johnson (1925) identified acetic and lactic acids in bread and cracker doughs. Wiseblatt and Kohn (1960) succeeded in isolating a number of volatile carbonyls from bread by subjecting freshly baked bread to a vacuum and condensing the vapors in cold traps. The 2,4-dinitrophenyl-hydrazones of the carbonyl compounds were prepared after obtaining the condensate. They were resolved and identified by column and paper chromatography. The identified aldehydes were acetaldehyde, crotonaldehyde, 2-ethyl hexanal, and furfural. The identified keto compounds were acetone, hexanone-2, heptanone-3, diacetyl, methyl glyoxal, and pyruvic and levulinic acids were also present. These same authors identified acetic and propionic acids. The identification of alcohols other than ethanol could not be made with confidence.

Following quantitative estimation of the various compounds from bread, Wiseblatt and Kohn (1960) attempted in two ways to improve the bread-like flavor of chemically leavened bread. They first obtained a condensate of the volatile substances from conventional bread. This aqueous solution was concentrated sevenfold by distillation to concentrate the aroma substances. The concentrate was used as part of the water in the preparation of chemically leavened bread. Wiseblatt and Kohn also exposed slices of bread to the vapors of the concentrate as well as to the vapor of a synthetic mixture prepared on the basis of their identification work. In no instance was bread flavor imparted to the experimental bread. It was concluded that further work was needed before a synthetic bread flavor could be prepared.

Ng *et al.* (1960) studied the carbonyls present in an ethanol extract of white bread. As in other work, the carbonyls were precipitated as the

TABLE 20

KETONES ASSOCIATED WITH WHITE BREAD

Ketone	Source			
	Brew	Dough	Bread	Oven Vapors
Acetone	Linko et al. (1962B) Smith and Coffman (1960)	Kohn et al. (1961)	Linko et al. (1962B)	Baker et al. (1953)
Methyl ethyl	Miller et al. (1961) Linko et al. (1962B)		Kohn et al. (1961) Linko et al. (1962B) Miller et al. (1961)	Ng et al. (1960) Baker et al. (1953)
Methyl ethyl n-butyl		Kohn et al. (1961)	Wiseblatt (1960A) Wick et al. (1964)	
Ethyl n-butyl			Wiseblatt (1960A)	
Diacetyl	Smith and Coffman (1960)		Kohn et al. (1961) Baker et al. (1953) Wiseblatt (1957) Wiseblatt (1960A) Thomas and Rothe (1957)	Baker et al. (1953)
Acetoin	Smith and Coffman (1960)		Wick et al. (1964) Thomas and Rothe (1957) Visser'T Hooft and DeLeeuw (1935)	
Maltol (heterocyclic)			Backe (1910)	

2,4-dinitrophenylhydrazones and identified by column and paper chromatography.

Linko and Johnson (1963) studied the change in amino acid concentration and carbonyl formation during baking. They observed that the formation of carbonyl compounds in bread crust was accompanied by a significant decrease in all amino acids, particularly aspartic and glutamic acids. These findings lend support to the view that the Maillard reaction plays a role in bread flavor and aroma. This reaction takes place chiefly in the crust.

Cole et al. (1962) found that pre-ferment made with a high percentage of yeast and sugar led to a brew which had a higher than normal content of acids, carbonyls, and alcohols. The flavor and aroma of the bread made from such pre-ferments was more pronounced than that of bread made from a "normal" brew. Conclusions concerning the merit of the stronger flavor were not drawn because Cole et al. (1962) did not make organoleptic evaluations.

Wick et al. (1964) made an extensive investigation of the volatile components of white bread prepared with a pre-ferment. Wick's efforts were directed toward the concentration, resolution, and identification of the volatile substances. Concentration was accomplished by removing the bread volatiles, using a high vacuum technique to obtain an aqueous condensate. This procedure was similar to that described by Wiseblatt and Kohn (1960). The condensate was then extracted with ether which was removed later by fractional distillation. The final concentrate of bread volatiles was studied by gas-liquid chromatography and the resolved and isolated fractions were identified by infrared spectroscopy. The major constituents were chiefly alcohols, acetone, furfural, and ethyl acetate. The carbonyl compounds were precipitated as the 2,4-dinitrophenylhydrazones which were separated and identified by gas-liquid and thin-layer chromatography. These carbonyl substances were present in the condensate in trace quantities.

In addition to the analytical studies on the bread volatile components, sensory evaluations of various breads also were made by Wick et al. (1964). These studies were largely directed toward observing changes in flavor and aroma through the addition of various amino acids. Only the addition of 1-proline caused an improvement in bread aroma. The substances identified in this study are summarized in the Tables 16 through 20.

OVEN GASES

A study of the components evolved from bread during baking has merit for several reasons. One reason is the generally recognized characteristic and attractive aroma coming from the ovens during baking, and freshly baked bread. Thus, it may be concluded that bread aroma substances are volatile. Another factor in favor of studying oven gases is that the volatile substances from a large number of loaves of bread are recoverable immediately upon formation.

In 1952, E. A. Pence published the first study on the gross composition of the aqueous condensate obtained from bread oven vapors. The only components isolated and identified were formic and acetic acids. Colorimetric tests indicated the presence of esters, carbonyls, and alcohols. At about the same time, Baker *et al.* (1953) described a rather extensive study on the composition of oven gases. This was accomplished by analyzing the aqueous condensate for a variety of substances. No isolation work was carried out. Rather, the components were identified primarily by colorimetric tests.

Ng *et al.* (1960) carried out preliminary work on the carbonyls present in oven gases. These workers passed the vapors into a trap containing 2,4-dinitrophenylhydrazine and analyzed the precipitated hydrazones by column and paper chromatography. They found isobutyraldehyde and *n*-valeraldehyde which were not present in the alcohol extract of the bread from which the vapors were derived.

Wiseblatt (1960A) obtained an aqueous condensate from the oven gases. He was able to identify ethanol, acetaldehyde, and acetic acid after the removal of the carbonyl compounds.

Wiseblatt also published (1960B) a paper concerned with the volatile organic acids in bread oven vapors, in doughs, and in bread. In the condensate from the oven the only acid which was identified was acetic acid. Doughs, however, contained C_2, C_4, i-C_5, and C_6 acids, and bread contained C_2, C_4, and i-C_5 acids. The identification of the acids was accomplished using gas-liquid chromatography.

In the research laboratories of General Mills, Inc., investigations concerning the fundamental chemistry of bread flavor and aroma have been in progress since 1958. Initially, the neutral components of a simple pre-ferment were concentrated from the cell-free fermentation mixture by an ether extraction. The resulting concentrates were resolved into their components by gas-liquid chromatography. The individual components from the mixture were isolated in cold traps and their identity determined by infrared spectroscopy. The findings were published by Smith and Coffman in 1960. Such information led to a reasonable knowledge of the nature of the major, and some of the minor, components that should be present in a dough.

Efforts were then concentrated on determining the nature of the substances evolved during the baking of bread. To simplify the problem, a basic straight dough was prepared and baked in an electrically heated oven. During the baking process the vapors were drawn from the oven by a vacuum pump with the rate of vapor removal being regulated by pump capacity and inlet air vent adjustment. All top oven openings were closed except one from which the vapors were led into the condensing and trapping system.

In early experiments six glass traps were arranged in series. This system resembled that described by Wiseblatt (1960A). The oven vapors were passed first through a glass condenser chilled with circulating ice water. The condensate and vapors then passed to a trap immersed in an ice bath. A second ice-chilled trap was placed in the system. This second trap was followed by two traps chilled in a dry ice-ethanol bath. Finally, the vapors passed into two traps chilled in liquid nitrogen. Approximately 97% of the total condensate was retained in the two wet ice traps, 2.5% in the dry ice traps, and 0.5% in the liquid nitrogen chilled vessels.

Initial examination of the aroma of the head space gases from the wet ice traps was disappointing and confirmed the observations of Wiseblatt and Kohn (1960). The odor of this condensate was quite objectionable and appeared to have no relationship to bread aroma. However, when this solution was placed in an atomizer and sprayed into the room air, the aroma constituents were sufficiently diluted so that the typical characteristic bread aroma was readily detected. The condensates present in the two other types of cold traps were similarly examined. However, the odor of these condensates was chiefly fruity in nature. In subsequent work, therefore, bread aroma and flavor research on the oven volatiles has been limited to the aqueous condensate. This condensate has a gross composition of approximately 95% water and 5% ethyl alcohol and 50 to 100 ppm. of the bread aroma constituents.

Initial attempts to concentrate bread aroma substances by pH adjustment of the condensate and ether extraction to separate the acids from the neutrals was not satisfactory. From approximately one liter of oven condensate there was obtained, after removal of the ether, a brown colored concentrate having a volume of approximately 40 ml. After diluting this concentrate with water and noting the aroma of the atomized solution, it was observed that the typical bread aroma had disappeared and in its place was an odor which resembled that of cinnamon rolls. Subsequently, it was found that this change was caused by an oxidation reaction, presumably catalyzed by ether peroxide. This change in aroma, coupled with the presence of a large quantity of ethyl alcohol and tarry substances, left much to be desired in the purification and concentration of the bread aroma substances.

In view of these difficulties a different approach was undertaken with gratifying results. The oven condensate from baking 48 loaves of bread has a volume of approximately 1.2 liters and a pH value of 3.5 to 3.6. The pH is adjusted to 9.2 and the solution is shell frozen, and lyophilized overnight. The sublimate upon melting has the delightful aroma of the original oven condensate and is free from acids and tars. Thus, the aroma substances, even those compounds having boiling points higher than 200°C, readily accompany the subliming ice. This sublimate has a pH of approximately 8.5, caused by the presence of ammonia. After pH adjustment of the melted sublimate to 6.0–6.5, the solution is placed in a liquid-liquid extractor contained in an ice bath and continuously extracted with purified ethyl chloride for a period of seven to eight hours. The extracted aqueous sublimate, after removal of the solvent, is totally odorless. The ethyl chloride is then removed by slow distillation on a water bath at 15° to 18°C. under a nitrogen atmosphere. The resulting concentrate of aroma substances derived from 400 loaves of bread has a volume of approximately 1 ml. Upon dilution with 5% aqueous ethanol adjusted to a pH of 3.5 by the addition of 10% acetic acid, the aroma of the concentrate is that of the original oven gas condensate. In addition, the concentrate is free of water has only a small quantity of ethanol, and is neutral.

Special mention should be made concerning the purification of the ethyl chloride. This solvent contains a varying quantity of hydrogen chloride which is readily removed by magnetically stirring the ethyl chloride with a quantity of powdered anhydrous sodium carbonate overnight in a refrigerator. The resulting HCl free solvent is recovered by slow distillation through an ice-water-chilled condenser leading into a flask immersed in an ice bath. The purified solvent is stored in a refrigerator with practically no loss and is stable to water and alcohol without the formation of free hydrochloric acid.

While we have not investigated the contribution of the acidic material to the oven volatile aroma, there is evidence which shows that the presence of the acids leads to a harsher odor than when they are absent from the condensate.

The main emphasis, therefore, has been applied to the neutral material. Gas-liquid chromatography has been used exclusively. The chromatographic column packing is 45–60 mesh Chromosorb W, containing 15% Ucon 75H 90000. Seventy peaks have been observed on a typical chromatogram. Many of the more clearly resolved components have been recovered and identified. These have been found to be the same substances which are present in the pre-ferment. They include ethanol, acetaldehyde, n-propyl alcohol, isobutyl alcohol, isoamyl alcohol, d-amyl alcohol, gamma-butyrolactone, the 2,3-butanediols, and beta-phenyl ethanol. This array of compounds is not surprising since during baking, the fermentation products are either volatilized or are steam distilled by the water which is driven off from the dough.

A synthetic mixture of these substances does not have an aroma resembling bread. Thus, many other substances present in the oven condensate have yet to be isolated and identified. The resolution and identification of certain of these will undoubtedly require special techniques which have yet to be devised.

SOURCE OF BREAD FLAVOR AND AROMA COMPONENTS

In numerous studies involving the identity of bread flavor substances, consideration has also been given to the source of the various flavor compounds. There is little doubt that some fermentation reaction products remain in the loaf and contribute to flavor. Another source of flavor and aroma is the Maillard reaction during crust formation. It is generally believed that this type reaction is chiefly responsible for the browning of the bread crust. Johnson and Miller (1961) reviewed this type of browning reaction, particularly as it applies to baked products. Volatile and nonvolatile substances are formed during crust development and both types exist in bread crust.

The identity, particularly of the volatile substances, has yet to be established. It is likely that no single compound is responsible for crust aroma and/or flavor.

Studies have been made by Kiely et al. (1960) using model browning reaction systems. It was observed that the reaction of glucose with leucine, histidine, and arginine led to the production of fresh bread aroma.

Further studies concerned with the browning reaction were those reported by Wiseblatt and Zoumut (1963). They reacted dihydroxy acetone with proline and obtained a strong cracker-like aroma. This aroma apparently is the same type of odor obtained from a boiled pre-ferment brew and from bread.

LOSS OF BREAD FLAVOR AND AROMA

It is well known that bread rapidly loses its freshly baked aroma and flavor upon cooling and standing. A variety of views have been expressed as to how this loss takes place. It is believed by some that the aroma and flavor substances are lost by volatilization or possibly by chemical reactions such as oxidation. Militating against this view is the fact that the aroma of bread may be partially renewed by the simple process of heating. Schoch (1965) has recently expressed the view that many of the bread flavor substances may become "locked" within the linear fraction of wheat starch. Lansky *et al.* (1949) described the separation of the linear fraction of starch by precipitating it with amyl and butyl alcohols. In this reaction the alcohol molecule enters into the helical structure of the amylose. The resulting complex then separates from the nonlinear starch fraction. This reaction is reversed by heating.

From the published literature it is well established that during fermentation a variety of alcohols is produced. Among these alcohols are ethanol, *n*-propanol, isoamyl and *d*-amyl alcohols, isobutyl alcohol, and beta-phenyl ethanol.

Coffman *et al.* (1964) found that these substances appeared in the condensate from oven vapors and that the amyl alcohol content of the condensate may possibly be related to the intensity of bread aroma. Thus, there is reason to believe that such compounds exist in bread, and that these could complex with the linear starch molecule. The "capture" of some bread flavor components by the starch may account, in part, for the loss of flavor and aroma as well as flavor rejuvenation upon the heating of a "flavorless" bread.

Schoch (1965) also pointed out that starch in the natural or added form is a component of many foods. For this reason he suggests that fundamental studies to evaluate flavor changes may be related to the mechano-chemistry of linear molecules.

In the author's opinion the views of Schoch have considerable merit, particularly from the standpoint of the fermentation products and their contribution to bread flavor.

CONCLUSION

Knowledge concerning the fundamental chemistry of bread flavor and aroma has been advanced extensively during the past 12 years. In spite of available information, however, no one has yet synthesized bread flavor and aroma.

A large portion of the current knowledge concerning bread flavor and aroma is the result of identifying those compounds which are the most abundant and/or the easiest to obtain. It is now necessary to identify the minor components which are more difficult to obtain. While these unknown substances are present in very small quantities they may have a pronounced influence upon the flavor and aroma of bread.

ACKNOWLEDGMENTS

The capable assistance of William Jones is greatly appreciated. The contributions of Delores Bell, Robert Fisher, and James White for infrared spectroscopy and mass spectrometry analysis have been most helpful. I am also most grateful to Byron S. Miller for his helpful suggestions.

DISCUSSION

D. A. Kendall.—Dr. Coffman, I enjoyed your presentation, and particularly your examination of the concentrates by dilution techniques for their flavor contribution. The question I have is, did you collect a total chromatographic eluent and spray this into the room?

J. R. Coffman.—Yes, the collected total eluent does possess the characteristic bread aroma.

H. W. Schultz.—I have two questions. One is, you put this interpretation on the substances which you put in one location and then got at a distance to smell them. You interpreted this to mean that it was a matter of concentration. Might it possibly be that only certain volatiles reach that distance? So in a sense you have experienced an air chromatography?

J. R. Coffman.—This is possible. We don't know.

H. W. Schultz.—The second question is, I know you are interested more in the odors than you are in the taste of the bread. Might you not degrade the flavor of the bread if you were to confine these odors? I'm basing this on the experience of cooking cabbage. If you cook cabbage in a closed vessel the flavor of the cabbage is undesirable. You do not have a good pot roast of beef if you close the vessel and confine these materials, obviously volatiles, which are emitted into the air and smell very good. Might you therefore experience a degrading of the flavor if you confine all of these flavors and odors, let us say, to the bread?

J. R. Coffman.—You have a point there. The only thing that I can say at the moment is that we have been able to add the total concentrate back to bread, and it very markedly improves the flavor. So from that standpoint, we have reason to believe that we not only have the aroma concentrate but also the flavor.

D. A. Forss.—I have a question and a comment. Have you done any sort of adding back of synthetic flavors to bread?

J. R. Coffman.—Yes, they are not very impressive. To a degree these will approximate the flavor and aroma of the bread crumb, but that is only part of the picture. The crust aroma has to be there, and we know nothing about the crust at the moment. I hope, as I said during the presentation, that we will have some knowledge on some of these substances that seem to have importance as far as the crust aroma and flavor are concerned.

D. A. Forss.—I gather this could be a quantitative rather than a qualitative problem.

J. R. Coffman.—It could be. This is another problem really. We are using a flame ionization detector. We know from some of the work that we have done that while there are reports in the literature that these detectors are linear, I think they are linear only over relatively narrow ranges, so that from the quantitative standpoint, as you mentioned, we do not know exactly how much of each component to put together because there are different responses, depending upon the rate at which they come through the gas chromatograph, and apparently upon the structure of the molecule. We have to guess at the moment. Once we are able to identify those substances that we are seeking, then we will have to run a known mixture and get a correction factor for quantitative work.

D. A. Forss.—My comment is somewhat related to that, in that we have had a similar problem to yours and developed a technique where we do avoid the use of solvents altogether.

C. R. Evans.—You mentioned compounds boiling as high as 200° and 300°C. Do you feel that they contribute anything to the odor aroma?

J. R. Coffman.—I'm quite certain that for instance, beta-phenyl ethanol which boils at 206°C. does. We know that stearic acid also comes over and this boils at 361°C. I don't think stearic acid is going to have anything to do with the flavor and aroma of bread, at least in the small quantities that are present. The thing that I was interested in bringing out is the fact that lyophilization will bring over with the subliming ice many, many substances which have high boiling points, some of which we probably do not care a thing about. Some of the other substances that we are interested in have boiling points far in excess of 206°C.

L. J. Minor.—You mentioned that the sublimate baked-bread aroma compounds boil in excess of 300°C. What liquid phase do you use to separate these?

J. R. Coffman.—Perhaps it is a case of sematics. I do not know that they boil in excess of 300°C. I merely mentioned the point of 300°C. to point out that substances having high boiling points can accompany the subliming ice. We do know that some of these substances that are very aromatic and are associated in one way or another with bread, boil over 200°C. We do not know their identity at present. The stationary phase that we use is a Yukon lubricant which is the 75H 90,000. We have used this for about seven years. We have looked at many others but keep returning to this because it gives us the best resolution. However, we do use other stationary phases for separating the compounds that are not separated by the 75H 90,000.

BIBLIOGRAPHY

Backe, A. 1910. A new compound contained in food products. Compt. rend. 150, 530–543.

Baker, J. C., and Mize, M. D. 1939. Some observations regarding the flavor of bread. Cereal Chem. 16, 295–297.

Baker, J. C., Parker, H. K., and Fortmann, K. L. 1953. Flavor of bread. Cereal Chem. 30, 22–36.

Coffman, J. R., Meisner, D. F., and Terry, D. E. 1964. Aroma of continuous mix bread—a preliminary study. Cereal Sci. Today 9, 305–307.

Cole, E. W., Hale, W. S., and Pence, J. W. 1962. The effect of processing variations on the alcohols, carbonyls, and organic acid contents of pre-ferments for bread making. Cereal Chem. 39, 114–122.

Collyer, D. M. 1964. Bread flavor—a review. Baker's Digest 38, No. 1 43–54.

De Figueiredo, M. P. 1964. Volatile components of bread—a review. Baker's Digest 38, No. 6 48–51.

Hodge, J. E., and Moser, H. A. 1961. Flavor of bread and pastry upon addition of maltol, isomaltol, and galactosyl isomaltol. Cereal Chem. 38, 221–228.

Hunter, I. R., Ng, H., and Pence, J. W. 1961. Volatile organic acids in pre-ferments for bread. J. Food Sci. 26, 578–580.

Johnson, A. H. 1925. Identification and estimation of the organic acids produced during bread dough and cracker dough fermentation. Cereal Chem. 2, 345–364.

JOHNSON, J. A. 1963. Bread flavor factors and their control. Proc. 39th Annual Meeting—American Society of Bakery Engineers, 78–84.

JOHNSON, J. A., and MILLER, B. S. 1957. Pre-ferments—their role in bread baking. Baker's Digest *31*, No. 3, 29–35; 76–77.

JOHNSON, J. A., and MILLER, B. S. 1961. The browning of baked products. Baker's Digest *35*, No. 5, 52–59.

JOHNSON, J. A., MILLER, B. S., and CURNUTTE, B. 1958. Pre-ferments in bread making—organic acids and esters produced in pre-ferments. J. Agr. Food Chem. *6*, 384–387.

KIELY, R. J., NOWLIN, A. C., and MORIARTY, J. H. 1960. Bread aromatics from browning systems. Cereal Chem. *5*, 273–274.

KOHN, F. E. 1961. A study of the volatile aryl and alkyl carbonyl compounds arising during panary fermentation. Ph.D. dissertation, Northwestern Univ. Dissertation Abst. 1962. *22*, No. 7, 2174–2175.

KOHN, F. E., WISEBLATT, L., and FOSDICK, L. S. 1961. Some volatile carbonyl compounds arising during panary fermentation. Cereal Chem. *38*, 165–169.

LANSKY, S., KOOI, M., and SCHOCH, T. J. 1949. Properties of the fractions and linear subfractions from various starches. J. Am. Chem. Soc. *71*, 4066–4075.

LINKO, Y., and JOHNSON, J. A. 1963. Changes in amino acids and formation of carbonyl compounds during baking. J. Agr. Food Chem. *11*, 150–152.

LINKO, Y., JOHNSON, J. A., and MILLER, B. S. 1962A. The origin and fate of certain carbonyl compounds in white bread. Cereal Chem. *39*, 468–476.

LINKO, Y., MILLER, B. S., and JOHNSON, J. A. 1962B. Quantitative determination of certain carbonyl compounds in pre-ferments. Cereal Chem. *39*, 263–272.

LUERS, H. 1948. The formation of flavor substances in fermentation. Brewers Digest *23*, No. 9, 45–49.

McLAREN, L. H. 1954. The practical aspects of the stable ferment baking process. Baker's Digest *28*, No. 3, 23–24.

MENGER, A. 1960. Baking technology and nutritional trends in Germany. Cereal Sci. Today. *5*, 275–277.

MILLER, B. S., JOHNSON, J. A., and ROBINSON, R. J. 1961. Identification of carbonyl compounds produced in pre-ferments. Cereal Chem. *38*, 507–515.

NG, H., REED, D. J., and PENCE, J. W. 1960. Identification of carbonyl compounds in an ethanol extract of fresh white bread. Cereal Chem. *37*, 638–645.

ORCHARD, W. J. 1953. The continuous manufacture of bread doughs. Baker's Weekly *158*, No. 7, 29–32.

OTTERBACHER, T. J. 1959. A review of some technical aspects of bread flavor. Baker's Digest *33*, No. 3, 36–42.

PENCE, E. A. 1952. A study of baking oven gases. Masters Thesis, Kansas State Univ., Manhattan, Kansas.

PENCE, J. W., and KOHLER, G. O. 1961. Investigations of bread flavor in the U.S. Department of Agriculture. Brot und Geback *15*, 129–134.

ROTHE, M., and THOMAS, B. 1959. The formation, composition, and determination of aromatic substances of bread. Die Nahrung *3*, 1–17.

Rothe, M., and Thomas, B. 1963. Aroma of bread. Evaluation of chemical taste analyses with the aid of threshold value. Z. Lebensm. Untersuch. Forsch. *119*, 302–310.

Rotsch, A., and Dorner, H. 1958. Identification of aromas produced during the baking process. Brot und Geback *12*, 138.

Schoch, T. J. 1965. Starch in bakery products. Baker's Digest *39*, No. 2, 48–57.

Smith, D. E., and Coffman, J. R. 1960. Analysis of food flavors by gas-liquid chromatography—separation and identification of the neutral components from bread pre-ferment liquid. Anal. Chem. *32*, 1733–1737.

Thomas, B., and Rothe, M. 1957. Participation of acetoin and diacetyl in the aroma of white bread. Ernahrungsforsch *2*, 751–757.

Thomas, B., and Rothe, M. 1960. Recent studies on bread flavor. Baker's Digest *34*, No. 4, 50–57.

Visser'T Hooft, F., and De Leeuw, F. J. G. 1935. The occurrence of acetyl methyl carbinol in bread and its relation to bread flavor. Cereal Chem. *12*, 213–229.

Wick, E. L., De Figueiredo, M., and Wallace, D. H. 1964. The volatile components of white bread prepared by a pre-ferment method. Cereal Chem. *41*, 300–315.

Wiseblatt, L. 1956. Identities of substances which contribute to the flavor of bread. 41st Annual Meeting American Assoc. Cereal Chemists. Abstract No. 64.

Wiseblatt, L. 1957. The flavor of bread. Northwest Miller Milling Production Section *258*, No. 11, 1A–16A.

Wiseblatt, L. 1960A. Some aromatic compounds present in oven gases. Cereal Chem. *37*, 728–733.

Wiseblatt, L. 1960B. The volatile organic acids found in dough, oven gases, and bread. Cereal Chem. *37*, 734–739.

Wiseblatt, L. 1961A. Bread flavor research. Baker's Digest *35*, No. 5, 60–63.

Wiseblatt, L. 1961B. Flavor research in bread baking field. Cereal Sci. Today *6*, 298–300.

Wiseblatt, L., and Kohn, F. E. 1960. Some volatile aromatic compounds in fresh bread. Cereal Chem. *37*, 55–66.

Wiseblatt, L., and Zoumut, H. F. 1963. Isolation, origin, and synthesis of bread flavor constituent. Cereal Chem. *40*, 162–169.

CHAPTER 9

A. Dinsmoor Webb

Wine Flavor:
Volatile Aroma Compounds of Wines

INTRODUCTION

The word "flavor" is not precisely defined, commonly being used to indicate either taste as perceived in the mouth or aromas perceived by the sense of smell. While it might be advantageous, with respect to certain foods, to consider flavor as primarily the result of taste *or* odor, certainly in the case of wine, it seems more logical to consider flavor as the complex impression created by both the sensations of taste and odor. Thus, while we may say that we find the flavor of a certain wine attractive, probably what we really mean is that our nose tells us that it smells good, and, on drinking, our taste tells us that there is a harmonious balance of acidity, saltiness, sweetness, and bitterness. In addition, to the person who is accustomed to having wine with his food, there will be some subconscious evaluation of the viscosity of the wine and an assessment of the astringency or puckery character of the wine. Viscosity is probably assessed by noting the way wine behaves when it is swished about in the mouth, while astringency is perceived as a drawing or drying sensation in the mouth. Although neither of these characteristics of the wine can be considered a taste, each probably would be considered as contributing to the overall flavor.

The question of flavor in wines is further complicated, both for the consumer and the wine maker, in that there are two fundamentally different philosophical approaches to flavor in wines. On the one hand, the large winery producing price competitive wines attempts to determine for each wine type what the maximum number of customers will buy and then to produce wines having these characteristics year after year without regard to variations in composition of the grape raw material. In contrast, other wineries will produce small lots of wine which are made exclusively from a single grape variety grown within a small delimited area in a given year. Here there will be obviously large variations in the flavors of the different wines according to the grape variety, the area of growth, and year of production. Both detailed chemical analyses and skillful sensory analyses are required to maintain constancy in wine flavor in spite of variations in composition of the grape raw materials. In the case of the production of vintage wine lots, laboratory analyses are needed only to assure that the wine meets legal requirements, the overall quality of the wine being critically dependent upon the decisions

203

of a skilled wine taster in the direction of the cellar operations in its vintage. Vintage wines, that is, wines made from fruit grown in a single season in a delimited area and from a single variety are usually produced only from grapes. Other fruit and berry wines normally are designed to have uniform characteristics year after year. In fact, most nongrape fruit and berry wines lose the characteristic smell and taste of the fruit on aging. While this same loss of fruity character also occurs in grape wines, there is a compensating development of bouquet on aging. However, aged bouquet does not develop in all grape wines. It is necessary to start with wine from one of the selected varieties that is capable of yielding this particular character upon aging. A number of the commoner grape varieties, in parallel with the other fruits and berries, yield wines which upon aging simply lose their fruity characteristics and do not develop any compensating bottle or aged bouquet character.

FLAVOR CLASSIFICATION

Perhaps the single characteristic most important in making wines attractive beverages is the complexity of flavors (Singleton and Ough 1962). In parallel with most other foods, wine flavors can be divided into two general classes, those that derive from the raw material and those that are produced by processing operation. However, the enologist or wine chemist differentiates wine flavors more critically (Austerweil 1946). There is a group of flavor materials that is common to the raw fruits and comes through the processing operations unaltered in some of the grape varieties and most of the nongrape fruits and berries that are used for wine production. Thus, for example, wines produced from Muscat or Concord grapes have the characteristic flavor of these particular grapes. Similarly, blackberry wine should taste and smell of the fresh blackberry fruit. A second group of flavor compounds consists of those aroma substances of the raw material which are altered during the fermentation. For example, at the height of fermentation there is an excess of reduced NAD produced by the yeast which escapes from the cells and is available for reduction of aldehydes, acids, and possibly other aroma substances coming from the raw material. A third group of flavors consists of those aroma materials produced by action of the yeast during fermentation from the sugars and other odorless substrates of the starting fruit. The fusel oil alcohols produced by the yeast from the sugars and amino acids of the raw fruit are an example of this type of flavor substance. The fourth group of flavor substances consists of those that result directly from cellar operations. In this class may be listed the materials that are extracted from the oakwood during storage, sulfur dioxide and other sulfur containing compounds derived from sulfur dioxide, acetaldehyde or acetic acid that results from improper storage conditions in which the wine becomes subject to the action of oxygen, and changes in flavor due to removal of certain components through fining operations or filtrations. A fifth group of flavor materials consists of those that are produced during aging. This group may be divided into two sub-categories the first of which would be those compounds produced by aging in large wooden containers, and the second, those compounds produced by the slow aging in glass bottles. Despite many years of study by many different workers, very little is known with certainty about the identity of the materials produced by aging, nor the chemical reactions that occur during aging (Singleton 1962).

The contributions of taste to the overall flavor impression in a wine presumably are limited to those taste sensations of acidity, sweetness, saltiness, and bitterness, supplemented to a certain extent by the chemical sense receptors in the mouth which are sensitive to substances such as sulfur dioxide and the kinesthetic sensors through which the viscosity or density of the wine is assessed. A proper balance of the four basic taste characteristics and the other flavor attributes is essential to palatability and acceptability in wines. While grape juices are known to contain about 250 mg. per liter of glutamic acid, according to Castor (1953) about 95% of this amount is lost during fermentation. The quantity present in the wine, thus, is well below the figure of 0.1 to 0.2% indicated by Nielson and Caul (1965) as appropriate for the flavor enhancing action by monosodium glutamate.

Finer distinctions of the intrinsic quality of wines are made on the basis of the aroma, the characteristics perceived by smelling the wine. Even so, much more is known about the substances responsible for the taste sensation in wines than is known about aroma compounds since these former materials, in general, are present in relatively larger quantities, and analytical methods have existed for some time capable of their quantitative measurements. The odor or aroma components of wines, in contrast, are present in extremely small proportions and, until very recently, there were no analytical methods sensitive enough to detect or measure them. The only method for aroma estimation and, indeed, the standard or reference method still employed was the technique of having a trained enologist carefully smell and taste the sample. Development of gas chromatographic analytical techniques during the recent past has finally given enologists a method sensitive enough to isolate and identify certain of the aroma components of wines. In the case of some substances, the gas chromatograph approaches or may surpass the nose in sensitivity, but for many of the important aroma components of wines the nose is still more sensitive than the gas chromatograph by a very considerable factor. Gas chromatographic technique cannot, of course, determine when a harmonious balance of aroma compounds is present in a wine—thus the use of the gas chromatograph always relies upon the abilities of a skilled wine taster for reference or standardization.

Since odor perceptors in man are so located that they are well protected from access by liquid, any substance to be smelled must have sufficient vapor pressure to assure that at least a few molecules reach the odor sensitive area in the gaseous or vapor state. It is observed, however, that even among compounds with very similar vapor pressures there is a tremendous range in the threshold values for odor perception. This means that the intrinsic odorous character of various chemical molecules differ greatly. For example, there is a big difference in threshold values between the two compounds, ethanol and ethylmercaptan, although there is relatively little difference between the two molecules structurally and in many chemical properties. Similarly, water and hydrogen sulfide have a tremendous difference in threshold values. Indeed, it may be that water has no threshold value at all—being undetectable by the odor sensors since they themselves presumably are bathed in an aqueous medium. Any theory of the mechanism of odor perception naturally must take into account these examples as well as numerous others of equally challenging difficulty (Amerine et al. 1965).

Many analyses of the aroma compounds in fruits, berries, and other food products have been published. Analyses of the aroma components of wines are fewer, although there has been great interest in wine aromas since very early times (Windisch 1906; Amerine and Singleton 1965), Ribéreau-Gayon and Peynaud (1958), Amerine (1954), Amerine and Cruess (1960), and Garoglio (1959) among many others have discussed wine flavors and aromas. Detailed analyses of the aroma materials are available only for wines produced from apples, passion fruit, several grape species and varieties, sake (rice wine), and buffered sugar solutions including bread pre-ferments. Of course, wines have been made from many other fruits and vegetables but analyses of the aromas of these wines remain to be done.

AROMA COMPOUND ISOLATION

Instrumental analyses, as contrasted with human olfactory analyses of wine aroma materials, have always been complicated by the presence of the large amount of water and ethanol in wine. Indeed, analyses of the aroma materials in unfermented food products are simpler than wine aroma analyses because of the lack of the large amount of ethyl alcohol in the former. In general, aroma analyses can be considered to consist of two phases—isolation and identification. It is the isolation phase that requires the greatest amount of skill when aroma materials are to be separated from the large amounts of water and ethanol, present in wine. Normally, low-temperature distillation at reduced pressure is employed first to separate the volatile aroma materials, the ethanol, and a good portion of the water from the nonvolatile dissolved materials of the wine. This reduced pressure distillation can be accomplished either in batch-type equipment or on a continuous basis, depending upon the amount of material being processed (Kepner and Webb 1956). Following the low-pressure distillation, solvent extraction is normally used to separate the aroma materials from the water and the bulk of the ethyl alcohol. The solvent extraction step must always be a compromise in that some of the lower molecular weight organic aroma materials will remain in the aqueous ethanol phase and some of the ethanol will be transferred to the aroma solvent phase. Solvents normally employed for this extraction are hydrocarbons such as isopentane, pentane, or isohexane, halogenated compounds such as methylene chloride, ethyl chloride, methyl bromide, or Freon MS (trichloromonofluromethane). Ether has been employed as a solvent, but it extracts so much of the ethyl alcohol that it is not very satisfactory as a separating solvent. The ether-pentane azeotropic mixture extracts much less ethanol into the organic phase and has been employed satisfactorily as a solvent (Mecke and de Vries 1959). The partition coefficients for the many aroma materials and the several different solvents are not known, and thus the choice of the solvent is usually dictated on the basis of empirical trials. Factors such as solvent boiling point, flammability, availability in pure form at reasonable costs, and stability during the extracting operations are also very important. While there is no ideal solvent for all applications, a suitable solvent for each extraction problem can usually be selected from among those mentioned.

Having selected a solvent, the next point of consideration is the type of extractor to be used. Ideally, the equipment should provide for complete and rapid extraction of the aroma materials from the aqueous ethanol into the organic phase without exposing the aroma materials to heat and the action of the oxygen in air. In addition, it may be desirable to protect the extract from light and to take into consideration the possible difficulty of emulsion formation. Since a distillation step is required to separate the extracting solvent from the concentrated aroma fraction, a low boiling extracting solvent is desirable to avoid heat damage to the extracted aroma. Similarly, design of the apparatus should minimize the quantity of extracting solvent required. A multi-stage continuous system utilizing recovered solvent from the stripping section as feed to the first stage of the extractor is desirable. The smaller the drops of the extracting solvent are as they are dispersed in the aqueous phase, the more rapid will be the extraction. A practical limit is reached, however, as with smaller and smaller drops one approaches the state of an emulsion which will not mechanically separate. As the composition of the dilute aqueous ethanol solution containing the aroma materials will vary from one case to another, and as it may be desirable to use different extracting solvents, the extractor itself should be designed mechanically so that the operating parameters may be varied over rather wide ranges to suit the condition of the particular extraction problem.

The bulk of the extracting solvent is separated from the aroma component mixture by distillation. In the normal case, where not too much attention is being paid to the low boiling aroma materials, the solvent will be removed through a simple distillation column of approximately five to ten theoretical plates efficiency. At intervals, especially toward the end of the concentrating step, aliquots of the separated solvent should be examined gas chromatographically to insure that no aroma materials are being lost azeotropically. At this point it is not desirable to remove all of the solvent but simply to reduce the bulk of the concentrated essence to a volume that can be conveniently handled in the laboratory. There is no point in removing all of the solvent or in trying rigorously to dry the essence because acids must be extracted from the concentrated essence before it can be stored or before it can be further processed.

Acids and phenols can be extracted from the concentrated essence by means of dilute potassium hydroxide solutions at 0°C. An exhaustive back extraction of the basic solution is necessary to return water soluble nonacidic materials to the main essence fraction. Traces of alcohols which cannot be back extracted can be eliminated by taking the basic extract nearly to dryness in a rotary film evaporator at very low pressure. The free acids can be separated from the phenols by a technique involving acidification of the basic extract and extraction into ether followed by a sodium bicarbonate extraction of this organic acid and phenol-containing solution. Examination by gas chromatography of the various fractions thus separated will show that the functional group separations are not perfect. In other words, there will be traces of the free acids and phenols left in the neutral fraction, traces of neutral compounds in the acid and phenol fractions, and both the acids and phenols will be mutually contaminated to a minor degree. The neutral fractions, after being dried over magnesium sulfate, can be further stripped of solvents and either analyzed gas chromatographically or stored over a drying agent, under nitrogen, at low temperature, and in the dark. Similarly the separated acids and phenols can be dried, concentrated, and analyzed immediately or stored for future analysis.

The neutral essence concentrate obtained from approximately ten gal. of wine or 100 lb. of other fruit will usually amount to something between 1 and 5 gm. The bulk of this essence concentrate is very likely to be residual solvent, ethanol, ethyl acetate, and possibly acetaldehyde—the minor portion remaining being the higher boiling essence components of primary interest. The analytical techniques necessary for the identification of the higher boiling, more interesting, components of the mixture must, of necessity, be very sensitive. The period since the last war has fortunately seen the development of many very sensitive microchemical techniques, and, perhaps of more importance, the development of the techniques of gas-liquid chromatography. Application of these sensitive techniques has permitted identification of a wide range of aroma components in wines.

AROMA COMPOUND ANALYSIS BY GAS CHROMATOGRAPHY

The techniques for identifying traces of aroma materials by gas chromatography are reviewed in detail in Chapter 7 by Teranishi. While some early workers in the field of gas chromatography reported identification of an unknown on the basis of coincidence of its retention time with a known material on a single column at one temperature, it is generally recognized today that the identification must remain tentative even though there is coincidence of retention times for the unknown and known materials on 3 or 4 columns of distinctly different absorption characteristics. Positive identification of the unknown material depends upon further confirmatory evidence such as mass spectrometric analysis, infrared spectrometric analysis, nuclear magnetic resonance analysis, combustion analysis, or the preparation of derivatives and determination of melting points and mixed melting points. The coupling of a time-of-flight mass spectrometer to a gas chromatograph provides much more information than the simple gas chromatographic analysis. Similarly, a fast-scan infrared instrument has been recently developed which should permit determination of the infrared spectra of individual peaks as they are eluted from the gas chromatographic columns (Beckman Instruments 1965). Presumably this type of instrument would be operated with a split in the column effluent line so that eluted samples would arrive at both the gas chromatograph detector and the infrared cell at the same time. Preparative scale gas chromatographs utilizing columns of larger diameter and lengths of 20 to 50 ft. are of great value in obtaining 0.1 to 1.0-ml. samples of highly purified components from aroma mixtures. Samples of this size not only permit positive identification by the techniques mentioned above but also provide enough sample, in many cases, to permit sensory analyses (Wilkins Instrument and Research 1965).

WINE AROMAS—COMPOSITION

Volatile Acids and Amides

The volatile acids and amides that have been identified in wine aromas are listed in Table 21. Detailed volatile acid studies have been made on

TABLE 21

VOLATILE ACIDS AND AMIDES OF WINE AROMA[1]

Compound	Apple	Caber-net	Ries-ling	Cham-pagne	Sake	Sherry	Sugar
Formic	1	2	2	3		6, 7	10
Acetic	1	2	2	3		6, 7	9, 10
Propionic	1	2	2	3		6	10
Butyric	1	2				6, 7	10
Isobutyric	1	2	2	3		6, 7	10
Valeric	1					7	10
Isovaleric	1	2	2	3		7	10
2-Methylbutyric							
Caproic	1	2	2	3		7	10
Isocaproic							10
Enanthic	1					7	10
Caprylic	1	2	2	3		7	10
Pelargonic						7	10
Capric		2					10
Lauric							10
Myristic							10
Palmitic							10
Crotonic							10
Ferulic					4		
Vanillic					4		
p-Hydroxycinnamic					5		
Ethyl acid succinate						7	
Ethyl acid tartrate						32	
Ethyl acid malate						32	
N-(2-phenethyl)-acetamide						8	
N-Isoamylacetamide						8	

[1] The numbers in the tables indicate the sources of the data.　(1) Sugisawa, Matthews, and MacGregor 1962; (2) Pisarnitskii 1964;　(3) Rodopulo and Pisarnitskii 1963;　(4) Yamamoto, Sasaki, and Saruno 1961;　(5) Yamamoto 1961D;　(6) Diemair and Schams 1960;　(7) Webb, Kepner, and Galetto 1964A;　(8) Webb, Kepner, and Galetto 1965A;　(9) Wick, de Figueiredo, and Wallace 1964;　(10) Hunter, Ng, and Pence 1961;　(32) Webb, Kepner, and Maggiora 1965.

eight different wine samples; one each of apple, Cabernet Sauvignon grape, champagne, sake, two different samples of sherry, and two different fermented buffered sugar solutions. The even carbon number, saturated, straight chain acids, acetic, butyric, caproic, and caprylic are found to be the most common acids in these volatile aroma materials. Acetic acid, of course, is a well-known minor by-product of fermentation. It is also the product of air oxidation of ethanol or acetaldehyde in wines which are improperly stored under conditions permitting aeration. Acetic acid also is produced by several of the bacteria which occasionally cause trouble in wines. The even carbon numbered acids from butyric through palmitic probably result from the normal fatty acid synthetic processes either in the raw materials or in the yeast which are conducting the fermentation. In either case this process undoubtedly involves an initial acetyl-coenzyme-A reaction with bicarbonate and transfer to the sulfhydryl group of a soluble multienzyme system. Successive condensations of this malonyl enzyme complex with either acetyl-coenzyme-A or even carbon number acyl soluble enzyme complexes would yield enzyme bound products increased by multiples of two carbon units. The carboxyl group of the malonyl enzyme complex is lost as carbon dioxide in each successive condensation. The oxo group produced by the condensation is reduced to an alcohol, the secondary alcohol is dehydrated, and the olefin thus produced is further reduced to the saturated hydrocarbon skeleton. All of these reactions occur while the acid is still bound to the sulfhydryl group of the soluble enzyme. In many systems, the acid is not detached from the enzymes surface until it reaches a carbon number of 16 or 18 (Brady 1963; Brodie et al. 1963). The presence of the large amounts of butyrate, caproate, and caprylate in fermented beverage systems suggest that either the longer chain saturated acids initially produced are degraded or that there is some leakage from the enzyme bound systems before the acids reach the 16 to 18 carbon stage. Indeed, the detection of crotonic acid in one of the fermented buffered sugar solutions suggests that unsaturated acids escape from the enzyme surface and thus make it more plausible that some of the oxo, hydroxy, and shorter chain saturated fatty acids likewise do so.

The presence of isobutyric, isovaleric, and isocaproic acids among the volatiles isolated from wines suggests that, in addition to the head to tail condensation of acetyl-coenzyme-A involved in the straight chain fatty acid syntheses, there may be some head to head condensation with subsequent loss of CO_2 resulting in branched chain carbon skeletons. Such condensations are akin to those involved in the production of mevalonic acid. Perhaps equally probable, however, is an oxidation rather than a reduction of the isobutanal and isopentanal intermediates involved in the biosynthesis of the fusel oil alcohols and in the amino acid metabolism of yeasts. The identification of 2-methylbutyric acid lends additional weight to this hypothesis. The four common alcohol components of the fusel oil complex are propanol, isobutanol, isopentanol, and 2-methylbutanol. Isohexyl alcohol and isocaproic acid are not recognized as regular components in the fusel oil metabolic pathway (Webb and Ingraham 1963).

The metabolic pathways accounting for the presence of the saturated straight chain odd carbon numbered acids in relatively small amounts in comparison with the even carbon numbered acids is not readily apparent.

Propionic acid, as mentioned above, could arise from oxidation of propanal, but the formic, enanthic, and pelargonic acids are produced by pathways at present not clear.

Ferulic, vanillic, and hydroxycinnamic acids identified in the samples of sake (rice wine) probably are produced from glucose through the shikimic acid pathway.

Although Ribéreau-Gayon and Peynaud (1958) have indicated that there must be some acid esters among the total ester components of wines, it is only recently that the presence of ethyl acid succinate has been definitely demonstrated (Webb et al. 1964A). It is not known whether the ethyl acid succinate results from chemical esterification of the succinic acid produced as a by-product of normal alcoholic fermentation or whether the acid ester is produced directly as a minor component by the yeast. Among the volatile acids present in wines, however, ethyl acid succinate is a major component. Of course, ethyl acid succinate is too high boiling and too water soluble to be appreciably steam distilled with the acetic and lactic acids that make up the commonly accepted "volatile acids" of fermented beverage analyses. Ethyl acid tartrate and at least one of the isomers of ethyl acid malate have been identified in a sample of flor sherry (Webb et al. 1965B). It is thought quite likely that the acid esters of the other trace acids of grapes and fruits will be found as analytical techniques improve. Thus we may look forward to identification of traces of the several isomers of mono and diethyl acid citrates, certain of the isomers of ethyl acid citramalate, ethyl acid glutarate, and very probably others. It is also quite probable that the propyl, isobutyl, iso, and active amyl acid esters of at least some of these di and tri basic acids will be identified in fermented beverages.

Two N-substituted amides have recently been identified in a submerged culture sherry. One of these compounds is N-(2-phenethyl)-acetamide, while the second is the simpler N-isoamylacetamide (Webb et al. 1965A). The amides, asparagine, and glutamine have been recognized as plant constituents for some time. The more recent literature reports increasing numbers of examples of N-substituted asparagine and glutamine. Sakato (1950) and Cartwright et al. (1954) find that N-ethyl glutamine (theanine) constitutes 1 to 2% of the total dry matter of tea leaves and that it is the principal component of the amino acid fraction in both fermented and unfermented tea. Casimir et al. (1960) finds in large quantities the same material, N-ethylglutamine, in the mushroom Xerocomus badius. Mushrooms of the genus, Agaricus, and in particular, Agaricus hortensis, according to Jadot et al. (1960) contain significant amounts of N-(p-hydroxyphenyl)glutamine. N-ethyl-L-asparagine was identified by Gray and Fowden (1961) in the squirting cucumber

Ecballium elaterium and also in *Bryonia diocia.* It is likely that further substituted amides will be identified in fermented beverages as investigations continue. Although the metabolic pathways involved in the production of these substituted amides in wines is unknown, the fact that the two substituting groups, 2-phenethyl and isoamyl, are present in relatively high concentrations in fermented beverage systems suggests that the substitution may occur during or after the fermentation.

Datunashvili (1963) described a defect in champagne type wines which he called "over oxidation." This flavor is ascribed to deamination of the amino acids present in the wine, and subsequent reaction of the ammonia with ethyl acetate in the wine to yield acetamide. The peculiar defective flavor is ascribed to the presence of acetamide. Although Datunashvili did not actually isolate and identify any acetamide, it is of considerable interest that he describes the flavor resulting from supposed presence of acetamide as "over oxidation." The interesting coincidence lies in the fact that substituted amides have been first positively identified in wines in a type that is produced by a technique involving generous aeration, a procedure that might be presumed to lead to over oxidation. Irregardless of whether acetamide itself was ever identified as a constituent of wine aromas, it seems unlikely that it would be produced by reaction of ammonia and ethyl acetate in a wine medium. The relatively very low concentrations of ethyl acetate and ammonia, the relatively high concentration of ethyl alcohol, and the low pH are all unfavorable for the production and high concentration of acetamide.

Volatile Carbonyls and Acetals

The volatile carbonyls and acetals that have been identified in wine aromas are listed in Table 22. Including the fermented buffered sugar solutions and sake there are 11 different wine types in which carbonyl and acetal analyses have been made. As might be expected, acetaldehyde has been identified in 9 of the 11 different wine samples. Acetaldehyde, of course, is the next to the last intermediate in the transformation of glucose to ethanol by the yeast enzymes. Acetaldehyde, in addition, is the first oxidation product of ethanol when wines are improperly stored so that they are subject to the action of atmospheric oxygen. Propionaldehyde, isobutyraldehyde, and isovaleraldehyde are the aldehydes corresponding to three of the principal alcohols in the fusel oil mixture and these aldehydes represent the next to the last intermediate in the formation of these fusel oils.

2-Hexenal is a frequent component of plant materials. According to Winter and Sundt (1962), however, 2-hexenal may be an artifact resulting from isomerization of 3-hexenal, and this aldehyde can be ob-

TABLE 22

VOLATILE CARBONYLS AND ACETALS OF WINE AROMAS[1]

Compound	Apple	Cabernet Sauvignon	Grape	Müller-Thurgau	Passion Fruit	Rotundifolia	Sake	Sherry	Sylvaner	Sugar	Zinfandel
Formaldehyde										32	
Ethanal	11		13	14	15	16		6, 18, 7		21, 32	
Propanal										20	
Butanal										32	
Isobutanal						16			19	32	
Pentanal										32	
Isopentanal									19	32	
2-Methylbutanal										32	
Hexanal						16			19	20, 22	
2-Hexenal						16					
Vanillin							17				
Cinnamaldehyde				14			17		19		
Benzaldehyde				14			17				
p-Hydroxybenzaldehyde							17				
Phenylacetaldehyde							17				
Furfural								7			
Acetone	11			14				6	19	9	
2-Butanone					15	16				21, 32	
2,3-Butandione					15	16				32	23
1,1-Diethoxyethane		12	13		15	16	7			21	23

[1] The numbers in the tables indicate the sources of the data. (6) Diemair and Schams 1960; (7) Webb, Kepner, and Galetto 1964A; (9) Wick, de Figueiredo, and Wallace, 1964; (11) Matthews, Sugisawa, and MacGregor, 1962; (12) Webb, Ribéreau-Gayon, and Boidron 1964C; (13) Lipis and Mamakova 1963; (14) Hennig and Villforth 1942; (15) Muller, Kepner, and Webb 1964; (16) Kepner and Webb 1956; (17) Yamamoto 1961C; (18) Webb and Kepner 1962; (19) Mecke, Schindler and de Vries, 1960; (20) Linko, Miller, and Johnson 1962; (21) Smith and Coffman 1960; (22) Suomalainen and Nykänen 1964; (23) Haagen-Smit and Hirosawa 1950; (32) Miller, Johnson, and Robinson 1961.

tained by oxidation from the cis-3-hexenol which is frequently present in aroma mixtures. How these materials are related to the other metabolic pathways in plant systems or in yeasts is not known for certain. However, it may be that 2-hexenal and 3-hexenol arise through successive reductions of the terminal carboxylic acid function of an unsaturated six carbon acid which escapes from the enzyme surface during the course of normal saturated fatty acid build-up.

Hexanal, the aldehyde corresponding to n-hexyl alcohol, is, like the alcohol, found widely distributed in fruits, berries, and wines. While neither of these compounds seems to be involved in fusel oil metabolic pathways, it is also true that other modes of formation and use remain obscure.

The five compounds containing the alkyl benzene carbon skeleton, vanillin, cinnamaldehyde, benzaldehyde, p-hydroxybenzaldehyde, and phenylacetaldehyde were all identified in the rice wine, sake. Vanillin and cinnamaldehyde, in addition, were identified in the sample of Müller-Thurgau wine. Each of these compounds has an intense aroma, and, even though they are present in very small concentrations in the wines, they are probably of significance in adding to the flavor complex. Although definite evidence is not available, it seems likely that these compounds arise through the shikimic acid pathway from glucose. Rather extensive oxidations, reductions, and substitutions are required to account for all of the five components, however. The three ketones identified, acetone, 2-butanone, and 2,3-butanedione are common components in fermented beverages. Acetone probably arises through decarboxylation of acetoacetic acid, while 2-butanone could result from reduction of the carboxylate group of the same compound. 2,3-Butanedione represents the highest oxidation state of the series of three compounds in which 2-oxo-3-hydroxy-butane and 2,3-butanediol represent the successively more reduced members. The ketones have only mild aromas, with the exception of the butanedione, which in very small concentrations has a buttery flavor, but the presence of which in beer is considered a defect.

Diethylacetal, the compound resulting from reaction of two molecules of ethanol and one molecule of acetaldehyde, was found in five of the wine samples investigated. This acetal has a very definite aroma, and has been suggested as being a critical component in the flavor of flor sherry by Russian workers (Sisakian et al. 1950). Recently, evidence has been secured for the presence of a number of mixed acetals in a sample of flor sherry (Galetto et al. 1965). A number of simpler mixed acetals has been reported present in strawberry essence (Teranishi et al. 1963). It seems highly likely that further acetals will be identified in wine aromas as investigations continue.

TABLE 23

VOLATILE ALCOHOLS OF WINE AROMAS[1]

Alcohol	Apple	Cabernet Sauvignon	Champagne	Grape	Passion Fruit	Riesling	Rotundifolia	Sake	Sherry	Sylvaner	Sugar	Zinfandel
Methanol		2			15	2	16		6			23
Ethanol		24, 12, 2			15	2	16		6		9, 21, 22	
Propanol		24, 12, 2	3, 25	27, 13					6, 7		9, 21	
2-Propanol	11		3, 25	13						19		
Butanol	11	12	3, 25	27, 13								
Isobutanol	11	24, 12, 2	3, 25	27, 13	15	2	16		18, 7	19	9, 21, 22	
2-Butanol				13								
Amyl	11	24, 12, 2	3, 25						6			
Isoamyl	11	24, 12, 2	3, 25	27, 13	15	2	16		18, 7	19	9, 21, 22	23
2-Methylbutyl		24, 12		27, 13	15				18, 7			23
Hexyl	11	24, 12	25		15		16		18, 7			
2-Phenethyl		24, 12	25	26, 27	15	2	16	29	18, 7		21, 22	
Heptyl			25									
Octyl									7			
Acetoin											9, 21	
(—) 2,3-Butanediol											21	
meso-2,3-Butandiol											21	

[1] The numbers in the tables indicate the sources of the data. (2) Pisarnitskii 1964; (3) Rodopulo and Pisarnitskii 1963; (6) Diemair and Schams 1960; (7) Webb, Kepner, and Galetto 1964A; (9) Wick, de Figueiredo, and Wallace 1964; (11) Matthews, Sugisawa, and MacGregor 1962; (12) Webb, Ribéreau-Gayon, and Boidron 1964B; (13) Lipis and Mamokova 1963; (15) Müller, Kepner, and Webb 1964; (16) Kepner and Webb 1956; (18) Webb and Kepner 1962; (19) Mecke, Schindler, and de Vries 1960; (21) Smith and Coffman 1960; (22) Suomalainen and Nykänen 1964; (23) Haagen-Smit and Hirosawa 1950; (24) Webb, Ribéreau-Gayon, and Boidron 1963; (25) Rodopulo and Egorov 1964; (26) Ayräpaa 1962; (27) Sihto, Nykänen, and Suomalainen 1962; (29) Yamamoto, 1961A.

Volatile Alcohols

Table 23 lists the volatile alcohols which have been identified in the eighteen samples of eleven different types of wines investigated. Ethanol (without which wine is not wine) represents, of course, one of the two principal products of the action of the yeast on hexose sugars. Carbon dioxide, the second principal product, while of great importance in the closely related panary fermentation, is of relatively little value to the enologist, and indeed, is sometimes considered a problem in fermentation cellars. n-Propyl, isobutyl, isoamyl, and active amyl alcohols, as mentioned previously, are the principal components of the fusel oil or "higher alcohol" mixture obtained as a by-product during the distillation of wines to make brandies. These alcohols are produced during the main alcoholic fermentation of the wine, and apparently represent waste or by-product materials of the yeast's synthesis and metabolism of amino acids. It is quite clear today that Ehrlich's proposal that all fusel oil alcohols resulted directly from the breakdown of the corresponding amino acid is only a portion of the picture, and that in fact, most of the carbon skeleton of these alcohols comes from the hexose sugars being fermented. n-Butyl and n-amyl alcohols, according to Ingraham et al. (1961), can also be considered part of the fusel oil or higher alcohol mixture and to be produced by pathways closely related to those by which the main components of the mixture are produced. Valaize (1951) has attempted to correlate wine quality, through intensity of bouquet, with the concentration of amino acids in the must.

n-Hexyl alcohol was found in many of the wines examined in relatively high concentrations. It does not seem to be a normal component of the fusel oil mixture (Ingraham et al. 1961), and, while it is attractive to speculate that the relatively large amounts of hexanol would result from reduction of caproic acid during fermentation, hexanol may come, principally, from the raw material without alteration during the fermentation.

Analyses of unfermented grapes and other fruit aroma materials have shown the presence of n-hexyl alcohol, as well as several other alcohols. Indeed, in nearly every case, n-propyl, isobutyl, and isoamyl alcohols have been identified. Active amyl alcohol has not been identified so frequently, perhaps because of the difficulties of separating it from isoamyl alcohol. Thus, while it is recognized that the principal amount of the fusel oil alcohols is produced during alcoholic fermentation, a portion at least, exists in the raw material. It is not known what role these alcohols play in fruits and berries, but it may be that they are by-products of amino acid metabolism here just as they are in fermenting yeasts. How n-hexyl alcohol is involved metabolically in fruits remains unknown.

TABLE 24

VOLATILE ESTERS OF WINE AROMAS[1]

Ester	Apple	Cabernet Sauvignon	Champagne	Grape	Passion Fruit	Rotundifolia	Sake	Sherry	Sylvaner	Sugar	Zinfandel
Methyl formate								6			
Methyl acetate									19	21	
Ethyl formate				13				6	19	9, 22	23
Ethyl acetate	11	24, 12	25	28	15	16		6, 18, 7	19		
Ethyl propionate			3, 25	28					19		
Ethyl isobutyrate			25	28				18, 7			
Ethyl valerate			25		15				19		
Ethyl isovalerate		12	25	28	15		29	18, 7	19	22	
Ethyl caproate			3, 25		15				19	22	
Ethyl heptanoate		12			15		31	18, 7	19	22	
Ethyl caprylate	11		3, 25						19	22	
Ethyl pelargonate										22	
Ethyl caprate		12			15			7		22	
Ethyl undecanoate					15					22	
Ethyl laurate									19	22	
Ethyl myristate									19	22	
Ethyl palmitate										22	
Ethyl palmitoleate										22	
Ethyl stearate										22	
Ethyl linoleate		24, 12						18, 7		21	
Ethyl lactate				27							
Ethyl pyruvate							29				
Ethyl α-ketobutyrate							30				
Ethyl α-ketoisovalerate							30				
Ethyl α-hydroxyisocaproate							29				
Ethyl α-ketoisocaproate							30				

Compound							
Ethyl cinnamate					18, 7		
Diethyl succinate	24, 12				18		
Diethyl malate	11						
Propyl propionate	11						
1,3-Propandiol-monoacetate						19	21
Butyl acetate	11						
Butyl caproate	11						
Isobutyl acetate	11				7		
Isobutyl propionate	11						
Isobutyl isobutyrate				15			
Isobutyl caproate		25			18		21
Isobutyl caprylate					18, 7		22
γ-Butyrolactone	24, 12			15	7		
Isoamyl acetate	12		27		18, 7		
Isoamyl butyrate	11				18, 7		
Isoamyl isovalerate	11	3, 25			18		
Isoamyl caproate	12				18, 7		22
Isoamyl caprylate	12				18, 7		22
Isoamyl caprate							22
Isoamyl lactate	24, 12				7		
act.-Amyl lactate	24				18, 7		
Hexyl acetate	12				7		
Hexyl isobutyrate					7		
Hexyl caproate							
Hexyl caprylate	12						
2-Phenethyl acetate	12				18, 7		
2-Phenethyl caproate	12				18		

The numbers in the tables indicate the sources of the data. (3) Rodopulo and Pisarnitskii 1963; (6) Diemair and Schams 1960; (7) Webb, Kepner, and Galetto 1964A; (9) Wick, de Figueiredo, and Wallace 1964; (11) Matthews, Sugisawa, and MacGregor 1962; (12) Webb, Ribéreau-Gayon, and Boidron 1964B; (13) Lipis and Mamakova 1963; (15) Müller, Kepner, and Webb 1964; (16) Kepner and Webb 1964; (18) Webb and Kepner 1962; (19) Mecke, Schindler, and de Vries 1960; (21) Smith and Coffman 1960; (22) Suomalainen and Nykänen 1964; (23) Haagen-Smit and Hirosawa 1950; (24) Webb, Ribéreau-Gayon, and Boidron 1963; (25) Rodopulo and Egorov 1964; (27) Sihto, Nykänen, and Suomalainen 1962; (28) Bayer and Bässler 1961; (29) Yamamoto 1961A; (30) Yamamoto 1961B; (31) Yamamoto 1961E.

Similarly, ethyl alcohol and 2-phenethyl alcohol, while known to be produced principally by action of fermenting yeasts, are also well recognized as normal constituents of unfermented ripe grapes (Kepner and Webb 1956). It has been demonstrated that ethyl alcohol is not produced by the Ehrlich mechanism from alanine during fermentation (Yamada et al. 1962), but the possibility remains that this pathway could be involved in the fruit. 2-Phenethyl alcohol, first identified in Rotundifolia grapes by Kepner and Webb (1956), has been more recently shown to be a common by-product of alcoholic fermentation (Webb and Ingraham 1963). It seems reasonable to assume that this alcohol is related to the metabolism of phenylalanine both in the fruit and during fermentation.

Methyl alcohol is found in small amounts in sound ripe fruits (Webb and Kepner 1957) and also in wines (Kepner and Webb 1956). How this alcohol is formed is not known with certainty, but two possibilities suggest themselves. Deamination, decarboxylation, and reduction of glycine would yield methyl alcohol, but this reaction has not been demonstrated to occur. In certain animal systems methionine has been shown to be the donor of methyl groups for O-methylation of several phenols (Senoh et al. 1959). It seems likely that the methyl alcohol observed in wines results from hydrolysis of portions of O-methylated tannins, pigments, and pectin materials.

Volatile Esters

The volatile esters which have been identified in wines are listed in Table 24. Sixteen individual samples of 11 different wine types have been analyzed. Of the esters positively identified, approximately half are ethyl esters which suggests that they are formed during or shortly after the alcoholic fermentation when ethyl alcohol is being produced or is present in higher concentrations. n-Propyl, isobutyl, isoamyl, active amyl, hexyl, and 2-phenethyl alcohols are the next most common alcohol portions of the esters identified. Here again, one notes that the alcohols are those common to fermentation systems. All of the straight chain saturated acids from formate through laurate are represented among the acid portion of the esters. In addition myristic, palmitic, and stearic acids are present as esters. A number of unsaturated, hydroxy, and oxo acids also have been identified as ester components. Sake has been shown to contain the ethyl esters of phenylacetic, salicylic, and cinnamic acids.

Nordström (1964) has studied the production of esters during fermentation in considerable detail. He finds that ester formation is dependent upon yeast metabolic activity, and that it proceeds through reaction of an acyl-CoA (activated acid) with alcohols of the medium. Acetyl-

CoA is found to come from pyruvate, but the other oxo acids do not give rise to the corresponding acyl-CoA product. Immediately after fermentation, certain ester concentrations can greatly exceed the equilibrium value. In these cases, aging would result in ester hydrolysis rather than the traditionally postulated ester formation.

Ribéreau-Gayon and Peynaud (1958) indicate that, generally in wines, esters are produced in small amounts by the yeasts and bacteria, and subsequent to the fermentation, by simple chemical esterification. As a result of detailed studies, they concluded that wines very seldom, if ever, contain the quantities of esters that could exist at equilibrium if given the observed alcohol, acid, and proper pH.

Gas chromatographic analysis of fruit and berry aroma fractions have established that there are a very large number of esters in these materials. Passion fruit, for example, contains relatively large concentrations of hexyl butyrate and hexyl caproate (Hiu and Scheuer 1961), pears contain methyl and ethyl decadienoates (Heinz *et al.* 1964), and Concord grapes owe their characteristic flavor to the presence of methyl anthranilate (Power and Chesnut 1921). The biosynthesis of these esters in the various fruits is not the subject of this review, but it is germane to consider what changes might occur during fermentation and aging of the wines. The most likely alteration would seem to be a trans-esterification converting nonethyl esters to ethyl esters. The relatively high concentration of ethyl alcohol naturally favors such reactions, but the concentration of hydrogen ions to catalyze the interesterification at the pH's of wines is very low. The reactions, therefore, would be expected to be quite slow.

Navara (1958) investigated a number of different grape varieties during the course of fermentation and aging in attempts to correlate bouquet with ester content. Using the technique of converting the esters to the hydroxamic acid-ferric iron complexes to facilitate their detection, the esters were separated by paper chromatography. Significant differences among wines were found although none of the esters were identified. Two possibilities exist with this chromatographic technique, the esters themselves may be chromatographed and after the separation on the paper is accomplished, the paper can be sprayed with the reagents to produce the ferric-hydroxamic colored complexes. Here, the esters would be the species separated chromatographically. Alternatively, the paper can be impregnated with the reagents and the hydroxamic acids themselves chromatographed, in which case it would be the acid moieties of the esters that would be separated.

In the older literature concerning wine aroma and bouquet, esters are accorded a very important place, it being held that their slow development through oxidation of alcohol to acid and subsequent esterification was, in large part, the source of bouquet. Ribéreau-Gayon and Peynaud more recently hold, however, that the importance of esters in bouquet and aroma has been exaggerated, and that bouquet development, in particular, is related to reduction processes rather than oxidations. The most recent findings by gas chromatographic techniques are interesting in that they demonstrate the presence of many more esters than had been expected by earlier researchers. It is still impossible, however, to evaluate the importance of esters in aroma and bouquet without knowing the sensory threshold values for the various individual esters and the quantities of each present in the various wines. It may be that certain ones of the esters present only in trace quantities have such strong intrinsic odors that they are significant in the overall aroma and bouquet.

WINE AROMA AND BOUQUET: CONCLUSIONS

Gas chromatographic techniques have given the analytical chemist the means of isolating and identifying hundreds of volatile compounds in wines. Where a thermal conductivity detector is employed and a keen nosed analyst sniffs at the exit line, some idea of the aroma qualities of the separated components may be obtained. The fact remains, however, that for the many new substances identified the enologist has either very little or no idea as to their importance in the overall aroma and bouquet of the wine. The problem of trying to determine the threshold and minimum detectable difference values for each of some hundred volatile substances in model wines and using statistically controlled tasting panels is staggering. When one considers that there are probably sensory interactions among the various substances, and that detection of these interactions requires panel testing of the many substances in combinations and permutation, the problem assumes impossible dimensions.

Because of the slowness of panel testing methods, improvements in wine aroma and bouquet will be made on the basis of empirical or semi-empirical experimentation for some time, at least. Components isolated from the aroma mixture of a wine and having interesting aroma notes might be added to similar wines to enhance or improve the overall aroma. Similarly more neutral flavored wines might be significantly improved by the addition of a mixture of aroma components. The recent modification of Federal regulations (U.S. Treasury Decision 1964) concerning wines to permit these or similar operations opens the door to a whole new spectrum of wine flavors.

DISCUSSION

E. L. Pippen.—I would like to ask you if you found any significant relationship between the types of compounds identified and the grape or type of wine?

A. D. Webb.—Actually, back in the early days, Professor Kepner and I thought we had identified the key flavor material in the *Rotundifolia* grape. I believe, this was work done in 1954 and we identified 2-phenethyl alcohol in these grapes. As you all know, 2-phenethyl alcohol is in everything now, so I have to hedge the question by saying that when we do examine any wine type or grape variety, we do find new compounds. This simply may be the result of improved techniques rather than the fact that they are exclusive to that particular wine. Philosophically, since the wines are different and can be distinguished from one another by trained tasters, there has to be differences, and we have to find them. We may have to work at more sensitive levels—1000 or 10,000 or even 1,000,000 times more sensitive than we are, in order to find these differences.

E. A. Day.—I would like to extend that question. Could not some of these differences be essentially quantitative rather than qualitative?

A. D. Webb.—I imagine that they probably are, but at present, we do not know. I think Professor Kepner agrees with me that our role in this problem is simply to isolate, identify, and catalog. If we live long enough, we will get around to the place where we have a large trained taste panel and a source of these compounds in absolutely pure state so that we are tasting the material and not some trace impurity. Then maybe we will get at the quantitative aspects and the key components—the other half of this problem.

D. D. Bills.—Is it possible that esters other than esters of acetic acid may be formed in excess of their equilibrium concentration during the fermentation by some biosynthetic means? There are reports in the literature that some fungi and microorganisms are able to form esters in relatively high concentration. Do you have an insight into this?

A. D. Webb.—Yes, Nordström's work did not restrict this ester formation to acetate esters. He simply demonstrated that you had to have an acyl coenzyme A complex before you got the reaction with the alcohol. This could take place with any acid radical attached to the coenzyme A.

BIBLIOGRAPHY

AMERINE, M. A. 1954. Composition of wines. I. Organic Constituents. *In* Advances in Food Research 5, 353–510. Academic Press, New York.

AMERINE, M. A., and CRUESS, W. V. 1960. Technology of Wine Making. Avi Publishing Co., Westport, Conn.

AMERINE, M. A., and SINGLETON, V. L. 1965. Wine—An Introduction for Americans. University of California Press, Berkeley, Los Angeles.

AMERINE, M. A., PANGBORN, R. M., and ROESSLER, E. B. 1965. Principles of Sensory Evaluation of Foods. Academic Press, New York.

AUSTERWEIL, G. 1946. Some observations on the aromas of wines (in French). Ind. de la Parfumerie *1*, 195–199.

AYRÄPAA, T. 1962. Phenethyl alcohol in wines. Nature *194* 472–473.

BAYER, E., and BÄSSLER, L. 1961. Systematic identification of esters in wine aroma (in German). Z. Anal. Chem. *181*, 418–424.

BECKMAN INSTRUMENTS. 1965. The IR-102 Infrared Spectrophotometer. Bull. 7073.

BRADY, R. O. 1963. The role of malonyl coenzyme A in fatty acid synthesis. Proc. 5th Intern. Congr. Biochem., Moscow 7, 44–47.

BRODIE, J. D., WASSON, G. W., and PORTER, J. W. 1963. Formation of malonyl enzyme and its conversion of fatty acids and β-hydroxy-β-methyl glutaryl coenzyme A. Biochem. Biophys. Res. Commun. 12, 27–33.

CARTWRIGHT, R. A., ROBERTS, E. A. H., and WOOD, D. J. 1954. Theanine, an amino acid N-ethyl amide present in tea. J. Sci. Food Agr. 5, 597–599.

CASIMIR, J., JADOT, J., and RENARD, M. 1960. Separation and characterization of N-ethyl glutamine from Xerocomus badius (in French). Biochem. Biophys. Acta 39, 462–468.

CASTOR, J. G. B. 1953. The free amino acids of musts and wines. II. The fate of amino acids of must during alcoholic fermentation. Food Research 18, 146–151.

DATUNASHVILI, E. N. 1963. The over-oxidation of wine (in Russian). Biokhim. Vinodeliya 1963, No. 7, 91–101.

DIEMAIR, W., and SCHAMS, E. 1960. Gas chromatography in food analysis. I. Determination of trace volatile fatty acids in foods (in German). Z. Lebensm.-Utersuch.-Forsch. 112, 457–463.

GALETTO, W. G., KEPNER, R. E., and WEBB, A. D. 1965. Identification of some acetals in an extract of submerged culture for sherry. Am. J. Enol. Viticult. 17, 11–19.

GAROGLIO, P. G. 1959. The New Enology (in Italian). Instituto di Industrie Agrarie, Firenze.

GRAY, D. O., and FOWDEN, L. 1961. N-ethyl-L-asparagine: a new amino acid amide from Ecballium. Nature 189, 401–402.

HAAGEN-SMIT, A. J., and HIROSAWA, F. N. 1950. Progress report on analysis of constituents of Zinfandel wine. Unpublished private communication. Calif. Instit. Technology, Pasadena, Calif.

HEINZ, D. E., PANGBORN, R. M., and JENNINGS, W. G. 1964. Pear aroma: Relation of instrumental and sensory techniques. J. Food Sci. 29, 756–761.

HENNIG, K., and VILLFORTH, F. 1942. Aroma materials of wines. I. Isolation. Aldehydes, ketones (in German). Vorratspflege Lebensmittelforsch, 5, 181–199.

HIU, D. N., and SCHEUER, P. J. 1961. The volatile constituents of passion fruit juice. J. Food Sci. 26, 557–563.

HUNTER, I. R., NG, H., and PENCE, J. W. 1961. Volatile organic acids in pre-ferments for bread. J. Food Sci. 26, 578–580.

INGRAHAM, J. L., GUYMON, J. F., and CROWELL, E. A. 1961. The pathway of formation of n-butyl and n-amyl alcohols by a mutant strain of Saccharomyces cerevisiae. Arch. Biochem. Biophys. 95, 169–175.

JADOT, J., CASIMIR, J., and RENARD, M. 1960. Separation and identification of L(+)-γ-(p-OH) anilide of glutamic acid from Agaricus hortensis (in French). Biochim. Biophys. Acta 43, 322–328.

KEPNER, R. E., and WEBB, A. D. 1956. Volatile aroma constituents of Vitis rotundifolia grapes. Am. J. Enol. Viticult. 7, 8–18.

LINKO, Y-Y, MILLER, B. S., JOHNSON, J. A. 1962. Quantitative determination of certain carbonyl compounds in preferments. Cereal Chem. 39, 263–272.

Lipis, B. V., and Mamakova, Z. A. 1963. Analysis of volatile components of wine, brandy, and raw alcohols by gas-liquid chromatography (in Russian). Vinodelie i Vinogradarstvo 23, No. 3, 7–11.

Matthews, J. S., Sugisawa, H., and MacGregor, D. R. 1962. The flavor spectrum of apple-wine volatiles. J. Food Sci. 27, 355–362.

Mecke, R., Schindler, R., and de Vries, M. 1960. Gas chromatographic investigations of wines (in German). Wein-Wiss. Beil. Fachz. Deut. Weinbau 15, 183–191.

Mecke, R., and de Vries, M. 1959. Gas chromatographic investigations of alcoholic drinks (in German). Z. anal. Chemie 170, 326–332.

Miller, B. S., Johnson, J. A., and Robinson, R. J. 1961. Identification of carbonyl compounds produced in pre-ferments. Cereal Chem. 38, 507–515.

Muller, C. J., Kepner, R. E., and Webb, A. D. 1964. Some volatile constituents of passion fruit wine. J. Food Sci. 29, 569–575.

Navara, A. 1958. Bouquet of Slovakian wines (in Slovak). Kvasny prumysl 4, 14–17.

Nielson, A. J., and Caul, J. F. 1965. Minor constituents as major flavor agents. Perf. Ess. Oil Record 56, 321–324.

Nordström, K. 1964. Studies on the formation of volatile esters in fermentation with brewer's yeast. Svensk Kemisk Tidskrift 76, 510–543.

Pisarnitskii, A. F. 1964. On bouquet materials in riesling and cabernet (in Russian). Vinodelia i Vinogradarstvo 24, No. 7, 23–5.

Power, F. B., and Chesnut, V. K. 1921. The occurrence of methyl anthranilate in grape juice. J. Am. Chem. Soc. 43, 1741–1742.

Ribéreau-Gayon, J., and Peynaud, E. 1958. Traité d'Oenologie. Ch. Béranger, Paris.

Rodopulo, A. K., and Egorov, I. A. 1964. Bouquet substances in wine (in Russian). Probl. Evolyutsionnoi i Tekhn. Biokhim. 341–7. Chem. Abstr. 61, 11291f.

Rodopulo, A. K., and Pisarnitskii, A. F. 1963. Identification of esters, volatile acids, and alcohols in champagne by gas chromatography (in Russian). Vinodelie i Vinogradarstvo 23, No. 8, 9–12.

Sakato, Y. 1950. The chemical constituents of tea. III. A new amide, theanine. J. Agr. Chem. Soc. Japan 23, 262–267.

Senoh, S., Daly, J., Axelrod, J., and Witkop, B. 1959. Enzymatic p-O-methylation by catechol O-methyl transferase. J. Am. Chem. Soc. 81, 6240–6245.

Sihto, E., Nykänen, L., and Suomalainen, H. 1962. Gas chromatography of the aroma compounds of alcoholic beverages. Teknillisen Kemian Aikakauslehti 19, 753–762.

Singleton, V. L. 1962. Aging of wines and other spiritous products, acceleration by physical treatments. Hilgardia 32, 319–392.

Singleton, V. L. and Ough, C. S. 1962. Complexity of flavor and blending of wines. J. Food Sci. 27, 189–196.

Sisakian, N. M., Egorov, I. A., and Saakian, R. G. 1950. On the intensity of the biochemical reactions in sherry wine production (in Russian). Biokhim. Vinodeliya 3, 57–68.

Smith, D. E., and Coffman, J. R. 1960. Separation and identification of the neutral components from bread pre-ferment liquid. Anal. Chem. 32, 1733–1736.

SUGISAWA, H., MATTHEWS, J. S., and MacGREGOR, D. R. 1962. The flavor spectrum of apple wine volatiles. II. Volatile fatty acids. J. Food Sci. 27, 435–440.

SUOMALAINEN, H., and NYKÄNEN, L. 1964. The formation of aroma compounds by yeast in sugar fermentation. Suomen Kemistilehti B 37, 230–232.

TERANISHI, R., CORSE, J. W., McFADDEN, W. H., BLACK, D. R., and MORGAN, A. I., JR. 1963. Volatiles from strawberries. I. Mass spectral identification of the more volatile components. J. Food Sci. 28, 478–483.

UNITED STATES TREASURY DEPARTMENT, INTERNAL REVENUE SERVICE, DECISION 6769. 1964. Use of volatile fruit-flavor concentrates. Federal Register, Nov. 6, 1964.

VALAIZE, H. 1951. Amino acids and the bouquet of wines (in French). Ind. agric. aliment. 68, 245–250.

WEBB, A. D., and INGRAHAM, J. L. 1963. Fusel Oil. In Advances in Applied Microbiology, vol. 5, 317–353. Academic Press, New York.

WEBB, A. D., and KEPNER, R. E. 1957. Some aroma constituents of Vitis vinifera var. Muscat of Alexandria. Food Research 22, 384–395.

WEBB, A. D., and KEPNER, R. E. 1962. The aroma of flor sherry. Am. J. Enol. Viticult. 13, 1–14.

WEBB, A. D., KEPNER, R. E., and GALETTO, W. G. 1964A. Comparison of the aromas of flor sherry, baked sherry, and submerged-culture sherry. Am. J. Enol. Viticult. 15, 1–10.

WEBB, A. D., KEPNER, R. E., and GALETTO, W. G. 1965A. Volatile components of sherry wine. Isolation and identification of N-(2-phenethyl)acetamide and N-isoamyl-acetamide. Am. J. Enol. Viticult. 17, 1–10.

WEBB, A. D., KEPNER, R. E., and MAGGIORA, L. 1965B. Isolation and identification of half-esters of malic and tartaric acids in California wines. Annual Meeting, American Society of Enologists, Sacramento, Calif.

WEBB, A. D., RIBÉREAU-GAYON, P., and BOIDRON, J-N. 1963. Preliminary observations in the odorous substances of wines (in French). Compt. rend. Acad. Agr. France 49, 115–123.

WEBB, A. D., RIBÉREAU-GAYON, P., and BOIDRON, J-N. 1964B. Composition of essence extracted from V. vinifera var. Cabernet Sauvignon (in French). Bull. Soc. Chim. France 1964, 1415–1420.

WICK, E. L., DE FIGUEIREDO, M., and WALLACE, D. H. 1964. The volatile components of white bread prepared by a pre-ferment method. Cereal Chem. 41, 300–315.

WILKINS INSTRUMENT and RESEARCH. 1965. Preparative G. C. with long columns. Research Notes, summer 1965.

WINDISCH, K. 1906. The chemical processes in the development of wines. Eugen Ulmer, Stuttgart.

WINTER, M., and SUNDT, E. 1962. Aroma research. Analysis of aroma of raspberries. I. Volatile carbonyl constituents (in French). Helv. chim. Acta 45, 2195–2211.

YAMADA, M., SHITARA, J., YOSHIDE, H., KOMODA, H., KOSAKI, M., and YOSHIZAWA, K. 1962. Amino acid fermentation by yeasts. I. A new pathway of fusel oil formation. J. Agr. Sci., Tokyo Nogyo Daigaku 7. 97–102.

YAMAMOTO, A. 1961A. Flavors of sake. II. Separation and identification of a hydrocarboxylic acid. Nippon Nogeikagaku Kaishi 35, 619–623.

YAMAMOTO, A. 1961B. Flavors of sake. III. Separation and identification of ketocarboxylic acids. Nippon Nogeikagaku Kaishi 35, 711–715.

YAMAMOTO, A. 1961C. Flavors of sake. V. Separation and identification of some nonvolatile carbonyl compounds. Nippon Nogeikagaku Kaishi 35, 819–823.

YAMAMOTO, A. 1961D. Flavors of sake. VI. Separation and identification of p-hydroxycinnamic acid. Nippon Nogeikagaku Kaishi 35, 824–826.

YAMAMOTO, A. 1961E. Flavors of sake. VII. Separation and identification of ethyl phenylacetate and ethyl caprylate. Nippon Nogeikagaku Kaishi, 35, 1082–6.

YAMAMOTO, A., SASAKI, K., and SARUNO, R. 1961. Flavors of sake. IV. Separation and identification of ferulic acid, vanillic acid, and vanillin. Nippon Nogeikagaku Kaishi 35, 715–719.

CHAPTER 10

I. Hornstein | Flavor of Red Meats

INTRODUCTION

Meat flavor is an artifact produced by heating a heterogeneous system containing nonodorous precursors. Meat flavor research has therefore centered on (a) locating the sites of flavor production, (b) identifying the precursor systems, and (c) identifying the flavor compounds. Moncrieff (1951) has defined flavor as a "complex sensation" composed of taste, odor, roughness or smoothness, hotness or coldness, and pungency or blandness. The factor however that exerts the greatest influence on flavor is odor. If odor is lacking, the flavor is primarily a function of bitter, sweet, sour, and salt. Meat flavor research in common with almost all flavor research has therefore equated odor with flavor and the flavor volatiles and their precursors have been the systems studied.

Early studies were primarily concerned with the location of flavor precursors. Crocker (1948) concluded that meat fiber on heating produced typical meat flavor and that expressed meat juices produced a nontypical low intensity flavor. Jones (1952), however, reported that cooking lean meat produced little flavor and attributed the flavor to the fat. Howe and Barbella (1937) considered both lean and fat important and related the time and temperature of heating to the quality of the flavor. In a more recent study, Barylko-Piekielva (1957) repeated Crocker's work and concluded that meat fiber is not the exclusive carrier of typical meat flavor. Kramlich and Pearson (1958) reported that pressed fluid from raw beef yielded a concentrated meat flavor on cooking. Hornstein et al. (1960B) blended ground lean beef with water at 0°C., centrifuged the slurry, reextracted, then recentrifuged the slurry and finally heated the protein residue at 100°C.—no meat-like aromas were noted. In fact, heating this residue for one hour at 100°C. under vacuum and trapping the volatiles at liquid nitrogen temperature yielded only traces of ammonia. However, heating the initial extract to 100°C. produced typical meaty aromas proving rather conclusively that regardless of the site the flavor precursors were water soluble and that the insoluble proteins did not contribute to flavor.

BEEF FLAVOR PRECURSORS

The nature of the flavor precursors in meat has been studied by several groups. Hornstein and Crowe (1960) prepared a water extract, free of

228

fat, from lean beef, concentrated the extract by freeze drying and then dialyzed the solution overnight at 0°C. against an equal volume of water. The dialysis procedure was repeated several times and the combined diffusates were lyophilized to yield a white, fluffy powder that rapidly browned on exposure to air.

Heating this powder produced aromas reminiscent of roast meat, boiling a water solution produced an aroma characteristic of meat broth. The nondialyzable solutes were also freeze-dried to yield a red-brown, friable powder. Heating this powder, essentially a mixture of the sarcoplasmic proteins, in air, vacuum, or in water solution did not yield meatlike aromas and indicated that the water soluble proteins on heating did not contribute to meat flavor. The diffusate which contained the low molecular weight precursors was in turn separated by ion exchange chromatography into an amino acid fraction and a neutral fraction containing reducing sugars. Neither of these fractions upon heating produced meat-like aromas. However, when these subfractions were recombined typical meat aromas were obtained. Based upon these observations it was concluded that the flavor of lean beef was produced by an "interaction between amino acids and the low molecular weight carbohydrates", i.e. a nonenzymatic browning reaction was responsible for lean meat flavor. To eliminate the possibility that reducing sugars and water soluble protein might react to produce meat-like aromas several model systems were studied. Mixtures of gelatin and glucose, egg albumin and glucose, the water soluble beef proteins and glucose, and the water insoluble beef proteins and glucose were heated at 100°C. under vacuum and the volatiles trapped. No meat-like aromas were obtained, again indicating that only low molecular weight compounds were the precursors for the development of cooked meat flavor. Wood and Bender (1957) and Bender et al. (1958) analyzed commercial beef muscle extract and fresh beef muscle for nonprotein constituents. The major differences between the two preparations were in the free amino acids and reducing sugar concentrations. Amino acids totaled 11% of the fresh extract and only 2.4% of the commercial material; the reducing sugars totaled 2% of the fresh extract but were absent in the commercial extract. Presumably the loss of amino acid and reducing sugars was due to a browning reaction. The composition of fresh and commercial muscle extracts are compared in Table 25. The commercial extract, Wood and Bender (1957), was a concentrate of the extract obtained when chopped beef was immersed for 30 minutes in water at 95° to 100°C. during the initial stages of corned-beef manufacture. The meat consisted entirely of muscle and connective tissue. The first stage of concentration of the liquor to 45% solids was carried out under reduced pressure, the second

TABLE 25

COMPOSITION OF MUSCLE EXTRACTS[1]

	Per Cent of Fresh[2,3] Muscle Extract	
Amino Acids		
α-Alanine	1.27	(1.48)
Aspartic acid	0.25	...
Glutamic acid	0.78	...
Glycine	0.25	...
Isoleucine	0.24	(0.09)
Leucine	0.63	(0.09)
Lysine	0.07	...
Methionine	0.21	(0.01)
Phenylalanine	0.40	...
Serine + threonine + asparagine	2.59	(0.11)
Tyrosine	0.21	...
Taurine	1.67	(0.36)
Citrulline	...	(0.29)
Valine	0.39	...
Phosphoserine	0.39	...
Phosphoethanolamine	0.94	...
Glycerophosphoethanolamine	1.68	...
Peptides		
Carnosine	4.86	(4.15)
Anserine	1.12	(0.84)
Iminazole peptide	...	(2.10)
Guanidines		
Creatine	9.45	(5.40)
Creatinine	0.75	(6.18)
Purines		
Hypoxanthine	1.46	(2.52)
Organic Acids		
Lactic	23.04	(16.40)
Glycollic	2.34	(1.10)
Succinic	0.88	(1.42)
Carnitine	3.45	(3.70)
Urea	0.68	(0.12)
Ammonia	0.37	(0.47)
Inorganic matter	27.50	(33.00)
Coloring matter	15.80	(20.58)
Reducing sugars as glucose	2.10	...

[1] Bender *et al.* (1958).
[2] Original extract contained 40.69% protein.
[3] Commercial meat extract concentration given in parenthesis.
··· represents none present.

and final stage at atmospheric pressure and 75°C. over a period of 7 to 14 hours. During this final stage of concentration, at which there was free access of air, the commercially desirable flavors and color were developed.

Fresh meat extract as compared to commercial meat extract contained qualitatively and quantitatively greater amounts of amino acids and reducing sugars and a higher percentage of organic acids. The commercial extract contained more creatinine and hypoxanthine, and an iminazole peptide absent in the fresh extract and greater concentrations of inorganic and coloring matter. Wood (1961) used this data as a point of departure for a study of meat flavor. Minced muscle from a freshly killed animal was blended with 6 volumes of 3% perchloric acid at 0°C. The slurry was neutralized with 10% KOH, the potassium perchlorate removed by filtration and the filtrate freeze dried. Using paper chromatography the reducing substances in this protein free extract of fresh beef muscle were identified as glucose, fructose-6-phosphate, glucose-6-phosphate, and diphosphopyridine nucleotide. Ribose-5-phosphate was not detected in fresh muscle although ribose was liberated by treatment of the extract with alkaline phosphatase. In aged muscle, glucose, fructose, and ribose were present, the sugar phosphates were found in only trace amounts. When fresh, protein free, muscle extract was freeze dried, then moistened and allowed to stand at room temperature, browning took place. Paper chromatography of the mixture showed that all of the free sugars and diphosphopyridine nucleotide had disappeared. When a similar mixture was heated on a steam bath for ten minutes the characteristic smell and flavor of meat extract appeared. With continued heating the flavor became more pronounced. The increase in flavor was accompanied by an increase in inorganic phosphate, a loss of organic phosphate, and a decrease in reducing substances. The behavior of model systems was also studied. Glucose and mixtures of amino acids did not brown at room temperature but only on heating. A similar result was obtained from a synthetic mixture approximating the composition of an authentic sample of beef extract (Bender et al. 1958) but containing glucose as the only reducing substance. On heating this mixture, flavor similar to that of beef extract developed. The rate of reaction of amino acids with other reducing sugars and sugar-phosphates was studied. Of the sugars tested, ribose-5-phosphate reacted most readily and liberated inorganic phosphate. Further experiments with this phosphate revealed that it could react under extremely mild conditions and cause rapid browning with mixtures of amino acids. In another model system it was shown that one mole of reducing sugar combined with as many as six moles of amino acid. These two experiments could well explain the observations that an increase in flavor was accompanied by a decrease in organic phosphate, an increase in inorganic phosphate, a loss of reducing sugar and a large decrease in free amino acids. Heating mixtures of amino acids or of their complete synthetic beef extract equivalent in the absence of reducing sugars produced neither browning nor meaty flavor. Browning of glucose and simple mixtures of amino acids, i.e. alanine, serine, methionine, leucine, isoleucine, and taurine did not produce authentic meaty aromas. To obtain meaty aromas synthetically, a mixture of all of the compounds identified in beef extract was required. Wood concluded, "it is shown beyond reasonable doubt that the development of the brown color and meaty flavor characteristic of these extracts is a result of the Maillard reaction."

Hornstein and Crowe (1960, 1963), Hornstein et al. (1963) using the same procedures developed in their study of beef looked at flavor precursors in lean pork, lamb, and whale. In each instance, the flavor precursors were water soluble, and dialyzable. Again, separation of the lyophilized diffusates by ion exchange chromatography into amino acids and reducing sugars yielded subfractions that on heating produced nonmeaty aromas; recombination of these subfractions followed by heating produced meaty aromas similar to each other and to that of beef. Macy et al. (1964A) also studied the water soluble flavor and odor precursors of meat in beef, pork, and lamb. Paper and ion exchange chromatography were used to qualitatively determine amino acids, carbohydrates, nonamino nitrogen compounds, and phosphoric acid esters in lyophilized diffusates from cold water extracts of beef, lamb, and pork muscle. They identified 31 compounds and concluded that qualitatively the low-molecular weight organic constituents in tissue from the three species were remarkably similar. The only qualitative differences observed were (a) the presence of glutathione in lamb, but not in pork and beef and (b) the presence of cysteic acid and ornithine in pork and lamb, but not in beef. Macy et al. (1964B) also studied the effect of heat on the amino nitrogen constituents and carbohydrates in the lyophilized diffusates. The amino nitrogen compounds in the diffusates were found to be qualitatively and quantitatively similar in beef, lamb, and pork. Taurine,

TABLE 26

MAJOR AMINO COMPOUNDS IN HEATED AND UNHEATED LYOPHILIZED DIFFUSATES FROM BEEF, LAMB AND PORK[1]

| | Mg/100 Gm. Tissue | | Change From Unheated |
Amino Compounds	Unheated	Heated	Sample (%)
Beef			
Taurine	9.05	4.02	−55.6
Alanine	11.28	6.22	−44.9
Anserine + Carnosine	90.14	38.17	−57.7
Lamb			
Taurine	26.25	16.47	−37.3
Alanine	9.18	6.53	−28.9
Anserine + Carnosine	25.55	16.28	−36.3
Pork			
Taurine	12.58	7.94	−36.9
Alanine	4.19	2.80	−33.2
Anserine + Carnosine	67.94	58.38	−14.1

[1] From Macy et al. (1964B).

alanine, and anserine plus carnosine were the major constituents of un-heated samples.

Table 26 shows the decrease of these compounds after heating the extracts for one hour in a boiling water bath. Decreases in taurine, anserine plus carnosine, and alanine accounted for 69, 72, and 45% of the total loss during the heating of the amino nitrogen compounds in beef, pork, and lamb, respectively.

The carbohydrate concentration in lyophilized diffusates from beef, lamb, and pork before and after heating are shown in Table 27. Glucose

TABLE 27

CONCENTRATION OF VARIOUS CARBOHYDRATES IN LYOPHILIZED DIFFUSATES
FROM BEEF, LAMB AND PORK BEFORE AND AFTER HEATING[1]

	Concentration Mg/100 Gm. Tissue					
	Beef		Lamb		Pork	
Carbohydrate	Unheated	Heated	Unheated	Heated	Unheated	Heated
Glucose	43.86	25.5	32.87	21.33	43.56	28.02
% loss		42.4		35.1		35.7
Fructose	3.56	3.21	2.68	2.61	2.08	2.02
% loss		9.8		2.6		2.9
Ribose	1.09	Trace	0.52	Trace	0.20	Trace
% loss		100.00		100.00		100.00
Unknown nucleoside (as ribose)	0.15	None	0.35	None	0.06	None
% loss		100.00		100.00		100.00
Total	48.66	28.46	36.42	23.94	45.90	30.04
% loss		41.5		34.3		34.6

[1] Macy et al. (1964B).

was initially present in the greatest concentration followed by fructose, ribose, and an unknown nucleoside thought to be inosine. Ribose appeared to be the most labile to heating and fructose the most stable. Heating solutions of the lyophilized diffusates from pork, beef, and lamb produced typical meaty aromas. Batzer et al. (1960, 1962) also reported that beef flavor precursors were found in the dialyzable portion of a water extract of raw ground beef. Only the diffusate yielded beef aromas and flavor on heating. This fraction was further separated through a cellulose membrane of a smaller pore size. The second membrane retained low-molecular weight proteins but permitted the small carbohydrate, amino acid, and peptide molecules to diffuse through. The procedure for separating fraction "A," the original diffusate, is shown in Figure 64. Fraction Aa, the nondialyzable material (on the second dialysis) was further separated on Sephadex G-25 into a high-molecular weight protein Aa_1, and a protein of intermediate molecular weight Aa_2. Fraction Aa_2 on heating produced an aroma of freshly cooked beef. This

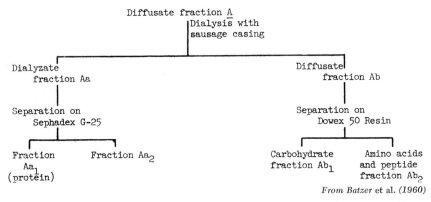

From Batzer et al. (1960)

FIG. 64.　SEPARATION OF FRACTION A TO YIELD A SUBFRACTION CONTAINING MEAT
FLAVOR PRECURSORS

fraction consisted mostly of a low molecular weight protein identified as a glycoprotein. The amino acid composition of this glycoprotein is given in Table 28. The sugar moiety was glucose. Fraction Aa_2 also contained inosinic acid. Inosinic acid is a potent flavor enhancer that is discussed in some detail by Dr. Kuninaka (cf. Chapter 24, this volume). Mixtures of either the glycoprotein and inosinic acid or complete hydrolysates of the glycoprotein and inosinic acid when heated in fat produced a broiled steak odor. However, mixtures of the authentic constituent acids of the protein when heated with glucose and inosinic acid did not produce the desired odor, an indication that other amino acids may serve as flavor precursors. Fraction Ab, the dialyzable material from the second dialysis, browned rapidly on standing. Separation of Ab on Dowex 50 gave an amino acid fraction, Ab_2, and a carbohydrate fraction, Ab_1. Both subfractions were stable and did not darken on standing.

Wasserman and Gray (1965) recently repeated the fractionation procedure described by Batzer et al. (1960). Beef extract was dialyzed

TABLE 28

IDENTITY AND APPROXIMATE MOLE EQUIVALENTS OF AMINO ACIDS OF
HYDROLYZED GLYCOPROTEIN BEEF FLAVOR PRECURSOR[1]

Amino Acid	Mole Equivalent
Serine	0.130
Glutamic acid	0.010
Glycine	0.025
Alanine	0.100
Isoleucine	0.016
Leucine	0.030
Proline	Not estimated

[1] Batzer et al. (1962).

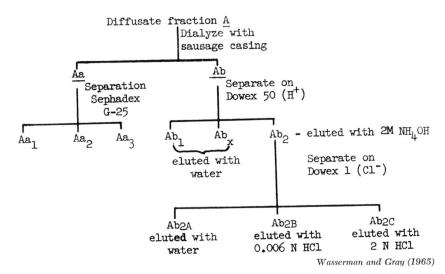

FIG. 65. FRACTIONATION PROCEDURE FOR OBTAINING A FRACTION FROM BEEF EXTRACT
CONTAINING A MEATY AROMA

through ordinary cellulose dialysis tubing and the diffusate A was re-
dialyzed through a smaller pore membrane similar to that used by Batzer
et al. (1960). The separation scheme for fraction A is given in Fig. 65.
Contrary to the results previously reported by Batzer et al. (1960) both
the diffusate Aa and dialysate Ab proved similar in composition and both
subfractions upon heating developed meat-like aromas. Separation of
the diffusate Aa by fractionation on Sephadex G-25 yielded three subfractions, Aa_1, Aa_2, and Aa_3. Only Aa_2 produced a meaty aroma on
heating. This fraction on standing darkened quickly and the solution
developed an aroma reminiscent of commercial meat extract. Further
studies on this fraction were not reported.

The dialysate Ab from fraction A, found to be similar to the diffusate
Aa, was separated on Dowex 50 (H^+). Water eluted a carbohydrate
fraction and a ninhydrin positive fraction, neither of which yielded meaty
aromas. A third fraction Ab_2 was eluted with $2N$ ammonium hydroxide.
Ab_2 produced meaty aromas on heating but did not contain any reducing
sugars. Ab_2 was separated on Dowex 1 (Cl^-). Water and dilute acid
eluted two fractions that produced meaty aromas on heating. A third
fraction, eluted with concentrated acid, was not a flavor precursor. The
free amino acid composition of fraction Ab_2 changed during hydrolysis indicating that peptides as well as amino acids were present. Hypoxanthine as well as traces of inosine, compounds previously isolated, but
normally not considered significant in the development of meat flavor,

TABLE 29

THE AMINO ACID COMPOSITION OF MEAT EXTRACT FRACTION Ab$_2$[1]

	μMoles/mg.		
	Unhydrolyzed	Hydrolyzed	Δ
Aspartic acid	0.0156	0.0933	0.0777
Threonine	0.0483	0.070	0.0217
Serine	0.186	0.105	−0.081
Glutamic acid	0.082	0.357	0.277
Proline	0.0184	0.071	0.0526
Glycine	0.101	0.412	0.311
Alanine	0.300	0.319	0.019
Valine	0.0695	0.104	0.0345
Methionine	0.0277	0.0319	0.0042
Isoleucine	0.047	0.054	0.007
Leucine	0.092	0.107	0.015
Tyrosine	0.0352	0.053	0.0178
Phenylalanine	0.0375	0.048	0.0105
Unknown No. 1	. . .[2]	. . .	. . .
Lysine	. . .[2]	0.110	. . .
Unknown No. 2	. . .[2]	. . .	. . .
Histidine	. . .[2]	1.141	. . .
NH$_3$	0.437	1.38	0.943
Arginine	0.0388	0.0495	0.0107
Tryptophan	0.0076	. . .	−0.0076

[1] Wasserman and Gray (1965).
[2] Unknown No. 1 and lysine were unresolved; unknown No. 2 and histidine were unresolved.

were also found in fraction Ab_2. The amino acid composition of fraction Ab_2 before and after hydrolysis is given in Table 29.

We can conclude from these studies on lean meat flavor precursors: (1) Only low-molecular weight, water-soluble materials are the meat-flavor precursors. (2) The high-molecular weight proteins do not contribute to meat-flavor precursors. (3) The amino acid and carbohydrate composition of lean pork, beef, and lamb are similar and this is reflected in the similarities of the lean meat odor from these species. (4) A specific glycoprotein and inosinic acid may be the precursors for beef flavor or parts thereof. (5) A browning-type reaction may not be the sole mechanism responsible for the production of lean meaty flavors since, in at least one instance, it has been reported that meat flavor was produced from a mixture of amino acids, polypeptides, and hypoxanthine.

VOLATILE COMPOUNDS

The volatile constituents of cooked beef, pork, lamb, and whale have been studied by one or more investigators. Yueh and Strong (1960) refluxed equal volumes of ground beef and water, filtered the mixture, adjusted the broth to pH 1, and distilled the volatile organic acids. The acids were esterified with diazomethane and the methyl esters separated by gas liquid chromatography (GLC) on diisodecylphthalate. Formic, acetic, propionic, and 2-methyl propionic acids were identified by comparison of the retention times of the unknowns with those of authentic methyl esters. Distillation of a similar broth at pH 5 to 6 yielded dimethyl sulfide, ammonia, acetone, acetaldehyde, diacetyl, and hydrogen sulfide.

Kramlich and Pearson (1960) also investigated beef flavor. They too refluxed a mixture of ground beef and water. The volatiles generated were swept from the reaction flask by a stream of nitrogen, condensed in cold traps, and identified by GLC. Methyl mercaptan, methyl sulfide, acetaldehyde, and acetone were identified by retention volumes and chemical tests.

Bender and Ballance (1961) studied the volatiles from a commercial beef extract. A 1:1 solution of extract and water was warmed to 60°C. Nitrogen was bubbled through the solution at slightly reduced pressure for four hours. The emergent gas was dried by passing through U-tubes cooled with solid carbon dioxide and the volatile components were collected in a U-tube cooled with liquid nitrogen. The condensed volatiles were analyzed by GLC on dinonyl phthalate and on polyethylene glycol 400. The peaks were identified by retention volumes relative to 2-methylpropanal and by comparison with the retention volumes of known samples. Compounds identified included hydrogen sulfide, methyl mercaptan, acetaldehyde, propionaldehyde, 2-methylpropanal, acetone, 3-methylbutanal, 2-butanone, ethyl mercaptan, dimethyl sulfide, methanol, and ethanol.

Hornstein et al. (1960B) and Hornstein and Crowe (1960) blended lean beef with water at 0°C., filtered the slurry, lyophilized the filtrate, and obtained a red-brown hygroscopic powder representing 3 to 4% of the weight of the muscle sample. This powder was heated to 100°C. under 10^{-5} mm. Hg. The volatiles were trapped in liquid nitrogen and the total condensate was fractionated under vacuum to yield two major fractions: one collected at −196°C. and the other, the residue remaining in the trap in which the total volatiles were initially condensed. The low-boiling volatiles had a rather disagreeable odor; the high-boiling volatiles were distinguished by a pleasant meaty aroma. Ammonia and traces of methylamine were the sole nitrogen containing compounds, and hydrogen sulfide and methyl mercaptan were the only sulfur containing compounds isolated from the low-boiling fraction. Formaldehyde, acetaldehyde and acetone were also identified in this fraction. Lactic acid and its ammonium salt were the only compounds positively identified in the high-boiling volatiles despite the marked meaty aroma of this fraction. GLC separations of the high-boiling volatiles on either castorwax or SE 30 were extremely poor presumably because of the high lactic acid concentration. Headspace analysis of the high-boiling fraction yielded only trace amounts of the same low-boiling materials isolated from the highly volatile fraction. A modified procedure for flavor development eliminated lactic acid interference. The lyophilized diffusate was heated to 100°C. and the volatiles were swept by nitrogen gas into a small trapping coil cooled by liquid nitrogen. The trapping coil (Hornstein and Crowe 1962) was a detachable part of the 6 ft $\times$ $^1/_8$ in O.D. stainless steel GLC column used in the subsequent analysis, both portions of the column were filled with the identical column packing. After trapping the volatiles, the column was reassembled, placed into the column oven and the sample chromatographed using temperature programming. At least 11 small unidentified peaks estimated to be in the microgram or submicrogram range were recorded above 75°C. The flame detector was bypassed and the odors of the emerging solutes were observed. No distinctive meaty aroma was noted, although the range of odors as they followed one another was truly impressive, encompassing new mown hay, grass, fish, butter—everything except meat! The aroma of the collective fraction above 75°C. was much more characteristic of meat than the collected volatiles below 75°C.

Many of the compounds present in cooked beef volatiles also have been identified in the volatiles of raw beef. Stahl (1957), in the course of a study on irradiation flavor damage in beef, analyzed unirradiated raw beef volatiles. Vacuum fractionation was used to collect condensables of increasing volatility in successively colder traps. These fractions were separated by GLC. The individual compounds were identified by mass spectrometry and included hydrogen sulfide, methyl mercaptan, ethyl mercaptan, carbon dioxide, and carbon monoxide. Merritt *et al.* (1959), using similar techniques, reported hydrogen sulfide, methyl mercaptan, ethyl mercaptan, acetaldehyde, acetone, 2-butanone, methanol, and ethanol in unirradiated raw beef volatiles. Burks *et al.* (1959) used both paper chromatography and GLC to study the amine volatiles from raw beef. The volatiles consisted of 99.9% ammonia and 0.1% of an unidentified compound with retention time less than that of ammonia. Thus, at least 9 of the 20 compounds identified in cooked-beef volatiles have also been identified in the volatiles of raw beef.

The volatile compounds obtained by heating the lyophilized extracts of pork (Hornstein and Crowe 1960), lamb (Hornstein and Crowe 1963) and whale (Hornstein *et al.* 1963) have also been studied. Organoleptically and chemically the volatiles from pork and lamb extracts were similar to the beef-extract volatiles. The volatiles of whale extract contained trimethylamine in addition to the compounds identified in the volatiles from the other species. The enrichment technique described (Hornstein

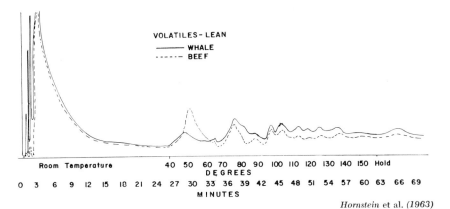

Hornstein et al. *(1963)*

FIG. 66. COMPARISON OF BEEF AND WHALE CHROMATOGRAM

and Crowe 1962) was used to collect volatiles from pork, lamb, and whale. The GLC patterns in each instance were almost indistinguishable from that of the beef volatiles. The GLC patterns obtained from beef and whale using temperature programming, a castorwax column, and a flame ionization detector are compared in Fig. 66. The patterns are practically identical, particularly above 75°C. This is indeed interesting in view of the fact that the two mammalian species live in completely different environments and eat completely dissimilar foods. The trimethylamine found in whale meat extracts is probably a result of the relatively high concentration of trimethylamine oxide in this creature's food. Jacobson and Koehler (1963) studied the volatiles contributing to roast lamb flavor. Mixtures of ground lean and subcutaneous fat were roasted for seven hours under vacuum at 80°C. Volatiles were swept by a stream of air into a series of cold traps. Compounds identified by GLC, infrared and confirmatory chemical tests were ammonia, hydrogen sulfide, *n*-hexanal, 3-methyl-2-butanone, propanal, and acetaldehyde. Water-soluble components from raw and cooked lamb exhibited no distinctive lamb flavor.

The precursors of a substantial portion of meat flavor are presumably the amino acids and sugars present in raw meat. It is therefore of considerable interest to see whether or not the relatively simple carbonyl compounds, alcohols, acids, and nitrogen and sulfur compounds identified, for example, in cooked beef volatiles, can be accounted for on the basis of either the Maillard reaction or by other interactions involving amino acids and sugars.

According to Speck (1952) the function of amino acids in the Maillard reaction is to serve both as a dealdolization and dehydration catalyst for the production of α-dicarbonyls from reducing sugars. The α-dicarbonyl compounds produced undergo complex polymerizations to give the browning characteristic of the Maillard reaction. In addition, oxidative deamination-decarboxylation of the α-amino acids in these mixtures via the Strecker degradation also takes place and results in the formation of aldehydes. The aldehyde produced by the Strecker degradation corresponds to the carbon chain of the amino acid minus the carbon atom lost by decarboxylation.

The Strecker degradation may be presented as follows:

$$R-\overset{\overset{O}{\|}}{C}-\overset{\overset{O}{\|}}{C}-R + R'CHNH_2COOH \rightarrow R'CHO + CO_2 + RCHNH_2COR$$

Nonenzymatic browning is discussed in Chapter 22.

TABLE 30

Compound	Boiling Point °C.		Precursors
Formaldehyde		−19.5	Glycine
Acetaldehyde[2]		21.0	Alanine
Propanal		49.0	α-Amino butyric acid
2-Methylpropanal		64.0	Valine
3-Methylbutanal		92.0	Leucine
Formic acid		100.5	Formaldehyde
Acetic acid		118.0	Acetaldehyde
Propionic acid		141.0	Propanal
2-Methylpropionic acid		153.0	2-Methyl propanal
Lactic acid	b_{15}	122.0	Glycogen
Acetone[2]		56.5	Sugars
Diacetyl		88.0	Sugars
2-Butanone[2]		79.6	Sugars?
H_2S[2]		−60.0	"S" containing amino acids
Methyl mercaptan[2]		6.1	Methionine
Ethyl mercaptan		37.0	Ethionine
Dimethyl sulfide		38.0	Methionine
Ammonia[2]		−33.5	Proteins
Methylamine		−6.3	Methyl mercaptan + NH_3
Methanol[2]		64.7	Sugars
Ethanol[2]		78.5	Sugars?

[1] Composite data; see text for sources.
[2] Also identified in raw beef volatiles.

Table 30 lists the volatiles found in cooked beef, their boiling points and their probable precursors. The Strecker degradation can account directly or indirectly for the formation of ten of the compounds listed. Thus, *formaldehyde* is obtained from glycine, *acetaldehyde* from alanine, *propanal* from α-amino butyric acid, *2-methylpropanal* from valine, and *3-methylbutanal* from leucine. Ballance (1961) has shown that the Strecker degradation of methionine leads to the formation of methional and this in turn breaks down to form *methyl mercaptan* and acrolein. Casey *et al.* (1965) have reported that *ethyl mercaptan* can be obtained from ethionine presumably by a similar reaction. The Strecker degradation indirectly accounts for the formation of *formic, acetic,* and *2-methyl propionic* acids since these can be produced by air oxidation of the corresponding aldehydes. *Hydrogen sulfide* can be obtained by heating the sulfur containing amino acids. Obata and Mizutana (1961) have reported that trace amounts of *dimethyl sulfide* can be obtained by heating methionine. Casey *et al.* (1965) observed that *acetone* and *methanol* can be obtained by heating sugars. *Ammonia* is readily produced by hydrolysis of the dicarboxylic amino acids present in protein. The anaerobic end product of glycolysis in animal tissues is *lactic acid* and this in turn can be the precursor of ethanol. The reaction of methyl mercaptan and ammonia may account for the formation of methylamine. Diacetyl is produced from sugars by the Maillard reaction. A somewhat fanciful picture of the formation of *2-butanone* may start with the conversion of sugars to 2,3-butylene glycol and its dehydration via a pinacol rearrangement to give the ketone. Thus, there is good experimental evidence that the amino acids and sugars may indeed be the precursors for at least 17 of the 21 compounds identified in cooked beef volatiles. These same precursors exist in many foods and compounds isolated from beef volatiles will also be found in the volatiles of a great many cooked foods. One must therefore conclude either that the qualitative and quantitative distribution of these low-boiling volatile compounds are all important in determining the flavor of a great many foods or that these compounds provide the flavor background and that other volatile compounds provide the distinctive flavor notes. The observation that a composite of trace amounts of high boiling materials separated by GLC from meat volatiles has a relatively "meaty" odor, while the composite flavor of the lower boiling volatiles is not meaty supports the idea that the flavor compounds identified to date do not provide the basic flavor notes associated with cooked lean meats and that the compounds identified to date play a secondary role in the characterization of meat flavor. There is also evidence that a basically similar meat aroma is developed on cooking red lean meats from different animals. The similarity of the amino acids and sugars identified in pork, lamb, and beef and the similarity organoleptically and chemically of the several fractions isolated from these species make this a reasonable hypothesis.

LIPID CONTRIBUTION TO MEAT FLAVOR

Hornstein and Crowe (1960, 1963) examined the volatiles from beef, pork, and lamb fat. Subcutaneous fats were rendered under nitrogen and then heated at 100°C. in vacuum, in nitrogen and in air. Heating fat from pork and beef in vacuum and in nitrogen produced nonmeaty aromas; heating in air produced characteristic odors associated with beef and pork. Lamb fat, on the other hand, produced typical lamb or mutton aromas under all conditions of heating. Later work (Hornstein and Crowe 1964) has shown that typical lamb aroma is not produced by all samples of lamb fat. In those instances where no lamb odor is developed, a bland odor is obtained under all heating conditions. Since fat oxidation appeared to be important in the development of flavor, the composition of the free fatty acids (FFA) which reportedly are more easily oxidized than the triglycerides (Badings 1960) as well as the volatile carbonyl compounds produced by oxidation was studied. FFA were determined by the method of Hornstein et al. (1960A). The fat was dissolved in hexane, a known amount of the C_{17}^0 fatty acid added as an internal standard, the acids absorbed on a strongly basic ion exchange resin, and the acids then methylated directly on the resin. The methyl esters were identified by GLC. Quantitative estimations were based on C_{17}^0 recoveries. Carbonyl compounds were converted to their dinitrophenylhydrazones (DNPH). The paper chromatographic procedures of Gaddis and Ellis (1959) and Ellis and Gaddis (1959) were used to separate the monocarbonyl DNPH into classes based on the degree of unsaturation. Each class was further separated by the use of different solvent systems.

TABLE 31

FREE FATTY ACIDS IN PORK, BEEF, AND LAMB FAT BEFORE AND AFTER HEATING IN AIR FOR FOUR HOURS AT $100°C$.[1] (MG./GM.)

Acid[2]	Beef		Pork		Lamb	
	Before Heating	After Heating	Before Heating	After Heating	Before Heating	After Heating
C_{12}^0	0.04	0.16	0.08	0.56	. . .	0.003
C_{14}^0	0.49	2.04	0.54	1.39	0.010	0.012
$C_{14}^{1=}$	0.36	2.24	. . .	. . .	0.001	0.001
C_{15}^0	0.06	0.15	. . .	. . .	. . .	. . .
C_{16}^0	2.24	4.91	2.89	3.62	0.650	0.865
$C_{16}^{1=}$	1.31	4.98	1.64	3.45	0.010	0.009
$C_{17}^{1=}$	0.19	0.44	. . .	. . .	. . .	. . .
C_{18}^0	0.96	1.37	0.77	3.21	0.920	1.141
$C_{18}^{1=}$	9.24	19.74	17.01	28.52	1.490	1.910
$C_{18}^{2=}$	0.58	1.34	5.45	13.27	0.017	0.020
$C_{18}^{3=}$	. . .	. . .	1.54	1.45	. . .	. . .
Totals	15.47	37.37	29.43	55.47	3.08	3.961

[1] Hornstein and Crowe (1960, 1963).
[2] Superscript denotes number of double bonds.

TABLE 32

DISTRIBUTION OF FREE FATTY ACIDS FROM BEEF, PORK AND LAMB HEATED IN AIR AT 100°C.
IN TERMS OF UNSATURATION[1]

No. Double Bonds	Per Cent of Total Free Fatty Acids		
	Beef	Pork	Lamb
0	23.03	15.65	51.07
1	73.10	57.64	48.31
2	3.87	23.92	0.62
3	1.45	2.79	...

[1] Hornstein and Crowe (1960, 1963).

Table 31 gives the changes in the FFA concentration in fat from beef, pork, and lamb after heating in air. Only quantitative changes were observed. The FFA in beef increased from 1.5 to 3.7%, in pork from 2.9 to 5.5%, and in lamb from 0.3 to 0.4%. After heating, the FFA concentration in pork and beef fat was respectively 7 and 14 times as great as in lamb fat. Table 32 shows the percentage composition in terms of unsaturation. FFA containing two or more double bonds were practically absent in lamb fat, constituted approximately 5% of beef fatty acids and approximately 26% of the FFA in pork. In terms of acids containing two or more double bonds, pork had 700 times and beef had 100 times the amount present in lamb.

This difference was reflected in the nature and amount of volatile carbonyl compounds isolated from beef, pork, and lamb fat. Table 33 shows the carbonyl compounds identified in the volatiles of beef, pork, and lamb fat heated in air. As expected, the carbonyl compounds were

TABLE 33

CARBONYL COMPOUNDS IDENTIFIED IN THE VOLATILES OF BEEF, PORK AND LAMB FAT HEATED
IN AIR AT 100°C.[1]

	Beef	Pork	Lamb
Acetone	+[2]	+	
Propanal	+	+	
Acetaldehyde	+	+	
Hexanal	+	+	+
Octanal		+	
Nonanal	+	+	+
Undecanal		+	
Hepta-2-en-1-al	+	+	
Octa-2-en-1-al	+	+	
Nona-2-en-1-al	+	+	+
Deca-2-en-1-al	+	+	+
Undeca-2-en-1-al	+	+	+
Hepta-2,4-dienal		+	
Nona-2,4-dienal		+	
Deca-2,4-dienal	+	+	

[1] Hornstein and Crowe (1960, 1963).
[2] + denotes presence of carbonyl compounds.

most numerous in pork and beef and practically absent in lamb. Table 34 gives the carbonyl distribution according to unsaturation. Pork-fat volatiles contained the greatest number and concentration of carbonyl compounds. Deca-2,4-dienal reported to have a deep-fat-fried aroma (Patton *et al.* 1959) was the dominant 2,4-dienal in both beef and pork. The concentration of this compound was five times as great in pork as in beef. No 2,4-dienals were detected in lamb volatiles. Volatile mono-carbonyl compounds derived from lamb, beef, and pork fat were present in the ratio of 1:5:14. These carbonyl compounds were present in organoleptically significant amounts. Lea and Swoboda (1958) found for example that the C_8-C_{12} aldehydes and the C_9 2-enal were detectable in water at dilutions as high as 10^8 or 10^9. Patton *et al.* (1959) reported

TABLE 34

CARBONYL COMPOUNDS, ACCORDING TO CLASS, IN VOLATILES OF BEEF, PORK AND LAMB FAT
HEATED IN AIR AT $100\,^\circ$C. IN MICROMOLES PER TEN GRAMS OF FAT
Compound in Parenthesis Major Carbonyl in Class[1]

Class	Beef	Pork	Lamb
Alkanals[2]	0.11	0.51	0.01
	(hexanal)	(hexanal)	(hexanal)
2-Enals	0.10	0.18	0.04
	(deca-2-en-1-al)	(5 equal)	(3 equal)
2,4-Dienals	0.02	0.09	. . .
	(deca-2,4-dienal)	(deca-2,4-dienal)	

[1] Hornstein and Crowe (1960, 1963).
[2] Includes acetone.

that the flavor threshold for deca-2,4-dienal in water was 0.5 part in 10^9. The threshold for these carbonyl compounds is about 100 times more when they are dissolved in fat instead of water. However, the concentrations found in beef and pork are considerably higher than these threshold values. For example, a concentration of 0.01 μ moles of deca-2,4-dienal in 10 gm. of fat is 1.5 parts in 10^7, about 30 times the threshold value cited for this compound dissolved in fat; this is somewhat less than the concentration actually found in beef fat volatiles and considerably less than the concentration determined in pork fat volatiles. Therefore at the concentrations found these carbonyl compounds must affect meat flavor.

The studies of lean meats and of adipose tissue omitted an evaluation of the possible contribution to flavor of phospholipids and neutral lipids in the lean. Hornstein *et al.* (1961) extracted the total lipids from lean beef and lean pork using a mixture of chloroform-methanol according to the procedure of Folch *et al.* (1957). The lipid extract was separated into three major fractions by column chromatography on silicic acid using increasingly polar mixtures of chloroform-methanol as eluants. These fractions were characterized by infrared absorption, total phosphorus, total nitrogen, amino nitrogen, reducing sugars, and fatty acid composition. In general, beef muscle contained 2 to 4% triglycerides and pork muscle contained 5 to 7%. The phospholipid content varied from 0.5 to 1.0% in beef and pork. The approximate composition of the phospholipid fraction in both beef and pork was cephalin 40 to 45%, lecithin 40 to 45%, sphingomyelin 10 to 15%, and protein 5 to 10%. The fatty acids of the triglycerides of intramuscular lipids were similar to the fatty acids of adipose tissue triglycerides, but were very different in composition from the phospholipid fatty acids. Unsaturated acids with two or more double bonds made up less than 10% of the triglyceride fraction and approximately 50% of the phospholipid fraction. Table 35

TABLE 35

PHOSPHOLIPID COMPOSITION OF LEAN BEEF, AND PORK (% OF TOTAL FATTY ACIDS)[1]

Fraction	Beef	Pork
Saturated Acids	31.4	33.0
Mono-unsaturated Acids	24.3	18.8
Dienoic + Trienoic Acids	25.2	31.9
Tetraenoic + Higher Unsaturated Acids	19.1	16.3

[1] Hornstein et al. (1961).

shows the types of unsaturated fatty acids that are present in the phospholipid fractions of pork and beef. The aromas developed by heating these lipid fractions in air were evaluated. The triglycerides produced aromas associated with beef and pork, the cephalin fraction produced strong, fishy odors, and the odors of the combined lecithin-sphingomyelin fraction were somewhat fishy, but superimposed on an aroma suggestive of broiled liver. The combined intramuscular lipid extracts as well as the separated fractions were also exposed to air and their odors noted at 24-hour intervals. Off-odors developed quickly in the phospholipid fractions. The total lipids developed off-odors at a much slower rate, and the odor of lean-pork total lipids, at all stages, was less objectionable than that of lean-beef total lipids. Perhaps the larger amount of triglycerides in pork lipids limited the surface available for phospholipid oxidation and/or served to cut down the vapor pressure of the generated volatiles. It was concluded that phospholipids did not contribute to desirable meat flavor and that the possibility existed that in excessively lean meat the phospholipids might contribute to poor flavor. An interesting example of the influence of lipid composition on flavor was noted in whale meat (Hornstein *et al.* 1963). A sample of lean whale meat was obtained less than 20 hours after the animal was killed. The sample was frozen, packed in dry ice, and flown to the laboratory. Steaks were prepared and evaluated organoleptically. Evaluations were uniformly poor, flavors were described as fishy, metallic, oily, and rancid. Off-flavors were traced to the intramuscular lipids. The profound difference in the fatty acid composition of the intramuscular whale triglycerides as compared, for example, to beef was particularly striking. Whale triglycerides contained approximately 37% C_{20} and C_{22} fatty acids, and 75% of these contained four or more double bonds. Beef triglycerides contained no appreciable concentration of fatty acids above C_{18}. In fact, the intramuscular whale triglyceride fraction contained more unsaturated fatty acids, with two or more double bonds, than the phospholipid fraction and rather than retard the development of oxidative off-flavors as observed in pork and beef, the triglycerides probably enhanced the development of these off-flavors.

Lipids affect meat flavor not only by virtue of their chemical composition but also by acting as a reservoir for fat soluble substances. Two examples are of interest. Hornstein and Crowe (1964) isolated a polar fraction that exhibited typical lamb aroma from unheated lamb fat by column chromatography on silicic acid using chloroform and increasing amounts of methanol as the developing solvent. Although this fraction was not found in every sample of lamb fat, where present, it influenced flavor by virtue of its solubility in fat.

Craig *et al.* (1962) studied so-called "sex" or "boar" odor, an objectionable odor produced by heating the flesh of certain swine. Cold saponification of boar fat yielded a small quantity of unsaponifiable matter that produced a concentrated, permeating sex odor on heating. It was concluded that the agent responsible for sex odor in pork is located in the lipid unsaponifiables. In both these examples this fat was affecting flavor not by virtue of chemical reactivity but simply by acting as a storage depot for odorous materials.

Further research should elucidate some of the secrets of meat flavor by isolating and identifying the following factors: (1) amino acids and sugars that are most important in flavor development; (2) high-boiling volatiles that contribute to meat flavor; (3) compounds that are responsible for flavor differences among broiled, roasted, fried, and boiled meats; and (4) factors that develop flavors that are characteristic of meats from different species of animals.

We can readily predict that the answers to these questions will be obtained, however, we cannot with equal ease predict when the answers will be obtained.

SUMMARY

Two approaches have been used to study meat flavor. Precursors have been isolated from raw meats and flavor compounds have been isolated from cooked meats. Both methods of attack have been fruitful.

These facts are reasonably well established. Lean meat flavor precursors are the diffusable compounds present in meat extracts. Nonenzymatic browning reactions between amino acids and sugars are important contributors to meat flavor but may not be the sole mechanism by which meat flavor is developed. Most of the volatiles identified in studies of cooked beef can be readily accounted for by known reactions of the amino acids and sugars identified in beef extract. The similarity in composition of the free amino acids and reducing sugars in pork, beef, and lamb and the similarity of organoleptic qualities obtained from water extracts of these meats suggest that a basic meaty flavor is common to the lean portion of all meats regardless of species.

Fats can influence meat flavor in at least two ways. Oxidation, principally of the unsaturated fatty acids, results in the formation of carbonyl compounds that are present in organoleptically significant amounts. These compounds may at one level of concentration produce characteristic and desirable flavors and at another concentration level produce undesirable off-flavors. Fats also serve as a depot for fat soluble compounds that volatilize on heating and strongly affect flavor.

DISCUSSION

A. M. Pearson.—I would like to ask if you feel that the difference in aroma between different methods of cookery are qualitative, quantitative, or both?

I. Hornstein.—I think the safest answer is both.

A. M. Pearson.—We have a little information on the carbonyl compounds, and we have found that it is a quantitative difference.

I. Hornstein.—Not both?

A. M. Pearson.—Not both.

I. Hornstein.—Do you have any information on sulfur compounds?

A. M. Pearson.—We don't know about the sulfur compounds and some of the other compounds, but qualitative and quantitative changes in these could affect the aroma.

R. Self.—I would like to ask you from the work you quoted of Macy's how long and at what temperatures were these amino acids and sugars reacted because of the very large decomposition rates?

I. Hornstein.—At boiling water temperature for one hour.

L. Khatri.—Dr. Hornstein, what is the contribution of some of these aromatic compounds in the meat flavor?

I. Hornstein.—You mean benzene ring type compounds?

L. Khatri.—Right.

I. Hornstein.—I know they have been reported, but I don't know their effect.

L. Khatri.—Also, when you mentioned that the lamb fractions did not have the typical lamb odor, I was wondering whether there was some sort of reaction between these components and some flavor enhancers which were originally present in the meat, like glutamates?

I. Hornstein.—The lipid fraction was separated by chromatography and I doubt if enhancers had anything to do with it. I think it's simply something that is fat soluble.

M. Gianturco.—I am surprised that so few nitrogen containing compounds have been found in the mixtures obtained by heating carbohydrates and proteins. We have found large amounts of high-boiling nitrogen compounds in coffee, that is 20 to 25 compounds, and none of them smell like meat, but they certainly have interesting odors. I would like to suggest that perhaps it might be fruitful to look for these compounds in other systems resulting from the heating of carbohydrates and proteins; or peptides and amino acids.

I. Hornstein.—What temperature did you heat your material?

M. Gianturco.—Coffee is generally roasted up to 200°C.

I. Hornstein.—We took some protein material in this high vacuum system that we talked about before and we heated it to 180°C. We obtained very unpleasant aromas and the material decomposed. At high temperatures you probably would get a completely different set of compounds. I know you get a completely different set of aromas.

BIBLIOGRAPHY

BADINGS, H. T. 1960. Principles of autoxidation processes in lipids with special regard to the development of autoxidation off-flavors. Neth. Milk and Dairy J. *14*, 215–242.

BALLANCE, P. E. 1961. Production of volatile compounds related to the flavour of foods from the Strecker degradation of DL-methionine. J. Sci. Food Agr. *12*, 532–536.

BARYLKO-PIEKIELVA, N. 1957. On the components of meat flavor. Przem. Spozyw. *11*, 26–30.

BATZER, O. F., SANTORO, A. T., and LANDMANN, W. A. 1962. J. Agr. Food Chem. *10*, 94–96.

BATZER, O. F., SANTORO, A. T., TAN, M. C., LANDMANN, W. A., and SCHWEIGERT, B. S. 1960. Precursors of beef flavor. J. Agr. Food Chem. *8*, 498–501.

BENDER, A. E., and BALLANCE, P. E. 1961. A preliminary examination of the flavour of meat extract. J. Sci. Food Agr. *12*, 683–687.

BENDER, A. E., WOOD, T., and PALGRAVE, J. A. 1958. Analysis of tissue constituents extract of fresh ox muscle. J. Sci. Food Agr. 9, 812–817.

BURKS, R. E., BAKER, E. B., CLARK, P., ESSLINGER, J., and LACEY, J. C., JR. 1959. The detection of amines produced on irradiation of beef. J. Agr. Food Chem. 7, 778–782.

CASEY, J. C., SELF, R., and SWAIN, T. 1965. Factors influencing the production of low-boiling volatiles from foods. J. Food Sci. *30*, 33–34.

CRAIG, H. B., PEARSON, A. M., and WEBB, N. B. 1962. Fractionation of the component(s) responsible for sex odor/flavor in pork. J. Food Sci. *27*, 29–35.

CROCKER, E. C. 1948. Flavor of meat. Food Research *13*, 179–183.

ELLIS, R., and GADDIS, A. M. 1959. Paper chromatography of 2,4-dinitrophenylhydrazones. Estimation of 2-alkanone, n-alkanal, alk-2-enal, and alk-2,4-dienal derivatives. Anal. Chem. *31*, 1997–2000.

FOLCH, J., LEES, M., and STANLEY, G. H. S. 1957. A simple method for the isolation and purification of total lipids from animal tissue. J. Biol. Chem. 226, 497–509.

GADDIS, A. M., and ELLIS, R. 1959. Paper chromatography of 2,4-dinitrophenylhydrazones. Resolution of 2-alkanone, n-alkanal, alk-2-enal and alk-2,4-dienal derivatives. Anal. Chem. 31, 870–875.

HORNSTEIN, I., ALFORD, J. A., ELLIOT, L. E., and CROWE, P. F. 1960A. Determination of free fatty acids in fat. Anal. Chem. 32, 540–542.

HORNSTEIN, I., and CROWE, P. F. 1960. Flavor studies on beef and pork. J. Agr. Food Chem. 8, 494–498.

HORNSTEIN, I., and CROWE, P. F. 1962. Gas chromatography of food volatiles—an improved collection system. Anal. Chem. 34, 1354–1356.

HORNSTEIN, I., and CROWE, P. F. 1963. Meat flavor: lamb. J. Agr. Food Chem. 11, 147–149.

HORNSTEIN, I., and CROWE, P. F. 1964. Unpublished material.

HORNSTEIN, I., CROWE, P. F., and HEIMBERG, M. J. 1961. Fatty acid composition of meat tissue lipids. J. Food Sci. 26, 581–586.

HORNSTEIN, I., CROWE, P. F., and SULZBACHER, W. L. 1960B. Constituents of meat flavor: beef. J. Agr. Food Chem. 8, 65–67.

HORNSTEIN, I., CROWE, P. F., SULZBACHER, W. L. 1963. Flavour of beef and whale meat. Nature 199, 1252–1254.

HOWE, P. E., and BARBELLA, N. G. 1937. Flavor of meat and meat products. Food Research 2, 197–202.

JACOBSON, M., and KOEHLER, H. H. 1963. Composition and flavor of lamb. J. Agr. Food Chem. 11, 336–339.

JONES, O. 1952. The flavoring of meat and meat products. I. Perf. and Ess. Oil Rec. 43, 336–337.

KRAMLICH, W. E., and PEARSON, A. M. 1958. Some preliminary studies on meat flavor. Food Research 23, 567–575.

KRAMLICH, W. E., and PEARSON, A. M. 1960. Separation and identification of cooked beef flavor components. Food Research 25, 712–719.

LEA, C. H., and SWOBODA, P. A. T. 1958. The flavor of aliphatic aldehydes. Chem. and Industry 1289–1290.

MACY, R. L., NAUMANN, H. D., and BAILEY, M. E. 1964A. Water-soluble flavor and odor precursors of meat. I. Qualitative study of certain amino acids, carbohydrates, non-amino acid nitrogen compounds, and phosphoric acid esters of beef, pork and lamb. J. Food Sci. 29, 136–141.

MACY, R. L., NAUMANN, H. D., and BAILEY, M. E. 1964B. Water-soluble flavor and odor percursors of meat. II. Effects of heating on amino acid nitrogen constituents and carbohydrates in lyophilized diffusates from aqueous extracts of beef, pork and lamb. J. Food Sci. 29, 142–148.

MERRITT, C., JR., BRESNICK, S. R., BAZINET, M. S., WALSH, J. T., and ANGELINI, P. 1959. Determination of volatile components of food stuffs. Techniques and their application to studies of irradiated beef. J. Agr. Food Chem. 7, 784–787.

MONCRIEFF, R. W. 1951. The Chemical Senses. 2nd Edition. p. 437. Leonard Hill, London.

OBATA, Y., and MIZUTANA, J. 1961. Studies on degradation of proteins and their derivatives in foods. V. Volatile sulfur compounds in the soyabean meal hydrolyzates and the development of dimethyl sulfide. Bull. Agr. Chem. Soc., Japan, 25, 36–38.

PATTON, S., BARNES, I. J., and EVANS, L. E.   1959.   n-Deca-2,4-dienal, its origin from linoleate and flavor significance in fats.   J. Am. Oil Chemists' Soc. 36, 280–283.

SPECK, J. C., JR.   1952.   The browning program at Michigan State College. In Surveys of progress on military subsistence problems.   Series I.   Food stability, No. 1 Contributions of browning research to ration items stability. Quartermaster Food and Container Inst., Chicago, Ill., pp. 29–36.

STAHL, W. H.   1957.   Chemistry of natural food flavors symposium.   Quartermaster Food and Container Inst., Chicago, Ill., pp. 58–75.

WASSERMAN, A. E., and GRAY, N.   1965.   Meat flavor.   I.   Fractionation of water soluble flavor precursors of beef.   J. Food Sci. 30, 801–807.

WOOD, T.   1961.   The browning of ox-muscle extracts.   J. Sci. Food Agr. 12, 61–69.

WOOD, T., and BENDER, A. E.   1957.   Analysis of tissue constituents.   Commercial ox-muscle extract.   Biochem. J. 67, 366–373.

YUEH, M. H., and STRONG, F. M.   1960.   Some volatile constituents of cooked beef.   J. Agr. Food Chem. 8, 491–494.

CHAPTER 11

Eldon L. Pippen | Poultry Flavor

INTRODUCTION

What poultry flavor is depends on the point of view. The poultry producer sees flavor as a rather elusive factor that may depend on production variables such as diet, age, sex, and genetic factors. The poultry processor also sees flavor as an elusive factor that may be influenced by processing steps such as evisceration, chilling, freezing, packaging, cooking, canning, dehydration, irradiation, and storage. Ultimately, poultry flavor is a sensory experience. Discussion of poultry flavor from each of these points of view is beyond the scope of this chapter. However, several subjects in these areas will be considered when they are incidental to topics covered here.

The chemist sees in poultry flavor a puzzle that challenges him to define the reactants, products, and reactions that contribute to cooked poultry flavor and aroma. The fundamental information he obtains will make it possible to attack poultry flavor problems rationally and efficiently. This chapter summarizes and discusses literature that deals with poultry flavor from a chemical point of view. Volatile components, pH and poultry flavor, and off-flavor are the principal topics covered here. For reviews of chicken flavor from several other points of view, the reader is referred to articles by Peterson (1957), Kazeniac (1961), and Lineweaver and Pippen (1961).

VOLATILES

Identity of Compounds in Poultry Volatiles

Carbonyl Compounds Identified as 2,4-Dinitrophenylhydrazones.— The identity of carbonyl compounds found in "oxidatively cooked" chicken and in "normally cooked" chicken are shown in Table 36. During oxidative cooking, in which an air stream was passing through the simmering chicken, carbonyl compounds evolved formed 2,4-dinitrophenylhydrazones (2,4-DNPH's) about four times faster than they did during "normal cooking" when chicken was simmered with no air passing through (Pippen et al. 1958; Pippen and Nonaka 1960). Oxidative and normal cooking generally gave similar types of carbonyls with acetaldehyde, hexanal, decadienal, acetoin, and diacetyl being the principal carbonyls. The principal effect oxidative cooking has on carbonyls

TABLE 36

CARBONYL COMPOUNDS IDENTIFIED IN COOKED CHICKEN[1]

Class	Identified			Tentatively Identified	
n-Alkanal	Acetaldehyde[4]	O[2]	N[3]	Heptanal	N[3]
n-Alkanal	Propanal	O[2]		Hexadecanal	N[3]
n-Alkanal	Butyraldehyde	O[2]	N[3]	Octadecanal	N[3]
n-Alkanal	Pentanal	O[2]	N[3]		
n-Alkanal	Hexanal[4]	O[2]	N[3]		
n-Alkanal	Octanal	O[2]	N[3]		
n-Alkanal	Nonanal	O[2]			
n-Alk-2-enal	Pentenal	O[2]		Butenal	N[3]
n-Alk-2-enal	Hexenal	O[2]	N[3]	Octenal	N[3]
n-Alk-2-enal	Heptenal	O[2]	N[3]	Nonenal	N[3]
n-Alk-2-enal	Decenal	O[2]	N[3]		
n-Alk-2-enal	Undecenal	O[2]	N[3]		
n-Alka-2,4-dienals	Heptadienal	O[2]	N[3]		
n-Alka-2,4-dienals	Decadienal[4]	O[2]	N[3]		
Ketones	Acetone	O[2]	N[3]	2-Pentanone	N[3]
Ketones	2-Butanone	O[2]		2-Heptanone	N[i]
Ketones	Acetoin[4]	O[2]	N[3]		
Ketones	Diacetyl[4]	O[2]	N[3]		

[1] Pippen et al. (1958); Pippen and Nonaka (1960).
[2] O—Identified in "oxidatively cooked" chicken.
[3] N—Identified in "normally cooked" chicken.
[4] Principal carbonyl compounds (in terms of yield of 2,4-DNPH).

apparently is to produce them faster; however, they are similar to those found in normally cooked chicken. Some carbonyls found in oxidatively cooked chicken were not found in normally cooked chicken and vice versa. This difference has been attributed to the difference in cooking and isolation methods used (Pippen and Nonaka 1960). Recently the occurrence of carbonyls in oxidatively cooked chicken, similar to those listed in Table 36, has been reported (Minor et al. 1965A).

Compounds Identified with the Aid of Gas Chromatography.—In one chromatogram 23 volatile components were characterized in chicken muscle. Tentative identification of 15 of these indicated the presence of sulfides, thiols, aldehydes, and ketones (Shrimpton and Grey 1965).

Other chromatograms show 25 and 30 peaks in volatiles of cooked breast and leg muscles respectively (Minor et al. 1965B). Further characterization of the fractions separated by gas chromatography led to tentative identification of 25 compounds from breast muscle and 30 compounds from leg muscle (Table 37). The alkanes, 2,4-pentanedione, amines, methyl formate, alcohols, and sulfur compounds listed in Table 37 had not been previously reported. These investigators also identified n-hexanethiol in addition to the sulfur compounds listed in Table 37.

The chromatogram shown in Fig. 67 indicates there are more than 200 compounds in chicken meat volatiles chromatographed on a 300-ft. capillary column. By combining gas chromatography with mass spec-

TABLE 37

TENTATIVE IDENTITY OF VOLATILE COMPOUNDS ISOLATED FROM CHICKEN MUSCLE DURING 50-HR HEATING AT 88°C. IN A NITROGEN ATMOSPHERE[1]

Type	Breast Muscle	Leg Muscle
n-Alkanes	$C_{2,3}$	$C_{2,3}$
n-Alkanals	$C_{2,5,6,7}$	$C_{2,6,7}$
Methyl-n-alkyl-ketones	$C_{3,7}$	$C_{3,7}$
Dicarbonyls	Diacetyl	Diacetyl
	2,4-Pentanedione	2,4-Pentanedione
Keto-alcohols	Acetoin	Acetoin
Amines	Methylamine	Methylamine
		Ethanolamine
Esters	Methyl formate	
n-Alkanols	$C_{1,2,4,7}$	$C_{1,2,5,6,7}$
Alkanols (branched)	2-Methylpropanol	3-Methylbutanol
n-Alkyl-thiols (RSH)	$R = C_3H_7$	$R = CH_3, C_2H_5, C_3H_7$
$Sym.$-n-alkyl-sulfides (RSR)	$R = CH_3, C_2H_5, C_3H_7$	$R = CH_3, C_2H_5, C_3H_7$
$Unsym.$-alkyl-sulfides (RSR$'$)	Ethyl-n-propyl-sulfide	Methyl-ethyl-sulfide
		Methyl-n-propyl-sulfide
		Methyl-isopropyl-sulfide
Alkyl-disulfides (RSSR)	$R = CH_3, C_2H_5$	$R = CH_3, C_2H_5$
Miscellaneous		$Sym.$-trithiane

[1] Minor et al. (1965B).

trometry, many of the fractions shown in this chromatogram have been tentatively identified. They include sulfur compounds, aldehydes, methyl ketones, benzene derivatives, furans, esters, and alkanes. The details of this work will be reported elsewhere.

Precursors of Volatile Compounds

Sulfur Compounds.—A minimum list of the potential precursors in poultry meat would include methionine, cystine, cysteine, taurine, and glutathione. Other sulfur compounds common to natural foods such as biotin, thiamine, and coenzyme A are also possible precursors. How-

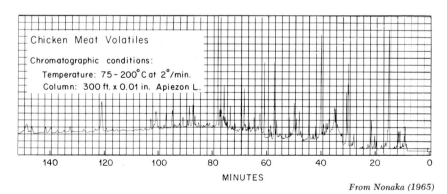

From Nonaka (1965)

FIG. 67. GAS CHROMATOGRAM OF COOKED CHICKEN MEAT VOLATILES

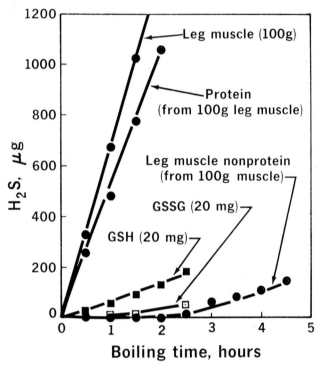

From *Mecchi* et al. *(1964)*

FIG. 68. H₂S PRODUCED BY BOILING THE FOLLOWING IN pH 6.5
BUFFER: REDUCED GLUTATHIONE (GSH), OXIDIZED GLUTA-
THIONE (GSSG), AND MUSCLE, MUSCLE PROTEIN, AND MUSCLE
NONPROTEIN OF CHICKEN LEG MUSCLE

ever, except for H_2S as described below, there is little direct evidence
that specifically links the volatile sulfur compounds of cooked chicken
to any of these sulfur sources.

It has been reported that Strecker degradation of methionine gives
rise to methanethiol and methyl disulfide (Ballance 1961). Hence, these
two sulfur compounds may be formed in cooked chicken by a similar
mechanism. However, formation of thiols and sulfides containing the
alkyl groups ethyl, *n*-propyl, isopropyl, and *n*-hexyl suggests a breakdown of sulfur amino acids by a mechanism more complex than those
apparent in the Strecker degradation.

The principal H_2S precursors in cooked chicken muscle are cystine and
cysteine residues in muscle protein (Mecchi *et al.* 1964). Figure 68
shows that leg muscle protein produces H_2S about 80% as fast as whole
leg muscle. Leg muscle nonprotein, on the other hand, did not start
to produce detectable amounts of H_2S until it had been boiled about

2½ hours (Fig. 68). Twenty milligrams of glutathione, which is approximately the maximum found per 100 gm. of leg muscle, produced only 2 to 9% of the total H_2S formed by leg muscle during two hours boiling (Fig. 68).

The efficiency with which various parent components produce H_2S has been calculated (Table 38). On a dry weight basis (Table 38,

TABLE 38

H_2S PRODUCED BY VARIOUS PARENT COMPONENTS BOILED IN PH 6.5 BUFFER[1]

	Average Production (in μg./hr./mg.) of H_2S from:		
	I	II	III
			Cystine + Cysteine
Parent Component	Dry Parent Component	Total Sulfur in Parent Component	Sulfur in Parent Component
Reduced glutathione (GSH)	3.65	35.03	35.03
Oxidized glutathione (GSSG)	1.01	9.66	9.66
Cysteine	4.96	24.39	24.39
Cystine	3.10	11.63	11.63
Muscle (chicken leg)	0.037	3.53	11.44
Protein (leg muscle)	0.023	2.92	6.74
Nonprotein (leg muscle)	0.0085	0.20	11.04
Muscle (chicken breast)	0.027	2.63	8.68
Protein (breast muscle)	0.021	2.52	5.96
Nonprotein (breast muscle)	0.0041	0.13	11.05

[1] Mecchi et al. (1964).

column I), and on a total sulfur basis (Table 38, column II), the rates for muscle and its protein and nonprotein fractions varied extremely. However, on a cystine plus cysteine sulfur basis (Table 38, column III), the rates for muscle and its fractions are fairly uniform and the range is only 51 to 98% of the cystine value. The values for glutathione, cystine, and cysteine (Table 38, column III), also indicate that the rates of H_2S production will depend somewhat on the type of peptide linkage in which cystine and cysteine occur and also on the sulfhydryl/disulfide ratio.

Hydrogen sulfide itself may be a precursor by reacting with carbonyls to form flavor substances (Barch 1952). A reaction of this type between acetaldehyde and H_2S will take place with chicken fat as the solvent (Pippen et al. 1965A).

Carbonyl Compounds.—Decadienal comes from chicken meat lipids (Lineweaver and Pippen 1961; Pippen and Nonaka 1963). Its principal precursor is probably linoleic acid (Patton et al. 1959). Marked increases in the quantity of this dienal were obtained during oxidative cooking and during storage of fried chicken in air (Pippen and Nonaka

1963; Nonaka and Pippen 1965). Hence, as expected, decadienal can be formed by a mechanism involving lipid oxidation. Apparently, decadienal can also be formed merely by heating linoleate in the presence of moisture (Patton *et al.* 1959). This may partially explain the occurrence of decadienal in normally cooked chicken (Table 36). There is little direct evidence linking the other carbonyl compounds to specific precursors in chicken meat lipids.

Diacetyl, glucose, and probably other compounds in chicken are effective agents in the Strecker degradation of alpha amino acids (Schönberg and Moubacher 1952). Therefore, the Strecker degradation provides a possible mechanism for the conversion of amino acids in chicken to the corresponding aldehydes. Acetaldehyde could form via degradation of alanine, asparagine, and aspartic acid (Ambler 1929; Schönberg and Moubacher 1952). The large yield of acetaldehyde obtained by degradation of alanine in the presence of glucose at 100°C with air passing through could explain the remarkably greater yield of acetaldehyde from oxidatively cooked chicken than from "normally cooked" chicken (Ambler 1929; Pippen *et al.* 1958; Pippen and Nonaka 1960). Although an attractive possibility, it has not been established that the Strecker degradation takes place in cooking poultry.

Mild acid hydrolysis of plasmalogens liberates fatty aldehydes of which the majority contain carbon skeletons containing 16 to 18 carbon atoms (Klenk and Debuch 1963). Perhaps therefore, the C_{16} and C_{18} aldehydes found in cooked chicken (Table 36), were released from plasmalogen precursors in chicken meat during several hours boiling at a pH of about 6.2 to 6.5.

Other Compounds.—Specific evidence revealing the identity of the precursors of ammonia, methylamine, and ethanolamine has not been reported. Ammonia itself, or its salts, occur in chicken muscle (Miller *et al.* 1965). In addition, many nitrogenous substances in chicken muscle probably degrade during cooking to produce ammonia. Bases occurring in phospholipids are possible precursors of methylamine and ethanolamine.

The precursors of the alcohols and methyl formate (Table 37), are probably lipids (Keeney 1962; Merritt *et al.* 1965).

Flavor Significance of Volatile Components

Remarkable progress has been made in identifying compounds in volatile fractions of cooked poultry. But, with few exceptions, we do not have the information required to bridge the gap between identification and flavor significance. Proof that the compound occurs at a significant concentration in poultry at the time poultry is eaten or smelled would help bridge this gap. An indiscriminate survey of this type on 50 to 200 compounds is obviously impractical. However, it would seem practical to obtain this information for selected compounds. We do know that H_2S contributes to chicken flavor. The odor of H_2S cannot be recognized in the total aroma carried by a nitrogen stream coming from a simmering mixture of water and chicken meat (Klose 1965). Removal of odorants other than H_2S from the nitrogen stream makes the odor of H_2S readily recognizable. The odor of H_2S can be detected in the headspace over water containing only ten parts per billion (p.p.b.) H_2S (Pippen et al. 1965A). Table 39 shows that chicken

TABLE 39

QUANTITY OF H_2S IN BOILED, ROASTED, AND FRIED CHICKEN[1]

Cooking Method	H_2S Found,[2] p.p.b.	
	Leg Meat	Breast Meat
Boiled (1 hr. at 100°C.)	730	320
Roasted (to 85°C. internal temperature)	590	180
Fried (to 85°C. internal temperature)	580	180

[1] Pippen et al. (1965A).
[2] Analysis was started about 5 min. after completion of cooking.

meat as typically prepared for eating contained 18 to 73 times more than this threshold value. It is remarkable that H_2S, one of the most volatile compounds, does accumulate in significant amounts in cooked chicken meat. Obviously, low-boiling volatiles in cooked meat cannot be dismissed to a role of secondary importance merely by assuming they are too volatile to accumulate.

Removal of sulfur compounds from cooked chicken volatiles causes nearly complete loss of "meaty" odor. This indicates that sulfur compounds contribute "meaty" character to cooked chicken aroma (Minor et al. 1965B).

Similar carbonyls occur in fresh, stale, and rancid chicken, but their quantity increases as these off-flavors develop. This indicates the contribution carbonyls make to cooked poultry flavor depends more on quantity than quality (Pippen and Nonaka 1963; Nonaka and Pippen 1965).

Removal of carbonyls from cooked chicken volatiles causes loss of "chickeny flavor." This indicates carbonyls are responsible for characteristic chicken flavor (Minor et al. 1965B).

Odor thresholds of carbonyls depend on whether they are being evaluated in water or lipid media (Lea and Swoboda 1958). In addition, Table 40 shows that vapor composition in the headspace over a

TABLE 40

EFFECT OF SOLVENT ON COMPOSITION OF HEADSPACE GAS AS DETERMINED BY DIRECT GAS
CHROMATOGRAPHIC ANALYSIS[1]

Compound Added,	Solvent, Relative Area	
200 p.p.m.	Water	Corn Oil
Acetone	10	47
2-Butanone	14	11
2-Pentanone	22	5.7
2-Hexanone	29	2.7
2-Heptanone	24	0.7

[1] W. W. Nawar and I. S. Fagerson (1962).

solvent containing a mixture of carbonyls depends on whether the carbonyls are dissolved in water or lipid. Therefore the contribution carbonyls make to chicken aroma will probably depend considerably on their distribution in aqueous and lipid portions of cooked poultry.

The threshold of 2,4-decadienal in water has been reported to be only 0.5 p.p.b. and its flavor has been described as "deep fried," "restaurant-like," and "oily" (Patton et al. 1959). It occurs not only in poultry but also in a wide variety of other food lipids (Patton et al. 1959; Hoffmann and Keppler 1960; Mookherjee et al. 1965). The circumstantial evidence linking 2,4-decadienal to food flavors is impressive and suggests that this compound deserves further investigation.

pH AND POULTRY FLAVOR

Muscle pH influences the rate of biochemical reactions that take place in muscle between slaughter and cooking. Therefore cooked muscle flavor will depend on muscle pH to the extent that those reactants and products influence cooked muscle flavor. But we know little about the relationship between the reactants and products involved in those reactions and cooked poultry flavor. Consequently, in the period between slaughter and cooking, the influence of pH on poultry flavor is rather obscure.

Figure 69 shows the ability of judges to discriminate between chicken broths became greater as the pH difference between broth samples became greater. Furthermore, judges associated more intense flavor with broth having the lower pH. This observation raised three questions. Was the flavor difference between broths caused by their pH difference? If so, did pH exert its principal influence before, during, or after cooking? Why should the broth cooked at the lower pH have the more intense flavor?

Adjustment of chicken broth pH by addition of sodium hydroxide or lactic acid after cooking causes no detectable effect on flavor if the

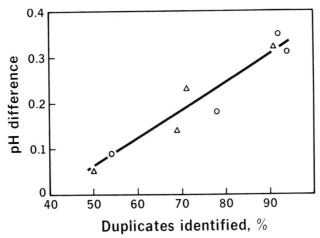

From Brant and Hanson (1962)

FIG. 69. CORRELATION BETWEEN THE PER CENT CORRECT
JUDGMENTS AND pH DIFFERENCE BETWEEN CHICKEN BROTHS
BEING COMPARED

△—Taste panel results at the Western Regional Research Laboratory O—Taste panel results at the University of California at
Davis, California

pH difference is 0.4 unit or less. The pH range found for typical
chicken broths is only about 0.31 pH unit. Therefore, pH itself, as
distinguished from its effects before or during cooking, probably has
little influence on chicken broth flavor. On the other hand pH differences
during cooking as little as 0.14 to 0.48 pH unit can influence chicken
broth flavor (Pippen *et al.* 1965B).

Biochemical properties of chicken muscle *post mortem*, including pH,
have been modified by cooking muscle immediately *post mortem* before
much lactic acid could form and also by *ante mortem* injection of
epinephrine which drastically limits *post mortem* lactic acid formation
(Pippen *et al.* 1965B). As expected, the pH of these muscles and of the
broth prepared from them, were significantly higher than muscle or
broth pH from control chickens aged 24 hours *post mortem*. The control broths were found to have the more intense flavor. It has been
suggested that some factor in addition to the pH difference during
cooking influenced flavor in these biochemically modified muscles.

Higher pH values during cooking favor the production of ammonia,
diacetyl, and H_2S (Kazeniac 1961; Mecchi *et al.* 1964). However, the
significance of these findings in terms of flavor is not known.

Fishy Flavor

Fishy off-flavor may occur in the cooked meat of poultry fed diets containing fish meal and fish oil (Cruickshank 1939; Murphy 1939). Fishy flavor can also occur in meat of roasted turkeys fed diets containing the highly unsaturated linseed oil (Klose *et al.* 1951). The degree of fishy off-flavor among various diet groups for turkeys is directly related to the amount of highly unsaturated (three or more double bonds) fatty acids in the carcass fat (Klose *et al.* 1953). This type of off-flavor is easily avoided by controlling diet composition.

Visceral Flavor

Off-flavor variously described as visceral, gutty, or gamey can occur in the cooked meat of poultry kept uneviscerated after slaughter. Nickerson and Fitzgerald (1939) suggested that diffusion of products of bacterial fermentation from the gut into the meat caused this type of off-flavor (Nickerson and Fitzgerald 1939; Fitzgerald and Nickerson 1939). Similar volatile compounds, including sulfur compounds, aldehydes, ketones, and alcohols occur in the meat and caeca of chickens (Shrimpton and Grey 1965). The quantity of these substances increased in the breast meat of chickens held uneviscerated after death at 15°C. In the United States, this type of off-flavor is now rare because practically all poultry is eviscerated before the taint can develop.

Oxidative Deterioration

Oxidative lipid deterioration has been reviewed (Schultz *et al.* 1962), and need not be dealt with here. It is oxidative deterioration that causes rancid and possibly stale off-flavor in poultry.

Peroxide values, carbonyl values, thiobarbituric acid (TBA) values, and other chemical methods are used to follow the extent of oxidative lipid deterioration. These are useful tests, but they correlate only inconsistently with subjective estimates of staleness and rancidity (Gaddis *et al.* 1959; Jacobson 1961).

Apparently the volatile products formed during lipid deterioration are directly responsible for rancid off-flavor (Berry and McKerrigan 1958; Gaddis *et al.* 1959). The quantity of volatile material in fried chicken undergoing oxidative flavor deterioration increases proportionally to the time and severity of exposure to oxygen (Nonaka and Pippen 1965). Figure 70 showing the increase in hexanal above the quantity present when no off-flavor was detectable reflects the extent of oxidative deterioration particularly well. Apparently hexanal can serve as an

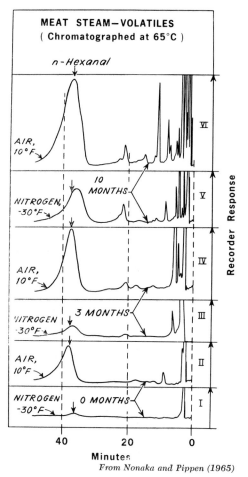

MEAT STEAM—VOLATILES
(Chromatographed at 65°C)

n-Hexanal

From Nonaka and Pippen (1965)

FIG. 70. THE QUANTITY OF HEXANAL IN FRIED CHICKEN AS A
FUNCTION OF TIME AND SEVERITY OF EXPOSURE TO OXYGEN

indicator of oxidative flavor deterioration in fried chicken as it does in potato granules (Boggs *et al.* 1964).

Turkey fat is chemically similar to chicken fat but turkey fat is much more prone to oxidative deterioration (Nutter *et al.* 1943). The fatty acid composition of the depot fats from the chickens and turkeys fed identical diets are similar and hence cannot explain the lesser stability of turkey fat (Mecchi *et al.* 1956). Chicken fat is more stable than turkey fat because chicken deposits the natural antioxidant tocopherol more efficiently than turkey (Nutter *et al.* 1943; Mecchi *et al.* 1956).

SUMMARY AND CONCLUSIONS

Gas chromatograms indicate there can be more than 200 compounds in cooked chicken volatiles. Carbonyl and sulfur compounds represent the principal classes identified.

Hydrogen sulfide, one of the lowest boiling compounds identified, contributes to cooked chicken flavor by accumulating in significant amounts in freshly cooked chicken meat. The principal H_2S precursors in cooked chicken are cystine and cysteine. Most of the cystine and cysteine residues in chicken muscle occur in protein, making muscle protein the principal H_2S precursor. Lesser amounts of H_2S come from free cystine and cysteine occurring in muscle or from the tripeptide glutathione. Specific precursors of the other volatile sulfur compounds of cooked chicken have not been reported.

Lipids are evidently the precursors of nearly all other volatile compounds that have been identified.

The characteristic aroma of cooked chicken consists of a blend of compounds. Whether the volatile compounds that have been identified in this blend are responsible for its characteristic aroma is still largely a matter for conjecture. Most of the compounds identified also occur in the aroma fraction of other foods. Therefore it is not evident from the chemical data why cooked chicken has a characteristic aroma. Limited evidence does suggest that sulfur compounds give "meaty" character and carbonyl compounds give "chickeny" character (Minor *et al.* 1965B).

During cooking pH can influence chicken broth flavor, and the sample cooked at the lower pH has generally been found to have the more intense flavor. It is not known how pH exerts its influence on broth flavor during cooking. Chicken muscles biochemically modified to give muscle with higher than normal pH during cooking also gave broths having less intense flavor than that of control broth.

Fishy off-flavor in poultry is associated with the degree of unsaturation in the fatty acids of carcass fat. Visceral off-flavor in poultry is evidently caused by the diffusion of compounds from the gut into the meat. The cause of fishy and visceral off-flavors in poultry are well known and hence are readily avoided. Oxidative deterioration of poultry lipids leads to stale and rancid off-flavor. The products partly responsible for this off-flavor are apparently volatiles formed during deterioration.

DISCUSSION

M. E. Stansby.—You discussed a type of flavor that you called "fishy." There are several kinds of fishy odors and flavors; some that resemble the fresh fish, some the spoiled fish like trimethylamine, some that are due to the oxidized oil, and very often products that are obtained from animals fed fish are described as fishy because they have an undesirable flavor even though it may not resemble fish at all. Therefore, could you tell us something about what type of a fishy flavor you were referring to?

E. L. Pippen.—I was warned that I should avoid the subject. No, I can't really classify it in any way except that a number of people on a taste panel agreed that this particular poultry had what they called a "fishy off-flavor." This has been noted not only in our laboratory, but by various other laboratories, so there is apparently a consensus of opinion agreeing that it is a fishy type of off-flavor that results from the feeding of certain types of components.

M. E. Stansby.—We noted in some pork that had been fed fish that it resembled more the flavor of old mutton than fish.

E. L. Pippen.—I think this illustrates very well the trouble we have with using subjective descriptions of flavor.

N. R. Artman.—Chicken is a unique experimental animal in that it is easy to control the diet and get the carcass the way you want it by manipulating the diet. It is generally observed that chickens fed a high fat diet are more palatable than those fed a low fat diet. I wonder if you have any evidence or experimentation indicating whether this increased palatability is related to actual flavor components or to simply the mechanical presence of that fat in the carcass?

E. L. Pippen.—I do not know of any evidence that can specifically answer your question. My guess is that the difference in palatability you mention is caused primarily by an obvious difference in the quantity of fat in the carcasses instead of by differences in actual flavor components. In connection with diet, it is well-documented that some ingredients of the diet can cause off-flavors. On the other hand, I don't know of any convincing evidence showing that certain ingredients in the diet can produce chicken having superior flavor.

N. R. Artman.—You mentioned an enhancement in the carbonyl compounds by cooking chicken under a stream of air. Did you do the same experiment with nitrogen so that you can say this increase in carbonyls is due to oxidation or simply due to a mechanical sweeping of volatiles during the cooking?

E. L. Pippen.—We have done a similar experiment under nitrogen and we did find similar types of carbonyl compounds, but in lesser amounts.

E. Lusas.—Will you comment on the apparent differences in flavor between young and old birds?

E. L. Pippen.—I believe the evidence indicates that there are very small flavor differences due to age. Minor demonstrated that the gas chromatograms of the volatiles from old and young chickens were similar, however, there was a larger amount of volatiles from the older birds than from the younger birds.

M. Gianturco.—You mentioned that aldehydes and hydrogen sulfide react

$$R-\overset{\displaystyle OH}{\underset{\displaystyle H}{\overset{|}{\underset{|}{C}}}}-SH$$

to give presumably compounds with the structure R—C—SH and of course

aldehydes also react with mercaptans to give analogous compounds. Some years ago, we were interested in this type of compound and found that com-

$$\text{OH}$$
$$|$$

pounds with the following structure R—C—SR regularly split into the cor-

$$|$$
$$\text{H}$$

responding aldehyde and mercaptan upon injection into the gas chromatograph. Since the organoleptic properties of these compounds are very pronounced they could be quite important. Do you have any particular comments on this, or any experience on the behavior of this class of compounds in gas chromatography?

E. L. Pippen.—My experience with these compounds is very limited and we have not run any of them on the gas chromatograph. The literature I have found concerning reaction of carbonyls with H_2S or mercaptans suggests the products are highly odorous and generally not well characterized chemically.

BIBLIOGRAPHY

Ambler, J. A. 1929. The reaction between amino acids and glucose. Ind. Eng. Chem. Ind. Edition 21, 47–50.

Ballance, P. E. 1961. Production of volatile compounds related to the flavor of foods from the Strecker degradation of DL-methionine. J. Sci. Food Agr. 12, 532–536.

Barch, W. E. 1952. Flavoring materials and method of preparing the same. U.S. Patent 2,594,379.

Berry, N. W., and McKerrigan, A. A. 1958. Carbonyl compounds as a criterion of flavor deterioration in edible fats. J. Sci. Food Agr. 9, 693–701.

Boggs, M. M., Buttery, R. G., Venstrom, D. W., and Belote, M. L. 1964. Relation of hexanal in vapor above stored potato granules to subjective flavor estimates. J. Food Sci. 29, 487–489.

Brant, A. W., and Hanson, H. L. 1962. Age, sex, and genetic effects on poultry flavor. Proc. 12th World's Poultry Cong., 409–413, Sydney, Australia.

Cruickshank, E. M. 1939. The effect of cod-liver oil and fish meal on the flavor of poultry products. Proc. 7th World's Poultry Cong., Cleveland, Ohio, Waverly Press, Baltimore, Md.

Fitzgerald, G. A., and Nickerson, J. T. R. 1939. Effect of time and temperature of holding undrawn poultry upon its quality. Proc. 7th World's Poultry Cong., Cleveland, Ohio, Waverly Press, Baltimore, Md.

Gaddis, A. M., Ellis, R., and Currie, G. T. 1959. Carbonyls in oxidizing fat. I. Separation of steam volatile monocarbonyls into classes. Food Res. 24, 283–297.

Hoffmann, G., and Keppler, J. G. 1960. The stereo-configuration of 2,4-decadienals isolated from oils containing linoleic acid. Nature 185, 310–311.

Jacobson, G. A. 1961. Some aspects of chemical assessment of fat and oil flavors. Proc. Flavor Chemistry Symposium, 165–178, Campbell Soup Co., Camden, N. J.

Kazeniac, S. J. 1961. Chicken flavor. Proc. Flavor Chemistry Symposium, 37–56, Campbell Soup Co., Camden, N. J.

Keeney, M. 1962. Secondary degradation products. In Symposium on Foods: Lipids and Their Oxidation. H. W. Schultz, E. A. Day, and R. O. Sinnhuber (Editors). Avi Publishing Co., Westport, Conn.

KLENK, E., and DEBUCH, H. 1963. Plasmalogens. Progress in the Chemistry of Fats and Other Lipids, Vol. 6. Macmillan Co., New York.

KLOSE, A. A. 1965. Direct olfactory demonstration of major fractions of chicken aroma. Abstracts of papers, 25th Ann. Mtg. Inst. Food Technologists, 97, Kansas City, Mo., May 16–20.

KLOSE, A. A., HANSON, H. L., MECCHI, E. P., ANDERSON, J. H., STREETER, I. V., and LINEWEAVER, H. 1953. Quality and stability of turkeys as a function of dietary fat. Poultry Sci. 32, 82–88.

KLOSE, A. A., MECCHI, E. P., HANSON, H. L., and LINEWEAVER, H. 1951. The role of dietary fat in the quality of fresh and frozen storage turkeys. J. Am. Oil Chemists' Soc. 28, 162–164.

LEA, C. H., and SWOBODA, P. A. T. 1958. The flavor of aliphatic aldehydes. Chem. and Ind., 1289–1290.

LINEWEAVER, H., and PIPPEN, E. L. 1961. Chicken flavor. Proc. Flavor Chemistry Symposium, 21–33, Campbell Soup Co., Camden, N. J.

MECCHI, E. P., PIPPEN, E. L., and LINEWEAVER, H. 1964. Origin of hydrogen sulfide in heated chicken muscle. J. Food Sci. 29, 393–399.

MECCHI, E. P., POOL, M. F., BEHMAN, G. A., HAMACHI, M., and KLOSE, A. A. 1956. The role of tocopherol content in the comparative stability of chicken and turkey fat. Poultry Sci. 35, 1238–1246.

MERRITT, C., WALSH, J. T., BAZINET, M. L., KRAMER, R. E., and BRESNICK, S. R. 1965. Hydrocarbons in irradiated beef and methyl oleate. J. Am. Oil Chemists' Soc. 42, 57–58.

MILLER, J. H., DAWSON, L. E., and BAUER, D. H. 1965. Free amino acid content of chicken muscle from broilers and hens. J. Food Sci. 30, 406–411.

MINOR, L. J., PEARSON, A. M., DAWSON, L. E., and SCHWEIGERT, B. S. 1965A. Separation and identification of carbonyl and sulfur compounds in the volatile fraction of cooked chicken. J. Agr. Food Chem. 13, 298–300.

MINOR, L. J., PEARSON, A. M., DAWSON, L. E., and SCHWEIGERT, B. S. 1965B. Chicken flavor: the identification of some chemical components and the importance of sulfur compounds in the cooked volatile fraction. J. Food Sci. 30, 686–696.

MOOKHERJEE, B. D., DECK, R. E., and CHANG, S. S. 1965. Relationship between monocarbonyl compounds and flavor of potato chips. J. Agr. Food Chem. 13, 131–134.

MURPHY, R. R. 1939. Flavor of turkey meat as affected by feeding fish meal and fish oil. Proc. 7th World's Poultry Cong., Cleveland, O., Waverly Press, Baltimore, Md.

NAWAR, W. W., and FAGERSON, I. S. 1962. Direct gas chromatographic analysis as an objective method of flavor measurement. Food Technol. 16, 107–109.

NICKERSON, J. T. R., and FITZGERALD, G. A. 1939. Problems arising during holding of poultry prior to evisceration and freezing. Proc. 7th World's Poultry Cong., Cleveland, O., Waverly Press, Baltimore, Md.

NONAKA, M. 1965. Gas chromatographic and mass spectral investigation of cooked chicken meat volatiles. Manuscript in preparation.

NONAKA, M., and PIPPEN, E. L. 1965. Volatiles and oxidative flavor deterioration in fried chicken. Manuscript in review.

NUTTER, M. K., LOCKHART, E. E., and HARRIS, R. S. 1943. The chemical composition of depot fats in chickens and turkeys. Oil Soap 20, 231–234.

PATTON, S., BARNES, I. J., and EVANS, L. E.   1959.   n-Deca-2,4-dienal, its origin from linoleate and flavor significance in fats.   J. Am. Oil Chemists' Soc. 36, 280–283.

PETERSON, D. W.   1957.   The source of chicken flavor.   Chemistry of natural food flavors.   A symposium sponsored by the National Academy of Sciences, National Research Council for the Quartermaster Food and Container Institute for the Armed Forces, 167–173, Washington, D. C.

PIPPEN, E. L., DE FREMERY, D., LINEWEAVER, H., and HANSON, H. L.   1965B. Chicken broth flavor and pH.   Poultry Sci. 44, 816–824.

PIPPEN, E. L., MECCHI, E. P., and LINEWEAVER, H.   1965A.   Cooked chicken aroma.   The origin and contribution of hydrogen sulfide.   Manuscript being reviewed.

PIPPEN, E. L., and NONAKA, M.   1960.   Volatile carbonyl compounds of cooked chicken.   II.   Compounds volatilized with steam during cooking. Food Res. 25, 764–769.

PIPPEN, E. L., and NONAKA, M.   1963.   Gas chromatography of chicken and turkey volatiles.   The effect of temperature, oxygen, and type of tissue on composition of the volatile fraction.   J. Food Sci. 28, 334–341.

PIPPEN, E. L., NONAKA, M., JONES, F. T., and STITT, FRED.   1958.   Volatile carbonyl compounds of cooked chicken.   I.   Compounds obtained by air entrainment.   Food Res. 23, 103–113.

SCHÖNBERG, A., and MOUBACHER, R.   1952.   The Strecker degradation of α-amino acids.   Chem. Rev. 50, 260–261.

SCHULTZ, H. W., DAY, E. A., and SINNHUBER, R. O.   1962.   Symposium on Foods: Lipids and Their Oxidation.   Avi Publishing Co., Westport, Conn.

SHRIMPTON, D. H., and GREY, T. C.   1965.   Speculations on the origin and nature of flavor precursors in chicken muscle.   World's Poultry Sci. J. 21, 180.

CHAPTER 12

N. R. Jones | Fish Flavors

INTRODUCTION

Of the commodities to be discussed in this symposium, fish covers potentially the broadest range of material. There are many edible species of true fish and shellfish; and each has its own characteristic flavor. Furthermore, sea foods are notoriously perishable. Each arrives at the table in a condition that varies with the efficiency of initial preservation, if any, and the skill of the cook.

The reviewer's task is simplified, to some extent, by the sparsity of information on some key areas of his subject. Coverage of others has been restricted to avoid overlap with detailed past and present reports in these symposia. In particular, the oxidation of fish fats has been the subject of a previous comprehensive report (Olcott 1962), and is to be discussed, in a mechanistic sense in Chapter 23. Some of the older areas of research have received less detailed treatment than the recent developments.

Taking the field as a whole, we know very little about the compositional derivations of the innate differences between fresh flavors of fish. With the exception of well-recognized general differences between fatty and nonfatty tissues, this lack of knowledge extends to differences between fish of different species undergoing deteriorative changes during processing or storage. However, studies on the chemistry and biochemistry of fish flesh have shown that certain similarities in flavor characteristics exist irrespective of species.

Most of the recent compositional work on fish has been related to organoleptic evaluations of the flesh, and hence it is not open to a common criticism of flavor chemists. This was not true of many of the earlier studies, although there were notable exceptions. For instance, Kodama's (1913) organoleptic observations on an inosine 5'-monophosphate salt, isolated from dried bonito, were the foundation of a burgeoning flavor enhancing industry. Much of this review will be concerned with areas of common ground, where compositional changes relate to flavor irrespective of species.

CHARACTERISTICS OF FISH FLAVORS

Some fish that are cooked within seconds or minutes of death, before the onset of *rigor mortis*, have a pronounced "metallic" flavor. This is lost extremely rapidly, so that most descriptions of the flavors of the freshest sea foods emphasize sweetness and a somewhat loosely-described "meaty" character. This is often weak. Superimposed upon these are delicate flavors characteristic of the individual species.

The potential for producing this composite flavor at cooking is often lost in a matter of hours or days, whatever the effort made to conserve the material. In some species, however (e.g., plaice), there is a transient improvement in flavor.

Chill storage in ice, or refrigerated sea water, is a common practice on fishing vessels and ashore. Under these conditions, the progressive loss in the characteristic fresh sweetness is followed by a loss of the other flavors until the cooked flesh becomes quite flavorless. Such changes are accelerated at higher temperatures of storage.

Freezing and thawing usually result in progress along a similar pathway of flavor deterioration. Cold storage can result in further changes of this nature and more serious deterioration. Such flavor loss appears to be inescapable with conventional methods of fish preservation, since all secondary processing (e.g., canning) is subject to some delay after catching.

Subsequent flavor change depends on the method of conservation or preservation, if any. In chill-stored fish, off-odors develop, and these are carried over to the odor and flavor of the cooked product. Shewan et al. (1953), for instance, described the successive appearance in cod (Gadus callarias) of "wood shavings, wood sap, vanillin, or terpene-like odors;" "slight salt-fish or cold storage odors," "condensed milk caramel, or toffee-like odors," "milk jug, boiled potato, boiled clothes, or metallic odors," "lactic acid, sour milk, or o-toluidine-like odors," "some lower fatty acid (e.g., acetic or butyric acid), grassy, soapy, turnipy, or tallowy odors," "ammoniacal (trimethylamine and lower amines) odors," "strong ammoniacal (trimethylamine, etc.) and some sulfide odors," and "strong putrid and fecal odors (ammonia, indole, etc.)." Accompanying these changes was a progressive increase in bitterness. Twelve years later, it is possible to put a chemical name to some of these odors and flavors. Rather similar flavor changes have been reported for a number of other sea foods (Fieger and Friloux 1954), but the individual peculiarities of species can exert overriding effects. In fatty species, and even in semi-fatty species, it is clear that the development of rancidity can outweigh other factors as the flavor change of major significance (Liston et al. 1961; Lerke et al. 1961). The dangers of confusion in descriptive terms such as those used by Shewan et al. (1953) are clearly recognized by the workers using them. Usually, they are used practically as a means of ensuring uniformity within a panel's assessment of quality rather than an attempt to convey more than a general idea of flavor change to other groups.

Changes that occur during frozen storage are similar in some respects to those of chill storage described as cold storage, metallic odors, soapy, bitter, caramel, and grassy. Fat oxidation is of great significance in frozen material, and the various descriptive terms employed by research groups in this field are strongly reminiscent of those first used by Shewan *et al.* (1953) such as "burnt," "green" (Stansby and Jellinek 1964), "soapy," "metallic" (Diemair 1964), and "metallic" (Forss 1963). From this and other descriptive material on cold-stored fish (Banks 1962) it is apparent that the main difference between the spoilage patterns of wet and frozen fish lies in the activity of the microflora.

"Bitterness" is a characteristic of the deterioration of dehydrated fish products as well as cold- and chill-stored material. The reviewer's impression is that there is some confusion in the usage of this term, particularly in relation to astringency and even to a form of burning aftertaste. This may account in part for some of the disagreements that have characterized research on this quality. There are possibilities also of confusion with "sweetness." For instance, it seems likely that the sweetness to which Stansby (1962), and Stansby and Jellinek (1964) refer in relation to material verging upon putridity, describes a very different flavor characteristic from the term as understood by other groups in relation to fresh fish, if not from that understood by Banks (1962) in relation to cold storage.

There is a fairly extensive literature on various off-flavors that can occur in fresh fish muscle. This subject lies separate from the main stream of flavor research and it will not be reviewed in detail. Undesirable flavors can rise from a number of causes such as the pollution of the habitat by industrial effluents or fungal metabolites, contact with tarry nets, and the consumption of food components that taint the flesh (Beet 1916; Ebeling 1931; Thaysen 1936; Thaysen and Pentelow 1936; Bandt 1946; Westfall 1946; Mann 1951; Jones, G.I. 1961; Sipos and Ackman 1964).

CHEMICAL COMPOSITION OF FISH AS IT AFFECTS FLAVOR

Nitrogenous Constituents

Amino Acids and Peptides.—Claims have been made that certain amino acids can occur in fish muscle at concentrations such that they contribute to flavor independently of other constituents. Thus glycine can contribute to sweetness (Amano and Bito 1951; Hashimoto 1964) and histidine to "meaty" character (Simidu *et al.* 1953 A, B). However, this is not always the case. The individual amino acids of gadoid muscles were found to occur below the flavor threshold, but they were readily detectable in a composite simulated extract (Jones 1961). Similarly, Konosu *et al.* (1960) found that a simulated amino acid fraction (which included histidine) of an extract of "Katsuobushi" (dried bonito) was almost flavorless. This group noted a pronounced mutual enhancing of flavor in combinations of the amino acid fraction with inosine 5′-monophosphate. In a further study, on fractionated extracts of abalone meat, Konosu and Hashimoto (1964) demonstrated a similar key inter-relationship to meaty character between glutamic acid and adenosine 5′-monophosphate. Komata (1964) obtained similar results with "Uni," the unripe gonad of the sea urchin. Of the amino acid fraction in combination with mononucleotides, he found glycine, valine, alanine, glutamic acid and, particularly, methionine to be important. The elimination of glycine resulted in an increase in bitterness and a decrease in sweetness.

Such findings tend to confirm the feelings of earlier workers that amino acids were likely to be important contributors to overall flavor. However, there are some very unsatisfactory aspects. For instance, taurine is a major constituent in most fish muscle. This substance is variously reported as serumy, somewhat astringent (Kazeniac 1961), slightly bitter (Konosu and Hashimoto 1964) and tasteless (Udo and Sato 1962).

Free amino acids undergo carbonyl-amino reactions in dehydrated, frozen, and canned fish. Consequently, they are precursors of other flavorous compounds.

Anserine (β-alanyl-*l*-1-methylhistidine), a major extractive of some muscles (Shewan and Jones 1957) is also highly susceptible to reaction with sugars (Jones 1959A). This dipeptide contributes also to "mouth satisfaction" in flesh foods (Kazeniac 1961; Jones 1961).

Amines and Ammonia.—The "fishy" character of a number of amines has been recognized for many years. It is well established that the quality of the perceived odor of trimethylamine varies with concentration (Moncrieff 1951; Stansby 1962), and it seems probable that this compound is the most important of the amines organoleptically. There is some debate as to whether the amine contributes to odor directly, or indirectly *via* reaction with lipids (Davies and Gill 1936; Lea and Rhodes 1951; Stansby 1962). It may well be that either view is correct, according to conditions. A major factor that has been ignored in much of this work is the effect of pH. This may be expected to control both reaction rates and perception. Another factor is the very considerable difference in the thresholds of the compound when solutions of trimethylammonium hydroxide are tasted and smelled (Jones 1961). The other methylamines occur in fish muscle in concentrations such that they are less significant as flavor components. Shewan (1951) reviewed the early work comprehensively. More recently, Hughes (1959) described the formation of monomethylamine in herring muscle, and Amano and Yamada (1964) discussed dimethylamine formation as a corollary of the splitting of formaldehyde from trimethylamine oxide.

Histamine is a major "extractive" component of many spoiling fatty fishes, where it is a decarboxylation product of the original free histidine of the flesh. Igarashi (1938, 1939) attributed the "pungent" off-flavor of such material to the high concentration of the amine. Perhaps more interest in the compound has resulted from the toxicological implications of its presence. Kimata (1961) has reviewed the factors controlling histamine concentration in fish muscle.

Cadavarine, putrescine, agmatine, and *iso*-amylamine are minor odoriferous constituents that have been identified in frozen salmon, and in canned and frozen crab (Tanikawa 1958, 1959; Tanikawa and Motohiro 1959).

Mononucleotides and Their Derivatives.—Interest in the contribution of mononucleotides to fish flavors dates back over half a century since Kodama (1913) concluded from his studies on dried bonito that the histidine salt of inosine 5'-monophosphate was the key flavor component. During the last ten years, there has been a resurgence of interest in the mononucleotides of fish muscle in the contexts both of flavor and of quality control.

Detailed compositional studies have been carried out on fresh muscle (Jones and Murray 1960) and there has been a rapid acquisition of a general picture of the patterns of degradation that occur in different species *post-mortem*. The sequences of compositional changes will be discussed in those parts of this review that introduce explanations of flavor change and the possibilities of quality control tests derived from a knowledge of flavor chemistry.

The nucleotide of primary interest in the muscles of the true fish is inosine 5'-monophosphate. While there is evidence that adenosine 5'-triphosphate can act as a flavor enhancer (Hashimoto 1964) the reviewer's experience of the analysis of muscles from trawled fish indicates that concentrations are too low to be significant (Jones and Murray 1960; Kassemsarn *et al.* 1963). Similarly, concentrations of guanosine 5'-monophosphate, which is highly active in model systems, are likely to be too low to be of significance under practical conditions (Jones and Murray 1960). Adenylate deaminase appears to be lacking in invertebrate muscle so that adenosine 5'-monophosphate accumulates rather than inosine 5'-monophosphate, and fulfills a similar function.

While inosine 5'-monophosphate can occur in fresh fish muscle and meat extracts at concentrations at which solutions are strongly flavorous in a "meaty" sense (Saito 1960; Jones 1960A, 1961; Wood 1961), it is apparent from the more recent studies that such compounds are of greater significance through their inter-relations with other compounds. These can be purely physiological, (Konosu et al. 1960; Hashimoto 1964) or in flavor-precursoring reactions (Batzar et al. 1962).

Following the work on the relation of structure to flavor-enhancing potential (see Kuninaka et al. 1964 for a review), it appeared that phosphorylation in the 5' position of the ribose and hydroxylation at position 6 of the purine was necessary for activity. However, numbers of invertebrate species, that have a meaty-flavored character, lack enzymatic activity in the muscle to deaminate adenosine 5'-monophosphate at position 6. Consequently, the adenine nucleotide, rather than the hypoxanthine-containing compound predominates (Saito et al. 1958; Arai 1960). These findings could be taken as an argument against a major contribution of mononucleotides to meaty flavor generally, but a recent report suggests that this is not the case. Hashimoto (1964) confirmed an earlier observation (Toi et al. 1961) that there is a strong natural enhancement of flavors between adenosine 5'-monophosphate and glutamate, and related this combination to invertebrate flavors. Obviously, the environment imposed by the other compounds of a musculature has a critical effect on mononucleotide flavor and vice versa.

A very recent report (Rhodes 1965) suggests that there is no relationship between flavor and nucleotide degradation in irradiated mammalian flesh. The analytical data presented were not correlated with organoleptic evaluations directly, but Rhodes argued from flavor work in previous experiments on irradiated material that the flavor of his samples would remain unchanged relative to frozen controls. Apparently, it was not established that the controls themselves remained unchanged. Such treatment induces flavor change in fish.

While there is a considerable measure of unanimity among workers about the flavor significance of mononucleotides in the flesh foods, and a growing acceptance of their value to the general food industry as flavor enhancers, there is disagreement between workers on the relevance of degradation products such as inosine and hypoxanthine. Thus, while Kazeniac (1961) considered inosine to contribute bitterness to chicken, Jones (1961) found the compound to be flavorless at the concentrations and pH obtaining in chill-stored fish muscle. Both workers agreed that hypoxanthine solutions were bitter and suggested that they were of relevance to these meats; but Komata (1964) found that the purine was not a "positive taste substance" in "Uni" (sea urchin gonad), and Udo and Sato (1962) reported it to be tasteless. Spinelli (1966) appears to have clarified the point somewhat. In agreement with Jones and Kazeniac, he found that solutions of the purine were bitter at concentrations such as occur in muscle *post-mortem*. He found, however, that effects of the purine added to fish muscle were detectable organoleptically only when the bacterial count in the latter indicated incipient spoilage. This degree of deterioration is similar to that at which fish muscle usually begins to show bitterness under commercial conditions of chill storage. Jones (1961) in a discussion of critical hypoxanthine concentrations found this to be close to ten days' of storage. Clearly, the situation is complicated by the masking and/or enhancing effects of other compounds and this may explain the findings of Rhodes (1965).

In view of the probabilities of changes in the degree of ionization of the compound under the conditions of acid and base formation that occur in muscle *post-mortem*, future studies should take into account the pH of the preparations. Variations in pH in the physiological region could affect the ionization of the purine itself and that of other compounds, including proteins which can bind ionizable substances.

Other Nitrogenous Bases.—Suzuki (1951) and Yoshimura and Kubo (1953) considered that trimethylamine oxide was responsible for the sweetness of clams and cuttlefish, but this view has been contested by Simidu *et al.* (1953A). In support of Simidu's group, Jones (1961) found that freshly prepared trimethylamine oxide was almost flavorless at concentrations and pHs such as commonly occur in fish muscle. Possibly, the inherent instability of the compound is relevant to this conflict of views.

Betaines are bitter, in general, but the simplest, glycine betaine, is sweetish (Moncrieff 1951). Hashimoto (1964) reported that the compound contributes a meaty and sweet flavor to abalone extracts. γ-Butyrobetaine, homarine, trigonelline, and stachidrine are known to be constituents of some marine organisms (Kapeller-Adler and Krael 1930).

Obata and his colleagues (Obata and Matano 1952; Obata *et al.* 1949; Obata *et al.* 1950; Obata and Yamanishi 1952) demonstrated the occurrence of pyridine, piperidine and its derivatives, pyrollidine, δ-aminovaleric acid, and δ-aminovaleraldehyde in fish products. By admixture of these compounds with each other, and other compounds, such as mercaptans, indole and trimethylamine, these workers were able to simulate the odors of fresh water fish, sea fish, "rather old fish," "fish-shop smell," "fish well below fresh," putrid fish, and dried fish. Bramstedt (1959) has reviewed this work in some detail.

The flavorous properties of the imidazoles of fish muscle have been discussed (Simidu *et al.* 1953B).

Indole and skatole occur in fish tissues in increasing concentration as putrefaction proceeds (Reay and Shewan 1949).

Non-nitrogenous Constituents

Volatile Carbonyls.—Early studies varied in specificity, and usually had quality testing as an objective. Thus Farber (1952) examined the steam-volatile carbonyls of tuna by iodometric titration; Yu and Sinnhuber (1957) related storage time to carbonyl development by the 2-thiobarbituric acid test which they developed later to estimate malonaldehyde specifically (Sinnhuber and Yu 1958); Schwartz and Watts (1957) examined the spoilage of cooked oysters by a similar procedure; Ota (1958), and Mendelsohn and Steinberg (1962) trapped the carbonyl compounds from spoiling fish as the 2,4-dinitrophenylhydrazones, and the latter workers showed that the majority were of relatively high molecular weight, and were liberated at maximum concentration in haddock fillets after 8 to 11 days' storage at 2°C.

Of the individual carbonyl compounds present in fish muscle, much attention has been given to formaldehyde, which is a product primarily of the degradation of trimethylamine oxide. Amano and Yamada (1964) have presented a modern view of this field.

Jones (1959B) reported the presence of pyruvate in fresh and spoiling muscle, on the basis of the classical partition fractionation of 2,4-dinitrophenylhydrazones. Recent studies, (Jones and Burt 1965) by the specific lactate-dehydrogenase assay, confirmed these observations for fresh cod muscle but suggested that the values were artifactually high for spoiling material, probably due to the presence of other compounds.

Apart from reports on malonaldehyde and δ-aminovaleraldehyde in fish products, our knowledge of other carbonyl compounds in fish tissues is largely of recent origin and a result of improvements in the fractionation and chromatography of 2,4-dinitrophenylhydrazones and general gas chromatography. It had been suspected for some time (Lundberg 1957) that the odor and flavor of oxidized fish oils was derived mainly from the presence of unsaturated carbonyl and dicarbonyl compounds; and it was reasonable to suppose that the carbonyl fraction would be of considerable significance in fish products generally.

Mangan (1959A, B), and Mangan et al. (1959) reported the presence of acetaldehyde, and probable dicarbonyl and α-hydroxycarbonyl compounds in frozen haddock. Merritt and Mendelsohn (1962) found both acetaldehyde and methyl ethyl ketone in chill-stored haddock. Hughes (1961) isolated acetaldehyde, propionaldehyde, acetoin, iso-butyraldehyde, and 2-methylbutyraldehyde as the main components of the neutral volatile fraction of cooked herrings, with smaller quantities of longer-chain carbonyl compounds. Groninger (1961), also, found acetoin in chill-stored fish. Subsequently, Hughes (1963) confirmed the presence of these compounds and identified tentatively: undecanal, nonanal, C_6-, C_7-, C_8-, C_9-, and C_{11}-alkan-2-ones, n- and *iso*-valeraldehyde, ethyl methyl ketone, hex-2-enal, hept-2-enal, pent-2-enal, and formaldehyde. He also isolated a group of fractions that were probably dicarbonyl and dienal in nature, and others that were branched-chain C_8-, and C_9-aldehydes and branched-chain C_6-, C_7-, C_8-, C_9-, and C_{11}-alkan-2-ones. These findings were similar in some respects to those of Yu *et al.* (1961) on isolates from oxidized salmon oil, and to the reports of Diemair and Schams (1962) and Diemair (1964) on uncooked stored fish. Hughes reported also on changes occurring in uncooked herring. His results were in agreement with other workers (Mendelsohn and Steinberg 1962; Ota 1958) in that there is a general increase in the concentration of carbonyls during chill storage, but it is apparent that proportional increases in different constituents can vary from species to species. Groninger (1961) failed to detect an increase in the acetaldehyde concentration in whole fish when they had been in chill storage for ten days.

Although he noted early work on the thresholds of some carbonyl compounds, Hughes (1963) concluded, after his extensive study, that nothing was known regarding the influence of "these carbonyls" on the flavor of cooked fish. Nevertheless, he did make the very pertinent observation, that the fall in rancidity, that occurs during post-canning storage, is accompanied by a decrease in the concentration of carbonyls. Almost concurrently with this work Guadagni *et al.* (1963) published further threshold data on some of the compounds reported upon by Hughes.

Evidence relating to the flavors of individual carbonyls to specific attributes of fish flavor has been reported by Diemair and Schams (1962), Diemair (1964), and Stansby and Jellinek (1964). On the basis of his work, Diemair suggested that the carbonyls of low molecular weight are associated with fresh flavor. The "tranig" odor components of fat-containing species come mainly from hexanal, heptanal, and hexenal, while the rancid and "talgigen" components belong to the higher constituents of the saturated and unsaturated fatty acids (e.g., nonanal, heptadienal, decanal). A strongly "metallic" component discussed by Diemair has many of the properties of oct-1-en-3-one (n-amyl vinyl ketone) (Forss 1963). Diemair and Schams isolated from stored fish also a carbonyl component with a "mushroom" odor. From its properties this was thought to have a dihydroxypropane skeleton. Forss (1963) has pointed out that there are strong similarities between certain components of fishy flavor in dairy products, and those isolated from stored fish by the German workers.

Alcohols.—Methanol and ethanol are constituents of chill-stored and cold-stored haddock fillets (Mangan 1959A, B; Mangan *et al.* 1959).

Free Lower Fatty Acids and Other Acids.—A considerable body of work has been carried out on increases in total lower fatty acid concentration and on individual acids, particularly acetic acid, formic acid, propionic acid, *n*-butyric acid, and *iso*-valeric acid (Hillig and Clark 1938; Hillig 1939A, B; Hillig *et al.* 1959; Clague 1942; Charnley 1945; Sigurdsson 1947; Hillig *et al.* 1958; Hughes 1960; Miyahara 1961). The flavors of the lower fatty acids are well in evidence in spoiling wet fish. Patton (1964) has recently reported on the thresholds of pure solutions.

Hashimoto (1964) reviewed Japanese work on the relevance of succinic acid and concluded that this compound is a "potent substance giving the 'meaty' taste in shellfish." He noted that the disodium salt can be used as a flavor additive but that its application is far more limited than monosodium glutamate because an excess confers too much of a shellfish-like flavor to foods. Hillig and his collaborators (Hillig *et al.* 1959) reported a fair degree of correlation between succinate concentration and an overall organoleptic evaluation in the flesh of tuna. Results with other species were insignificant.

Opinion varies as to the relevance of lactic acid as a flavor constituent of flesh foods. Wood (1961) considered that the compound contributes nothing to the flavor of meat extract, but Kazeniac (1961) reported that it contributes to the "sour, astringent" character in chicken broths. It has been recognized for many years that high concentrations can occur in fish muscle (Sharp 1934, 1935).

Volatile Sulfur Compounds.—The presence of hydrogen sulfide in fish products has been reported by a number of workers (Almy 1925; Tanikawa 1958; Hughes 1964A). Mangan (1959A, B) and Mangan *et al.* (1959) identified dimethyl sulfide in raw haddock. Merritt and Mendelsohn (1962) found diethyl sulfide and other sulfides in similar material in an advanced state of spoilage. These workers noted that the presence of large amounts of hydrogen sulfide, methyl mercaptan, and organic sulfides is a characteristic of "well aged, spoiled fish." Miyahara (1961) identified methyl mercaptan as a constituent of spoiling mackerel and tuna flesh.

Hughes (1964A) reported that there is also a progressive liberation of such compounds during the cooking of flesh. There has been general agreement that sulfur compounds are of considerable significance to fish flavor since the Obata school's study on the effects of admixture with other compounds in model systems.

Carbohydrates, Sugar Phosphates, etc.—Glycogen, while itself flavorless is claimed to contribute "body, harmony, and smoothness in taste" to a simulated extract of abalone meat (Hashimoto 1964). As is well known, however, this substance is substantially degraded in most fish muscle within a short period after death, if it has not disappeared before-hand during the death struggle in a commercial catching operation.

Glucose, ribose, and a trace of maltose are the sugars commonly occur-ring in fish muscle (Tarr 1953, 1955, 1958A, B, 1964; Jones 1958A, B; Burt 1961; Tarr and Leroux 1962; Hughes 1964B). Considerably greater quantities of glucose than that which occur in the true fish have been reported to be present in canned crab, together with rhamnose, galactose, and other sugars (Nagasawa 1958, 1960). Jones (1961) suggested that much of the characteristic sweetness of fresh fish flesh results from the presence of high initial concentrations of glucose. Hashimoto (1964) re-ported that a weak sweetness in "Uni" extracts was derived from glucose.

Very little work has been carried out on the flavors of sugar phosphates. While emphasizing the difficulties of simulating conditions in the food-stuff, Jones (1961) concluded from a study on solutions of these com-pounds at their maximum concentration, that they contributed "sweetish salty" character to fresh or chill stored fish. While there is some dis-cussion as to the validity of certain findings, a body of data has become available in recent years on concentrations of glucose 1-and 6-phosphates, fructose 1- and 6-phosphates, and ribose 1- and 5-phosphates in fish muscle (Jones and Burt 1960; Burt 1961; Burt and Jones 1961; Tarr and Leroux 1962; Burt 1964; Tarr 1964; Jones and Burt 1964).

BASES OF FLAVOR CHANGE DURING STORAGE AND PROCESSING

Chill Storage

The chemical changes that occur during chill storage result from the separate or combined effects of autolysis, the spoilage microflora, leaching by water from melting ice and spontaneous chemical reactions.

Shewan (1962) and Jones (1962A) have reviewed the activities of the spoilage by microflora and the tissue enzymes respectively. The effects of the former have been recognized for many years and expressed in chemical terms by the production of amines, lower fatty acids, mercap-tans, indole, skatole etc.

However, considerable flavor change occurs before the development of an active spoilage microflora. A loss of muscle constituents occurs as a result of leaching (Cutting 1951; Jones 1955A) and there is little doubt that both desirable and unwanted compounds are lost from the flesh in this way. Indications from work with an inert "marker," taurine, (Jones 1955A) show that, as one might expect, losses are most rapid in the initial phases. Conceivably, losses to the atmosphere could be important during early flavor deterioration.

Cann *et al.* (1962) showed that the flavor of unleached, sterile cod flesh lost its initial meaty sweetness and developed bitterness in a manner similar to the flesh of fish iced under conventional conditions. This lent support to earlier suggestions (Fieger and Friloux 1954) that autolysis could be implicated in initial flavor changes, and specific indications (Saito 1960; Jones 1960A, 1961) of the relevance of enzymatic activities toward nucleotides and sugar phosphates. Subsequent work on nucleotide interrelations with other compounds of the flesh (Hashimoto 1964) and flavor enhancement (Kuninaka *et al.* 1964) would appear to add further substance to these views although these have been questioned by Rhodes (1965). It is clear that concentrations of inosine 5′-monophosphate in fish muscle fall rapidly during early chill storage (Shewan and Jones 1957; Saito *et al.* 1959B; Saito 1961; Jones and Murray 1957, 1961, 1962; Jones 1963; Kassemsarn *et al.* 1963). The key enzymes in the complete sequence of flavor changes have been discussed recently (Jones 1962B). Many of the enzyme systems concerned in nucleotide degradation in Pacific species have been described by Tarr and his colleagues (Tarr 1955, 1958A, B, 1964; Tarr and Leroux 1962; Tomlinson and Creelman 1960). As noted above, adenosine 5′-monophosphate accumulates in shellfish muscle where it is a major flavor constituent (Arai 1960; Hashimoto 1964). Although the deaminating system is not operative in such tissues, the nucleotide is still subject to dephosphorylation by 5′-nucleotidase.

Burt (1964) and Tarr (1964) have discussed the autolytic systems governing hexose phosphate concentrations which, as indicated above, are significant during early storage. Shibata and Yoshimura (1962) carried out a detailed study of the limiting factors in glycolysis. In general the more important compounds, from a flavor standpoint, disappear more rapidly than the 5′-mononucleotides.

Perhaps it is in the interrelations between autolytic activities and the development of the spoilage microflora that the most fruitful area of mechanistic research into flavor change may lie in the near future. For instance, it is now apparent that the concentrations of many free amino acids in the muscles of chill-stored fish are controlled by the rate of utilization of the autolytically liberated compounds rather than by bacterial production (de Silva and Hughes 1960; Jones 1955B; Siebert and Schmitt 1964; Sanz Perez and Jones 1962; Shewan and Jones 1957). The significance of such control of amino acid concentrations to fish flavor is readily apparent from reference to such reviews as Bramstedt (1959, 1962A, B) and Hashimoto (1964).

Interrelationships between autolytic and bacterial activity are also clearly apparent in the field of nucleotide degradation. Kassemsarn *et al.* (1963) have summarized the known pathways. Both autolytic and bacterial agencies can liberate hypoxanthine. The latter also remove the purine by oxidation and ring cleavage (Kassemsarn *et al.* 1963; Avery *et al.* 1962).

From the known courses of development of the spoilage microflora (Shewan 1962) it seems likely that the dramatic compositional changes that take place during the 8 to 12 day storage period are associated with the development of particular groups of bacteria, principally *Pseudomonads*. Much work remains to be carried out before the composite activities of the microflora as a whole are clearly understood. A little progress has been made in one or two fields such as trimethylamine oxide reduction.

Little information is available on the full extent of "spontaneous" chemical reactions that may occur without the intervention of bacterial and tissue enzymes. Certain aspects of fat oxidation, and the cleavage of trimethylamine oxide to dimethylamine and formaldehyde are well-authenticated examples.

Frozen Storage

Of the chemical reactions leading to flavor deterioration in frozen fish, the most important is often the development of oxidative rancidity in the lipid constituents (Banks 1952).

Many of the enzymes that control the concentrations of other compounds, that are believed to be of significance to flavor, are active in frozen material. There is some temperature differential among activities along the principal pathway of nucleotide degradation (Jones 1963) but complete reaction can occur rapidly at temperatures just below the freezing point (Saito and Arai 1957, 1958). Changes in sugar phosphate concentrations indicate that certain enzymes along the glycolytic pathway are also active (Burt 1964). Enzymes affecting amino acid composition can be active in frozen fish (F. Bramstedt, personal communication).

From the development of brown discolorations in some frozen fish, it is likely that (apart from blood contamination considerations) carbonyl-amino reactions occur and, that they affect flavor. Little information is available on these reactions. For instance, the relative contributions of carbonyl compounds derived from fats and the carbohydrate fraction have not been established (Olcott 1962). Information is also lacking on the reactivity of different amino constituents under the conditions of frozen storage. Possibly, some parallel may be drawn from reactions in freeze-dried material. Such reactions are known to result in the development of bitterness. While it has been suggested that hypoxanthine liberation may be implicated in bitterness in frozen fish (Jones 1963) it seems very likely that carbonyl-amino reactions are at least as important under some conditions.

Freezing and thawing produce, in themselves, a significant deterioration in the flavor of very fresh fish. This has been related to enzymatic changes known to occur under these conditions (Jones 1963; Saito and Arai 1957, 1958). For instance, substantial production of hypoxanthine from mononucleotide occurs during the conventional plate freezing of eviscerated cod.

Dehydrated Fish

Matheson (1962) demonstrated the activity of tissue ferments in freeze-dried material. He suggested that the great differences between the storage properties of raw and pre-cooked fish are derived from differences in enzymic activity. It appears, therefore, that the situation is analogous to that of frozen fish in many respects.

Undoubtedly, much of the flavor deterioration that occurs in dehydrated material results from carbonyl-amino reactions. The relative contributions of different sugar reactants varies with the condition of the material to be dehydrated. Glucose and the hexose phosphates are of primary importance in fresh fish: ribose and ribose 5'-phosphate increase in relative concentration as the flesh stales, and they are inherently more potent "browners" (Tarr 1953, 1954, 1964; Jones 1958A, 1962C; Burt and Jones 1961). Some work has been carried out on the reactivities of amino constituents in freeze-dried fish muscle preparations and related model systems (Jones 1959A, C). Amino constituents that are not commonly studied in such reactions (e.g., anserine and 1-1-methylhistidine) were shown to be of considerable reactivity with ribose in phosphate-buffered systems. Browning reactions in dried fish products have been reviewed in some detail (Jones 1962C).

Canned Fish

Tarr (1953, 1954) examined sugar-amino reactions in canned fish and emphasized the key significance of ribose and phosphorylated sugars. Nagasawa (1960) summarized a series of investigations on crab canning, which presents certain differences, particularly in relation to sugar composition. Nagayama (1960A, B, 1962) carried out a series of investigations on model systems related to fish canning. Results were reminiscent of those reported by Jones (1959B, C) on dried material, particularly in relation to the high reactivity of imidazoles.

Hughes (1959, 1960, 1961, 1963, 1964A, B) examined changes in the concentration of a number of flavor constituents in herring muscle under conditions that simulated commercial canning operations. The results of this work have been indicated above under the headings of different groups of compounds. Probably its major contribution to the subject is a clear demonstration of a progressive disappearance of rancidity from canned herring, as a corollary of a decrease in the concentrations of individual carbonyl compounds. The studies on volatile sulfur compounds, free amino acids, and sugars indicated a strong similarity to reactions in other products.

CHEMICAL INDICES OF QUALITY

Analyses for many of the compounds discussed above have been carried out in a systematic manner to ascertain their potentials as indices of the quality of fish products. Thus the estimation of total volatile bases has exercised a number of workers (Wierzhchowski 1956; Sato 1960) with varying success according to the species of fish examined. Considerable attention has been given to the estimation of specific bases such as ammonia and trimethylamine. Well over 60 papers have been reported on the relation of freshness to the concentration of the latter compound in different species (e.g., Sigurdsson 1947; Luijpen 1958; Shewan and Ehrenberg 1957). It would appear that the general correlations were as good as or better than those obtained with the other older methods. Dimethylamine would appear to have certain advantages as an index, however: the concentrations increase during the period of the initial lag phase of the microflora (Shewan 1951).

A considerable body of work has been carried out by Hillig and his collaborators, and other workers (Hillig 1939A, B; Hillig et al. 1950; Hillig et al. 1958; Sigurdsson 1947; Clague 1942; Suzuki 1953) on concentrations of total and individual acids as quality indices. General observations on such procedures have been favorable, but some workers (Tomiyama and Yone 1953; Fieger and Friloux 1954) reported unsatisfactory correlations for such different materials as "Kamaboko" fish loaf and shrimp.

The presence of hydrogen sulfide in uncooked fish is invariably an indicator of definite spoilage (Farber 1965).

Analyses of volatile substances that react with strong oxidizing agents, have been examined by a number of groups, but particularly by Farber and his colleagues (Lang et al. 1944, 1945; Farber 1949; Farber and Cederquist 1953; Farber and Lerke 1958). Obviously, such analyses estimate a wide variety of volatile compounds, so that they may reasonably be expected to correlate with overall odor perception.

The estimation of total and individual volatile carbonyls, trapped as the 2,4-dinitrophenylhydrazones relates directly to freshness (Ota 1958).

Farber (1952) had shown the promise of such an approach from earlier observations on bisulfite binding.

As explained elsewhere, the mechanism of fat oxidation is not considered in this review. Specific tests for oxidation as a quality index have been discussed by numerous workers: peroxide tests (Lea 1931, 1938, 1952; Banks 1944; Fiedler 1941), aldehyde tests (Lea 1931; Yu and Sinnhuber 1957; Sinnhuber and Yu 1958; Andresson and Danielson 1961; Ryan and Stansby 1959; Schwartz and Watts 1957), Kreis test (Watts and Major 1946).

Of the nonvolatile, nitrogenous constituents, interest has centered on indole and skatole, histamine, free amino acids, and nucleotides and their derivatives.

From his own studies and those of numerous other workers, Farber (1965) concluded that indole and skatole were poor indicators of incipient spoilage. He considered also that the potential value of histamine estimation was limited in this respect.

The more recent work on quality indices often has been concerned with the estimation of individual amino acids. Shewan and Jones (1957) demonstrated that concentrations varied during chill storage, and suggested that the determination of free lysine was potentially more useful than that of other amino acids. The findings of Bramstedt and his colleagues (Bramstedt 1962A, B; Bramstedt and Wurtzbacher 1960) were in general agreement. From a further consideration of the innate seasonal variation of free amino acid composition (Jones 1959D) and a variability in some aspects of spoilage patterns (Shewan and Jones 1957; Miyauchi and Malins 1957; Ranke 1960) it seems to the reviewer that prospects for amino acid tests are less hopeful than they appeared a decade ago. The earlier "tyrosine value" procedures are of variable applicability, lacking sensitivity during early spoilage (Soudan 1950).

Shewan and Jones (1957) related the freshness of cod (on a time scale) to nucleotide dephosphorylation in the muscle. Dephosphorylation was determined from colorimetric ribose measurements on extracts fractionated by the classical barium procedure. This simple approach met with some success for other species (e.g., Sawant and Magar 1961). Subsequently, Saito et al. (1959A) correlated dephosphorylation in frozen fish with organoleptically determined quality. These workers estimated dephosphorylation by a more sophisticated but more time consuming technique involving the ion-exchange chromatography of extracts to separate a combined inosine + hypoxanthine fraction from mononucleotide. Separated fractions were evaluated by ultraviolet absorption measurements. Jones and Murray (1964) simplified this approach to a differential adsorption of phosphorylated compounds on to a suitable ion-exchange resin in suspension, leaving inosine and hypoxanthine in solution. Very rapid estimations of inosine 5′-monophosphate concentration and nucleotide dephosphorylation are obtainable.

From the time scale of the different stages of nucleotide degradation in true fish (Saito et al. 1959B; Kassemsarn et al. 1963; Jones 1963) it became apparent that the measurement of hypoxanthine, specifically, was likely to be of more general value as a quality index, as its appearance monitors both the rate of destruction of a compound known to confer desired flavor properties (inosine 5′-monophosphate) and probably the development of bitterness. A comparison with other methods of analysis for the purine indicates that specific enzymatic deterioration with xanthine oxidase is the method of choice (Anon. 1959, 1961, 1962; Jones 1960B, 1963, 1964; Jones et al. 1964; Spinelli et al. 1964). Very good correlations with flavor ratings have been obtained with cod, haddock, coalfish, and whiting. Correlations were good for flavor changes in sole during early storage but decreased with storage. Relationship to freshness on a time scale has been excellent for all the species of true fish examined to date.

While there was a reasonable expectation, on the properties of the compounds concerned, that such a test would be a useful index of quality, Jones et al. (1964) concluded from their results on different species, that the main value of the test lies in its monitoring of both autolytic and bacterial activities in a general sense. In this respect, hypoxanthine measurement appears to be more valuable than most others. However, it has been apparent for many years that patterns of spoilage can vary widely even within a species. In a situation where flavor is derived from a multiplicity of compounds, it is most unlikely that the analysis of any single compound would be an adequate cover for all eventualities. For instance it is unlikely that the hypoxanthine test will be as effective on invertebrates where the key autolytic nucleotide deaminating system is missing.

Farber (1965) has reviewed all but the latest developments in freshness testing *in extenso*.

CONCLUSIONS

Within the main categories of fish—fatty and nonfatty—there is some measure of uniformity in the character of fresh flavor. This can be explained (or at least, argued about) in terms of broad similarities among the free amino acids, free sugars, sugar phosphates, mononucleotides, etc. There is some evidence that known variations in composition with respect to such nonvolatile compounds can account for some of the flavor differences between species, and within species.

In general, however, most of the finer nuances of flavor, that distinguish species, appear to be associated with the "volatile" fraction of the flesh. Useful investigations have been carried out in the fields of carbonyl, sulfide, fatty acid, and amine chemistry but it will require much more work, particularly on the organoleptic evaluation of these compounds in the presence of others, to establish with any certainty whether the really important compounds have yet been examined at all. In some respects there appears to be a depressing similarity between the volatile fractions isolated from widely disparate foodstuffs.

More progress has been made in identifying many of the causative factors in the development of off-odors and off-flavors. This has resulted primarily from a search for objective indices of quality. While there has been a considerable "fall-out" to flavor chemistry from such research, the object of these exercises, a universally applicable quality test, is far from realization. Our developing understanding of the basic mechanisms of flavor changes indicates that there is every reason to believe that this state of affairs will continue, although we shall probably approach nearer to the ideal.

One cannot but reflect that the science might well have advanced a little further if some of the considerable quality test effort had been directed toward a more systematic approach to flavor chemistry, and to the underlying bases of changes and their control. Some progress has been made in the fields of chill- and frozen-storage, canning, and dehydration. Probably, the most significant advances have been made in lipid oxidation. Certain relevant areas of bacterial metabolism are reasonably well ventilated, but others are still obscure. Current trends in the industry may render some aspects of this field less pressing than they appeared in the past. There is evidence that autolysis exercises control over various aspects of flavor change, either directly, or through its effects on precursor systems. Perhaps further developments in this field will demonstrate direct liberations and removals of volatile components by autolytic systems.

A point of considerable relevance to general flavor research has emerged recently. Compounds have been isolated and found to be flavorful in pure solutions or in simple mixtures with other compounds present in the flesh. The flavors were similar to those observable in the flesh under some conditions. However, admixture of compounds and flesh resulted in no flavor change in the latter. Under the conditions of other experiments, concentrations of the compounds have changed considerably in the flesh with reportedly no flavor change. Obviously, if such reports can be substantiated under experimental conditions that withstand critical scrutiny (at both the physiological and chemical levels), the extensive observations that have been made on numerous compounds and mixtures of compounds will require re-evaluation. Masking, binding, and enhancing phenomenas are well-recognized, of course, but logically such observations suggest a complete analysis and reconstitution of flesh may be a necessary preliminary to a correct appraisal of the contributions of individual compounds to the flavor.

DISCUSSION

J. D. Ponting.—Does hypoxanthine have a flavor of its own, and if not how did you use it as a test compound for flavor?

N. R. Jones.—There is some dispute on this which relates to the pH at which the compound is tasted. I find it is bitter in pure solution at the concentration that occurs after ten days of chill storage of cod. Dr. Kazeniac finds it to be one of the bitter constituents of chicken flesh. Dr. Spinelli's recent work also indicates that the substance is bitter. However, some Japanese work suggests otherwise. The value of the estimation of hypoxanthine as a quality index is that it monitors effectively both the disappearance of inosine 5'-monophosphate a desirable compound from the muscle and the appearance of the bitter base. We have a very rapid method for determining hypoxanthine using a specific xanthine oxidase and we have recently automated the system using the Auto-Analyzer.

J. A. Dassow.—In connection with your comments on the nonprotein nitrogenous constituents, the nucleotide breakdown products, do you have an explanation for this?

N. R. Jones.—We have indications that variations in sweetness, for instance, relate to the glucose concentration. As you know, fish can feed on different constituents which can impart different flavors. The "blackberry" problem in fish, for instance, is where the organism it is feeding on, ultimately contributes enough dimethyl sulfide to the flesh to make it rather unpleasant.

J. A. Dassow.—How does this relate to nucleotide breakdown products, assuming that we are getting at some substances that contribute desirably or adversely to flavor?

N. R. Jones.—We actually found that the appearance of hypoxanthine in the flesh and the disappearance of IMP were not affected by external circumstances, such as variation in nutritional status, which do in fact affect overall flavor. Obviously there are large numbers of substances, other than hypoxanthine, which are important here.

R. O. Sinnhuber.—Could you comment on the iodine or iodoform-like flavor that we occasionally encounter in shrimp or sole? Would you say this is entirely feed or is this some other problem?

N. R. Jones.—Quite honestly, I do not know.

B. M. Slabyj.—Would you happen to know what is responsible for the radiation flavor in irradiated fish and what is the explanation for its disappearance during storage?

N. R. Jones.—No sir, I do not know. As far as I know, no one else does either.

BIBLIOGRAPHY

Almy, L. H. 1925. A method for the estimation of hydrogen sulfide in proteinaceous food products. J. Am. Chem. Soc. 47, 1381–1390.

Amano, K., and Bito, M. 1951. Consequence of free amino acids generated from decomposing fish muscle. Bull. Japan. Soc. Sci. Fisheries 16, No. 12, 10–16.

Amano, K., and Yamada, K. 1964. The biological formation of formaldehyde in cod flesh. F.A.O. symposium on the significance of fundamental research in the utilization of fish, Husum, Germany. Paper No. WP/II/9.

Andresson, K., and Danielson, C. E. 1961. Storage changes in frozen fish: a comparison of objective and subjective tests. Food Technol. 15, 55–57.

Anon. 1959. Ann. Rept. Dept. Sci. Industr. Res. Lond., Torry Research Station, p. 26. H.M. Stat. Office, London.

Anon. 1961. Ann. Rept. Dept. Sci. Industr. Res. Lond., Torry Research Station, p. 8. H.M. Stat. Office, London.

Anon. 1962. Ann. Rept. Dept. Sci. Industr. Res. Lond., Torry Research Station, p. 6. H.M. Stat. Office, London.

Arai, K. 1960. Acid-soluble nucleotides of marine invertebrates. I. Contents of nucleotides and their decomposition in shellfish muscle. Bull. Fac. Fisheries Hokkaido Univ. 11, 67–72, 225–229.

Avery, K. W. J., Cann, D. C., Hobbs, G., Murray, C. K., Jones, N. R., and Shewan, J. M. 1962. Quoted by Kassemsarn, B. O., Sanz Perez, B., Murray, J., and Jones, N. R. 1963. Nucleotide degradation in the muscle of iced haddock (Gadus aeglefinus), lemon sole (Pleuronectes microcephalus) and plaice (Pleuronectes platessa). J. Food Sci. 28, 28–37.

Bandt, H. J. 1946. Damage to the taste of fish. Beitr. Wass. Abwasser Fischereichem. No. 1, 36–39.

Banks, A. 1944. Method for studying the effects of antioxidants on the oxidation of aqueous suspension of unsaturated fatty acids. J. Soc. Chem. Ind. 63, 8.

Banks, A. 1952. The freezing and cold storage of herrings. Dept. Sci. Indus. Res. Lond. Food Invest. Bd. Spec. Rept. 55. H.M. Stat. Off., London.

Banks, A. 1962. Identifying quality changes in frozen fish. Bull. Inst. Intern. Froid. Suppl. 1.

Batzer, O. F., Santoro, A. T., and Landmann, W. A. 1962. Identification of some beef flavor precursors. J. Agr. Food Chem. 10, 94–96.

Beet, T. A. L. 1916. Phenolic odor in fish Z. Fleisch-u. Milchhyg. 36, 254.

Bramstedt, F. 1959. Substances responsible for taste and smell in fish. Arch. Fischereiwissen. 8, 94–103.

Bramstedt, F. 1962A. Amino acid composition of fresh fish and influence of storage and processing. In Fish in Nutrition, 61–67, E. Heen and R. Kreuzer (Editors). Fishing News (Books) Ltd., London.

Bramstedt, F. 1962B. The significance of variation in nucleotide, amino acid and carbohydrate contents of fish muscle in relation to quality evaluation. Fette, Seifen Anstrichmittel 64, 820–825.

Bramstedt, F., and Wurtzbacher, J. 1960. Biochemical investigations into the problem of establishing quality standards for sea fishes (in German). Fette, Seifen Anstrichmittel 62, 513–517.

Burt, J. R. 1961. Free sugars and sugar phosphates in muscle of chill-stored aquarium cod (Gadus callarias). J. Food Sci. 26, 462–468.

Burt, J. R. 1964. Sugar phosphates as indicators of fish quality. F.A.O. symposium on the significance of fundamental research in the utilization of fish. Husum, Germany. Paper No. WP/IV/3.

Burt, J. R., and Jones, N. R. 1961. Changes in sugar phosphates of chilled codling (Gadus callarias) muscle. J. Sci. Food Agr. 12, 344–348.

Cann, D. C., Jones, N. R., and Shewan, J. M. 1962. Quoted by Kassemsarn, B. O., Sanz Perez, B., Murray, J., and Jones, N. R. 1963. Nucleotide degradation in the muscle of iced haddock (Gadus aeglefinus), lemon sole (Pleuronectes microcephalus) and plaice (Pleuronectes platessa). J. Food Sci. 28, 28–37.

Charnley, F. 1945. The measurement of spoilage in herring stored under moderately low temperature conditions. Analyst 70, 168–172.

Clague, J. A. 1942. Application of volatile fatty acid determination to a study of canned Maine sardines. Food Research. 7, 56–67.

Cutting, C. L. 1951. Loss of weight and shrinkage of cod fish on trawlers. Fishing News (London). No. 1975, 10–13.

Davies, W. L., and Gill, E. J. 1936. Investigations on fishy flavor. J. Soc. Chem. Ind. 55, 141T–146T.

de Silva, N. N., and Hughes, R. B. 1960. Effects of tetracycline antibiotics on the proteolysis of fish muscle. Nature (London) 188, 663.

Diemair, W. 1964. Gas chromatography in the analysis of volatile odor and flavor components in fish flesh. F.A.O. symposium on the significance of fundamental research in the utilization of fish, Husum, Germany. Paper No. WP/4/9.

Diemair, W., and Schams, F. 1962. The application of physical research methods for the analysis of volatile odor and taste substances in foods. II. Investigations of carbonyl compounds in fresh and stored fish. Z. Anal. Chem. 189, 161–175.

Ebeling, G. 1931. Chemical investigation of waste waters from cellulose factories as regards fisheries. Wasser, 5, 192.

Farber, L. 1949. Chemical evaluation of odor intensity. Food Technol. 3, 300–304.

Farber, L. 1952. A comparison of various methods for the determination of spoilage in fish. Food Technol. 6, 319–324.

Farber, L. 1965. Freshness tests. In Fish as Food, Vol. 4, Part 2, 65–126, G. Borgstrom, (Editor). Academic Press, New York and London.

Farber, L., and Cederquist, A. 1953. The determination of volatile reducing substances (VRS) as an aid in quality control of fish products. Food Technol. 7, 478–480.

Farber, L., and Lerke, P. A. 1958. A review of the value of volatile reducing substances for the chemical assessment of the freshness of fish and fish products. Food Technol. 12, 677–680.

Fiedler, R. H. 1941. Peroxide test as a measure of oxidative liberation of fish oil. U.S. Fish Wildlife Service Admin. Rept. No. 41, 230–235.

Fieger, E. A., and Friloux, J. 1954. A comparison of objective tests for quality of Gulf shrimp. Food Technol. 8, 35–37.

Forss, D. A. 1963. Paper presented at 58th American Dairy Science Association Meeting, Purdue University, Lafayette, Indiana. (Abstract) Compounds with mushroom flavors in dairy products. J. Dairy Science 46, 614.

Groninger, H. S. 1961. Formation of acetoin in cod and other bottom-fish fillets during refrigerated storage. Food Technol. 15, 10–12.

GUADAGNI, D. G., BUTTERY, R., and OKANO, S. 1963. Odor thresholds of some organic compounds associated with food flavors. J. Sci. Food Agr. 14, 761–765.

HASHIMOTO, Y. 1964. Taste-producing substances in marine products. F.A.O. symposium on the significance of fundamental research in the utilization of fish, Husum, Germany. Paper No. WP/II/6.

HILLIG, F. 1939A. Determination of volatile acids as an approach to the evaluation of spoilage in canned herring roe. J. Assoc. Offic. Agr. Chemists 22, 116–118.

HILLIG, F. 1939B. Determination of volatile fatty acids as an approach to the evaluation of spoilage in canned sardines. J. Assoc. Offic. Agr. Chemists 22, 414–418.

HILLIG, F., and CLARK, E. P. 1938. A chemical procedure for evaluating spoilage in canned fish, especially salmon and tuna fish. J. Assoc. Offic. Agr. Chemists 21, 688–695.

HILLIG, F., PATTERSON, W. I., and MacLEAN, M. 1950. Succinic acid as an index of decomposition in tuna. J. Assoc. Offic. Agr. Chemists 41, 763–776.

HILLIG, F., SHELTON, L. R., and LOUGHREY, J. H. 1959. Chemical indices of decomposition in haddock. J. Assoc. Offic. Agr. Chemists 42, 702–708.

HILLIG, F., SHELTON, L. R., LOUGHREY, J. H., and EISNER, J. 1958. Chemical indices of decomposition in cod. J. Assoc. Offic. Agr. Chemists 41, 763–776.

HUGHES, R. B. 1959. Chemical studies on the herring (Clupea harengus). 1. Trimethylamine oxide and volatile amines in fresh, spoiling and cooked herring flesh. J. Sci. Food Agr. 10, 431–436.

HUGHES, R. B. 1960. Chemical studies on the herring (Clupea harengus). III. The lower fatty acids. J. Sci. Food Agr. 11, 47–53.

HUGHES, R. B. 1961. Chemical studies on the herring (Clupea harengus). VI. Carbonyl compounds formed during the heat processing of herring. J. Sci. Food Agr. 12, 822–826.

HUGHES, R. B. 1963. Chemical studies on the herring (Clupea harengus). VIII. Further observations on the production of carbonyls in heat-processed herring. J. Sci. Food Agr. 14, 893–904.

HUGHES, R. B. 1964A. Chemical studies on the herring (Clupea harengus). IX. Preliminary gas chromatographic study of volatile sulphur compounds produced during the cooking of herring. J. Sci. Food Agr. 15, 290–292.

HUGHES, R. B. 1964B. Chemical studies on the herring (Clupea harengus). X. Histidine and free sugars in herring flesh. J. Sci. Food Agr. 15, 293–299.

IGARASHI, H. 1938. The pungent principles of fishes produced by decrease in freshness. I. (in Japanese). J. Chem. Soc. Japan, 59, 1258–1259.

IGARASHI, H. 1939. The pungent principles of fishes produced by decrease in freshness. II. Bull. Japan. Soc. Sci. Fisheries 8, 158–160.

JONES, G. I. 1961. Phenol-like odors in fish. Their origin and avoidance. Pacific Fisherman, 59, No. 6, 45.

JONES, N. R. 1955A. The free amino acids of fish. Taurine in the skeletal muscle of codling (Gadus callarias). J. Sci. Food Agric. 6, 3–9.

JONES, N. R. 1955B. The free amino acids of fish. 1-Methylhistidine and β-alanine liberation by skeletal muscle anserinase of codling (Gadus callarias). Biochem. J. 60, 81–87.

JONES, N. R. 1958A. Free sugars in chill stored trawled codling (Gadus callarias) muscle. J. Sci. Food Agr. 9, 672–677.

JONES, N. R. 1958B. The estimation of free sugars in skeletal muscle of codling (*Gadus callarias*) and herring (*Clupea harengus*). Biochem. J. 68, 704–708.

JONES, N. R. 1959A. Kinetics of phosphate-buffered ribose-amino reactions at 40° and 70% relative humidity: systems related to the "browning" of dehydrated and salt cod. J. Sci. Food Agr. 10, 615–624.

JONES, N. R. 1959B. Pyruvic acid in the skeletal muscle of fresh and chill-stored, trawled codling (*Gadus callarias*). J. Sci. Food Agr. 10, 472–474.

JONES, N. R. 1959C. "Browning" reactions and the loss of free amino acid and sugar from lyophylised muscle extractives of fresh and stored codling. Food Research 24, 704–710.

JONES, N. R. 1959D. The free amino acids of fish. II. Fresh skeletal muscle from lemon sole (*Pleuronectes microcephalus*). J. Sci. Food Agr. 10, 282–286.

JONES, N. R. 1960A. Muscle biochemistry and fish flavors. New Scientist 7, 783–785.

JONES, N. R. 1960B. The separation and determination of free purines, pyrimidines and nucleoside in cod muscle. Analyst 85, 111–115.

JONES, N. R. 1961. Fish flavors. Proc. Flavor Chem. Symp. pp. 61–81. Campbell Soup Co., Camden, N. J.

JONES, N. R. 1962A. Fish muscle enzymes and their technological significance. *In* Recent Advances in Food Science, Vol. 1—Commodities, 151–166. J. Hawthorn and J. Muil Leitch (Editors). Butterworths, London.

JONES, N. R. 1962B. Enzyme systems in fish muscle related to flavor. (Proc. 1st. Intern. Congr. Food Sci. and Technol.) London (in press).

JONES, N. R. 1962C. Browning reactions in dried fish products. *In* Recent Advances in Food Science. Vol. 2. Processing, 74–78. J. Hawthorn and J. Muil Leitch (Editors). Butterworths, London.

JONES, N. R. 1963. Interconversion of flavorous nucleotide catabolites in chilled and frozen fish. Proc. XI Int. Cong. Refrig. Munich. Paper IV-5.

JONES, N. R. 1964. Hypoxanthine and other purine-containing fractions in fish muscle as indices of freshness. F.A.O. Symposium on the significance of fundamental research in the utilization of fish. Paper No. WP/IV/4.

JONES, N. R., and BURT, J. R. 1960. The separation and determination of sugar phosphates, with particular reference to extracts of fish tissue. Analyst 85, 810–814.

JONES, N. R., and BURT, J. R. 1964. A note concerning the occurrence of ribose 1-phosphate and fructose 1-phosphate in cod muscle post-mortem. F.A.O. Symposium on the significance of fundamental research in the utilization of fish, Husum, Germany. Paper No. WP/1/5.

JONES, N. R., and BURT, J. R. 1965. Unpublished data, Torry Research Station, Aberdeen, Scotland.

JONES, N. R., and MURRAY, J. 1957. Nucleotides in the skeletal muscle of codling (*Gadus callarias*). Biochem. J. 66, 5.

JONES, N. R., and MURRAY, J. 1960. The acid-soluble nucleotides of codling (*Gadus callarias*) muscle. Biochem. J. 77, 567–575.

JONES, N. R., and MURRAY, J. 1961. Nucleotide concentration in codling (*Gadus callarias*) muscle passing through rigor mortis at 0°. Z. vergleich. Physiol. 44, 174–183.

JONES, N. R., and MURRAY, J. 1962. Degradation of adenine- and hypoxan-thine-nucleotide in the muscle of chill-stored trawled cod (*Gadus callarias*). J. Sci. Food Agr. *13*, 475–480.

JONES, N. R., and MURRAY, J. 1964. Rapid measures of nucleotide dephos-phorylation in iced fish muscle. Their value as indices of freshness and of inosine 5′-monophosphate concentration. J. Sci. Food Agr. *15*, 684–690.

JONES, N. R., MURRAY, J., LIVINGSTON, E. I., and MURRAY, C. K. 1964. Rapid estimations of hypoxanthine as indices of the freshness of chill-stored fish. J. Sci. Food Agr. *15*, 763–774.

KAPELLER-ADLER, R., and KRAEL, J. 1930. Researches on the distribution of nitrogen in the muscles of different classes of animals (in German). Biochem. Z. *221*, 437–460.

KASSEMSARN, B. O., SANZ PEREZ, B., MURRAY, J., and JONES, N. R. 1963. Nu-cleotide degradation in the muscle of iced haddock (*Gadus aeglefinus*) lemon sole (*Pleuronectes microcephalus*) and plaice (*Pleuronectes platessa*). J. Food Sci. *28*, 28–37.

KAZENIAC, S. J. 1961. Chicken flavor. Proc. Flavor Chem. Symp. pp. 37–59. Campbell Soup Co., Camden, N. J.

KIMATA, M. 1961. The histamine problem. *In* Fish as Food, Vol. 1, 329–352, G. Borgstrom (Editor). Academic Press, New York and London.

KODAMA, S. 1913. On a procedure for separating inosinic acid. J. Tokyo Chem. Soc. (Tokyo Kwagaku Kwai Shi) *34*, 751.

KOMATA, Y. 1964. Unpublished data quoted by HASHIMOTO, Y. 1964. Taste-producing substances in marine products. F.A.O. Symposium on the significance of fundamental research in the utilization of fish, Husum, Ger-many. Paper No. WP/II/6.

KONOSU, S., and HASHIMOTO, Y. 1964. Unpublished data quoted by HASHI-MOTO, Y. 1964. Taste-producing substances in marine products. F.A.O. Symposium on the significance of fundamental research in the utilization of fish, Husum, Germany. Paper No. WP/II/6.

KONOSU, S., MAEDA, Y., and FUJITA, T. 1960. Evaluation of inosinic acid and free amino acids as tasting substances in the katsuobushi stock. Bull. Japan. Soc. Sci. Fisheries *26*, 45–48.

KUNINAKA, A., KIBI, M., and SAKAGUCHI, K. 1964. History and development of flavor nucleotides. Food Technol. *18*, 287–293.

LANG, O. W., FARBER, L., BECK, C., and YERMAN, F. 1944. Determination of spoilage in protein foodstuffs, with particular reference to fish. Ind. Eng. Chem. Anal. Ed. *16*, 490–494.

LANG, O. W., FARBER, L., and YERMAN, F. 1945. The "Stinkometer"—a new tool. Food Inds. *17*, 8–9, 116–118.

LEA, C. H. 1931. Oxidation of fats. Rept. Food Invest. Bd. Gt. Brit. 1930, 44. H. M. Stat. Office, London.

LEA, C. H. 1938. Rancidity in edible fats. Food Invest. Bd. Spec. Rept. *46*, 1–230. H. M. Stat. Office, London.

LEA, C. H. 1952. Methods for determining peroxides in lipids. J. Sci. Food Agr. *3*, 586–594.

LEA, C. H., and RHODES, D. 1951. Trimethylamine oxide and the autoxida-tion of unsaturated esters. J. Sci. Food Agr. *2*, 556–561.

LERKE, P. A., FARBER, L., and HUBER, W. 1961. Preservation of fish and shellfish by relatively low doses of beta radiation and antibiotics. Food Technol. *15*, 145–151.

Liston, J., Chapel, J. G., and Stern, J. A. 1961. The spoilage of Pacific Coast rockfish. 1. Spoilage in ice storage. Food Technol. *15*, 19–22.

Luijpen, A. F. M. G. 1958. Objective spoilage tests for fish stored under conditions other than normal chilling in ice. J. Sci. Food Agr. *9*, 410–417.

Lundberg, W. O. 1957. Fish oil research at the Hormel Institute. Com. Fisheries Rev., *19* (4a), 5–8.

Mangan, G. F. 1959A. Flavor and odor of fish—progress report. Com. Fisheries Rev. *21* (b), 21–27.

Mangan, G. F. 1959B. Dicarbonyl compounds as components of fish odor. Com. Fisheries Rev. *21*, No. 7, 21–23.

Mangan, G. F., Merritt, C., and Walsh, J. T. 1959. Chemical components of the odor of fish. Paper presented at 135th National Am. Chem. Soc. Meeting, Boston, Mass., April 5–10, p. 13A.

Mann, H. 1951. The influence of pollution of the Hamburg harbor on the taste of fresh fish-flesh. Städtehygiene Staufen Breissau 2, 123–125.

Matheson, N. A. 1962. Enzymic activity at low moisture levels and its relation to deterioration in freeze-dried foods. J. Sci. Food Agr. *13*, 248–254.

Mendelsohn, J. M., and Steinberg, M. A. 1962. Development of volatile carbonyls in haddock (*Melanogrammas aeglefinus*) flesh during storage at 2°C. Food Technol. *16*, 113–115.

Merritt, C., and Mendelsohn, J. M. 1962. Flavor of fish. Paper presented before the Division of Agricultural and Food Chemistry, Am. Chem. Soc., 142nd National Meeting, Atlantic City, N. J.

Miyahara, S. 1961. Gas liquid chromatographic separation and determination of volatile fatty acids in fish meat during spoilage. Bull. Japan. Soc. Sci. Fisheries *27*, 42–47.

Miyauchi, D. T., and Malins, D. C. 1957. Chemical compounds formed during the spoilage of fish. Com. Fisheries Rev. *19*, 26–29.

Moncrieff, R. W. 1951. The Chemical Senses. Leonard Hill, London.

Nagasawa, Y. 1958. The difference in the chemical composition of normal and browned crab meat. Bull. Japan. Soc. Sci. Fisheries *24*, 535–540.

Nagasawa, Y. 1960. Studies on the browning of canned crab meat (*Paralithodes camtschatica Til.*). Mem. Fac. Fisheries Hokkaido Univ. 8, No. 2, 1–98.

Nagayama, F. 1960A. Studies on the browning of fish flesh. II. Change of sugar content by heat process and browning. Bull. Japan. Soc. Sci. Fisheries *26*, 1026–1031.

Nagayama, F. 1960B. Studies on the browning of fish flesh. III. Browning caused by sugar with amino acid in phosphate buffer solution. Bull. Japan. Soc. Sci. Fisheries *26*, 1107–1113.

Nagayama, F. 1962. Studies on the browning of fish flesh. VII. Fluorescence and flavor of autoclaved sugar-amino acid system. Bull. Japan. Soc. Sci. Fisheries *28*, 45–48.

Obata, Y., Hoshi, K., and Matsuno, K. 1949. Chemical studies on the substance of fish smell. I. Substances concerned with fishy smell and natural coloration of fish-oil. Bull. Japan. Soc. Sci. Fisheries *15*, 412–414.

Obata, Y., and Matano, K. 1952. The flavor of katsuobushi. 2. Identification of volatile substances by paper chromatography (Japanese, English summary). J. Agr. Chem. Soc. Japan. *26*, 184–185.

OBATA, Y., and YAMANISHI, T. 1952. Chemical studies on the substance of fish smell. V. Aroma of cooked fish. Bull. Japan. Soc. Sci. Fisheries 17, 326–328.

OBATA, Y., YAMANISHI, T., and ISHIDA, M. 1950. Chemical studies on the substance of fish smell. II. Pyridine compounds as the substances concerned with fishy smell. Bull. Japan. Soc. Sci. Fisheries 15, 551–554.

OLCOTT, H. S. 1962. Marine products. In Symposium on Foods: Lipids and Their Oxidation, 173–189. H. W. Schultz, E. A. Day and R. O. Sinnhuber (Editors). Avi Publishing Co., Westport, Conn.

OTA, F. 1958. Carbonyl compounds in fish as related to deterioration. I. Detection of volatile carbonyl compounds formed in fish flesh. Bull. Japan. Soc. Sci. Fisheries 24, 334–337.

PATTON, S. 1964. Flavor thresholds of volatile fatty acids. J. Food Sci. 29, 679–688.

RANKE, E. 1960. The influence of storage on the free amino acids and peptides of ling (Molva vulgans) and coalfish (Gadus virens). (In German). Arch. Fischereiwiss. 11, 18–47.

REAY, G. A., and SHEWAN, J. M. 1949. The spoilage of fish and its preservation by chilling. Adv. Food Res. 2, 343–398.

RHODES, D. N. 1965. Nucleotide degradation during the extended storage of lamb and beef. J. Sci. Food Agr. 16, 447–451.

RYAN, B. A., and STANSBY, M. E. 1959. Measurement of rancidity in fishery products by 2-thiobarbituric acid method. Com. Fisheries Rev. 21, No. 1, 21–23.

SAITO, T. 1960. Tastes of fishes. Fishery products and inosinic acid. (In Japanese) Kagaku (Kyoto). 15, 101–107.

SAITO, T. 1961. Adenosine triphosphate and the related compounds in the muscles of aquatic animals. Bull. Japan. Soc. Sci. Fisheries 27, 461–470.

SAITO, T., and ARAI, K. 1957. Studies on the organic phosphates in muscle of aquatic animals. 5. Changes in muscular nucleotides of carp during freezing and storage. Bull. Japan Soc. Sci. Fisheries 23, 265–272.

SAITO, T., and ARAI, K. 1958. Slow freezing of carp muscle and inosinic acid formation. Arch. Biochem. 73, 315–319.

SAITO, T., ARAI, K., and TANAKA, T. 1958. Changes in adenine nucleotides of squid muscle. Nature (London) 181, 1127–1128.

SAITO, T., ARAI, K., and MATSUYOSHI, M. 1959A. A new method for estimating the freshness of fish. Bull. Japan. Soc. Sci. Fisheries 24, 749–750.

SAITO, T., ARAI, K., and YAJIMA, T. 1959B. Changes in purine nucleotides of red lateral muscle of rainbow trout. Nature (London) 184, 1415.

SANZ PEREZ, B., and JONES, N. R. 1962. Effects of tetracycline antibiotics on the products of anserinase action in chill stored haddock (Gadus aeglefinus) muscle. J. Food Sci. 27, 69–72.

SATO, Y. 1960. Examination on the freshness of bottom fish. Bull. Japan Soc. Sci. Fisheries 26, 312–316.

SAWANT, P. L., and MAGAR, N. G. 1961. Studies on frozen fish. 2. Some chemical changes occurring during frozen storage. Food Technol. 15, 347–350.

SCHWARTZ, M. G., and WATTS, B. M. 1957. Application of the thiobarbituric acid test as a quantitative measure of deterioration in cooked oysters. Food Research 22, 76–82.

SHARP, J. G. 1934. Post mortem breakdown of glycogen and accumulation of lactic acid. Proc. Roy. Soc. London B114, 506–512.

SHARP, J. G. 1935. Post mortem breakdown of glycogen and accumulation of lactic acid in fish muscle at low temperatures. Biochem. J. 29, 850–853.

SHEWAN, J. M. 1951. The chemistry and metabolism of the nitrogenous extractives of fish. Biochem. Soc. Symp. 6, 28–48.

SHEWAN, J. M. 1962. The bacteriology of fresh and spoiling fish and some related chemical changes. In Recent Advances in Food Science. Vol. 1—Commodities 167–193. J. Hawthorn and J. Muil Leitch (Editors). Butterworths, London.

SHEWAN, J. M., and EHRENBERG, A. S. C. 1957. Volatile bases as quality indices of iced North Sea cod. J. Sci. Food Agr. 8, 227–231.

SHEWAN, J. M., and JONES, N. R. 1957. Chemical changes occurring in cod muscle during chill storage and their possible use as objective indices of quality. J. Sci. Food Agr. 8, 491–498.

SHEWAN, J. M., MACINTOSH, R. G., TUCKER, C. G., and EHRENBERG, A. S. C. 1953. The development of a numerical scoring system for the sensory assessment of the spoilage of wet white fish stored in ice. J. Sci. Food Agr. 4, 283–298.

SHIBATA, T., and YOSHIMURA, K. 1962. Enzymic studies of the muscle of aquatic animals. IV. Limiting step in aerobic fructose 1,6-diphosphate glycolysis and the formation of α-glycerophosphate in fish and mollusk muscle. Bull. Japan. Soc. Sci. Fisheries 28, 514–517.

SIEBERT, G., and SCHMITT, A. 1964. Fish tissue enzymes and their role in the deteriorative changes in fish. F.A.O. symposium on the significance of fundamental research in the utilization of fish, Husum, Germany. Paper No. WP/II/3.

SIGURDSSON, G. T. 1947. Comparison of chemical tests on the quality of fish. Anal. Chem. 19, 892–902.

SIMIDU, W., HIBIKI, S., SIBATA, S., and TAKEDA, K. 1953A. Studies on muscle of aquatic animals. XVI. Distribution of extractive nitrogen in muscle of several kinds of Gastropod. Bull. Japan Soc. Sci. Fisheries 19, 871–881.

SIMIDU, W., KUROKAWA, Y., and IKEDA, S. 1953B. Studies on muscle of aquatic animals. XVII. Imidazole compounds in fish muscles with special reference to the taste of red muscle fishes (Japanese, English summary). Bull. Research Inst. Food Sci. Kyoto Univ. No. 12, 40–48.

SINNHUBER, R. O., and YU, T. C. 1958. 2-Thiobarbituric acid method for the measurement of rancidity in fishery products. II. The quantitative determination of malonaldehyde. Food Technol. 12, 9–12.

SIPOS, J. C., and ACKMAN, R. G. 1964. The association of dimethyl sulphide with the "blackberry" problem in cod from the Labrador area. J. Fish. Res. Bd. Canada, 21, 423–425.

SOUDAN, F. 1950. The deterioration of fish. Preservation of its freshness. Proc. Cong. Int. Poisson Aliment. (Paris) pp. 448–496.

SPINELLI, J. 1966. Effect of hypoxanthine on the flavor of fresh and stored low-dose irradiated petrale sole fillets. J. Food Sci. 30, 1063.

SPINELLI, J., EKLUND, M., and MIYAUCHI, D. 1964. Measurement of hypoxanthine in fish as a method of assessing freshness. J. Food Sci. 29, 710–714.

STANSBY, M. E. 1962. Speculations on fishy odors and flavors. Food Technol. 16, No. 4, 28–32.

STANSBY, M. E., and JELLINEK, G. 1964. Flavor and odor characteristics of fishery products with particular reference to early oxidation changes in menhaden oil. F.A.O. Symposium on the significance of fundamental research in the utilization of fish, Husum, Germany. Paper No. WP/IV/2.

SUZUKI, T. 1951. Water-soluble extract of shellfish Asari (*Venerpis semidecussata*) in winter. 1. Nitrogen-containing substances in the water boiled with living shellfish Asari. J. Pharm. Soc. Japan *71*, 195–198.

SUZUKI, T. 1953. Determination of volatile fatty acids for judging the freshness of fish. Bull. Japan. Soc. Sci. Fisheries *19*, 102–105.

TANIKAWA, E. 1958. Studies on the technical problems in the processing of canned salmon. Mem. Fac. Fisheries Hokkaido Univ. *6*, No. 2, 67–138.

TANIKAWA, E. 1959. Studies on the technical problems in the processing of canned crab. Mem. Fac. Fisheries Hokkaido Univ. *7*, 95–155.

TANIKAWA, E., and MOTOHIRO, T. 1959. Odorous components in refrigerating warehouses. Proc. X Int. Cong. Refrig. Copenhagen, 442–447.

TARR, H. L. A. 1953. Ribose and the Maillard reaction in fish muscle. Nature (London) *171*, 344–345.

TARR, H. L. A. 1954. The Maillard reaction in flesh foods. Food Technol. *8*, 15–19.

TARR, H. L. A. 1955. Fish muscle riboside hydrolases. Biochem. J. *59*, 386–391.

TARR, H. L. A. 1958A. Biochemistry of fishes. Ann. Rev. Biochem. *27*, 223–244.

TARR, H. L. A. 1958B. Lingcod muscle purine nucleoside phosphorylase. Can. J. Biochem. Physiol. *36*, 517–530.

TARR, H. L. A. 1964. Enzymatic degradation of glycogen and adenosine triphosphate in fish muscle. F.A.O. symposium on the significance of fundamental research in the utilization of fish, Husum, Germany. Paper No. WP/II/7.

TARR, H. L. A., and LEROUX, M. 1962. A note concerning the origin and quantitative distribution of acid-soluble phosphorus compounds and free sugars in fish muscle. J. Fish. Res. Bd. Canada, *19*, 519–520.

THAYSEN, A. C. 1936. The origin of an earthy or muddy taint in fish. 1. The nature and isolation of the taint. Ann. Appl. Biol. *23*, 99–104.

THAYSEN, A. C., and PENTELOW, F. T. K. 1936. The origin of an earthy or muddy taint in fish. II. The effect on fish of the taint produced by an odoriferous species of *Actinomyces*. Ann. Appl. Biol. *23*, 105–109.

TOI, B., IKEDA, S., and MATSUNO, T. 1961. Paper presented at the meeting of the Japan Home Economics Association, October. Quoted by HASHIMOTO, Y. 1964. Taste-producing substances in marine products. F.A.O. symposium on the significance of fundamental research in the utilization of fish, Husum, Germany. Paper No. WP/II/6.

TOMIYAMA, T., and YONE, Y. 1953. Studies on methods of determining freshness of foods. VI. A comparative study of methods of determining freshness of "Kamaboko." Bull. Japan. Soc. Sci. Fisheries *18*, 521–524.

TOMLINSON, N., and CREELMAN, V. M. 1960. On the source of free ribose formed post mortem in the muscle of lingcod (*Ophiodon elongatus*). J. Fish. Res. Bd. Canada, *17*, 603–606.

UDO, S., and SATO, T. 1962. J. Agric. Chem. Soc. Jap. *36*, 838. Quoted by HASHIMOTO, Y. 1964. Taste-producing substances in marine products.

F.A.O. symposium on the significance of fundamental research in the utilization of fish, Husum, Germany. Paper No. WP/II/6.

WATTS, B., and MAJOR, R. 1946. Comparison of a simplified quantitative Kreis test with peroxide values of oxidizing fats. Oil and Soap 23, 222–225.

WESTFALL, B. A. 1946. Stream pollution hazards of wood pulp mill effluents. U. S. Fish and Wildlife Service, Fish Leaflet No. 174.

WIERZHCHOWSKI, J. 1956. Some chemical indications of fish spoilage. Przemysl. Spozywczy. 10, No. 4, 162–165.

WOOD, T. 1961. The browning of ox-muscle extracts. J. Sci Food Agr. 12, 61–69.

YOSHIMURA, K., and KUBO, S. 1953. Biochemical studies on "surume-ika" (Ommastrephes sloani pacificus). 1. Nitrogen fraction and contained amino acids in muscle and in extracted matter with water. Bull. Fac. Fisheries Hokkaido Univ. 3, 205–210.

YU, T. C., DAY, E. A., and SINNHUBER, R. O. 1961. Autoxidation of fish oils. 1. Identification of volatile monocarbonyl compounds from autoxidized salmon oil. J. Food Sci. 26, 192–197.

YU, T. C., and SINNHUBER, R. O. 1957. 2-Thiobarbituric acid method for the measurement of rancidity in fish products. Food Technol. 11, 104–108.

CHAPTER 13

O. W. Parks | Milk Flavor

INTRODUCTION

The flavor of fresh fluid milk is difficult to describe because basically milk is a bland product. From a gustatory standpoint, it can have either a slight sweet character as a result of its lactose content, or a slight salty character due to the presence of chloride salts. Fresh milk imparts a pleasant smooth sensation to the mouth and there should be no evidence of astringency (Keeney 1961). A basic olfactory quality, characteristic of all fresh milks, exists, but the normal intensity of the flavor is such, that for all practical purposes, milk has very little flavor. This is not to suggest that all milks are flat since the flavor of milk is highly suscepti-ble to change as a result of farm and manufacturing practices, in addition to changes which occur spontaneously in the milk itself. Off-flavors resulting from these practices and spontaneous changes, although abnormal, are eventually accepted by the consumer as the normal flavor when their presence and intensity is consistent. It is only when the intensity of the normal flavor changes or the sudden presence of other flavors appear that the consumer objects. The dairy manufacturer is confronted, therefore, with the problem of marketing a product with uniform flavor, whether it be free of or contain slight off-flavors. A knowledge of the characteristic flavor and the off-flavors which can arise, including the conditions conducive to formation, are of utmost importance to the dairy industry.

CHARACTERISTIC FLAVOR OF MILK

At present, it is not definitely known what compounds contribute to the characteristic flavor of milk. Low molecular weight compounds present in trace amounts such as acetone, acetaldehyde, butyric acid, and certain other low molecular weight fatty acids have been suggested (Jenness and Patton 1959) as contributors to the flavor. Methyl sulfide, shown to be a constituent of fresh milk and detectable on cows breath, imparts a flavor highly characteristic of fresh milk (Patton *et al.* 1956). Other low molecular weight compounds identified in fresh milk include formaldehyde, butanone-2, pentanone-2, hexanone-2, and heptanone-2 (Wong and Patton 1962). Studies not related to the characteristic flavor, but employing fresh milk as control have resulted in the identifica-tion of the C_3 to C_{12} normal, saturated aldehydes and the C_{13} to C_{16}

normal and branched chain saturated aldehydes (Parks *et al.* 1963; Wishner and Keeney 1963). At the concentrations detected, the individual aldehydes would not appear to affect the overall flavor of the product, but collectively their effect remains to be determined.

Several flavor compounds identified in fresh dairy products must also be given some consideration as to their contribution to the characteristic flavor of fresh fluid milk. Among these compounds are (1) diacetyl—an accepted flavor constituent of fresh butter (Jenness and Patton 1959), (2) isovaleraldehyde—observed in fresh cream (Wong 1963), (3) 4-*cis*-heptenal—reported to impart a creamy flavor to fresh butter (Begemann and Koster 1964), and (4) δ-lactones—flavor constituents of butter and shown to occur in fresh cream (Boldingh and Taylor 1962) and pasteurized milk (Patton 1961).

Most flavors, at least in dairy products, cannot be attributed to one compound, but rather to a mixture of compounds; whereas one compound will show different flavor characteristics at various concentrations, mixtures of compounds should accentuate this condition. It is significant that the compounds which have been implicated in the characteristic flavor of milk have also been observed in higher concentrations in many of the off-flavors which arise in milk. For example, methyl sulfide at concentrations distinctly above threshold imparts a cowy flavor to milk (Patton *et al.* 1956), an off-flavor which has also been associated with high concentrations of ketones (Josephson and Keeney 1947). Observations, such as these, must be considered when defining the characteristic or normal flavor of a bland product which is subject to various off-flavors. Some of the off-flavors of milk and how they arise to alter the flavor is the main topic of this presentation.

FEED FLAVORS

It was recognized as early as 1757 (Bradley 1757) that the feed consumed by the cow was a contributing cause of abnormal flavors in milk and the literature contains literally hundreds of publications and several comprehensive reviews on the subject (Strobel *et al.* 1953; Babcock 1938). The role of feeds in the flavor of milk does not, however, follow a standard pattern. The early literature clearly indicates that milk produced on certain feeds contains flavors characteristic of the feed consumed, while other feeds impart flavors which are not characteristic of the feed. Furthermore, certain highly flavored feeds do not impart flavors, or only marginal flavors, whereas some lightly flavored feeds impart strong off-flavors.

Feed flavors can be controlled to a certain extent by proper feeding practices such as removing animals from pasture a few hours prior to milking, feeding highly flavored feed immediately after milking, keeping barns well ventilated, providing high quality feeds essentially free of weeds, etc. (Jenness and Patton 1959; Babcock 1938). Although these practices have lessened, to a great extent, the intensity of feed flavors in milk, they do not in all cases prevent their appearance. It is quite evident that the feed consumed and the animals' physiological processes influence the final flavor.

Recently, a Cornell team conducted a series of experiments (Dougherty *et al.* 1962; Shipe *et al.* 1962) which demonstrated the role of three pathways in the transfer of feed flavors to milk. Two animals were fitted with tracheal and ruminal fistulae and the experiment was so designed that flavor substances under study could be added directly into the rumen or into the lungs. Furthermore, eructated gases from the rumen were allowed to pass into the lungs or prevented from doing so by passing fresh air into the tracheal fistula. The results of this study are summarized in Table 41. When the vapors of an onion slurry were intro-

TABLE 41

TRANSMISSION OF FLAVOR FROM ONIONS TO MILK[1]

Onion slurry → Tracheal cannula → lungs	No flavor up to 90 min.
Fresh air → Tracheal cannula Onion slurry → Ruminal cannula	Flavor intensity low up to 45 min.
Cow breathing normally Onion slurry → Ruminal cannula	Pronounced flavor in 15 min.
Onion slurry incubated 30 min. at 37°C. → lungs with rumen ingesta	Pronounced flavor in 15 min.
Rumen ingesta → lungs	No flavor up to 90 min.

[1] Dougherty *et al.* (1962).

duced into the trachea, no detectable off-flavor was observed in the milk after 90 minutes. When the slurry was introduced into the rumen and eructated gases prevented from entering the lungs, a low level of flavor was detected in the milk. A pronounced flavor occurred in the milk in a short period of time when the eructated gases were not excluded from the lungs. The role of the rumen in liberating flavor substances from onions which are transmitted to the milk becomes evident when the onion slurry is incubated with rumen ingesta and the vapors then passed through the tracheal fistula into the lungs. It must be noted here, that the off-flavor which occurred in the milk was not characteristic of the onion. Similar experiments on other substances gave rise to off-flavors which were rather typical of the feed. Employing the same techniques, the introduction of various low molecular weight alcohols, esters, aldehydes and ketones, compounds identified in the volatiles of grass and corn silage (Morgan and Pereira 1962A and B) resulted in off-flavors in the milk. There was no apparent difference between the methods of transmission, although it was observed that the flavors appeared in the milk much more rapidly when introduced into the lungs than through the digestive system. It must be noted that although, with a few exceptions the compounds administered in these studies gave rise to off-flavors, it was necessary to introduce 25 to 75 ml. of most of the compounds to attain these off-flavors. Honkanen and co-workers (Honkanen et al. 1964) have carried out similar experiments which are unique in several respects. The most unique aspect of their work is that the animals are producing milk on an odorless, purified diet consisting of cellulose, starch, sucrose, urea, inorganic ammonium salts, minerals, Vitamins A and D, and maize oil (Virtanen and Lampila 1962). The animals reportedly produce milk with the characteristic milk flavor, but more important, free of off-flavors as a result of feeds and feeding practices. Hence, the product is ideally suited for studying the transfer of flavor and potential flavor compounds into milk. The results of studies in which 1 to 2 gram quantities of various compounds were added to the rumen and recovered from the milk by vacuum distillation techniques and analyzed quantitatively by gas chromatography are reported in Table 42. Although the percentage transfer is low, the authors conclude that as a result of an additive effect, some classes of compounds can give distinct off-flavors to the milk. The results are interesting in many respects, since they may explain why certain feeds do not impart off-flavors to milk while others impart flavors which are not characteristic of the feed consumed. As can be observed, aliphatic alcohols with an odd-number of carbon atoms are transferred to the milk at a greater degree than others. Of the ethyl esters administered, only those with an even number of carbon atoms in the fatty acids enter the milk while the methyl esters are not transferred in detectable amounts. Only traces of the aldehydes administered, with the exception of 2-methylpropanal, were transferred. The maximum concentration of the higher molecular weight compounds is reached in the milk after a longer period of time following administration of these compounds. This latter observation may explain the differences in time elapsed between feeding and the presence of detectable off-flavors which occur when different feeds are consumed.

As mentioned previously, those methods employed to prevent or lessen the effect of feeds on the flavor of milk are, for the most part, those which lengthen the time between feeding and milking. Petersen and Brereton (1942), following experiments on the inhalation of various compounds, suggested that an equilibrium of flavor compounds from

TABLE 42

TRANSFER OF SOME ALIPHATIC COMPOUNDS TO MILK VIA THE RUMEN[1]

Substance	Amount Fed, Gm.	Con. at the Maximum, μg./liter Milk	Total Amount Transferred to Milk, μg.	Percentage of Total Amount Fed
Alcohols				
n-Pentan-1-ol	2	380	250	0.013
n-Hexan-1-ol	2	30	20	0.001
n-Heptan-1-ol	2	120	100	0.005
n-Octan-1-ol	2	?	...	...
n-Nonan-1-ol	2	75	100	0.005
cis-Hex-3-en-1-ol	2	45	25	0.0013
trans-Hex-3-en-1-ol	3	25	15	0.0005
dl-Oct-1-en-3-ol	1	20	15	0.0015
Aldehydes				
2-Methyl-propanal	2	1500	600	0.03
Hexanal	2	15	10	0.0005
Heptanal	2	20	10	0.0005
Octanal	2	30	10	0.0005
Ketones				
Pentan-2-one	2	1300	1000	0.05
Hexan-2-one	2	1100	800	0.04
Heptan-2-one	2	750	250	0.013
Octan-2-one	2	490	150	0.0075
Nonan-2-one	2	150	50	0.0025
Decan-2-one	2	60	30	0.0015
Undecan-2-one	2	40	25	0.0013
Octan-3-one	2	50	25	0.0013
Oct-1-en-3-one	2	...	...	...
Esters				
Methyl esters of C_6-C_{10} fatty acids	2	...	...	...
Ethyl esters of C_5, C_7, C_9 fatty acids	2	...	...	...
Ethyl butanoate	2	120	120	0.006
Ethyl hexanoate	2	60	60	0.003
Ethyl octanoate	2	120	100	0.005
Ethyl decanoate	2	120	100	0.005
Butyl 2-methyl-propanoate	1	300	160	0.016
Butyl butanoate	1	160	120	0.012
Butyl 3-methyl-butanoate	1	140	90	0.009
Butyl pentanoate	1	200	150	0.015
Butyl hexanoate	1	260	170	0.017
Butyl octanoate	1	110	75	0.0075

[1] Honkanen et al. (1964).

feeds exists between the lungs, blood, and milk. In time, the concentration in the lungs becomes low, shifting the equilibrium away from the milk; hence, decreasing the concentrations of these compounds in the final product.

RANCID FLAVOR

All raw milks are susceptible to the development of rancid flavors as a result of the liberation of fatty acids by lipases, enzymes native to milk.

At least two different lipase systems have been reported (Tarassuk and Frankel 1957) in milk, one irreversibly adsorbed on the fat globule membrane when freshly drawn milk is cooled and the other associated with the casein in the milk plasma. However, as many as four systems have been indicated (Gutfreund 1963). Despite the differences with regard to the number of systems which are present, one of which has been recently isolated (Chandran and Shahani 1963), it is obvious from the literature, that more than one system is operative.

The appearance of rancid flavor in market milk seems to follow a seasonal pattern. The greatest incidence of the off-flavor has been reported to occur in the late fall and early winter months (Hileman and Courtney 1935). This seasonal trait has been correlated with late stages of lactation and the practical observation that green pastures decrease and dry feeds increase the incidence of the off-flavor (Tarassuk et al. 1962).

Basically, raw milks can be classified into either one of two groups with regard to lipase activity, (1) those which develop rancid flavors spontaneously without any treatment other than cooling of the freshly drawn milk, and (2) those which develop rancid flavors only after activation treatments (Schwartz 1965). Nonspontaneous lipolysis occurs in raw milk by several activation treatments. These include, (a) excessive agitation, (b) homogenization, (c) separation or clarification, (d) warming cold milk to 27°C. or 32°C. and recooling to lower temperatures, (e) freezing and thawing, and (f) the addition of small amounts of raw milk to pasteurized, homogenized milk (Jenness and Patton 1959). Since pasteurization destroys the lipases of milk, the problem of rancidity is really one of handling the raw product. In recent years, the problem of hydrolytic rancidity has been aggravated by modern trends of handling raw milk, some of which are the pumping of milk from the milking machine to the holding vats through pipelines (Speer et al. 1958), the use of milk measuring devices in pipelines (Janzen 1963), and bulk tank hauling of milk (Jenness and Patton 1959) all of which create varying degrees of agitation.

Milkfat is unique among fats in that it contains substantial amounts of low molecular weight fatty acids. It has been suggested (Jenness and Patton 1959) that the release of these lower acids, especially butyric acid, imparts to milk its characteristic rancid flavor. There is available in the literature, indirect support for this contention. It has been demonstrated that butyric acid is a major constituent liberated from milkfat by lipase activity (Harper 1955). It was originally suggested by Harper that milk lipases showed a specificity for liberating butyric acid from milkfat triglycerides. Recent work has demonstrated, however, that the enzymes show a specificity for the alpha position of tri-glycerides (Gander and Jensen 1960) and most of the butyric acid is esterified in the alpha position (Jensen *et al.* 1960). Nevertheless, with our present knowledge of the additive effect of compounds in the same class on the flavor of a product (Day *et al.* 1963), it is difficult to ascribe the off-flavor to one particular fatty acid.

OXIDIZED FLAVOR

If any uncertainty remains that the milks from individual animals vary in their susceptibility to the spontaneous development of off-flavors, such doubt is removed when one considers the development of oxidized flavor in fluid milk. The freshly drawn milk of some animals develops an off-flavor within hours after cooling while that of others resists oxidative deterioration even though relatively large amounts of copper have been added to the product. Investigators have gone so far as to show (Guthrie and Brueckner 1934) that the milks from the individual quarters of the same animal differ in their susceptibility to oxidative deterioration. It has been reported (Potter and Hankinson 1960) that as many as 23% of the animals in a herd will produce milk which will develop an oxidized flavor within 24 to 48 hours storage and as was the case with rancid flavor, the incidence of the off-flavor increases when the animals are on dry feeds and decreases during pasture feeding (Greenbank 1948)—reportedly due to the differences in the antioxidative properties of the feeds (Krukovsky 1961).

It is not within the scope of this presentation to review the literature regarding the mechanisms involved in this phenomenon, since recent reviews on the subject are available (Riel 1952; Patton 1962; Parks 1965). It has been demonstrated (Greenbank 1940) that a correlation exists between the appearance of the off-flavor and conditions favoring a mild oxidation. The resistance of some milks to undergo oxidative deterioration, even in the presence of added copper, has been explained on its resistance to change in the oxidation-reduction potential (Greenbank 1940).

The site of oxidation in fluid milk is the phospholipids associated with the fat globule membrane (Smith and Dunkley 1959) and indeed the inhibition of spontaneous autoxidation in fluid milk is accomplished by homogenization which physically alters the membrane surrounding the fat globules. The constituents of milk which have been implicated in the mechanism include the ratio of ascorbic to dehydroascorbic acid, natural copper complexed with the proteins in the fat globule membrane, and the phospholipids and oxygen dissolved in the system.

The role of enzymes in the mechanism has been proposed on several occasions (Kende 1932; Aurand and Woods 1959) and rejected on just as many (Smith and Dunkley 1960 and 1962). Recently, Patton (1962) has compared the system previously described to an enzyme system and suggests that the controversy of enzymatic vs. nonenzymatic is a question of semantics regarding the definition of an enzyme.

TABLE 43

QUANTITATIVE CARBONYL ANALYSES ON THE BUTTEROIL FROM NONOXIDIZED AND SPON-
TANEOUSLY OXIDIZED FLUID MILK[1]

| Carbonyl | Concentration in Parts Per Billion of 4% Milk | |
	Nonoxidized Milk	Spontaneously Oxidized Milk
Pentanal	1.46	2.25
Hexanal	2.38	13.48
Heptanal	6.95	6.04
Octanal	1.84	1.95
Nonanal	1.65	3.04
Decanal	0.97	1.12
Undecanal	0.31	0.27
Dodecanal	0.74	2.06
C_{13}-C_{16} Sat. Ald.	8.90	11.25
2-Hexenal	. . .	0.09
2-Heptenal	. . .	0.39
2-Octenal	0.19	0.55
2-Nonenal	0.24	0.62
2-Decenal	0.59	1.17
2-Undecenal	0.58	1.08
2,4-Nonadienal	. . .	0.39
2,4-Decadienal	0.17	0.83
2,4-Undecadienal	. . .	0.12
2,4-Dodecadienal	. . .	0.22

[1] Parks et al. (1963).

Table 43 represents the carbonyl compounds identified and quantitized in the fat of nonoxidized and spontaneously oxidized fluid milk as judged by a 10 member taste panel. As one might expect, the compounds identified do not differ significantly from those reported in other oxidized dairy products (Forss et al. 1955; El-Negoumy et al. 1961). The differences in flavor of the two products can be attributed, for the most part, to the concentrations of some of the individual compounds. Although the compounds identified in the control did not impart an oxidized flavor to the milk, one cannot conclude that the carbonyls did not influence the flavor, which was judged to have a definite feed flavor.

SUNLIGHT FLAVOR

When milk is exposed to direct sunlight, for even very short periods of time, an off-flavor develops which has been described as resembling cooked cabbage and burning hair.   No one deliberately exposes milk to sunlight, but this can conceivably occur when glass bottled milk is delivered at the home doorstep or allowed to set out on the kitchen table in full view of the sun's rays.   Although direct sunlight is the most effective catalyst of the off-flavor, incandescent or fluorescent light to which milk is frequently exposed during handling, processing, and storage can be contributive (Smith and MacLeod 1955).   The early literature refers to the flavor defect under the general term of sunlight, but actually two distinct flavors occur in whole milk exposed: an oxidized flavor as a result of lipid oxidation and an activated flavor which originates in the proteins of milk.

The carbonyls in whole milk exposed to sunlight have been reported (Wishner and Keeney 1963) and they do not, for the most part, differ qualitatively from those reported for spontaneously oxidized milk or copper induced oxidation of skimmilk.   The authors do not report the presence of 2,4-dienals in the sunlight exposed milk but this may be the result of the size of samples analyzed (500 ml.).

The activated flavor has been shown to originate in the proteins of milk and is dependent, although not entirely, on the presence of riboflavin (Flake et al. 1940; Patton 1954).   The off-flavor has been attributed to the reaction of methionine with riboflavin and somewhat of a controversy exists as to the compound or compounds which arise to impart the characteristic flavor.   Methional, as a result of its formation from methionine by the Strecker degradation and the similarity in flavor with that of exposed milk was originally proposed as the compound responsible for the defect (Patton and Josephson 1953; Patton 1954).   The presence of methional could not be confirmed, however, in studies on the carbonyls in sunlight exposed milk (Wishner and Keeney 1963) despite methods capable of accomplishing this.   Ballance (1961) has reported that methional is further degraded to methyl mercaptan, dimethyl sulfide and acrolein during the Strecker degradation of methionine.   Samuelsson (1961 and 1962), although acknowledging that methional can result in milk by the Strecker degradation of free methionine, reported that the aldehyde is not liberated when methionine is present in a peptide linkage.   Instead, highly flavorful mercaptans, sulfides, and disulfides were shown to result from the irradiation of model peptides.

Recently, it has been reported (Zittle 1963; Zittle et al. 1964) that a loss of tryptophan, histidine, tyrosine, cystine, and methionine accompanies photo-oxidation of β-casein and α_s-casein.   This suggests that flavor compounds, in addition to those derived from methionine, may play a significant role in the activated flavor of milk.

TABLE 44

THE EFFECT OF HEATING ON THE OXIDATION-REDUCTION POTENTIAL, FLAVOR AND NITRO-
PRUSSIDE REACTION OF MILK[1]

Heat Treatment	O-R (Volts)	Flavor	Nitroprusside Reaction
None	0.2441	Normal	—
62.8°C., 30 min.	0.2423	Normal	—
71.1°C., momentarily	0.2426	Normal	—
76.7°C., momentarily	0.2349	Cooked ±	±
82.2°C., momentarily	0.2331	Cooked + +	+
87.8°C., momentarily	0.2025	Cooked + + + +	+ + +

[1] Josephson and Doan (1939).

HEATED FLAVORS

With few exceptions, all market milk is pasteurized at 61.7°C. for 30 minutes by the holding process or 71.7°C. for 15 seconds in the high-temperature, short-time process. An organoleptic comparison of milk before and after pasteurization readily demonstrates that the treatment is not without effect on the flavor of the product. Although little is known with regard to the changes which occur at pasteurizing temperatures, it is to be expected that the loss of volatile compounds is as much a contributing factor as is the formation of new heat generated flavor constituents.

When milk is heated to approximately 74°C. or higher, even momentarily, a distinct cooked flavor develops (Gould and Sommer 1939; Josephson and Doan 1939) the intensity of the flavor being a function of the temperature and duration of heating. The flavor is the result of volatile sulfides, hydrogen sulfide in particular (Jenness and Patton 1959), which are liberated from the activated sulfhydryl groups of β-lactoglobulin and to a lesser extent the proteins of the fat globule membrane (Hutton and Patton 1952). Table 44 demonstrates the effect of various heat treatments on sulfhydryl activity as measured by the nitroprusside test and the appearance of a cooked flavor. Accompanying the appearance of a cooked flavor, is a lowering of the oxidation-reduction potential of the system—a change which is beneficial when one considers the keeping quality of sterile milks.

As the heat treatment is prolonged at 74°C or increased to higher temperatures, the cooked flavor, at some undetermined point, gives way to a caramelized flavor and the initiation of Maillard type reactions take place.

DRY AND STERILE CONCENTRATED MILKS

Since World War II, considerable research has been conducted on preparing dry and sterile concentrated milks as a means of storing milk for future consumption, as a reconstituted fluid beverage. The major goal is to produce and maintain a product which, when reconstituted will have a flavor typical of fresh fluid milk. Various problems accompany such products, not the least important of which is changes which occur in the flavor as a result of heat processing and storage conditions.

Dry whole and sterile concentrated milks have much in common with regard to flavor changes which occur initially and during storage. However, several differences do exist. Concentrated milks, as a result of a need for sterilization, are subjected to more intense heat treatments than are dry milks, a treatment which renders the product more conducive to cooked and other off-flavors accompanying the Maillard reaction, but less susceptible to oxidative deterioration, a result of the reducing conditions which exist in cooked products. Dry milks, on the other hand, are prepared with heat treatments which minimize the development of heat induced off-flavors, making it, however, susceptible to oxidative deterioration. Heat treatment alone does not govern the susceptibility to oxidative deterioration or Maillard-type reactions. One must also take into account that one product exists in the dry state and the other in a concentrated liquid state. The problem of oxidized flavor in dry milks is academic, since the oxidative mechanism can be controlled by packaging the product in an atmosphere essentially free of oxygen.

Conventional evaporated milk is normally sterilized at 117°C. for 15 minutes, which is a substantial amount of heat regardless of what the product is. Recent trends, in an effort to minimize the effects of heat on the product, have been to sterilize at temperatures approaching 148°C. for one or two seconds. The effect of the higher temperature for a short

TABLE 45

FLAVOR COMPOUNDS IDENTIFIED IN VARIOUS DRY AND STERILE CONCENTRATED MILKS

Acetone	δ-decalactone	Formaldehyde
Butanone-2	δ-dodecalactone	Acetaldehyde
Pentanone-2	δ-tetradecalactone	Propanal
Hexanone-2	γ-dodecalactone	Pentanal
Heptanone-2		Hexanal
Nonanone-2		Heptanal
Undecanone-2	Caprylic acid	Octanal
Tridecanone-2	Caproic acid	Nonanal
Pentadecanone-2	Capric acid	Decanal
	Lauric acid	Dodecanal
	Myristic acid	Tetradecanal
	Palmitic acid	
Furfural	Vanillin	
Hydroxymethyl furfural	Benzaldehyde	
Diacetyl	o-Aminoacetophenone	
Maltol		
Methylpropanal		
3-Methylbutanal		

period of time is an easily noticeable improvement in the fresh sterilized product, and for the most part, this improvement continues throughout the storage life.

This is not to suggest that the newer products do not undergo flavor deterioration since other mechanisms, not related to the initial heat treatment of the product are still operative.

Table 45 lists the flavor compounds which have been reported in stale dry and sterile concentrated milks. The products, in which these compounds have been identified, were prepared under various manufacturing conditions and the table is presented only to demonstrate the apparent complexity of the reactions which can occur in stored dairy products.

The presence of the C_5 to C_{15} odd-numbered carbon methyl ketones and a series of lactones has been demonstrated in various studies concerned with the heat treatment and storage stability of milkfat and fat containing dairy products. Lactones have been observed in pasteurized milk and along with the methyl ketones are known flavor constituents of dry whole milks and sterile concentrated milks (Patton 1961; Keeney and Patton 1956; Parks and Patton 1961; Muck et al. 1963; Wong et al. 1958). In the latter products, the concentrations increase during storage and their contributions to the so-called stale flavor of these products have been adequately established. At present, only the C_{10}, C_{12}, and C_{14} δ-lactones and the C_{12} γ-lactone have been demonstrated in these products, but various other lactones are known to occur in heated milkfat (Parliment and Nawar 1965; Boldingh and Taylor 1962).

The mechanisms involved in the formation of butanone-2 and hexanone-2 have not been determined although the evidence clearly indicates that they originate from mechanisms completely divorced from the other methyl ketones. The presence of butanone-2 in gamma and solar irradiated skimmilk (Day et al. 1957; Wishner and Keeney 1963) has led to speculation that the ketone may arise as the result of a branched alkyl free radical derived from leucine. Hexanone-2 has recently been reported in sterile concentrated milks (Bingham 1964) and substantial quantities were observed in several dry whole milks examined (Parks and Patton 1961).

The presence of a homologous series of saturated aldehydes is not unexpected since they have been observed in fresh fluid milk. However, on the basis of the concentrations observed in dry milks and control samples (Parks and Patton 1961; Bassette and Keeney 1960), the majority of these aldehydes obviously occurred as the result of autoxidation of lipid material.

The presence of free fatty acids (Muck et al. 1963) is also to be expected since one would predict a certain amount of hydrolysis to take place over a period of time. Some thought has been given to the re-activation of lipases in sterile milks, but there is no evidence available to support this hypothesis.

Furfural, hydroxymethylfurfural, diacetyl, maltol, methyl propanal, and 3-methylbutanal (Parks and Patton 1961; Bassette and Keeney 1960; Potter and Patton 1956) are directly or indirectly the result of the heat treatment employed in preparing these products. Methyl propanal and 3-methylbutanal can result from the Strecker degradation of the amino acids valine and leucine while hydroxymethylfurfural, furfural, diacetyl, and maltol are known products of sugar fragmentation and dehydration during the Maillard reaction (Hodge 1953).

The identification of vanillin (Cobb et al. 1963) in commercial sterile concentrates suggests an interesting aspect of flavor development in dairy products. On the basis of its structure alone, it is difficult to assign a precursor among the normal constituents of milk to this highly flavorful compound. It has been reported that vanillin is a product of a mild oxidation or alkaline degradation of lignin (Richter 1952). Therefore, the possibly exists that some ligneous fragment or fragments from feed passes through the metabolic processes of the cow and finds its way into the milk. Heat treatments such as employed in sterilization or drying of milk may then give rise to this compound and contribute to the caramel-ized flavor. We have observed on occasions some fresh, pasteurized fluid milks with flavors which were highly suggestive of vanillin.

Benzaldehyde (Parks and Patton 1961) is another compound which may arise in dairy products as a result of feed constituents entering milk; this compound has been observed in both grass and corn silage (Morgan and Pereira 1962A and B).

o-Aminoacetophenone is one of the latest flavor compounds to be identified in dry and sterile concentrated milks (Parks et al. 1964). The synthetic compound has a grape-like odor and imparts a characteristic flavor to milk. The flavor threshold concentration of this compound has been determined to be in the order of 0.5 parts per billion in skimmilk. Little is known with regard to the mechanisms involved in the formation of this compound in dairy products. It has been reported to result from the alkaline degradation of tryptophan and kynurenine in model systems (Spacek 1954). Indican (indoxyl sulfate) has been suggested as a possible source of the flavor compound. The latter compound has been found in milk (Spinneli 1946) while the presence of kynurenine has not been established.

On the initial assumption that the compound may arise in dry milks as the result of high heat treatments, we prepared (Parks et al. 1965) a series of milk powders from skimmilk heated to temperatures ranging from 76.7° to 143.3°C. for fifteen seconds. However, we were not able to detect organoleptically any significant differences in the samples initially or after four months storage at room temperature when packed in either nitrogen or air. In addition to the flavor studies, we analyzed the original heated milks to determine the quantities of *o*-aminoacetophenone which could result from the alkaline degradation of the basic fraction of the nonprotein nitrogen compounds in milk by a modification of the method of Spacek (1954). The results of that study are reported in Table 46. The amount of *o*-aminoacetophenone which arises decreases

TABLE 46

RELATIVE AMOUNTS OF *o*-AMINOACETOPHENONE LIBERATED FROM THE BASIC FRACTION OF THE NONPROTEIN NITROGEN OF 500 ML. OF SKIMMILK HEATED TO VARIOUS TEMPERATURES

Heat Treatment °C.	O.D. at 353 mμ in 10 ml. of Hexane[1]
Raw milk	0.034
76.7°C., 15 sec.	0.039
93.3°C., 15 sec.	0.034
110°C., 15 sec.	0.026
126.7°C., 15 sec.	0.021
143.3°C., 15 sec.	0.008

[1] Average reading of four determinations.
Parks *et al.* (1965).

gradually as the milk is heated over 93.3°C. It is quite difficult to interpret these results at this time since we were not successful in generating the flavor compound to any significant degree, if at all, in the dry milks prepared. The data may reflect nothing more than the loss of free tryptophan in the milk as a result of the Maillard reaction during heating. Then again, the possibility exists that the heat treatment of the milk and the nonprotein nitrogen are not involved in the reactions leading to the presence of this compound in dairy products. We have observed that the concentration of this flavor compound appears to vary among commercial sterile concentrates despite similar temperatures employed in the sterilization treatment.

Milk as evidenced by the brief review of literature presented herein can have many flavors. In fact, milk free of off-flavor is the exception rather than the rule. Most slight off-flavors are not objectional to the consumer, although a few such as oxidized are more so than others. In fact, it is not uncommon to hear individuals say they like a slight rancid or a slight feed flavor in their milk. The consumer's rejection of dry and sterile concentrated milks can be traced to the rather pronounced off-flavors which develop in these products during storage despite the convenience of having such products available in the home at all times. Up until such time that the initial flavor of these products can be maintained over a period of time, dry and sterile concentrated milks will not be used as a fluid beverage to any degree. To quote Jenness and Patton (1959), "A food may be wholesome, nutritious, attractively packaged and reasonably priced, but if its flavor is poor, it will be rejected by the consumer."

DISCUSSION

W. F. Wilkens.—Is lipase destroyed by the flash pasteurization treatment of 148°C. for 1 to 2 seconds?

O. W. Parks.—I believe it would probably remain active.

A. M. Swanson.—There is definite evidence that you can get heat reactivation of lipolytic activity with high-temperature, short-time heat treatments.

R. Self.—I was very interested in the speculation that vanillin may arise from lignin. In consideration of some work by Goheen on commercial forestry products, where he studies the demethylation reactions, it would be interesting if you could also find dimethyl sulfide as a degradation product with vanillin.

W. F. Shipe.—Do you consider the development of the activated flavor as an oxidative process?

O. W. Parks.—It is to a certain extent, whether it is a completely oxidative reaction I couldn't say.

C. Wiener.—Do the plasmalogens actually play a role in the release of aldehydes to produce off-flavors in milk? Also are there enzyme systems present that release these aldehydes, or do you attribute the release to a rise in acidity of the milk. Have other aldehydes beside the C_{16} and C_{18} been found?

O. W. Parks.—The only place I know that the plasmalogens supposedly play a role is in the irradiation of milkfat. In most fresh milks there are free saturated aldehydes.

BIBLIOGRAPHY

AURAND, L. W., and WOODS, A. E. 1959. Role of xanthine oxidase in the development of spontaneously oxidized flavor in milk. J. Dairy Sci. 42, 1111–1118.

BABCOCK, C. J. 1938. Feed flavors in milk and milk products. J. Dairy Sci. 21, 661–668.

BALLANCE, P. E. 1961. Production of volatile compounds related to the flavor of foods from the Strecker degradation of dl-methionine. J. Sci. Food Agr. 12, 532–536.

BASSETTE, R., and KEENEY, M. 1960. Identification of some volatile carbonyl compounds from non-fat dry milk. J. Dairy Sci. 43, 1744–1750.

BEGEMANN, P. H., and KOSTER, J. C. 1964. 4-cis-heptenal—a cream flavored component of butter. Nature 202, 552–553.

BINGHAM, R. J. 1964. Gas chromatographic studies on the volatiles of sterilized concentrated milk. Ph.D. thesis. Univ. of Wisc., Madison, Wisc.

BOLDINGH, J., and TAYLOR, R. J. 1962. Trace constituents of butterfat. Nature 194, 909–913.

BRADLEY, R. 1757. A general treatise of agriculture. London. Cited by STROBEL, D. R., BRYAN, W. G., and BABCOCK, C. J. 1953. Flavors of milk. A review of literature. Publication of the U.S. Dept. of Agriculture, Washington, D. C.

CHANDRAN, R. C., and SHAHANI, K. M. 1963. Purification and characterization of milk lipase. I. Purification. J. Dairy Sci. 46, 275–283.

COBB, W. Y., PATTON, S., and GRILL, H. 1963. Occurrence of vanillin in heated milks. J. Dairy Sci. 46, 566–567.

DAY, E. A., FORSS, D. A., and PATTON, S. 1957. Flavor and odor defects of gamma irradiated skimmilk. II. Identification of volatile components by gas chromatography and mass spectrometry. J. Dairy Sci. 40, 932–941.

DAY, E. A., LILLARD, D. A., and MONTGOMERY, M. W. 1963. Autoxidation of milk lipids. III. Effect on flavor of the additive interactions of carbonyl compounds at subthreshold concentrations. J. Dairy Sci. 46, 291–294.

DOUGHERTY, R. W., SHIPE, W. F., GUDNASON, G. U., LEDFORD, R. A., PETERSON, R. D., and SCARPELLINO, R. 1962. Physiological mechanisms involved in transmitting flavors and odors to milk. I. Contribution of eructated gases to milk flavor. J. Dairy Sci. 45, 472–476.

EL-NEGOUMY, A. M., MILES, D. M., and HAMMOND, E. G. 1961. Partial characterization of the flavors of oxidized butteroil. J. Dairy Sci. 44, 1047–1056.

FLAKE, J. C., JACKSON, H. C., and WECKEL, K. G. 1940. Isolation of substances responsible for the activated flavor of milk. J. Dairy Sci. 23, 1087–1095.

FORSS, D. A., PONT, E. G., and STARK, W. 1955. The volatile compounds associated with oxidized flavor in skimmilk. J. Dairy Res. 22, 91–102.

GANDER, G. W., and JENSEN, R. G. 1960. The specificity of milk lipase toward the primary ester groups of some synthetic triglycerides. J. Dairy Sci. 43, 1762–1765.

GOULD, I. A., and SOMMER, H. H. 1939. Effect of heat on milk with especial reference to the cooked flavor. Mich. State Univ. Agr. Exp. Sta. Tech. Bull. 164.

GREENBANK, G. R. 1940. Variation in the oxidation-reduction potential as a cause for the oxidized flavor in milk. J. Dairy Sci. 23, 725–744.

GREENBANK, G. R. 1948. The oxidized flavor in milk and dairy products: A review. J. Dairy Sci. 31, 913–933.

GUTFREUND, H. 1963. Isolation and characterization of selected enzymes of milk. Progress report, October 1962 to September 1963, U. S. Dept. of Agriculture Public Law 480, Grant No. FG-UK-124-61.

GUTHRIE, E. S., and BRUECKNER, H. J. 1934. The cow as a source of "oxidized" flavors of milk. New York Agr. Exp. Sta. Bull. 606.

HARPER, W. J. 1955. Apparent selective liberation of butyric acid from milk fat by the various lipase systems. J. Dairy Sci. 38, 1391.

HILEMAN, J. L., and COURTNEY, E. 1935. Seasonal variations in the lipase content of milk. J. Dairy Sci. 18, 247–257.

HODGE, J. E. 1953. Chemistry of browning reaction in model systems. J. Agr. Food Chem. 1, 928–943.

HONKANEN, E., KARVONEN, P., and VIRTANEN, A. 1964. Studies on the transfer of some flavor compounds to milk. Acta Chem. Scand. 18, 612–618.

HUTTON, J. T., and PATTON, S. 1952. The origin of sulfhydryl groups in milk protein and their contribution to cooked flavor. J. Dairy Sci. 35, 699–705.

JANZEN, J. J. 1963. Milk flavor as affected by a milk metering device. J. Dairy Sci. 46, 567–569.

JENNESS, R., and PATTON, S. 1959. Principles of Dairy Chemistry. John Wiley and Sons, Inc., New York.

JENSEN, R. G., DUTHIE, A. H., GANDER, G. W., and MORGAN, M. E. 1960. Some evidence supporting the specificity of milk lipase for the primary hydroxyl ester positions of triglycerides. J. Dairy Sci. 43, 96–97.

JOSEPHSON, D. V., and DOAN, F. J. 1939. Observations on cooked flavor in milk. Its source and significance. Milk Dealer 29, No. 2, 35–36, 54–62.

JOSEPHSON, D. V., and KEENEY, P. G. 1947. Relationship of acetone bodies to "cowy" flavor in milk. Milk Dealer 36, No. 10, 40–42.

KEENEY, M. 1961. Flavor of milk and milk products. In Flavor Chemistry Symposium, 183–200. Campbell Soup Co., Camden, N. J.

KEENEY, P. G., and PATTON, S. 1956. The coconut-like flavor defect of milk fat. II. Demonstration of δ-decalactone in dried cream, dry whole and evaporated milk. J. Dairy Sci. 39, 1114–1119.

KENDE, S. 1932. Examinations of the "oily-tallowy" transformations of milk-fat. (In German.) Milchwirtschaft. Forsch. 13, 111–143.

KRUKOVSKY, V. N. 1961. Review of biochemical properties of milk and the lipide deterioration in milk and milk products as influenced by natural varietal factors. J. Agr. Food Chem. 9, 439–447.

MORGAN, M. E., and PEREIRA, R. L. 1962A. Volatile constituents of grass and corn silage. I. Steam distillates. J. Dairy Sci. 45, 457–466.

MORGAN, M. E., and PEREIRA, R. L. 1962B. Volatile constituents of grass and corn silage. II. Gas enriched aroma. J. Dairy Sci. 45, 467–471.

MUCK, G. A., TOBIAS, J., and WHITNEY, R. McL. 1963. Flavor of evaporated milk. I. Identification of some compounds obtained by the petroleum ether solvent partitioning technique from aged evaporated milk. J. Dairy Sci. 46, 774–779.

PARKS, O. W. 1965. Lipids of milk: Deterioration. In Fundamentals of Dairy Chemistry, 197–223, A. H. Johnson, and B. H. Webb (Editors), Avi Publishing Co., Westport, Conn.

PARKS, O. W., KEENEY, M., and SCHWARTZ, D. P. 1963. Carbonyl compounds associated with the off-flavor in spontaneously oxidized milk. J. Dairy Sci. 46, 295–301.

PARKS, O. W., NELSON, K., and SCHWARTZ, D. P. 1965. Unpublished data.

PARKS, O. W., and PATTON, S. 1961. Volatile carbonyl compounds in stored dry whole milk. J. Dairy Sci. 44, 1–9.

PARKS, O. W., SCHWARTZ, D. P., and KEENEY, M. 1964. Identification of o-aminoacetophenone as a flavor compound in stale dry milk. Nature 202, 185–187.

PARLIMENT, T. H., and NAWAR, W. W. 1965. Delta-caprolactone in heated milk fat. J. Dairy Sci. 48, 615–616.

PATTON, S. 1954. The mechanism of sunlight flavor formation in milk with special reference to methionine and riboflavin. J. Dairy Sci. 37, 446–452.

PATTON, S. 1961. Gas chromatographic analysis of flavor in processed milks. J. Dairy Sci. 44, 207–214.

PATTON, S. 1962. Dairy products. In Symposium on Foods: Lipids and Their Oxidation, H. W. Schultz, E. A. Day, and R. O. Sinnhuber, (Editors), Avi Publishing Co., Westport, Conn.

PATTON, S., FORSS, D. A., and DAY, E. A. 1956. Methyl sulfide and the flavor of milk. J. Dairy Sci. 39, 1469–1470.

PATTON, S., and JOSEPHSON, D. V. 1953. Methionine-origin of sunlight flavor in milk. Science *118*, No. 3060, 211.

PETERSEN, W. E., and BRERETON, J. G. 1942. Effect of inhaled substances on milk flavors. J. Dairy Sci. *25*, 381–387.

POTTER, F. E., and HANKINSON, D. J. 1960. The flavor of milk from individual cows. Abstract of paper presented at Eastern Division meeting of ADSA, Durham, N. H. J. Dairy Sci. *43*, 1887.

POTTER, F. E., and PATTON, S. 1956. Evidence of maltol and hydroxymethylfurfural in evaporated milk as shown by paper chromatography. J. Dairy Sci. *39*, 978–982.

RICHTER, G. H. 1952. Textbook of Organic Chemistry. 3rd ed., John Wiley and Sons, New York.

RIEL, R. R. 1952. Causative factors and end-products of oxidized flavor development in milk. Ph.D. thesis, Univ. of Wisc., Madison, Wisc.

SAMUELSSON, E. G. 1961. Degradation of methionine by light and its dependence on pH and presence of oxygen. Milchwissenschaft *16*, 344–347.

SAMUELSSON, E. G. 1962. Experiments on sunlight flavor in milk—S^{35} labelled milk. Milchwissenschaft *17*, 401–405.

SCHWARTZ, D. P. 1965. Lipids of milk: Deterioration. In Fundamentals of Dairy Chemistry, 170–197, A. H. Johnson, and B. H. Webb (Editors), Avi Publishing Co., Westport, Conn.

SHIPE, W. F., LEDFORD, R. A., PETERSON, R. D., SCANLAN, R. A., GEERKEN, H. F., DOUGHERTY, R. W., and MORGAN, M. E. 1962. Physiological mechanisms involved in transmitting flavors and odors to milk. II. Transmission of some flavor components of silage. J. Dairy Sci. *45*, 477–480.

SMITH, A. C., and MACLEOD, P. 1955. The effect of artificial light on milk in cold storage. J. Dairy Sci. *38*, 870–874.

SMITH, G. J., and DUNKLEY, W. L. 1960. Xanthine oxidase and incidence of spontaneous oxidized flavor in milk. J. Dairy Sci. *43*, 278–280.

SMITH, G. J., and DUNKLEY, W. L. 1962. Pro-oxidants in spontaneous development of oxidized flavor in milk. J. Dairy Sci. *45*, 170–181.

SMITH, L. M., and DUNKLEY, W. L. 1959. Effect of the development of oxidized flavor on the polyunsaturated fatty acids of milk lipids. Abstract of paper presented at 54th annual meeting of ADSA, Urbana, Ill. J. Dairy Sci. *42*, 896.

SPACEK, M. 1954. Simultaneous determination of kynurenine and *p*-phenetidine in human urine. Canadian J. Biochem. Physiol. *32*, 604–609.

SPEER, J. F., WATROUS, G. H., and KESLER, E. M. 1958. The relationship of certain factors effecting hydrolytic rancidity in milk. J. Milk and Food Technol. *21*, 33–37.

SPINNELI, F. 1946. The indican content of cow's and goat's milk. Boll. Soc. Ital. Biol. Sper. *22*, 211. Cited by Jenness, R., and Patton, S. 1959. Principles of Dairy Chemistry. John Wiley and Sons, New York.

STROBEL, D. R., BRYAN, W. G., and BABCOCK, C. J. 1953. Flavors of milk. A review of literature. Publication of the U. S. Dept. of Agriculture, Washington, D. C.

TARASSUK, N. P., and FRANKEL, E. N. 1957. The specificity of milk lipase. IV. Partition of the milk lipase system in milk. J. Dairy Sci. *40*, 418–430.

TARASSUK, N. P., and HENDERSON, J. L. 1942. Prevention of development of hydrolytic rancidity in milk. J. Dairy Sci. *25*, 801–806.

TARASSUK, N. P., LABEN, R. C., and YAGUCHI, M. 1962. Effect of feeding regime on susceptibility of milk to the development of hydrolytic rancidity. Proc. 16th Intern. Dairy Cong., 2, 609–616.

VIRTANEN, A. I., and LAMPILA, M. 1962. Production of cow's milk on purified nutrients without proteins. Suomen Kemistilehti B 35, 244.

WISHNER, L. A., and KEENEY, M. 1963. Carbonyl pattern of sunlight-exposed milk. J. Dairy Sci. 46, 785–788.

WONG, N. P. 1963. A comparison of the volatile compounds of fresh and decomposed cream by gas chromatography. J. Dairy Sci. 46, 571–573.

WONG, N. P., and PATTON, S. 1962. Identification of some volatile compounds related to the flavor of milk and cream. J. Dairy Sci. 45, 724–728.

WONG, N. P., PATTON, S., and FORSS, D. A. 1958. Methyl ketones in evaporated milk. J. Dairy Sci. 41, 1699–1705.

ZITTLE, C. A. 1963. Photooxidation of α_s-casein. J. Dairy Sci. 46, 607. Abstract of paper presented at 58th annual meeting of ADSA, Lafayette, Indiana.

ZITTLE, C. A., KALAN, E. B., WALTER, M., and KING, T. M. 1964. Photooxidation of β-casein. J. Dairy Sci. 47, 1052–1055.

CHAPTER 14

R. C. Lindsay | Cultured Dairy Products

INTRODUCTION

Lactic acid-producing bacteria have been used for centuries to convert fresh milk into edible fermented dairy products. Before the advent of pasteurization, refrigeration, and refined culturing procedures, man relied on the natural microbial flora or crude starters to carry out the fermentation processes. Through the years a great number of cheeses and fermented milk and cream products have evolved. This paper deals with a group of fresh dairy products which possess a common culture flavor. Typical examples of this group are butter culture, cultured buttermilk, cultured cream butter, sour cream, and creamed cottage cheese. The characteristic culture flavor of these products is primarily dependent upon flavor and aroma substances produced by certain lactic acid-producing bacteria.

FLAVOR CONTRIBUTIONS FROM NORMAL MILK CONSTITUENTS

Although culture flavor is dependent on microbial metabolism, it is generally recognized that a significant contribution to the overall flavor of cultured products is made by normal milk constituents. The compounds considered hereunder are naturally present in fresh milk or are produced from milk constituents during manufacture.

Milkfat possesses several characteristics which are believed to contribute to the flavor of cultured products. The glycerides of milkfat contain considerable quantities of butyric, caproic, caprylic, and capric acids. Work by Harper *et al.* (1961) and Khatri and Day (1962) has demonstrated that milk contains appreciable levels of unesterified fatty acids (straight chain C_{18} or less). At optimum concentrations these fatty acids are believed to add favorable notes to the flavor of dairy products. A number of less abundant fatty acids have also been found in the lipids of cows' milk (Magidman *et al.* 1962). The flavor significance of the majority of these acids is largely unknown. Of particular interest are several isomeric unsaturated 18 carbon atom fatty acids isolated from milkfat by de Jong and van der Wal (1964). These acids are believed to be precursors of 4-*cis*-heptenal, a compound isolated from milkfat which exhibits a cream flavor (Begemann and Koster 1964). The cream flavored component is formed through the autoxidation of the isolinoleic acids.

Work by Boldingh and Taylor (1962) on the trace constituents of milkfat has demonstrated the presence of several compounds which probably are of significance in butter flavor. These workers have isolated and identified several optically active lactones from milkfat. The delta-lactones with 8, 10, 12, 14, and 16 carbon atoms were found to comprise the major portion of the lactone fraction. Indirect evidence indicated that hydroxy-acids were esterified in normal glycerides. Hydrolysis of the hydroxy-acids from glycerides and subsequent ring closure would give rise to the corresponding lactones.

When milkfat is heated in the presence of water, an homologous series of methyl ketones with odd-numbers of carbon atoms is produced (Patton and Tharp 1959). The methyl ketones are formed through the de-carboxylation of even-numbered beta-ketoacids which are normally esterified to triglycerides of milkfat (Parks et al. 1964). It is generally accepted that methyl ketones contribute to the flavor of cultured products, and especially those containing significant quantities of milkfat. Recent work has indicated that butter cultures prepared from heated whole milk contained larger quantities of 2-pentanone and 2-heptanone than did control heated milk (Lindsay et al. 1965B). Since the beta-ketoacid decarboxylation reaction is pH dependent (Widmark 1920), it has been postulated that the lower pH of butter culture causes a more rapid formation of methyl ketones.

Patton and co-workers (1956) first isolated dimethyl sulfide from milk and found that at its flavor threshold (12 p.p.b. in water) it exhibited a typical milk odor. Day et al. (1964) have found dimethyl sulfide in butter cultures, cultured cream butter, and sweet cream butter. It was noted that dimethyl sulfide was a significant flavor component in fresh sweet cream butter, and that it had the capacity to smooth out the harsh flavor of diacetyl and acids associated with culture flavor.

All cultured dairy products receive some degree of heat treatment during the manufacturing processes. A variety of flavors develop when milk is heated. The severity of heat treatment determines the type and intensity of flavor that will be apparent. The flavor significance of compounds, such as 2-furfural, 2-furfuryl alcohol, maltol, and formic acid which are formed in milk by various degrees of heat treatment, is not yet clear. Undoubtedly, these compounds and other thermally induced compounds contribute to the flavor of cultured products which receive substantial heat treatment.

The term "butter flavor" has been used synonymously with culture or cultured cream butter flavor. At the present time, the assumption that the two flavors are the same is not entirely correct. In recent years the majority of high quality butter manufactured in the United States has been made from pasteurized sweet cream. While sweet cream butter possesses the unique and desirable characteristics peculiar to milkfat, it has a bland flavor and does not possess a culture flavor. The flavor of sweet cream butter, therefore, is due entirely to flavor compounds initially present in fresh cream and to those produced or added (for example, salt) during manufacture. As yet, it has not been possible to duplicate synthetically the natural flavor of sweet cream butter.

On the other hand, cultured cream butter was the usual product before the development of modern processing procedures. In many instances culture flavor production was brought about by the natural bacterial flora of the cream rather than sophisticated culturing techniques. Clearly, cultured cream butter flavor is due to both inherent natural flavor compounds and compounds produced by microbial activity. Therefore, it is proposed that the terms, "cultured butter flavor" or "cultured cream butter flavor," be used in describing the flavor of butter processing a true culture flavor. The term, "butter flavor," would then be a more meaningful description of the flavor of sweet cream butter.

ORGANISMS PRODUCING CULTURE FLAVOR

The bacteria found in starters used for the manufacture of cultured products can be placed into three general categories. These are (1) the lactic acid-producing streptococci, *Streptococcus lactis* and *Streptococcus cremoris;* (2) the associative citrate-fermenting aroma bacteria, *Leuconostoc citrovorum* and *Leuconostoc dextranicum;* and (3) the dual purpose lactic acid- and aroma-producing strains of *Streptococcus diacetilactis.* For convenience the term, "aroma bacteria," is used as a general term to describe those organisms which produce appreciable quantities of diacetyl when appropriately grown in a milk medium.

Commercially blended mixed-strain starter cultures contain combinations of the above mentioned species. The type of product that is to be manufactured determines the species of organisms to be included in the culture. For instance, in setting a vat of cottage cheese only lactic acid for coagulation of milk is necessary. In this case combinations of strains of S. cremoris and S. lactis may be quite satisfactory for the production of a bland flavored product. However, when culture flavor is desired some provision for the inclusion of aroma bacteria must be made. For creamed cottage cheese manufacture some culture flavor may be obtained by employing mixed-strain cultures containing aroma bacteria for cheese setting. Frequently aroma bacteria produce considerable quantities of carbon dioxide through citrate fermentation and this leads to problems with floating curd during the cooking process. Alternate natural culturing methods for producing culture flavor have been developed. These methods involve adding cultures of *L. citrovorum* (Mather and Babel 1959) or *S. diacetilactis* (Lundstedt and Fogg 1962 to the creaming mixture prior to final mixing. These processes eliminate floating curd problems caused by the aroma bacteria. Carbon dioxide production in the finished cheese is not objectionable.

Starter cultures are routinely propagated in milk media. Culture activity is maintained by frequent transfers. Experience has shown, however, that it is very difficult to achieve consistency in flavor production under normal dairy plant operations. Many factors are involved in the difficulties encountered in the production of high-quality aroma producing cultures. Changes in the balance of the microbial flora are directly reflected in the flavor and acid producing characteristics. Certain culturing procedures tend to favor the development of some bacterial strains over others (Galesloot 1962; Vedamuthu *et al.* 1964). Quite often a shift in the balance of organisms is experienced, and one or more strains predominate after a few transfers. The usual result is the loss of the ability of the culture to produce a desirable culture flavor. The use of culture rotation programs and single-use starters which do not require routine dairy plant propagation has been of value in cultured product manufacture. However, the dairy industry still is faced with starter problems.

STARTER DISTILLATE AS A SOURCE OF CULTURE FLAVOR

Starter distillates have been used for producing culture flavor in butter, sour cream, and creamed cottage cheese. These flavor concentrates are obtained from desirable mixed-strain butter cultures that exhibit high flavor-producing characteristics. In addition, culturing methods, such as the addition of citric acid to the medium, are employed to enhance flavor production. Steam distillation is used to recover the volatile flavor fraction from ripened cultures. The flavor intensity of such distillates can be standardized to meet market demands.

Although a starter distillate imparts a definite culture flavor, it is well accepted that it does not duplicate the balanced flavor obtained through the use of natural culturing procedures. Several factors may contribute to the inability of starter distillates to produce exact flavor duplication. Loss of desirable volatile flavor compounds and production of heat-induced components during steam distillation may change the flavor properties of starter distillates. Furthermore, the ratio of desirable flavor compounds found in natural intact butter cultures may be altered during distillation.

DIACETYL AND RELATED COMPONENTS

It was early recognized that diacetyl is the key component of culture flavor. Since the discovery of diacetyl in cultured butter (Van Niel *et al.* 1929), numerous workers have investigated the various aspects of its production and stabilization in cultured products. Two comprehensive reviews by Hammer and Babel (1943; Babel and Hammer 1944) adequately summarize the early work on culture flavor.

Citric acid fermentation and biosynthesis of diacetyl, acetoin, and 2,3-butanediol have been controversial subjects for many years. Recent work has led to a more complete understanding of the processes, and the reader is referred to recent reviews by Galesloot (1962), Marth (1962), and Reiter and Moller-Madsen (1963) for a summary of recent progress. The pathways for the conversion of citric acid by *S. diacetilactis* are shown in Fig. 71. Before citrate can be metabolized, it must be taken up from the medium. Aroma production occurs only when the pH of the medium is below 6.0 (Mizuno and Jezeski 1959). Harvey and Collins

Citric acid $\xrightarrow{\;1\;}$ Oxaloacetic acid + Acetic acid

Oxaloacetic acid $\xleftrightarrow{\;2\;}$ Pyruvic acid + CO_2

2 Pyruvic acid + 2 TPP^2 $\xrightarrow{\;3\;}$ 2 Acetaldehyde $\cdot$ TPP + $2CO_2$

Acetaldehyde $\cdot$ TPP $\xrightarrow{\;4\;}$ Acetaldehyde + TPP

Acetaldehyde $\cdot$ TPP + Acetaldehyde $\xrightarrow{\;5\;}$ Acetoin + TPP

Acetaldehyde $\cdot$ TPP + Pyruvic acid $\xrightarrow{\;6\;}$ α-Acetolactic acid + TPP

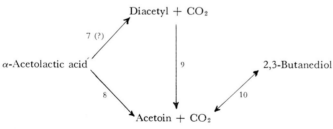

[1] Enzymes catalyzing each reaction:

1. Citritase
2. Oxaloacetate decarboxylase
3. Pyruvate decarboxylase
4. Non-enzymatic
5. Acetoin synthetase

6. α-Acetolactate synthetase
7. α-Acetolactate oxidase
8. α-Acetolactate decarboxylase
9. Diacetyl reductase
10. 2,3-butanediol dehydrogenase

[2] Thiamine pyrophosphate

From Seitz et al. (1963B)

FIG 71. PATHWAYS FOR CONVERSION OF CITRIC ACID BY *S. Diacetilactis*

(1962) have demonstrated that citrate uptake is mediated by an inducible pH dependent enzymatic transport system.

Diacetyl and acetoin are not produced from sugar alone, but are produced from a mixture of citrate and sugar (Harvey and Collins 1963). Pyruvate has been found to be a key intermediate in the synthesis of diacetyl and acetoin. The formation of pyruvate from sugar fermentation simultaneously yields reduced pyridine nucleotides. In order to permit the sugar fermentation to proceed, pyruvate must be reduced to lactic acid to allow reoxidation of reduced pyridine nucleotides. Thus, when the substrate is sugar alone no pyruvate is available for the synthesis of alpha-acetolactic acid, the immediate precursor of diacetyl and acetoin. On the other hand, citrate fermentation yields pyruvate without the corresponding production of reduced pyridine nucleotides. When the substrate is a mixture of sugar and citrate and the pH is sufficiently low, more pyruvate is present in the metabolic pool than is necessary for regeneration of reduced pyridine nucleotides. It is under these conditions that alpha-acetolactic acid is synthesized.

In the past, many workers have considered acetoin as the precursor of diacetyl. However, Pette (1949) and others have found that acetoin is not oxidized to diacetyl under conditions prevailing in starters. It is now generally accepted that alpha-acetolactic acid is the direct precursor of diacetyl (Seitz *et al.* 1963B). Alpha-acetolactic acid may be decarboxylated to yield acetoin or it may be oxidatively decarboxylated in some manner to give diacetyl. The mechanism for the production of diacetyl from alpha-acetolactic acid has not been resolved. Some workers (Pette 1949; deMan 1956) believe that the reaction is purely chemical requiring only atmospheric oxygen for the conversion, while others believe that the process is enzymatic (Seitz *et al.* 1963B).

S. *diacetilactis* possesses an enzyme, diacetyl reductase, which catalyzes the irreversible reduction of diacetyl to acetoin (Seitz *et al.* 1963A). This conversion is of great importance when considering flavor stability of cultured products. Diacetyl is accumulated during the first part of incubation but is destroyed on prolonged incubation. Improperly handled cultured products can suffer loss of aroma through diacetyl reductase activity. Furthermore, it has been demonstrated that common coliform and psychrophilic contaminants also possess diacetyl reductase and are a further hazard to culture flavor stability.

Some mention of 2,3-butanediol is in order since it is one of the compounds classically associated with culture organisms and culture flavor. It is formed by the reversible enzymatic reduction of acetoin. However, like acetoin, it appears to be only of physiological importance. Neither acetoin nor 2,3-butanediol contribute flavor or aroma to cultured products because they are flavorless and odorless at concentrations normally encountered in cultured products.

OTHER COMPOUNDS ASSOCIATED WITH CULTURE FLAVOR

Lactic acid is the main metabolic end-product of homofermentative lactic streptococci and is produced to a lesser extent by the heterofermentative aroma bacteria. Pure lactic acid is nonvolatile and odorless, and therefore does not contribute to the aroma. However, the acid taste of naturally cultured products is largely due to the presence of lactic acid.

The volatile acids produced by culture organisms are considered to contribute to the mildy acid aroma of cultured products. Acetic acid comprises the major portion of the volatile acid fraction of cultured products and is the most important in culture flavor. Acetic acid is produced during citrate fermentation, and it is also a terminal product of the hexose monophosphate pathway utilized by the heterofermentative aromatic bacteria (Kandler 1961). Formic, propionic, butyric, and valeric acids have been isolated from cultured buttermilk, but are present only in very small quantities (Chou 1962; Hammer and Sherwood 1923).

Acetaldehyde has been found to be responsible for the green or yogurt flavor defect in butter cultures and cultured butter (Badings and Galesloot 1962). Apparently, acetaldehyde production is a characteristic of lactic streptococci as all strains examined thus far have this capability (Harvey 1960; Keenan et al. 1966). A small amount of acetaldehyde is desirable for the full flavor of mixed-strain butter cultures (Lindsay et al. 1965A). The flavor balance of butter cultures was found to be closely related to the diacetyl:acetaldehyde ratio. Desirable full-flavored cultures exhibited ratios from 3:1 to about 5:1; a green flavor became apparent when the ratio dropped below 3:1, and when the ratio exceeded 5:1, a harsh diacetyl flavor was noted. The green flavor defect of butter cultures has been attributed to an overgrowth of S. diacetilactis, but it was found that high numbers of S. lactis in relation to the Leuconostoc population also gives rise to the flavor defect.

Acetaldehyde production by lactic streptococci appears to follow cell growth up to a point (Keenan et al. 1966). Typical acetaldehyde production curves for three single-strain cultures of lactic streptococci are shown in Fig. 72. S. diacetilactis continues to accumulate acetaldehyde on prolonged incubation while S. lactis and S. cremoris slowly remove acetaldehyde after 12 h of incubation. At this time there is tentative evidence suggesting an alcohol dehydrogenase system in lactic streptococci.

L. citrovorum has a much greater ability to remove acetaldehyde from

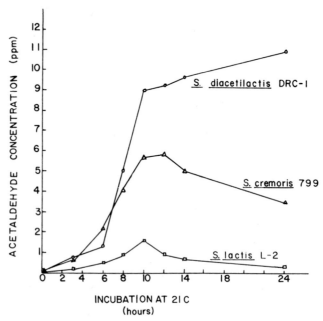

FIG. 72. ACETALDEHYDE PRODUCTION BY SINGLE-STRAIN LACTIC
STREPTOCOCCI

culture medium than either *S. lactis* or *S. cremoris* (Badings and Galesloot 1962; Lindsay *et al.* 1965A). These organisms rapidly remove acetaldehyde from both nonacidified (pH 6.5) and acidified (pH 4.5) milk medium. It also has been observed that the addition of acetaldehyde to the culture medium stimulates the growth of *L. citrovorum.* Apparently, the free acetaldehyde is utilized as a hydrogen acceptor by the heterofermentative *Leuconostoc* organisms. If such is the case reduced pyridine nucleotides can be regenerated without the loss of energy that takes place when acetylphosphate is converted to ethanol (Fig. 73). In mixed-strain starters the *Leuconostoc* bacteria could derive a growth stimulation from acetaldehyde produced by the lactic streptococci. Desirable full culture flavor is obtained only when the numbers of the two types of organisms maintain a proper balance.

A number of other aldehydes have been isolated from cultured products. Transamination and subsequent decarboxylation of amino acids by some lactic streptococci leads to the production of a number of aldehydes (MacLeod and Morgan 1958). Of these 3-methylbutanal is the most well known since it has been shown to contribute heavily to the malty flavor defect in cultures caused by *S. lactis* var. *maltigenes* (Jackson and

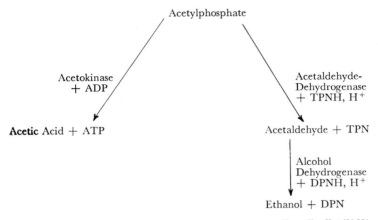

From Kandler (1961)

FIG. 73. TERMINAL COMPOUNDS OF HETEROFERMENTATIVE CARBOHYDRATE METABOLISM

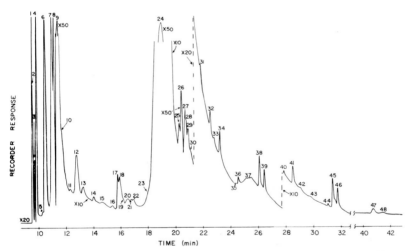

FIG. 74. TEMPERATURE-PROGRAMMED CAPILLARY COLUMN SEPARATION OF BUTTER CULTURE VOLATILES

Morgan 1954). Recent work has shown that these organisms also produce primary alcohols which are produced from the corresponding aldehydes (Morgan *et al.* 1966). However, neither the aldehydes nor the alcohols are thought to play a major role in normal culture flavor.

Several recent investigations have demonstrated that a large number of volatile flavor compounds can be isolated from cultured dairy products (Chou 1962; Winter *et al.* 1963; Lindsay *et al.* 1965B). A wide variety of compounds, including aldehydes, methyl ketones, alcohols, methyl and ethyl esters of aliphatic acids, and lactones, have appeared in the volatile flavor fractions obtained from natural cultured products.

In work carried out at Oregon State University (Lindsay et al. 1965B), high-quality butter cultures were used as a source of culture flavor. The volatile flavor fraction was isolated by reduced-pressure steam distillation. Flavor concentrates obtained by ethyl ether extraction of the aqueous distillates were separated by temperature-programmed capillary column gas-liquid chromatography (GLC). A typical GLC separation of volatiles obtained from butter culture is shown in Fig. 74. Most of the peaks were identified by GLC and mass spectral data, and it appeared that culture flavor was a very complex mixture. However, when control milk medium was similarly examined, it was found that a majority of the compounds were also present in the heated milk medium. Furthermore, no new or unusual compound with a highly characteristic culture flavor or aroma was represented in the mixtures.

SYNTHETIC CULTURE FLAVOR

Diacetyl has been used for imparting a culture flavor to butter (Riel and Gibson 1961) but the results were not satisfactory. Work by Andersen (1961) indicated that the addition of diacetyl to single-strain cultures of S. lactis and S. cremoris resulted in an improved flavor. However, the addition of formic, acetic, or citric acid to the cultures did not favorably influence the flavor. Propionic acid was found to improve the flavor, but the effect was not great. These examples indicate that attempts to synthetically reproduce culture flavor have not been very successful. In most instances starter distillate gave a more desirable flavor than the synthetic formulations. This emphasizes the fact that even though the flavoring properties of starter distillates are inferior to natural culturing procedures, the distillates contain a reasonably complete spectrum of culture flavor compounds.

The work mentioned earlier on the volatile flavor components of butter culture at Oregon State University indicated that only a few compounds were actually necessary for the duplication of culture flavor. However, the remainder of these flavor compounds which modify the overall effect exerted by diacetyl was considered to be of great importance. Determination of optimum levels of key flavor components present in natural high-quality butter cultures and cultured cream butter appeared to be the most logical approach to the problem.

A number of high-quality butter cultures and cultured cream butters were prepared and analyzed for diacetyl, acetaldehyde, short-chain acids and pH (Lindsay et al. 1966). The samples were also presented to small expert panels for flavor preference evaluation. Analysis of the data revealed that from 1.0 to 2.5 p.p.m. of diacetyl was the desirable concentration range for diacetyl in both butter culture and cultured cream butter. These findings were in general agreement with earlier reports (Hammer and Babel 1943; Swartling and Johannson 1954). The development of a rapid procedure for acetaldehyde determinations (Lindsay and Day 1965) made it possible to establish the optimum diacetyl: acetaldehyde ratio (about 4:1) in full-flavored butter cultures (Lindsay et al. 1965A).

Short-chain acids in butter culture and cultured cream butter were determined by the method of Wiseman and Irvin (1957). The average lactic acid content of the cultured cream butter samples was found to be about 500 p.p.m.; however, when this much lactic acid was added to butter the pH dropped significantly below 5.0. Further trails showed that about 250 p.p.m. of lactic acid was sufficient to obtain a final pH of near 5.2. The results of the acid analyses also showed that the cultured cream butters contained an average of about 30 p.p.m. of acetic acid while the butter cultures contained an average of 1250 p.p.m. Formic acid was also measured, but the levels found were not considered sufficient to contribute to culture flavor.

In earlier work (Day et al. 1964) dimethyl sulfide was reported to be an important flavor component of butter and culture flavor. Since sensitive chemical and instrumental methods were not available for dimethyl sulfide analysis, taste panel evaluations were conducted to give an approximation of levels which could be reasonably applied to synthetic formulations. The average flavor threshold of dimethyl sulfide was found to be about 24 p.p.b. in bland butter oil. Results also showed that in butter oil a level of 50 p.p.b. of dimethyl sulfide in the presence of 2.5 p.p.m. of diacetyl was preferred by the panel members.

Volatile esters of aliphatic acids have been considered by some to be highly significant in culture flavor (Babel and Hammer 1944). However, attempts to demonstrate levels of esters which could be of significance in culture flavor were unsuccessful (Lindsay 1965).

For initial trials on synthetic culture flavor formulations, chemically acidified milk systems were used. Delta-gluconolactone (a lactone which hydrolyzes slowly to the acid) was used as the acidogen in levels suggested by Deane and Hammond (1960). Several important considerations in the development of artificial butter cultures soon became evident. The final pH of the system is very important in obtaining a desirable flavor balance. Best results were obtained when the pH of the milk was between 4.50 and 4.65. It was also found that a high heat treatment of whole milk was necessary for producing background flavor which contributes to the full flavor of cultures. A small amount of carbon dioxide, obtained by adding about 0.15% of sodium bicarbonate, improved the flavor of the artificial butter culture by giving it a note of "tanginess."

Further trials were conducted utilizing flavor panels to arrive at satisfactory flavor formulations for butter culture, cultured butter, sour cream, and creamed cottage cheese. Some adjustments in formulation were necessary because the products differ in composition and physical structure. Recent work by Bennett *et al.* (1965) has shown that fat, pH, and volatile acids affect the flavor perception of diacetyl. This is also undoubtedly true for other culture flavor compounds. The flavor formulations that have given best results are presented in Table 47. Lactic acid was added only to butter (near pH 5.2). Lowered pH values in sour

SYNTHETIC CULTURE FLAVOR FORMULATIONS FOR DAIRY PRODUCTS

| | Concentration, Mg./Kg. | | | |
Compound	Cultured Butter	Sour Cream	Cottage Cheese	Buttermilk
Lactic acid	250.0	. . .	. . .	. . .
Acetic acid	30.0	30.0	30.0	1250.0
Acetaldehyde	0.2	0.2	0.2	0.5
Dimethyl sulfide	0.08	0.025	0.025	0.025
Diacetyl				
Low level	0.5	1.0	1.0	1.0
High level	2.0	2.0	2.0	2.0

cream (pH 4.6) and artificial buttermilk (pH 4.6) were obtained by employing combinations of citric acid and delta-gluconolactone (Deane and Thomas 1964). When normal dry cottage cheese curd was employed, it was not necessary to add acid (other than acetic acid) to achieve a desirable culture flavor in the final creamed product (pH 5.2). One per cent of salt added to butter and cottage cheese improved the flavor.

Samples of synthetically flavored products were prepared and presented to large flavor preference panels along with one sample each of a commercially obtained product and a high-quality natural product prepared in the University Creamery. A summary of the results of the flavor panel evaluations is given in Table 48. It can be seen that no significant preference was found between the synthetically flavored products and the high-quality natural products. Although flavor preference tests are not designed to distinguish differences in flavor, the results indicate that the flavors are very similar. This point has been strengthened by small panel evaluations. Most people found it difficult to distinguish between synthetically flavored and naturally cultured butter, creamed cottage cheese, or sour cream. However, experienced judges noted that the synthetic buttermilk lacked the exact character of natural buttermilk. Problems

TABLE 48

LARGE PANEL FLAVOR PREFERENCE SCORES FOR CULTURE FLAVORED DAIRY PRODUCTS

Sample Identification	Mean Score[1,2]			
	Cultured Butter	Sour Cream	Cottage Cheese	Buttermilk
Commercial	. . .[3]	5.25[4]	6.02[4]	3.72
OSU natural	6.38	5.73	6.22	3.69
Low synthetic	6.27	5.80	6.37	3.81
High synthetic	6.29	5.75	6.41	3.71

[1] Includes from 150 to 175 observations per sample.
[2] Nine-point hedonic scale from 9, like extremely, to 1, dislike extremely.
[3] Sample not available.
[4] Significantly lower than other samples at the 0.01 level.

associated with tactual properties may have been partly responsible. It is also interesting to note (Table 48) that the preference panel members (college students) did not like any of the samples of buttermilk. This indicates that buttermilk is not widely consumed by people of that age group.

In summary, recent work has shown that a desirable culture flavor can be produced synthetically and that the formulations for cultured butter, sour cream, buttermilk, and creamed cottage cheese are relatively simple. Future work in this area will probably be directed toward the definition of butter flavor. Then the two flavors may be combined and the many demands for cultured butter flavor can be fulfilled.

DISCUSSION

J. G. Keppler.—Have you analyzed different butters for the amount of diacetyl present, because this varies from one country to another?

R. C. Lindsay.—We made up a number of cultured butters with varying levels of diacetyl and evaluated them by small flavor panels for desirability, or acceptability, and levels of diacetyl. We found the acceptable range of diacetyl was from about 0.5 p.p.m. for a very mild diacetyl-type flavor to about 2.5 p.p.m. as an upper limit. The acceptable range depends upon the panel and to some extent on what the population is used to consuming. In this country, the majority of the younger generation do not know what cultured cream butter tastes like, as they are used to consuming sweet cream butter. The range of acceptability would be different in some parts of Europe where they are used to a cultured product.

E. A. Day.—I would like to comment a little further on the question. We analyzed a number of samples from Europe for diacetyl and I do not think we found any that were above 3 p.p.m.

R. C. Lindsay.—Three parts per million would be an upper limit even on European butters. In fact, we noted that the flavor intensity of many of these butters was lower than the ones that we were making experimentally, in which we were specifically trying for a higher flavor.

BIBLIOGRAPHY

ANDERSEN, V. B. 1961. Cultured buttermilk and sour cream from single-strain cultures of lactic streptococci. Milchwissenschaft 16, 128–130.

BABEL, F. J., and HAMMER, B. W. 1944. Action of butter cultures in butter: A review. J. Dairy Sci. 27, 79–141.

BADINGS, H. T., and GALESLOOT, T. E. 1962. Studies on the flavor of different types of butter starters with reference to the defect "yoghurt flavor" in butter. Proc. 16th Intern. Dairy Congr. B, 199–208.

BEGEMANN, P. H., and KOSTER, J. C. 1964. Components of butterfat. 4-cis-Heptenal: A cream-flavored component of butter. Nature 202, 552–555.

BENNETT, G., LISKA, B. J., and HEMPENIUS, W. L. 1965. Effect of other flavor components on the perception of diacetyl in fermented dairy products. J. Food Sci. 30, 35–37.

BOLDINGH, J., and TAYLOR, R. J. 1962. Trace constituents of butterfat. Nature 194, 909–913.

CHOU, T. C. 1962. The chemical nature of the characteristic flavor of cultured buttermilk. Ph.D. thesis, Ohio State University, Columbus, O.

DAY, E. A., LINDSAY, R. C., and FORSS, D. A. 1964. Dimethyl sulfide and the flavor of butter. J. Dairy Sci. 47, 197–199.

DEANE, D. D., and HAMMOND, E. G. 1960. Coagulation of milk for cheese making by ester hydrolysis. J. Dairy Sci. 43, 1421–1429.

DEANE, D. D., and THOMAS, W. R. 1964. Use of chemical compounds to replace lactic cultures in the manufacture of sour cream. J. Dairy Sci. 47, 684.

DE JONG, K., and VAN DER WAL, H. 1964. Identification of some isolinoleic acids occurring in butterfat. Nature 202, 556–560.

DEMAN, J. C. 1956. The formation of diacetyl in cultures of Betacoccus cremoris. Neth. Milk Dairy J. 10, 38–52.

GALESLOOT, T. E. 1962. The bacteriology and biochemistry of starters and ripened cream. Proc. 16th Intern. Dairy Congr. D, 143–167.

HAMMER, B. W., and BABEL, F. J. 1943. Bacteriology of butter cultures. A review. J. Dairy Sci. 26, 83–168.

HAMMER, B. W., and SHERWOOD, F. F. 1923. The volatile acids produced by starters and by organisms isolated from them. Iowa Agr. Expt. Sta. Res. Bull. 80.

HARPER, W. J., GOULD, I. A., and HANKINSON, C. L. 1961. Observations on the free volatile acids in milk. J. Dairy Sci. 44, 1764–1765.

HARVEY, R. J. 1960. Production of acetone and acetaldehyde by lactic streptococci. J. Dairy Res. 27, 41–45.

HARVEY, R. J., and COLLINS, E. B. 1962. Citrate transport system of Streptococcus diacetilactis. J. Bacteriol. 83, 1005–1009.

HARVEY, R. J., and COLLINS, E. B. 1963. Roles of citrate and acetoin in the metabolism of Streptococcus diacetilactis. J. Bacteriol. 86, 1301–1307.

JACKSON, H. W., and MORGAN, M. E. 1954. Identity and origin of the malty aroma substance from milk cultures of Streptococcus lactis var. maltigenes. J. Dairy Sci. 37, 1316–1324.

KANDLER, O. 1961. Metabolism of lactic acid organisms (in German). Milchwissenschaft 16, 523–581.

KEENAN, T. W., LINDSAY, R. C., MORGAN, M. E., and DAY, E. A. 1966. Acetaldehyde production by single-strain lactic streptococci. J. Dairy Sci. 49, 10–14.

KHATRI, L. L., and DAY, E. A. 1962. Analysis of free fatty acids of fresh milk fats and ripened cream butters. J. Dairy Sci. 45, 660.

LINDSAY, R. C. 1965. Flavor chemistry of butter cultures. Ph.D. thesis. Oregon State University, Corvallis, Ore.

LINDSAY, R. C., and DAY, E. A. 1965. Rapid quantitative method for determination of acetaldehyde in lactic starter cultures. J. Dairy Sci. 48, 665–669.

LINDSAY, R. C., DAY, E. A., and SANDINE, W. E. 1965A. Green flavor defect in lactic starter cultures. J. Dairy Sci. 48, 863–869.

LINDSAY, R. C., DAY, E. A., and SANDINE, W. E. 1965B. Identification of volatile flavor components of butter culture. J. Dairy Sci. 48, 1566–1574.

LINDSAY, R. C., DAY, E. A., and SATHER, L. A. 1966. Preparation and evaluation of synthetic culture flavor concentrates. J. Dairy Sci. (In press).

LUNDSTEDT, E., and FOGG, W. B. 1962. Citrated whey starters. II. Gradual formation of flavor and aroma in creamed cottage cheese after the addition of small quantities of citrated cottage cheese whey cultures of Streptococcus diacetilactis. J. Dairy Sci. 45, 1327–1331.

MACLEOD, P., and MORGAN, M. E. 1958. Differences in the ability of lactic streptococci to form aldehydes from certain amino acids. J. Dairy Sci. 41, 908–913.

MAGIDMAN, P., HERB, S. F., BARFORD, R. A., and RIEMENSCHNEIDER, R. W. 1962. Fatty acids of cows milk. A. Techniques employed in supplementing gas-liquid chromatography for identification of fatty acids. J. Am. Oil Chemists' Soc. 39, 137–142.

MARTH, E. H. 1962. Symposium on lactic starter cultures. III. Certain aspects of starter culture metabolism. J. Dairy Sci. 45, 1271–1281.

MATHER, D. W., and BABEL, F. J. 1959. A method for standardizing the diacetyl content of creamed cottage cheese. J. Dairy Sci. 42, 1045–1056.

MIZUNO, W. G., and JEZESKI, J. J. 1959. Studies on starter metabolism. IV. Effect of various substrates on the formation of acetoin by a mixed starter culture. J. Dairy Sci. 42, 251–263.

MORGAN, M. E., LINDSAY, R. C., LIBBEY, L. M., and PEREIRA, R. L. 1966. Identity of additional aroma constituents in milk cultures of Streptococcus lactis var. maltigenes. J. Dairy Sci. 49, 15–18.

PARKS, O. W., KEENEY, M. KATZ, I., and SCHWARTZ, D. P. 1964. Isolation and characterization of the methyl ketone precursor in butter fat. J. Lipid Res. 5, 232–235.

PATTON, S., FORSS, D. A., and DAY, E. A. 1956. Methyl sulfide and the flavor of milk. J. Dairy Sci. 39, 1469–1470.

PATTON, S., and THARP, B. W. 1959. Formation of methyl ketones from milk during steam distillation. J. Dairy Sci. 42, 49–55.

PETTE, J. W. 1949. Some aspects of the butter aroma problem. Proc. 12th Intern. Dairy Congr. 2, 572–579.

REITER, B., and MOLLER-MADSEN, A. 1963. Reviews of the progress of dairy science. Cheese and butter starters. J. Dairy Res. 30, 419–456.

RIEL, R. R., and GIBSON, C. A. 1961. The use of starter distillate for flavoring butter. Food Technol. 15, 137–140.

SEITZ, E. W., SANDINE, W. E., ELLIKER, P. R., and DAY, E. A. 1963A. Distribution of diacetyl reductase among bacteria. J. Dairy Sci. 46, 186–189.

SEITZ, E. W., SANDINE, W. E., ELLIKER, P. R., and DAY, E. A. 1963B. Studies on diacetyl biosynthesis by Streptococcus diacetilactis. Canadian J. Microbiol. 9, 431–441.

SWARTLING, P., and JOHANSSON, S. 1954. Treatmeint of winter cream at different temperatures with regard to butter aroma. Svenska Mejeritidn. 46, 309–312, 315–316.

VAN NIEL, C. B., KLUYVER, A. J., and DERX, H. G. 1929. Studies on butter aroma. Biochem. Zeitschrift. 210, 234–251.

VEDAMUTHU, E. R., SANDINE, W. E., and ELLIKER, P. R. 1964. Influence of milk citrate concentration on associative growth of lactic streptococci. J. Dairy Sci. 47, 110.

WIDMARK, E. M. P. 1920. Kinetics of the ketonic decomposition of acetoacetic acid. Acta med Scandinav. 53, 393–421.

WINTER, M., STOLL, M., WARNOFF, E. W., GREÜTER, F., and BUCHI, G. 1963. Volatile carbonyl constituents of dairy butter. J. Food Sci. 28, 554–561.

WISEMAN, H. G., and IRVIN, H. M. 1957. Determination of organic acids in silage. J. Agr. Food Chem. 5, 213–215.

CHAPTER 15

E. A. Day | Cheese Flavor

INTRODUCTION

The estimated hundreds of cheese varieties (Sanders 1953) available throughout the world provide a broad spectrum of flavors for the human palate. All varieties are made from the milk of mammals, so species determines some varietal differences. In addition, the manner in which the milk is manipulated to form curds and the subsequent dehydration and compaction of the curds into the final shape of the cheese, the normal and added microflora, and the procedure employed to ripen the cheese also are factors in determining varietal differences. Even though there are many cheese varieties, all have much in common in qualitative flavor composition and to orient subsequent discussions a partial classification of cheese varieties is given here.

CLASSIFICATION OF CHEESES

(I) Natural
  (A) Unripened
    (1) *Low Fat*—Cottage, Baker's
    (2) *High Fat*—Cream, Neufchatel
  (B) Ripened
    (1) *Hard Grating Cheese*—Romano, Parmesan, Asiago Old
    (2) *Hard*—Cheddar, Swiss, Gruyere, Provalone, Gouda
    (3) *Semi-Soft*—Roquefort, Blue, Gorgonzola, Brick, Limburger
    (4) *Soft*—Camembert, Brie, Liederkranz
(II) Whey Cheeses—Ricotta, Mysost

The unripened cheeses exhibit a mild delicate flavor that is derived from three sources; namely, the milk, heat degradation products of milk, and metabolic products of microorganisms used as cultures in the manufacturing process.

GROSS CHANGES IN THE MAJOR CONSTITUENTS OF RIPENED CHEESE

Ripening cheese represents a dynamic system in which many reactions are proceeding simultaneously. Many of the reactions are mediated through fermentation pathways of the microorganisms, through enzymes from lysed microbial cells, through enzymes native to milk, and finally, through chemical equilibria. In the course of these reactions, the protein, fat, and carbohydrate are degraded to varying degrees to yield a very complex mixture of compounds, some of which give rise to the varietal cheese flavors. Some components of milk may exert either a direct or indirect effect upon the final cheese flavor, either by serving as precursors or by influencing the balance of microorganisms in the ripening process. Most evidence suggests, however, that degradation of the major cheese constituents results in the main flavor components.

Protein

The proteins of cheese, with casein as the main component, provide much of the physical structure, body, and texture properties. The protein undergoes varying degrees of hydrolysis which is dependent upon the cheese variety and its state of maturity (Lindquist and Storgards 1959; Annibaldi 1959). The casein fractions are attacked and degraded in a sequential manner which is fairly common to most varieties and involves kappa, beta, and alpha respectively. Electrophoretic patterns of peptide fractions (Storgards and Lindquist 1953) are different, however, between cheese varieties and appear to be characteristic of variety. Variations in the peptide fractions can occur within a variety and account for the bitter flavor effects. Bitterness in Cheddar cheese has been ascribed by Czulah (1959) to the proteolytic activity of rennet to give bitter-tasting peptides in conjunction with a deficiency of suitable bacterial proteases for degradation of the peptides. Emmons et al. (1962) has shown that proper selection of starter bacteria of suitable proteolytic capacity can eliminate the defect.

Qualitatively, the amino acids resulting from proteolysis are the same in ripened cheese varieties as in casein (Kosikowski 1951; Kosikowski and Dahlberg 1954). There are quantitative differences but they are beyond the scope of this discussion. It is important to bear in mind that amino acids serve as substrates for the microorganisms of cheese and can undergo a variety of reactions to yield flavorful compounds.

Lipids

It has been repeatedly demonstrated that milkfat is essential for the typical flavor of most cheese varieties. The fat acts as a solvent for many of the flavor components, and the fat is known to modify the flavor properties of many compounds. In addition, the fat serves as a precursor for a variety of compounds. Lactones, methyl ketones, esters, alcohols, and fatty acids all can be derived from milk lipids during cheese ripening and all have been found.

Some fat hydrolysis appears to be beneficial to the flavor of most ripened cheese varieties. This has been well documented in the literature and reference should be made to the reviews by Sjostrom (1959) and Mabbitt (1961). As yet, no one knows which lipase systems are responsible for fat hydrolysis in Cheddar cheese. At least two lipase systems are known in milk but neither has a pH optimum in the range of Cheddar. The relative significance of the milk and microbial lipases is an area of research that could be very beneficial in extending our knowledge of Cheddar ripening. In blue-veined cheeses, lipolysis by natural milk lipases is induced in the manufacturing procedure and lipases also are elaborated by molds used for ripening. In the manufacture of Italian hard grating cheeses, lipases are added via the rennet paste or as special enzyme preparations, from the base of the tongue of lambs, kids, and calves. In each case the lipids are hydrolyzed to yield fatty acids which impart flavor. The acids also serve as substrates for molds and bacteria in the production of other flavor components.

Carbohydrate

Lactose, the major carbohydrate of milk and cheese, serves as a primary energy source of the lactic bacteria used in cheese making. Part of the lactose is utilized through fermentation and the remainder is expelled in the whey so that by the time most cheeses leave the press, no significant amount remains in the curd. This does not infer that products of sugar fermentation are not important in flavor because there is evidence that some are. When one deals with flavor, what was considered quantitatively insignificant in gross analysis, frequently becomes very important. Traces of sugar remaining in the curd can provide ample precursor for significant quantities of flavor components. The reader is referred to the review by Reiter and Moller-Madsen (1963) for details on products of sugar fermentation.

FLAVOR OF BLUE-VEINED CHEESE

Roquefort is the best known of the blue-veined cheeses but there are a number of other varieties that also employ the mold, *Penicillium roqueforti*, in their ripening and which also have similar flavors. Domestic Blue, imported Bleu, English Stilton, and Italian Gorgonzola are a few examples. For convenience in this discussion all of these will be referred to as Blue cheese. This group of cheeses is characterized by a sharp, peppery flavor and a semi-soft consistency. Of all the varieties of ripened cheeses, more is probably known about Blue cheese flavor than any other. In fact, based on current knowledge of flavor composition, many flavor houses have been able to develop reasonable facsimiles of the authentic flavor which are used widely in the food industry. In no case, however, are the synthetic blends a complete reproduction of the natural, hence the reason for continued interest in the flavor. Flavor chemists have investigated the flavor since the early part of the century and extensive reviews have been published by Sjostrom (1959) and Bakalor (1962).

Blue cheese contains 41 to 43% water, 30 to 32% fat, 21 to 23% nitrogenous compounds (mostly casein and its degradation products) and 4 to 5% salt. The flavor components of the cheese may be derived from three main sources: (1) the milk; (2) added materials such as salt; (3) through action of microbial and natural milk enzymes on the cheese components during manufacturing and ripening. The families of compounds that have been identified and related to flavor are the amino acids, fatty acids, carbonyls, alcohols, esters, and other compounds that will be called miscellaneous.

Amino Acids

The role of proteolysis and its affect on Blue cheese flavor has received limited attention. *P. roqueforti* and *Bacterium linens* both have active proteolytic enzymes that degrade casein (Nishikawa 1958; Foster *et al.* 1957) and relatively large quantities of amino acids have been reported

TABLE 49

FREE AMINO ACIDS IN ROQUEFORT AND BLUE CHEESE[1]
(milligrams per gram)

Amino Acids and Related Compounds[2]	Roquefort			Gorgonzola	Domestic Blue			
	1	2	3	1	1	2	3	4
Glutamic acid	>6.06	6.06	>6.06	>6.06	>6.06	>6.06	>6.06	>6.06
Aspartic acid	0.23	1.48	0.23	1.14	0.46	1.14	0.91	0.14
Leucine-methionine	5.13	. . .	2.85	>6.06	4.90	5.59	3.76	0.97
Basic	>6.06	4.60	1.86	0.46	0.23	>6.06	>6.06	1.23
Valine	>6.06	5.36	4.33	>6.06	5.01	5.59	4.67	0.88
Alanine	>6.06	0.57	3.76	4.60	2.62	1.71	5.36	0.70
Glutamine	0.91	>6.06	2.30	0.23	6.06	>6.06	>6.06	0.61
Phenylalanine	3.19	0.00	>6.06	0.00	0.23	0.23	0.57	0.60
Tyrosine	3.65	3.54	1.86	4.33	3.53	3.31	0.57	0.55
Glycine	0.34	0.11	0.11	0.34	0.57	0.11	0.23	0.00
Threonine	2.74	0.00	1.00	0.34	0.46	0.23	0.00	0.00
Proline	0.46	0.80	3.62	0.34	0.57	0.46	3.88	0.13
Tyramine	0.00	0.00	0.00	0.00	0.00	0.00	0.00	0.00
α-amino butyric acid	0.00	0.46	0.00	0.00	0.00	0.00	0.00	0.00
Methionine sulfoxide γ-amino butyric acid	1.93	>6.06	>6.06	4.79	>6.06	3.08	4.22	1.71
Asparagine	0.00	0.00	0.00	0.00	0.00	2.96	3.53	0.40
Serine	1.14	0.00	2.52	0.57	0.23	0.34	0.11	0.00
Flavor development	Strong	Strong	Strong	Strong	Strong	Strong, bitter	Medium	Mild

[1] From Kosikowski and Dahlberg (1954).
[2] Notation 0.00 indicates inability to obtain detectable amount of particular amino acid by this analytical method and not complete absence of amino acid.
. . . No observation made.

in several varieties of Blue cheese (Kosikowski and Dahlberg 1954). The amino acid composition is shown in Table 49.

Based on the observations of Dacre (1953) and Mabbitt (1955), the amino acids and peptide fractions isolated from cheese bear no resemblance to a typical cheese flavor. Rather, the fractions impart a "brothy" taste which constitutes an important background on which the typical flavor is superimposed and through which the flavor is enhanced as originally postulated by Mulder (1952). Flavor enhancement is still a nebulous subject and may include such things as alteration of the flavor properties of classes of compounds through physical bonding and related phenomena. A possible example will be discussed later in this paper. The amino acids also are converted to flavor components via microbial action to yield alcohols, aldehydes, sulfur compounds, and possibly other important compounds.

Fatty Acids

The fatty acids have long been recognized as important components of Blue cheese. The "peppery" taste has been attributed to the 4:0, 6:0, and 8:0 acids and many workers have qualitated the short chain acids: Thomasow (1947) found 4:0, 5:0, and 8:0; Coffman et al. (1960) identified 4:0, iso 5:0, 6:0, 7:0, 8:0 and 10:0; Simonart and Mayaudon (1959A) isolated 1:0, 2:0, lactic and succinic acids and in subsequent work (1956B) identified benzoic, p-hydroxybenzoic, and p-hydroxyphenylacetic acids. Several investigators have obtained quantitative data for the acids; Morris et al. (1955) measured butyric and the moles of higher

TABLE 50

AVERAGE OF DUPLICATE ANALYSES OF FREE FATTY ACIDS IN BLUE CHEESE[1]
(Mg. acid/kg. cheese)

| Acid | Cheese Sample | | | |
	A	B	C	D
2:0	1,417	715	345	826
4:0	1,269	558	2,517	338
6:0	887	369	1,471	447
8:0	786	291	1,237	676
10:0	1,414	514	2,026	1,414
12:0	1,686	619	2,458	965
14:0	6,199	2,044	9,324	2,291
16:0	13,212	4,848	20,308	5,162
18:0	4,880	1,610	6,239	2,011
18:1	14,347	4,819	18,199	7,480
18:2	1,336	266	1,615	1,175
18:3	1,358	283	1,320	1,587
pH of cheese	5.6	5.5	5.3	5.6

[1] From Anderson and Day (1965A).

molecular weight acids; Sjostrom and Willart (1959) reported values for the 2:0 and 4:0 acids.

In recent work, the individual free fatty acids from 2:0 to 18:3 were quantitated by Anderson and Day (1965A). The data are presented in Table 50. Samples A, B, and C were domestic Blue and Sample D was imported Roquefort.

As shown in Table 50, there was considerable variation in the free fatty acid content among the samples examined (23 to 67 gm. per kg. of cheese). This variation was reflected in the flavor and odor of the samples. Sample B was mild and had an atypical flavor; Sample D, which was Roquefort, had a different flavor than the domestic samples in that it lacked the butyric acid odor and was more characteristic of the 6:0, 8:0, and 10:0 acids. The fatty acid distribution in the Roquefort sample was indeed different from the others in that the mole per cent of 8:0 and 10:0 was higher than in the domestic samples (see Table 50). Roquefort cheese is made from sheeps' milk which is reported (Hilditch 1956) to contain a higher mole per cent of 8:0 and 10:0 in the fat than in cows' milkfat.

Aside from the variations in free fatty acids caused by the composition of the fat, variations in the specificity of lipase systems common to Blue cheese may account for differences in free fatty acid patterns. At least two lipases exhibiting different pH optima are present in all cows' milk (Schwartz 1965) and *P. roqueforti* strains also have active lipase enzymes that might alter the patterns (Morris and Jezeski 1953; Proks *et al.* 1956).

Carbonyls

The methyl ketones, especially 2-heptanone and 2-nonanone, are generally considered the key flavor components of Blue cheese. A number of investigators have contributed to our knowledge on this subject and the data are well documented through 1960 by Bakalor (1962). The methyl ketones that have been identified are C_3 to C_{11}, C_{13}, and C_{15}. Schwartz and Parks (1963) quantitated the odd numbered methyl ketones from C_3 to C_{15} in domestic Blue cheese and Schwartz *et al.* (1963) measured the same compounds in Roquefort cheese. In neither type of blue-veined cheese was there a definite ratio between the quantities of the various ketones; 2-heptanone was the major ketone in all domestic Blue cheese and in all Roquefort cheese samples except one which contained more 2-nonanone. Aged cheese did not necessarily have a higher ketone content, and the concentration of individual ketones varied appreciably between samples. Similar results were obtained by Anderson and Day (1966) and since the data will be used in subsequent discussions, they are presented in Table 51.

TABLE 51

CONCENTRATION OF METHYL KETONES IN BLUE-VEIN TYPE CHEESES[1]

Methyl Ketone Chain Length	Mg. Ketone/Kg. Cheese[2]						
	A[3]	B[3]	C[3]	D[3]	E[3]	F[4]	G[4]
3	3.4	2.8	3.9	1.7	2.7	2.7	...
5	18.4	7.2	20.9	6.5	17.5	19.2	3.6
7	40.8	19.0	71.8	17.9	39.1	69.9	17.6
9	28.0	22.3	88.3	19.8	42.5	78.	
11	6.4	6.0	29.9	4.9	12.3	6.7	2.4

[1] From Anderson and Day (1966).
[2] Average of duplicate analyses.
[3] Samples A to E are domestic Blue cheese.
[4] Samples F and G are imported Roquefort cheese.

Origin of Methyl Ketones.—It is now generally accepted that the methyl ketones result from β-oxidation of fatty acids. The spores of *P. roqueforti* are responsible for the conversion rather than the vegetative cells (Gehrig and Knight 1958). The same investigators (1963) found that when low concentrations of C^{14} labeled sodium octanoate were used as a

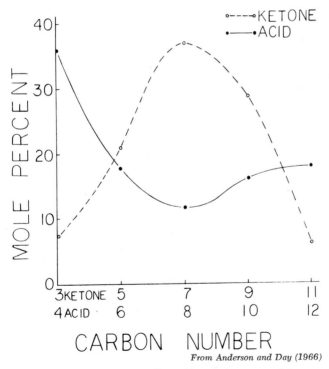

From Anderson and Day (1966)

FIG. 75. RELATIONSHIP OF FREE FATTY ACIDS AND METHYL KETONES IN BLUE CHEESE

spore substrate, most of the octanoate was recovered as CO_2 and no ketone was produced. When an excess of octanoate was used, part was converted to 2-heptanone and part was oxidized to CO_2. They were unable to isolate intermediates of the β-oxidation scheme but concluded their evidence supported such a mechanism. Support of such a mechanism was provided earlier by Bassett and Harper (1958) who detected β-keto acids in Blue cheese. It should be noted, however, that β-keto acids are normal components of milk lipids (Parks *et al.* 1964) and a portion of the ketones may arise from this source.

As shown in Figure 75, the mold spores are more specific in the conversion of certain acids to ketones than others. The fatty acid curve represents the free acids in cheese and closely resembles the distribution of these acids in milk glycerides. Whereas 2-heptanone is in highest concentration, octanoic acid is the least plentiful, both as the free acid and in milk glycerides. Girolami and Knight (1955) reported increasing O_2 uptake for *P. roqueforti* as the acid substrate went from 4:0 to 9:0 and a decrease as the carbon number of the acid increased further. The data presented in Figure 75 support this trend.

Substantial quantities of acetaldehyde, 2-methylbutanal, 3-methylbutanal, and furfural have been reported in Blue cheese (Day and Anderson 1965). Acetaldehyde could come from pyruvate via alanine or sugar fermentation whereas the branched chain aldehydes may be derived from amino acids. Furfural is a product of the browning reaction.

Primary Alcohols

While the alcohols have not received much attention in the past, recent work (Day and Anderson 1965; Anderson and Day 1965B) indicates they may be of significance in Blue cheese flavor both as flavor components *per se* and as reactants for ester formation.

Of the primary alcohols identified in Blue cheese, methanol and ethanol appear to be important in ester formation. While ethanol is a common metabolic product of many yeast and fungi, methanol is not. However, methyl esters have been identified in Blue cheese (Day and Anderson 1965) Cheddar cheese (Day and Libbey 1964) and in butter cultures (Lindsay *et al.* 1965). The literature is lacking as to a possible mechanism for methanol formation. 2-Phenylethanol, 2-methylbutanol, and 3-methylbutanol undoubtedly result from oxidative decarboxylation and deamination of phenylalanine, isoleucine, and leucine respectively. This reaction is well documented in the literature (Foster 1949) for yeast and fungi. The presence of *n*-pentanol, however, is less rapidly explained. Ingraham *et al.* (1961) related a metabolic pathway to *n*-

pentanol by mutant strains of *Saccharomyces cerevisiae*. The alcohol was thought to occur as an intermediate in amino acid synthesis. It is conceivable that similar reactions may be initiated by yeasts and molds common to Blue cheese.

Secondary Alcohols

The secondary alcohol analogs of methyl ketones have been identified in Blue cheese by Day and Anderson (1965). Jackson and Hussong (1958) obtained evidence that the secondary alcohols result from reduction of the ketone analogs by the mold mycelia. Research recently completed in our laboratory by Anderson and Day (1965B) supports and extends the findings of Jackson and Hussong. The effect of pure cultures of *P. roqueforti, B. linens, Geotricum candidum, Torulopsis sphaerica, Streptococcus lactis*, and a *Mycoderma* species, all of which are found in Blue cheese, on ketone-alcohol interconversion was determined. After incubation of the pure cultures in appropriate media, with and without hexanoic acid, 2-pentanone or 2-pentanol added as substrate, one-half milliliter of headspace from the culture flask was analyzed by gas liquid chromatography (GLC) for the presence of oxidation and reduction products.

The results of the analysis for *P. roqueforti* are shown in Figure 76. Chromatogram A represents the control mold culture with no acid, ketone, or alcohol added. No peaks representing 2-pentanone or 2-pentanol are evident; however, when hexanoic acid was added, 2-pentanone and 2-pentanol appeared in the culture medium as seen in Chromatogram B. The addition of 2-pentanone resulted in 2-pentanol (Chromatogram C) and when 2-pentanol was added as a substrate, 2-pentanone was formed, Chromatogram D. The data clearly show that the mold converts the acid to the ketone and that it could interconvert the alcohol and ketone. While the other organisms could not oxidize hexanoic acid to the ketone, all could interconvert the ketone and alcohol except *S. lactis* and *B. linens*. *S. lactis* did not act on the substrates and *B. linens* only was able to oxidize the alcohol to the ketone.

The peak identities given in Figure 76 were obtained by rapid scan mass spectrometric analysis of the (GLC) effluent and provide an example of the utility of this relatively new marriage of two powerful analytical tools. For the identification studies, five milliliters of headspace from the mold culture was injected onto a 1/8 inch O.D. by 12 ft. GLC column and the effluent from the column was split; half of the effluent was directed to the flame ionization detector and the remainder was directed to the EC-1 inlet of the Atlas CH-4 mass spectrometer (MS). The gas flow to the two legs of the split was regulated so that a

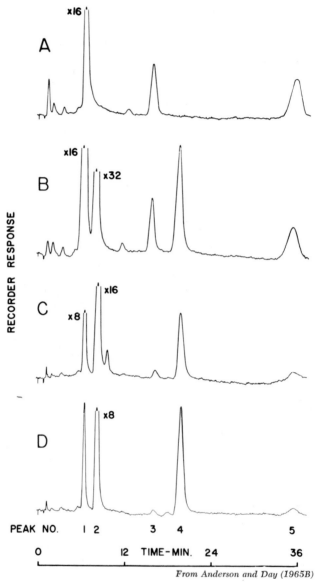

From *Anderson and Day (1965B)*

Fig. 76.   Headspace Chromatogram of *P. Roqueforti* Cultures

(A) *P. roqueforti* only; (B) Contained added hexanoic acid; (C) Contained added 2-pentanone; (D) Contained added 2-pentanol, peak (1) ethanol, (2) pentanone, (3) isobutanol, (4) 2-pentanol, (5) 2-methyl and 3-methylbutanol.
GLC conditions = 9 ft × ¹/₈ inch O.D., 15% Carbowax 1500 on 80/100 mesh acid-alkali washed Celite 545; 70 degrees C.

component eluting from the GLC column reached the flame detector and the MS source simultaneously. Mass spectra were taken concurrently with GLC analyses. Approximately five per cent of the GLC effluent passed to the EC-1 inlet was admitted to the ionization chamber. Hence only 2.5% of the 5 ml. of culture headspace was required to give interpretable mass spectra for those compounds identified in Fig. 76.

Quantitative Analysis of Secondary Alcohols.—The alcohols of cheese have been difficult to quantitate because of the lack of derivatives and chromatographic procedures such as is now available for the carbonyls (Day 1965). Anderson and Day (1965B) overcame this problem by resorting to GLC analysis and by using the methyl ketones as internal standards. The methyl ketones were quantitated via the DNP-hydrazones (data in Table 51). Aliquots of the same cheese samples were subsequently analyzed for alcohols. The resulting GLC peak areas of the methyl ketones represented a known molar concentration and the peak area of the alcohol analog could thus be quantitated. Corrections had to be made for recovery of the alcohol during sampling and for the nonlinearity of the GLC detector for the ketone and alcohol. The GLC analysis was conducted using the gas entrainment and on-column trapping technique of Morgan and Day (1965) with 5 gm. of Blue cheese fat as the sample. Gas chromatograms representative of the analysis are shown in Fig. 77. The quantitative data representing duplicate analyses are given in Table 52. The alcohol pattern is similar to the methyl ketone analogs in that 2-heptanol occurs in highest concentration. However, the alcohols occur at levels of less than ten per cent of the ketone analogs.

TABLE 52

CONCENTRATION OF SECONDARY ALCOHOLS IN BLUE-VEIN TYPE CHEESE[1]

Secondary Alcohol Chain Length	Mg. Alcohol/Kg. Cheese[2]						
	Cheese Sample[3,4]						
	A	B	C	D	E	F	G
C_5	0.6	0.3	1.9	1.3	0.3	0.6	0.2
C_7	6.3	8.2	9.1	9.8	3.0	3.4	4.2
C_9	3.9	3.7	4.3	2.5	2.5	...	...

[1] From Anderson and Day (1966).
[2] Average of duplicate analyses.
[3] Samples A to E are domestic Blue cheese.
[4] Samples F and G are imported Roquefort cheese.

Esters

Day and Anderson (1965B) have identified a rather extensive list of esters of the aliphatic acids in Blue cheese. Whether ester formation is the result of a chemical equilibrium or an enzyme catalyzed reaction remains to be elucidated. Pereira and Morgan (1958) found that ester formation in milk by *Pseudomonas fragi* was limited by ethanol concen-

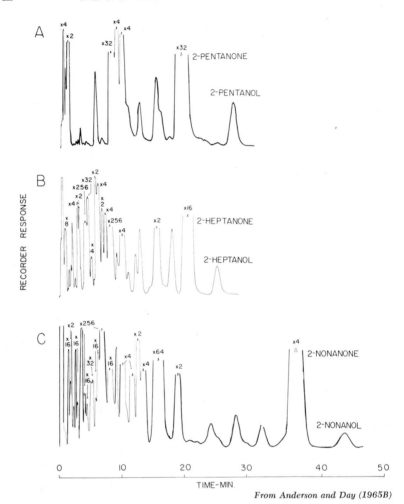

FIG. 77. GAS CHROMATOGRAMS OF BLUE CHEESE FAT SHOWING THE C₅, C₇,
AND C₉ METHYL KETONES AND SECONDARY ALCOHOLS

Column = 12 ft. x ¹/₈ inch O.D. packed with 20% 1,2,3- *tris*- (2-cyanoeth-
oxy propane on 60/80 mesh acid-alkali washed Celite 545. Temperatures
A = 50°C.; B = 80°C.; C = 90°C.

tration in the presence of the organism, thus suggesting the reaction is
enzyme catalyzed. A similar mechanism might be expected in cheese.

Miscellaneous Compounds

In the miscellaneous grouping of compounds is a series of poorly defined
alkyl and alkenyl substituted benzenes (Boyd *et al.* 1965). These com-

pounds exhibit an earthy, decayed wood odor and we believe they are important in Blue cheese flavor. A mass spectrum of one of the more important components exhibits a parent peak at mass/charge (m/e) 160, with major ions at succeeding 14 mass units and with the tropylium ion at m/e 91 all of which are suggestive of an alkenyl substituted benzene. A relatively large parent (P) minus 55 at m/e 105 originally suggested that the double bond might be located in the 4-5 position of the side chain. The *cis* and *trans* isomers of this compound did not fit the spectrum, however, because their P-15 fragment was much less intense. Further studies of the spectra have suggested a benzene substituted with a branched side chain. Additional studies are in progress to elucidate this point but it is apparent that the class of alkyl benzenes is important in the flavor of Blue cheese. They probably are synthesized by the mold.

Of the other compounds identified in Blue cheese (Day and Anderson 1965) the delta-lactones probably are the most important. These compounds are derived from milkfat and are commonly found in most cheeses and other dairy products. There are undoubtedly other important compounds that are still unidentified. Day and Anderson (1965) separated the volatile neutral components of Blue cheese into over 100 fractions by capillary column GLC. Less than half of the fractions were identified. Surely, other unidentified compounds are of importance and researchers will continue to unravel the complicated mixture.

Significance of Identified Compounds in Blue Cheese Flavor

Since qualitative and quantitative data had been obtained for Blue cheese flavor, it was logical to test the data with some preliminary flavor evaluations. The testing medium was composed of bland cottage cheese curd, milkfat, sweet cream, and three per cent salt blended into a homogeneous mixture. The flavor compounds were added at appropriate concentrations and evaluated after equilibration for 12 hr. The compounds used in the evaluation are listed in Table 53.

Initially, the complete series of fatty acids from 2:0 to 18:0, the secondary alcohols and the ketones were blended at the concentrations found in the cheese but the sample had a very intense soapy, bitter flavor. The soapy character was finally eliminated by including only the 2:0, 4:0, 6:0, and 8:0 acids at two-thirds their concentration in cheese. The flavor of subsequent samples became progressively more typical of Blue cheese as the concentration of ketones and secondary alcohols was doubled; by addition of 2-phenylethanol and by addition of the esters. The final mixture as listed in Table 53 closely resembles the natural flavor although there is a definite difference. The difference appears to be due to lack of the earthy-moldy note as well as other minor compounds.

TABLE 53

COMPOUNDS USED IN SYNTHETIC BLUE CHEESE FLAVOR[1]

| Compounds | Concentration (Mg./Kg.) | |
	Added to Mixture	Found in Cheese
Acetic acid	550	826
Butanoic acid	964	1448
Hexanoic acid	606	909
Octanoic acid	514	771
Acetone	6.2	3.1
2-Pentanone	30.3	15.2
2-Heptanone	69.5	34.8
2-Nonanone	66.3	33.1
2-Undecanone	17.0	8.5
2-Pentanol	0.9	0.4
2-Heptanol	12.1	6.1
2-Nonanol	7.0	3.5
2-Phenylethanol	2.0	...
Ethyl butanoate	1.5	...
Methyl hexanoate	6.0	...
Methyl octanoate		...

[1] From Anderson and Day (1966).

The data mentioned above point up an interesting problem encountered in this type of work. That is, the inability to exactly reproduce the natural flavor by strict adherence to the analytical data. The same problem has also been encountered in cultured dairy products (cf. Chapter 14). It can be argued, with justification, that the data are incomplete. Even so, the most striking discrepancy is the need to exclude, entirely, certain compounds from the mixture, i.e. 10:0 to 18:3 acids, and to adjust the concentration of others. This poses some interesting questions: first, is the physical distribution of compounds different in cheese than in the synthetic medium? If so, does the manner of incorporating the compounds into the medium affect the final flavor? Certainly the compounds have different flavor thresholds, depending upon whether they are in the fat or aqueous phase of the cheese. Second, do some of the flavor compounds form physical bonds with proteins, carbohydrates, etc., in such a manner that the equilibrium is altered or even the flavor properties of the compound are altered? Such bonds might dissociate as the food is masticated, thereby providing a regulator of aroma release to the olfactory receptors. These are but a few intriguing questions remaining to be answered on this subject.

FLAVOR OF CHEDDAR CHEESE

According to Kosikowski (1957) "the typical flavor of Cheddar cheese is associated with a pleasant, slightly sweet, aromatic, walnuty sensation without any outstanding single note. In aged cheese, a bitty quality, which is neither coarse nor unpleasant gives sharpness to the cheese." Much more research effort has been expended on elucidating the nature of Cheddar flavor than on Blue cheese but with less success.   The status of published research on Cheddar flavor through 1960 is given in reviews by Mabbitt (1961) and Marth (1963).   While the list of compounds isolated in the aroma fraction has become extensive, no complete description has been reported that satisfactorily reproduces Cheddar flavor. Endless failures in relating the aroma to a few discrete compounds has prompted adherence to Mulder's theory of balanced components (1952) which states that aroma is due to a combination of many compounds, which when in proper quantitative balance, give rise to a typical flavor.

Cheddar cheese usually contains 35 to 37% water, 33 to 36% fat, 23 to 25% casein, and 1.4 to 1.8% salt.   Practically all of the lactose is removed from the cheese via the whey or by fermentation by the time the cheese is removed from the hoops.   The flavor of freshly made Cheddar is quite bland and it is through the ripening process that flavor develops. Ripening is carried out by diverse groups of bacteria and the role of each

TABLE 54

A COMPARISON BETWEEN THE FREE AMINO ACID CONTENT AND FLAVOR OF RAW AND PASTEURIZED-MILK CHEDDAR CHEESE FROM THREE DIFFERENT LOTS
(COMMERCIAL LACTIC STARTER)[1, 2, 3]
(All cheeses ripened 3 mo. at 60°F.)

	(Mg./g. cheese)					
	Cheese 72949		Cheese 72849		Cheese 2491	
Amino acid	Raw	Past.	Raw	Past.	Raw	Past.
Glutamic acid	>6.06	>6.06	>6.06	>6.06	>6.06	>6.06
Aspartic acid	0.82	0.22	1.85	0.11	2.17	0.33
Leucine-methionine	>6.06	3.19	4.54	1.66	4.32	2.43
Basic	>6.06	>6.06	>6.06	>6.06	>6.06	>6.06
Valine	5.00	3.94	5.59	1.37	4.70	4.97
Alanine	1.90	0.23	3.65	0.16	1.66	0.06
Gutamine	0.36	0.25	2.19	0.32	0.27	0.42
Phenylalanine	3.98	3.93	3.42	1.33	1.25	0.73
Tyrosine	0.40	0.91	0.34	0.86	0.31	1.35
Glycine	0.36	0.27	0.14	0.14	0.15	0.14
Threonine	0.40	0.18	0.33	0.19	0.35	0.23
Proline	0.24	0.00	0.91	0.00	1.06	0.00
Tyramine	0.75	0.00	0.87	0.00	1.40	0.00
α-amino butyric acid	0.08	0.00	0.08	0.00	0.18	0.00
Asparagine	0.00	>6.06	0.00	2.43	0.00	>6.06
Serine	0.00	0.33	0.00	0.00	0.11	0.13
Cysteic acid	++	++	+++	++	0.00	0.00
Methionine sulfoxide, γ-amino butyric acid	++	+++	+++	++	++	+
Score	39.0	40.0	38.0	39.5	38.0	39.0
Flavor	Sl. unclean sharp	Med.	Sl. bitter Sl. fermented, sharp	Med.	Unclean sharp	Sl. acid med.
Score	29.0	29.5	27.5	29.0	29.5	29.5
Body	Sl. open		Open, gassy	Sl. open		

[1] Notation 0.00 indicates inability to obtain detectable amount of particular amino acid at analytical period in question.
[2] As + signs increase concentration of amino acid increases.
[3] From Kosikowski (1951).

group is not clear. Nevertheless, the protein, fat and minor constituents are degraded to various stages to give a variety of flavorful compounds. For this discussion, the compounds have been grouped into nitrogeneous, carbonyl, fatty acid, alcohol, ester, and sulfur containing.

Nitrogeneous Compounds

Proteolysis in Cheddar cheese has been studied extensively and many of the products of the reaction have been identified. These include ammonia (Kristoffersen and Gould 1960), amines (Silverman and Kosikowski 1956), and the amino acids common to casein (Kosikowski 1951) but with certain quantitative differences. As indicated in the discussions on Blue cheese, it is now well established that the amino acids, amines, and peptide fractions do not impart cheese flavor as such but appear to function by providing a brothy background on which the typical flavor is superimposed. However, further degradation of amino acids serves to introduce a variety of compounds of significance to typical Cheddar flavor. As shown in Table 54, larger concentrations of amino acids occur in raw-milk cheese as compared to pasteurized cheese. While no direct relation has been established, the higher level of amino acids may indirectly affect the flavor differences between the two types of Cheddar.

Fatty Acids

The relative significance of the free fatty acids (FFA) in Cheddar cheese flavor remains to be elucidated. The fact that Cheddar cheese made with skimmilk is practically devoid of Cheddar character suggests that lipid degradation products are essential. Peterson *et al.* (1949) noted that FFA of intermediate chain length were produced during the ripening process and were characteristic of the cheese flavor. Patton (1963) studied the volatile acids in cheese distillates and by use of various qualitative reagents for removal of specific classes of compounds, he was able to assess the importance of the various compounds in Cheddar aroma. He concluded that the volatile acids were the "backbone" of Cheddar aroma. Since acetic acid was the dominant acid in the volatiles, it was considered to be especially important.

Bills and Day (1964) quantitated the major FFA from 2:0 to 18:3 in 14 samples of Cheddar having a wide range in flavor quality. The samples were made from raw and pasteurized milk. The results are presented in Tables 55 and 56. Acetic acid showed the greatest variability in concentration and was usually the most abundant. Among the FFA that could arise through the hydrolysis of milkfat, butyric was always found in about twice the percentage reported for esterified 4:0. The individual FFA from 6:0 to 18:3, however, were present in nearly

TABLE 55

DESCRIPTIVE SUMMARY OF CHEDDAR CHEESES SELECTED FOR ANALYSIS[1]

Cheese No.	Flavor Criticism	pH	Milk
1	None	5.26	Raw
2	None	5.47	Past.
3	None[2]	5.35	Past.
4	Acid (slight)	5.19	Raw
5	Acid (slight)[2]	5.27	Raw
6	Acid, bitter (pronounced)	5.32	Raw
7	Bitter	5.33	Past.
8	Fermented	5.32	Past.
9	Fermented	5.35	Raw
10	Fruity	5.22	Past.
11	Fruity	5.22	Past.
12	Whey taint (pronounced)	5.36	Raw
13	Rancid (pronounced)	5.10	Raw
14	Rancid (pronounced)	5.24	Past.

[1] From Bills and Day (1964).
[2] Indicates cheeses ripened 3 to 4 months. Other cheeses were ripened 7 to 12 months.

TABLE 56

AVERAGES OF DUPLICATE ANALYSES OF FREE FATTY ACIDS IN 14 SAMPLES OF CHEDDAR CHEESE[1]
(Mg. free fatty acid per kilogram cheese)

Acid							Cheese No.							
	1	2	3	4	5	6	7	8	9	10	11	12	13	14
2:0	275	837	437	1103	1134	882	1170	1325	1316	663	811	429	858	437
4:0	94	127	76	178	102	80	119	145	207	71	80	106	913	751
6:0	35	33	29	79	37	39	27	48	61	18	18	36	744	333
8:0	34	43	36	74	36	37	50	44	55	24	21	34	462	472
10:0	45	53	55	75	50	48	80	57	62	42	40	58	708	860
12:0	60	83	87	109	69	55	123	90	93	58	60	81	738	808
14:0	176	236	191	309	215	170	315	235	264	143	134	233	2,237	1,576
16:0	443	510	516	689	522	427	620	498	548	358	300	599	3,978	2,445
18:0	160	192	104	237	144	136	216	219	246	124	118	163	1,181	795
18:1	360	458	319	590	361	420	819	630	502	368	312	464	5,390	5,852
18:2	48	81	63	87	46	37	125	93	91	70	41	45	366	536
18:3	33	43	28	57	26	21	60	62	52	25	31	41	536	618
Total	1763	2696	1941	3587	2742	2352	3724	3446	3497	1964	1966	2289	18,111	15,483

[1] From Bills and Day (1964).

the same ratio as the same esterified acids in milkfat. This suggests that the excessive amount of butyric acid is a product of selective hydrolysis or microbial synthesis, or both. Peterson et al. (1949) reported an increase in butyric acid without a corresponding increase in other FFA during the early period of Cheddar cheese ripening. The selective hydrolysis of short-chain fatty acids from milk triglycerides by milk lipase was reported by Harwalker and Calbert (1961). Both pancreatic lipase and milk lipase are known to selectively hydrolyze the 1-position of triglycerides (Jensen et al. 1963) upon which butyric acid is predominantly esterified (Clement et al. 1962).

With the exception of the two rancid samples listed in Table 55, the differences observed in the concentration of FFA from cheese to cheese are not as striking as one might expect, considering the difference in flavor, age, and manufacturing conditions of the cheese. Except for rancidity, there appeared to be no obvious correlation between given flavor defects and FFA concentration. There also is no marked differences in the range of FFA concentration between cheeses manufactured from raw milk and cheeses manufactured from pasteurized milk.

In view of the flavor properties of the cheeses listed in Table 55, and the variation in individual FFA concentrations for the respective samples, Table 56, Bills and Day concluded that over a still undefined range, the balance between the FFA and other flavor constituents is more important to Cheddar flavor than the concentration of FFA alone.

Carbonyls

A classical piece of research conducted over 50 years ago (Suzuki et al. 1910) still influences the thinking and direction of many investigators of Cheddar cheese flavor. Suzuki et al. (1910) studied the acids and neutral distillates of Cheddar and concluded that the "flavor solution" characterized by its close resemblance to Cheddar aroma, contained alcohols and esters. Failure in succeeding years to attribute Cheddar flavor to any of the major constituents, or to find "a Cheddar flavor compound," coupled with the conclusion of Dacre (1953) that the components of typical flavor are volatile and occur at p.p.m. concentration levels, has prompted investigators to examine the minor volatile components more closely. The carbonyls have been rigorously studied, primarily because analytical procedures have made them readily accessible (Day 1965).

Methyl ketones, containing odd-numbered carbon atoms from C_3 to C_{13} as well as butanone, have been reported in Cheddar cheese (Day and Keeney 1958). The significance of these compounds in Cheddar flavor is not certain. Walker (1961) reported that the flavor of a blend of methyl ketones, fatty acids and H_2S, when added to fresh cheese curd and aged three weeks corresponded to a three month old cheese. However, the actual presence of methyl ketones in Cheddar flavor at any significant concentration has been questioned (Lawrence 1963). Lawrence reported that a greater part of the methyl ketones found in Cheddar essentially are artifacts and result from degradation of β-keto esters which are normal constituents of milkfat (Ven et al. 1963). While this can certainly occur, it is doubtful that mild treatments such as employed by Libbey et al. (1963) would produce much ketone from the precursor. Atmospheric steam distillation or distillation at temperatures above 50°C. should be avoided to prevent degradation of the ketone precursor (Langler and Day 1964). The methyl ketones undoubtedly are derived from the natural β-keto esters of milk fat but it is plausible to conclude that hydrolysis of lipid during cheese ripening could also result in their formation. Butanone is found in relatively large concentration in Cheddar (Day *et al.* 1960; Scarpellino and Kosikowski 1962; Day and Libbey 1964) and it has been postulated that it results from reduction of acetoin to 2,3-butylene glycol which is in turn dehydrated to the ketone (Scarpellino and Kosikowski 1962).

Several aldehydes have been identified in Cheddar, the most prominent of which are methanal, ethanal, propanal, 3-methyl butanal, and 3-methyl thiopropanal (methional) (Day *et al.* 1960; Day and Libbey 1964). All of these compounds can result from transamination and decarboxylation of amino acids (MacLeod and Morgan 1958) by bacteria of the cheese. Methional has been implicated as an important flavor component in toasted Cheddar cheese and can form by the Strecker degradation of methionine (Keeney and Day 1957). Methional is very unstable and readily decomposes to acrolein, methyl mercaptan and dimethyl sulfide (Ballance 1961). The decomposition of methional may account for the methyl mercaptan (Libbey and Day 1963) and dimethyl sulfide (Patton *et al.* 1958) found in Cheddar cheese.

Diacetyl occurs in Cheddar cheese (Calbert and Price 1949) and within narrow concentration limits, less than 1 p.p.m, it has been considered necessary in Cheddar flavor. Certain starter bacteria used in the cheese operation readily ferment citrate to diacetyl (Reiter and Møller-Madsen 1963).

Alcohols

Ethanol and 2-butanol appear to be the major alcohols in Cheddar and they have been observed by a number of investigators (Dacre 1953; Patton *et al.* 1958; Scarpellino and Kosikowski 1962). In addition Day and Libbey (1964) identified traces of secondary alcohols corresponding to the methyl ketone analogs. Apparently some of the bacteria associated with ripening possess alcohol dehydrogenases capable of reducing the ketones and aldehyde analogs. All evidence obtained thus far (Bills and Day 1965) indicates that ethanol is a terminal product in the metabolism of glucose, through the hexosemonophosphate pathway the EMP glycolytic scheme or the Entner-Doudoroff pathway (Wood 1961) depending upon the bacteria involved.

Scarpellino and Kosikowski (1962) postulated that 2-butanol was a terminal product in the breakdown of acetoin. The proposed pathway was as follows:

$$CH_3-\underset{\overset{\|}{O}}{C}-\underset{\overset{|}{OH}}{CH}-CH_3 \xrightarrow{+2H} CH_3-\underset{\overset{|}{OH}}{CH}-\underset{\overset{|}{OH}}{CH}-CH_3 \xrightarrow{-H_2O} [CH_3-CH=\underset{\overset{|}{OH}}{C}-CH_3]$$

$$CH_3-CH_2-\underset{\overset{|}{OH}}{CH}-CH_3 \xleftarrow{2H} CH_3-CH_2-\underset{\overset{\|}{O}}{C}-CH_3$$

Large quantities of butanone are commonly found in Cheddar in addition to the alcohol analog.

Methanol has not been identified in Cheddar, yet methyl esters of fatty acids are quite common. It undoubtedy is present but has not been identified due to its solubility in water. At the present time, there is no metabolic scheme to explain its production by the bacteria associated with ripening of Cheddar cheese.

Esters

Esters of fatty acids and monohydroxy compounds have been somewhat ignored in Cheddar flavor. Suzuki et al. (1910) suggested that esters were present and recent work by Day and Libbey (1964) and Bills et al. (1965) has confirmed their presence and importance. In the analysis of neutral components in Cheddar volatiles by capillary GLC–rapid scan mass spectrometry, Day and Libbey (1964) identified a number of the methyl, ethyl, and n-butyl esters of fatty acids. The esters were exceeded in concentration only by the methyl ketones. The flavor properties of the esters coupled with their relatively large concentration in the volatiles tends to implicate them as contributors to flavor. In fact, the delicacy of the balance of Cheddar flavor components is best illus-

TABLE 57

RELATIVE AMOUNTS OF ETHANOL, ETHYL BUTYRATE, AND ETHYL HEXANOATE FOUND IN FOUR SAMPLES OF FRUITY CHEESE AND THEIR MATCHING NONFRUITY CONTROLS[1]

(Arranged in order of the intensity of the fruity defect as judged organoleptically)

Sample Pair		Relative Peak Height[2]		
		Ethanol	Ethyl Butyrate	Ethyl Hexanoate
1	Fruity	230	2.44	3.08
	Control	36	1.00[3]	0.27
2	Fruity	114	7.84	0.35
	Control	7	1.52	0.05
3	Fruity	95	0.53	[3]
	Control	18	0.22	[3]
4	Fruity	45	[3]	0.12
	Control	4	[3]	0.04

[1] From Bills et al. (1965).
[2] Full scale (1.0 mv) response equals relative peak height of 1.00 at 1x attenuation.
[3] Incomplete or doubtful resolution of the ester peak.

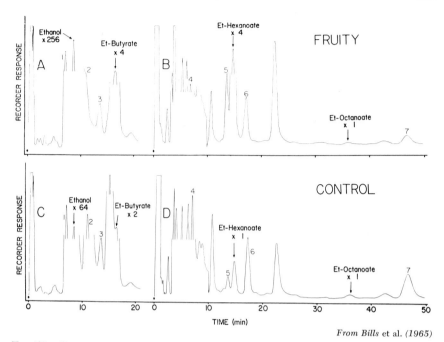

From Bills et al. (1965)

FIG. 78. CHROMATOGRAMS OF THE VOLATILE COMPONENTS OF A FRUITY CHEESE AND
ITS MATCHING NONFRUITY CONTROL (SAMPLE PAIR NO. 1)

Chromatograms A and C obtained at 50°C. Chromatograms B and D obtained at
80°C. A ⅛ inch O.D. x 10 ft. column packed with 20% 1,2,3-tris(2-cyanoethoxy)
propane on 80–100 mesh Celite 545 in an F&M Model 810 GLC.

trated by the fact that when the esters exceed some undetermined
concentration level, the cheese develops a fruity defect.

Bills et al. (1965) identified the fruity components as the ethyl esters
of fatty acids. Ethyl butyrate and ethyl caproate were found to be the
most important components. While these compounds occur in relatively
high concentrations in normal flavored Cheddar cheese, fruity samples
contain exceedingly high amounts. This is illustrated in Fig. 78 where
a fruity sample is compared to normal cheese. Both cheeses were made
from aliquots of the same batch of milk; the only difference was the
starter cultures used for manufacture. As can be seen in Fig. 78, the
levels of ethyl butyrate and ethyl hexanoate are higher in the fruity
sample than in the control. It is noteworthy that ethanol also occurs in
exceedingly high concentration in the fruity sample. A comparison of
the relative concentrations of the alcohol and the two esters in a series of
cheese samples is given in Table 57.

The peaks numbered 1 through 7 in the chromatograms of Fig. 78 were identified as follows: (1) acetone; (2) butanone; (3) 2-butanol; (4) diacetyl; (5) methyl hexanoate; (6) 2-heptanone; and (7) acetoin. In general, the level of volatile compounds appear to be higher in the fruity cheese. Individually, however, the volatile compounds, other than ethanol, ethyl butyrate, and ethyl hexanoate, did not appear to be consistently more abundant in the fruity samples; for example, 2-heptanone was larger in the fruity cheese in one sample series and smaller in another.

The higher level of ethanol in the fruity cheeses is probably indicative of the higher levels of esters in the fruity samples. Free fatty acids are present in relatively high concentration in Cheddar and vary over a narrow range (Bills and Day 1964). The increased ethanol production probably results in higher ester concentration via esterification with the fatty acids. Hence, ethanol probably is the limiting factor in ethyl ester formation. Whether esterification is enzyme catalyzed or the result of a chemical equilibrium remains to be elucidated.

Sulfur Compounds

Most of the work on sulfur containing compounds has been directed toward measuring H_2S. It has been observed by a number of investigators and Kristoffersen and Gould (1960) reported a significant correlation of the H_2S-free fatty acid ratios for characteristic Cheddar flavor. Certainly H_2S is detectable, organoleptically, in the concentration range found (1.6 to 2.3 μ moles/100 gm. cheese) so it must contribute to flavor. It is also very reactive and could form a variety of flavorful compounds in the cheese. This area of research has gone unattended and could provide interesting leads to the ambitious investigator.

The possible importance of methional in Cheddar flavor was first suggested by Keeney and Day (1957) and was subsequently implicated by Jackson (1958). Day et al. (1960) conclusively identified it in aged Cheddar and it recently has been found by McGugan (1964). There has been controversy over the significance of methional in Cheddar flavor and further work will be required before it, as well as other components, are placed in proper perspective. Methional is relatively unstable which makes it difficult to isolate. Ballance (1961) has shown that it readily decomposes to yield a number of compounds. Important among the degradation products are methyl mercaptan and dimethyl sulfide. Methyl mercaptan has been isolated (Libbey and Day 1963) and at its estimated concentration in Cheddar (25 p.p.b.) it would be detectable organoleptically. Dimethyl sulfide also has been isolated (Patton et al. 1958; Libbey and Day 1964) and it probably is important in flavor.

All of the sulfur compounds identified thus far could be derived from the sulfur containing amino acids. Trace compounds that may occur in milk should not be disregarded, however. Several likely precursors of dimethyl sulfide can be derived from plant materials that are consumed by the cow and subsequently might be secreted in the milk. These were discussed by Day *et al.* (1964).

Significance of Identified Compounds in Cheddar Flavor

At the present time, it can be stated with a reasonable degree of certainty that Cheddar cheese flavor has not been duplicated by use of analytical data. Many investigators have mixed various compounds isolated from cheese and have claimed varying degrees of success. In no case has a synthetic mixture been rigorously evaluated with proper taste panel procedures. This implies that no one is sufficiently satisfied with their data to put it to a rigorous test.

Apart from the additional qualitative data required to complete the picture, extensive quantitative data are needed before the true significance of various compounds can be assessed. Quantitative data are accumulating on several classes of compounds but the more difficult ones remain.

ANALYTICAL METHODS FOR CHEESE FLAVOR STUDIES

Space does not permit discussion of other cheese flavors in this chapter. In passing it seems appropriate, however, to mention briefly general procedures for handling cheese to study critically the flavor components. Certainly more elegant methods will be developed but the ones mentioned here have been very useful in our hands.

A scheme for isolation of the aroma of cheese follows:

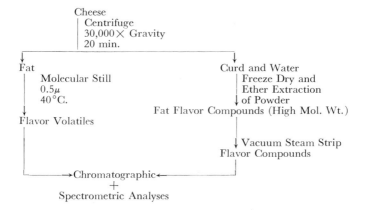

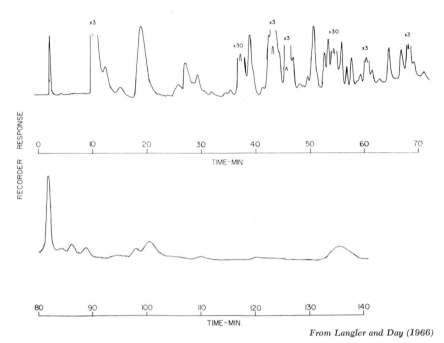

From Langler and Day (1966)

FIG. 79. SEPARATION OF SWISS CHEESE VOLATILES BY PACKED COLUMN GAS-LIQUID CHROMATOGRAPHY

Column conditions—20% Apiezon M on 100–120 mesh Celite 545; 12 ft. x ¹/₈ inch O.D. column. Isothermal at 55°C. for 15 min., then programmed at 3°/min. to 200°C.

The scheme is similar to that published earlier from our laboratory (Libbey *et al.* 1963) but with some additions. The cheese is packed into stainless steel centrifuge tubes and centrifuged to separate the fat phase. The fat is decanted off and passed through a molecular still as indicated. The aroma components generally move toward the vacuum pump and are trapped out in liquid nitrogen traps. The trapped components can be manipulated in a number of ways for subsequent analysis by chromatographic and spectrometric methods. Chromatography serves as the purification tool and it also can provide clues on the possible identity of compounds. Spectrometric analysis, which may include absorption spectrophotometry, nuclear magnetic resonance, and mass spectrometry, provide the data for establishing conclusive identification.

After most of the fat has been removed by centrifugation of the cheese, the protein plug and water remaining in the centrifuge tube can be slurried and lyophilized. The resulting powder is extracted with organic solvents, such as diethyl ether. If hydrocarbon solvents are used, it is necessary to wet the cheese powder to about ten per cent moisture level.

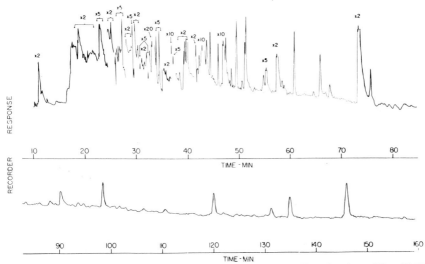

From Langler and Day (1966)

FIG. 80. SEPARATION OF SWISS CHEESE VOLATILES BY CAPILLARY COLUMN GAS-
LIQUID CHROMATOGRAPHY

Column conditions—alumina washed Apiezon L coated on a 0.01 inch I.D. x 300 ft.
capillary. Isothermal at 70°C. for 15 min., then temperature programmed at 10°C./
min. to 175°C.

The extracted powder is essentially odorless and when reconstituted it
has a brothy taste. The solvent extract of the powder contains some
cheese fat and usually contains some interesting flavor components of
high polarity or with very low vapor pressures. These compounds are
steam stripped from the fat with the apparatus described by Day and
Lillard (1960). The flavor components can be extracted from the
aqueous distillate and subjected to qualitative analyses.

Gas liquid chromatography is well suited for separation of the complex
mixtures encountered in flavor isolates and it therefore serves as the
major tool for separation and purification of components. We have
always believed in using any procedure that will help give reliable data
so that column, paper, and thin-layer chromatography are frequently
employed. We usually carry out the initial separations of flavor mixtures
on packed GLC columns. Flame detectors are used and the GLC column
effluent is split; 10% goes to the detector and 90% is vented to the outside of the oven. The portion of the effluent that is vented can be
smelled or the fractions can be collected for further purification. The
ability to smell the effluent is very important in determining where
emphasis should be placed in subsequent analytical steps. Also, the

ability to trap components for further purification on dissimilar packed columns or on capillary columns is of equal importance. For trapping, the melting point capillary is very useful. We also employ short packed columns which are connected to the column effluent vent and are dipped in a coolant. For subsequent transfer to capillary columns, a short piece of $1/_{16}$-inch O.D. by 0.03-inch I.D. column, which has been packed with stationary phase on treated Celite, is used to collect fractions from packed GLC columns. The trap is then connected to the front of the capillary and the separation on the capillary is carried out.

The new and powerful analytical combination of GLC with rapid scan mass spectrometry is used as the major tool for identifying components of the flavor mixtures. It is employed for both packed and capillary GLC analysis. Other spectrometric analyses are conducted when the data require it.

A single pass of a flavor mixture through a packed GLC column usually will not give adequate separation of the mixture. Figure 79 is the separation of the neutral volatiles from Swiss cheese (Langler and Day 1965). That many peaks contain more than one component is easily demonstrated by separating the same mixture on a capillary column. Such a separation is shown in Fig. 80 (Langler and Day 1965.) Obviously, neither the packed column nor the capillary column separation is adequate for complete analysis of the mixture. That is why trapping fractions and sometimes repeated trapping of the same fraction, is important to build up the concentration of minor components and to allow complete analysis.

DISCUSSION

O. Arakji.—The ketonic compounds in the synthetic Blue cheese flavor are practically half the concentration as found in the natural Blue cheese. On what basis did you pick this data?

E. A. Day.—This is the point that I was trying to make—you need to do a little compounding. You can't adhere strictly to the analytical data and of course this may be because your analytical data are still incomplete.

H. W. Schultz.—We are assuming that every one of these compounds has a distinctly different odor. Is this actually true?

E. A. Day.—We have not assumed that they do. In fact, the C_7, C_8, and C_9 ketones are all very similar and this may be one of the reasons why there is a synergistic effect with some of these compounds. They are similar and several of them in combination could give the effect of the same concentration of one compound by itself.

H. W. Schultz.—But if they are similar, one could make substitutions on that basis?

E. A. Day.—Yes.

R. L. Wasson.—You mentioned that amino acids can produce background flavor notes. Did you try incorporating these in your synthetic cheese?

E. A. Day.—Not in the Blue cheese. We realize that this has to be done. We have done this with Cheddar cheese. The addition of amino acids may help to smooth out the soapy flavor we encountered.

BIBLIOGRAPHY

ANDERSON, D. F., and DAY, E. A. 1965A. Quantitative analysis of the major free fatty acids in Blue cheese. J. Dairy Sci. 48, 248–249.

ANDERSON, D. F., and DAY, E. A. 1965B. Action of microorganisms in Blue cheese on 2-pentanone and 2-pentanol. J. Dairy Sci. 48, 784.

ANDERSON, D. F., and DAY, E. A. 1966. Quantitative evaluation and effect of certain microorganisms on flavor components of Blue cheese. J. Agr. Food Chem. 14, 241.

ANNIBALDI, S. 1959. Electrophoretic research on several Italian cheeses (in French). Lait, 39, 381.

BAKALOR, S. 1962. Research related to the manufacture of blue-veined cheese. Dairy Science Abst. 24; Part I, 529–535; Part II 583–593.

BALLANCE, P. E. 1961. Production of volatile compounds related to the flavor of foods from the Strecker degradation of DL-methionine. J. Sci. Food Agr. 12, 532–536.

BASSETT, E. W., and HARPER, W. J. 1958. Isolation and identification of acidic and neutral carbonyl compounds in different varieties of cheese. J. Dairy Sci. 41, 1206–1217.

BAVISOTTO, V. S., ROCK, L. A., and LESNIEWSKI, R. S. 1960. Gas chromatography of volatiles of fermented milk products. J. Dairy Sci. 43, 849.

BILLS, D. D., and DAY, E. A. 1964. Determination of the major free fatty acids of Cheddar cheese. J. Dairy Sci. 47, 733–738.

BILLS, D. D., and DAY, E. A. 1965. Unpublished data. Oregon S. Univ., Corvallis, Oreg.

BILLS, D. D., MORGAN, M. E., LIBBEY, L. M., and DAY, E. A. 1965. Identification of the compounds responsible for the fruity flavor defect of some experimental Cheddar cheeses. J. Dairy Sci. 48, 1168–1173.

BOYD, E. N., PATTON, S., and DAY, E. A. 1965. Unpublished data. Penn. State Univ., University Park, Pa.

CALBERT, H. E., and PRICE, W. V. 1949. A study of the diacetyl of cheese. I. Diacetyl content and flavor of Cheddar cheese. J. Dairy Sci. 32, 515–520.

CLEMENT, G., CLEMENT, J., BEGARD, J., COSTANGO, G., and PARIS, R. 1962. Hydrolysis of butter triglycerides by pancreatic lipase: Localization of butyric acid. Arch. Sci. Physiol. 16, 237.

COFFMAN, J. R., SMITH, D. E., and ANDREWS, J. S. 1960. Analysis of volatile food flavors by gas-liquid chromatography. I. The volatile components from dry Blue cheese and dry Romano cheese. Food Research 25, 663–669.

CZULAH, J. 1959. Bitter flavor in cheese. Australian J. Dairy Technol. 14, 177–179.

DACRE, J. C. 1953. Amino acids in New Zealand Cheddar cheese: Their possible contribution to flavor. J. Sci. Food Agr. 4, 604–608.

DAY, E. A. 1965. Some properties of carbonyl compounds encountered in the flavor isolates of dairy products. Food Technol. 19, 1585–1590.

DAY, E. A., and ANDERSON, D. F. 1965. Gas chromatographic and mass spectral identification of neutral components of the aroma fraction of Blue cheese. J. Agr. Food Chem. *13*, 2–4.

DAY, E. A., BASSETTE, R., and KEENEY, M. 1960. Identification of volatile carbonyl compounds from Cheddar cheese. J. Dairy Sci. *43*, 463–474.

DAY, E. A., and KEENEY, M. 1958. Identification of volatile carbonyls from Cheddar cheese. J. Dairy Sci. *41*, 718.

DAY, E. A., and LIBBEY, L. M. 1964. Cheddar cheese flavor: Gas chromatographic and mass spectral analysis of the neutral components of the aroma fraction. J. Food Sci. *29*, 583–589.

DAY, E. A., and LILLARD, D. A. 1960. Autoxidation of milk lipids. I. Identification of volatile monocarbonyl compounds from autoxidized milk fat. J. Dairy Sci. *43*, 585–597.

DAY, E. A., LINDSAY, R. C., and FORSS, D. A. 1964. Dimethyl sulfide and the flavor of butter. J. Dairy Sci. *47*, 197–199.

EMMONS, D. B., McGUGAN, W. A., ELLIOTT, J. A., and MORSE, P. M. 1962. Effect of strain of starter culture and of manufacturing procedure on bitterness and protein breakdown in Cheddar cheese. J. Dairy Sci. *45*, 595–600.

FOSTER, E. M., NELSON, F. E., SPECK, M. L., DOETSCH, R. N., and OLSON, J. C. 1957. Dairy Microbiology. Prentice-Hall, Englewood Cliffs, N. J.

FOSTER, J. W. 1949. Chemical Activities of Fungi. Academic Press, New York.

GEHRIG, R. F., and KNIGHT, S. G. 1958. Formation of ketones from fatty acids by spores of *Penicillium roqueforti*. Nature *182*, 1237.

GEHRIG, R. F., and KNIGHT, S. G. 1963. Fatty acid oxidation by spores of *Penicillium roqueforti*. J. Appl. Microbiology *11*, 166–170.

GIROLAMI, R. L., and KNIGHT, S. G. 1955. Fatty acid oxidation by *Penicillium roqueforti*. J. Appl. Microbiology *3*, 264–267.

HARWALKER, W. R., and CALBERT, H. E. 1961. Specificity of milk lipases. J. Dairy Sci. *44*, 1169.

HILDITCH, T. P. 1956. The Chemical Constitution of Natural Fats. John Wiley and Sons, New York.

INGRAHAM, J. L., GUYMON, J. F., and CROWELL, E. A. 1961. The pathway of formation of *n*-butyl and *n*-amyl alcohols by a mutant strain of *Saccharomyces cerevisiae*. Arch. Biochem. Biophys. *95*, 169–175.

JACKSON, H. W. 1958. Flavor of Cheddar cheese. *In* Flavor Research and Food Acceptance. L. B. Sjostrom (Editor). Arthur D. Little, Cambridge, Mass.

JACKSON, H. W., and HUSSONG, R. V. 1958. Secondary alcohols in Blue cheese and their relation to methyl ketones. J. Dairy Sci. *41*, 920–924.

JENSEN, R. G., SAMPUGNA, J., and PARRY, R. M., JR. 1963. Lipolysis of laurate glycerides by pancreatic and milk lipase. J. Dairy Sci. *46*, 907–910.

KEENEY, M., and DAY, E. A. 1957. Probable role of the Strecker degradation of amino acids in development of cheese flavor. J. Dairy Sci. *40*, 874–876.

KOSIKOWSKI, F. V. 1951. The liberation of free amino acids in raw and pasteurized milk Cheddar during ripening. J. Dairy Sci. *34*, 235–241.

KOSIKOWSKI, F. V. 1957. Cheese flavor. *In* Chemistry of Natural Food Flavors: A Symposium. Quartermaster Research and Engineering Center, Natick, Mass.

KOSIKOWSKI, F. V., and DAHLBERG, A. C. 1954. A quantitative appraisal of the free amino acids in foreign-type cheese. J. Dairy Sci. *37*, 167–172.

KRISTOFFERSEN, K., and GOULD, I. A. 1960. Cheddar cheese flavor. II. Changes in flavor quality and ripening products of commercial Cheddar cheese during controlled curing. J. Dairy Sci. 43, 1202–1215.

LANGLER, J. E., and DAY, E. A. 1964. Development and flavor properties of methyl ketones in milk fat. J. Dairy Sci. 47, 1291–1296.

LANGLER, J. E., and DAY, E. A. 1965. Unpublished data. Oregon S. Univ., Corvallis, Oreg.

LAWRENCE, R. C. 1963. Formation of methyl ketones as artifacts during steam distillation of Cheddar cheese and butter oil. J. Dairy Res. 30, 161–170.

LIBBEY, L. M., BILLS, D. D., and DAY, E. A. 1963. A technique for the study of lipid-soluble food flavor volatiles. J. Food Sci. 28, 329–333.

LIBBEY, L. M., and DAY, E. A. 1963. Methyl mercaptan as a component of Cheddar cheese. J. Dairy Sci. 46, 859–861.

LIBBEY, L. M., and DAY, E. A. 1964. Unpublished data. Oregon S. Univ., Corvallis, Oreg.

LINDQUIST, B., and STORGARDS, T. 1959. Changes in casein during cheese ripening. 15th Int. Dairy Cong. 2, Sec. 3, 679–684.

LINDSAY, R. C., DAY, E. A., and SANDINE, W. E. 1965. Identification of volatile flavor components of butter culture. J. Dairy Sci. 48, 1566–1574.

MCGUGAN, W. A. 1964. Private communication. Canada Department of Agriculture, Ottawa, Canada.

MABBITT, L. A. 1955. Quantitative estimation of the amino-acids in Cheddar cheese and their importance in flavor. J. Dairy Res. 22, 224–231.

MABBITT, L. A. 1961. The flavour of Cheddar cheese. J. Dairy Res. 28, 303–318.

MABBITT, L. A., and ZIELINSKA, M. 1956. Flavour production in Cheddar cheese. 14th Int. Dairy Congr. 2, No. 2, 323–334.

MACLEOD, P., and MORGAN, M. E. 1958. Differences in the ability of lactic streptococci to form aldehydes from certain amino acids. J. Dairy Sci. 41, 908–913.

MARTH, E. H. 1963. Microbiological and chemical aspects of Cheddar cheese ripening. A review. J. Dairy Sci. 46, 869–890.

MORGAN, M. E., and DAY, E. A. 1965. A simple on-column trapping procedure for gas chromatographic analysis of flavor volatiles. J. Dairy Sci. 48, 1382–1384.

MORRIS, H. A., and JEZESKI, J. J. 1953. The action of microorganisms on fats. II. Some characteristics of the lipase system of Penicillium roqueforti. J. Dairy Sci. 36, 1285–1298.

MORRIS, H. A., JEZESKI, J. J., COMBS, W. B., and KURANIOTO, S. 1955. Free fatty acids produced during Blue cheese ripening. J. Dairy Sci. 38, 590.

MULDER, H. 1952. Taste and flavour forming substances in cheese. Netherlands Milk and Dairy J. 6, 157–168.

NISHIKAWA, I. 1958. Studies on the proteolytic decomposition in cheese II. Report of research laboratory of Snow brand milk products. Japan. No. 36. Abstracted in Dairy Science Absts. 20, 2887.

PARKS, O. W., KEENEY, M., KATZ, I., and SCHWARTZ, D. P. 1964. Isolation and characterization of the methyl ketone precursor in butter fat. J. Lipid Res. 5, 232–235.

PATTON, S. 1950. The methyl ketones of Blue cheese and their relation to its flavor. J. Dairy Sci. *33*, 680–684.

PATTON, S. 1963. Volatile acids and the aroma of Cheddar cheese. J. Dairy Sci. *46*, 856–858.

PATTON, S., WONG, N. P., and FORSS, D. A. 1958. Some volatile components of Cheddar cheese. J. Dairy Sci. *41*, 857–858.

PEREIRA, J. N., and MORGAN, M. E. 1958. Identity of esters produced in milk cultures of *Pseudomonas fragi*. J. Dairy Sci. *41*, 1201–1205.

PETERSON, M. H., JOHNSON, M. J., and PRICE, W. V. 1949. Liberation of fatty acids during making and ripening of Cheddar cheese. J. Dairy Sci. *32*, 862–869.

PROKS, J., DOLEZALEK, J., and PECK, Z. 1956. Biochemical studies about *Penicillium roqueforti*. 14th Intern. Dairy Congr. 2, No. 2, 401–412.

REITER, B., and MOLLER-MADSEN, A. 1963. Reviews of the progress of Dairy Science. Section B. Cheese and butter starters. J. Dairy Res. *30*, 419–456.

SANDERS, G. P. 1953. Cheese varieties and descriptions. U. S. Dept. Agr. Agriculture Handbook *54*.

SCARPELLINO, R., and KOSIKOWSKI, F. V. 1962. Evolution of volatile compounds in ripening raw and pasteurized milk Cheddar cheese observed by gas chromatography. J. Dairy Sci. *45*, 343–348.

SCHWARTZ, D. P. 1965. The lipids of milk: Deterioration. Part 1. Rancidity. *In* Fundamentals of Dairy Chemistry, B. W. Webb and A. H. Johnson (Editors) Avi Publishing Co., Westport, Conn.

SCHWARTZ, D. P., and PARKS, O. W. 1963. Quantitative analysis of methyl ketones in Blue cheese fat. J. Dairy Sci. *46*, 989–990.

SCHWARTZ, D. P., PARKS, O. W., and BOYD, E .N. 1963. Methyl ketones in Roquefort cheese. J. Dairy Sci. *46*, 1422–1423.

SILVERMAN, G. J., and KOSIKOWSKI, F. V. 1956. Amines in Cheddar cheese. J. Dairy Sci. *39*, 1134–1141.

SIMONART, P., and MAYAUDON, J. 1956A. Chromatographic investigations of cheese II. Aliphatic acids. Netherlands Milk and Dairy J. *10*, 156–161.

SIMONART, P., and MAYAUDON, J. 1956B. Chromatographic investigations of cheese III. Aromatic acids. Netherlands Milk and Dairy J. *10*, 261–267.

SJOSTROM, G. 1959. Lipase problems in milk and dairy products: A review. Milk and Dairy Res. Alnarp. Sweden. Report No. 58.

SJOSTROM, G., and WILLART, S. 1959. Free fatty acids in Blue cheese and their influence on the determination of the dry matter in cheese. 15th Intern. Dairy Congr. 3, (3) 1474–1480.

STORGARDS, T., and LINDQUIST, B. 1953. A comparison of the ripening process of different cheese types, based on some new methods of investigation. 13th Int. Dairy Congr. 2, 625–628.

SUZUKI, S. K., HASTINGS, E. G., and HART, E. B. 1910. The production of volatile fatty acids and esters in Cheddar cheese and their relation to the development of flavor. Wisconsin State Agr. Expt. Sta. Bull. *11*.

THOMASOW, J. VON. 1947. Secondary breakdown products of Blue-mold cheese. Milchwissenschaft 2. *2*, 354–358.

VEN, B. VAN DER, BEGEMANN, P. H., and SCHOGT, J. C. M. 1963. Precursors of methyl ketones in butter. J. Lipid Res. *4*, 91–95.

WALKER, J. R. L. 1961. Some volatile compounds in New Zealand Cheddar cheese and their possible significance in flavor formation. IV. The addition of flavor compounds to cheese curd to simulate Cheddar flavor. J. Dairy Res. 28, 1–4.

WOOD, W. A., 1961. In The Bacteria. 2nd Edition. I. G. Gunsalus and R. Y. Stainer (Editors). Academic Press, N. Y.

CHAPTER 16

R. Self | Potato Flavor

INTRODUCTION

There are species of potatoes e.g., *Solanum tuberosum,* grown for food in most countries from the tropics to the northern tundra; and although the nutritive value of the potato varies with climatic conditions, it is usually very high (Burton 1948). In general therefore, with a yield per acre greater than most other crops, its sustaining power depends primarily on its acceptability. Not only should a variety of potato of high quality be capable of yielding more tons per acre of undamaged, virus free, regular shaped, clean tubers but also these tubers should have acceptable cooked qualities of flavor, texture and color. This viewpoint was pioneered by Lugt *et al.* (1962), who recommended to the European Association for Potato Research the inclusion of flavor among the properties of the potato used to assess its quality.

Studies of food acceptance involve many complex, psychological socioeconomic and "cultural" factors which affect attitudes toward foods. Investigations in this field were initiated in the United States by Dr. Margaret Mead and eventually formed an important part of the activities of the Food Acceptance Branch of the U.S. Quartermaster Food and Container Institute for the Armed Forces, in Chicago. Their studies of food preferences of U.S. Servicemen include placing about 400 foods in order of preference. Potatoes in various forms come high on that list (Peryam *et al.* 1960). Harper (1963) made certain comparisons between the United Kingdom and the United States with regard to a small selection of vegetables, including potatoes. In both countries the potato was highly popular and only rarely disliked. A recent consumer survey conducted for the United Kingdom Potato Marketing Board (Pickard and Cori 1964) confirmed this view and in addition provided information about the preference shown by the housewife and her family for different methods of cooking potates. From this report it was estimated that about 70% of the potatoes consumed in the home were eaten either boiled or boiled and then mashed, and 25% were cooked with fat as roast, French fried, fritters, etc. The remainder were mainly baked or boiled in their skins. Hampson (1965) has shown that in keeping with the statistics for the first half of this century, the *per capita* consumption rate continued to decline annually for most European countries, whereas

362

in the United States consumption tended to remain constant. A more detailed analysis of the U.S. figures showed that the consumption of fresh potatoes was still falling at the rate of 2.3% per year but this fall was counteracted by an equivalent increase in the consumption of processed potato products. These statistics will serve to indicate present and likely future eating habits and underline the relative importance of the topics listed below. The main aims of this review of the flavor of potatoes and edible potato products are to discuss: (1) the basic chemistry of the precursors likely to be involved in the production of potato odor; (2) the experimental methods used for measurement of the volatiles constituting the flavor stimulus; (3) the flavor of various commodities and products produced from potatoes (e.g., boiled, baked, and roast potatoes, chips and French fried potatoes, and dehydrated flakes and granules); and (4) changes occurring during storage of the above products.

Flavor Nomenclature

Because confusion often exists about the meaning of terms used in relation to flavor, the following scheme has been adopted. The word flavor has been reserved to mean the overall sensation resulting from the impact of the food on the chemical sense receptors in the nose and mouth. Taste is perceived in the mouth by the taste buds and is made up of a complex of at least four individual sensations namely sweet, sour, salt, and bitter. Odor is detected by the olfactory epithelium in the nose and is so called when the volatile molecules producing the sensation are inhaled directly through the nose: when the odorous molecules pass from the mouth to the nose, via the inner passages, during the eating process, then the complex sensation of taste and odor is called flavor.

THE CHEMISTRY OF FLAVOR PRECURSORS

Natural odorous substances always possess some degree of volatility and since the raw tuber has little or no cooked potato odor and only rather low intensities of "earthy" and "starchy" components it is evident that the odor of cooked potatoes must arise from odorless, enzyme-activated or heat sensitive precursors in the tuber (Swain and Self 1964). Enzyme-produced odors from potatoes have not been intensively studied, as with other vegetables (Schwimmer 1963), although the usual warming up period (from 20° to 100°C.) for potatoes being boiled may be several minutes, during which time a significant amount of enzymic action could occur. Thermal degradation processes would then take over and a different pattern of volatile substances would emerge. This problem was avoided in our own work by using small samples of potato (1 gm.), in a minimum of water, to facilitate rapid heating (Swain and Self 1964). In the following discussion enzyme systems in general will be ignored and emphasis laid on thermal and chemical degradations of the constituents of the tuber.

Amino Acids

The possible role of amino acids as precursors of odor substances (Herz and Shallenberger 1960) evolved from foods during cooking has been discussed (Bailey et al. 1962; Keeney and Day 1957; Mizutani et al. 1960) and analyses of the free and protein-bound amino acid contents of tubers have been reported in relation to nutritive value (Chick and Slack 1949; Mulder and Bakema 1956; Talley et al. 1964). By using the information available from these studies, the presence or absence, and to some extent the quantity, of some of the volatiles expected to be produced during the cooking process could be predicted. Rohan and Stewart (1965) used this approach when studying the distribution of amino acids among varieties of cocoa beans in relation to chocolate flavor. More detailed information, however, could not be extracted from a closer study, because the complex distribution and availability of these precursors in the tuber, combined with the very different effects of the various oxidants, oxidant precursors, and antioxidants also present, created an almost infinite number of possible variables. Nevertheless, model system studies of the reactions between single amino acids and naturally occurring substances capable of reacting with them has furnished valuable information leading toward an understanding of the flavor of potatoes. Examples of the production of volatiles from amino acids in such a model system are shown in Table 58. The well-known Strecker degradation of α-amino acids (Schonberg and Moubacher 1952) has been used as the central reaction around which other amino acid degradation systems may be orientated. In this reaction the α-amino acids are deaminated and decarboxylated by certain carbonyl and other compounds to yield aldehydes and ketones containing one carbon less (α-amino butyric acid, for example, yields propanal): all the alkanals listed in Table 58 could originate from their designated precursors in this way.

β-Amino acids also undergo oxidative deamination and decarboxylation to the ketone with one less carbon atom, e.g., β-amino n-butyric acid produces 2-propanone. 2-Propanone could also be formed by the Strecker degradation of α-amino isobutyric acid (Schonberg and Moubacher (1952) but as this acid has not been detected in potatoes it is unlikely to be a precursor of 2-propanone in this system (Table 58).

TABLE 58

LOW-BOILING VOLATILES PRODUCED BY THE DEGRADATION OF COMMON METABOLITES

Volatile	Precursor[1]
Ethanal	Alanine, cysteine, asparagine, glucose, fructose
Propanal	α-amino butyric acid
2-methylpropanal	Valine
2-methylbutanal	Isoleucine
3-methylbutanal	Leucine
2-propanone	Sugars, β-amino n-butyric acid, α-amino isobutyric acid, threonine
Butane-2,3-dione	Fructose
Pentane-2,3-dione	Fructose
Methanethiol	Methionine
Methyl ethyl sulfide	Ethionine
Ethanethiol	Ethionine
n-propanethiol	3-propylsulfinyl alanine[2]
Hydrogen sulfide	Cysteine, cystine, methionine
Dimethyl disulfide	Methionine
Dimethyl sulfide[3]	Methionine
Diethyl disulfide	Ethionine
Propenal[4]	Methionine
Methanol	Pectin, sugar, and amino acid fermentation
Ethanol	Sugar and amino acid fermentation

[1] Amino acids (0.01 M) and reactants (0.1 M) were heated in phosphate buffer (1 ml. 0.01 M, pH 6.5) in a 10-ml. flask for 30 min. in a bath at 110°C. under a water-cooled condenser, and 1 ml. of headspace vapor analyzed by gas chromatography (Self et al. 1963B) using a stainless steel capillary column. Reactants for amino acids, in order of efficiency (as judged by the production of 3-methylbutanal from leucine in 30 min.) are: Sorbose and dehydroascorbic acid > fructose > glucose > chlorogenic acid, and pyruvic acid > sucrose > rhamnose (see also Table 60).
[2] Both enzymically (Kupieki and Virtanen 1960) and by boiling (Self 1965).
[3] In trace amounts only unless pectin or certain other methylating agents are present (Casey et al. 1963).
[4] Methionine first yields methional which degrades to acrolein and methanethiol (Ballance 1961).

So far no small molecules have been identified in the headspace above a γ-amino butyric acid containing system: presumably the γ-acid undergoes cyclization to form one molecule of a pyrrolidone type compound.

Organic di- and tri-carbonyls are not the only oxidants effective in Strecker degradations. Substances like ozone, and hydrogen peroxide in the presence of ferrous sulfate, will also degrade α-amino acids at room temperature: glycine, for example, gives methanal (Schonberg and Moubacher 1952). A recent report of the co-oxidation of sulfur containing amino acids in an autoxidizing lipid system suggested that lipid peroxide intermediates may also function in this way (Wedemeyer and Dollar 1963).

One of the most interesting and important examples of the Strecker degradation is the production of methional from methionine (Hunter and Potter 1958). The significance of methional in food flavor has been discussed by Patton (1956), Keeney and Day (1957), Ballance (1961), and Patton and Barnes (1958). Its odor has been variously described by these authors, and others, as being "broth-like," "the sunlight flavor of milk," "onion-like," "raw pumpkin," and so on. The flavor threshold value for methional was found by Day *et al.* (1958) to be 16 p.p.b. in fresh pasteurized homogenized milk, and the potential importance in food flavor of a compound with so intense and clinging an odor is obvious.

Ballance (1961) suggested that the stability of methional was such that very little decomposition occurred on heating in water to 100°C. On the other hand the decomposition of methional to propenal (acrolein) and methanethiol at 100°C. certainly took place when ninhydrin was used (Ballance 1961), and would appear to occur also with many of the common reactant constituents of vegetables which have so far been tested in model systems, e.g., the glucose and fructose induced degradation of methionine to propenal has been measured (Table 59) (Casey

TABLE 59

QUANTITATIVE ANALYSIS OF VOLATILES PRODUCED FROM AMINO ACID-SUGAR MODEL SYSTEMS[1]

Amino Acid	Volatile Compound Estimated	B.P. (°C.)	Rate of Production[2] of Volatile Using	
			Glucose (nM/hr.)	Fructose (nM/hr.)
Alanine	Ethanal	21	14.6	48.1
α-amino butyric acid	Propanal	49	20.4	38.9
Valine	2-methylpropanal	64	10.3	28.4
Leucine	3-methylbutanal	92	26.0	57.7
Methionine	Propenal[3]	52.5	0.05	51.1

From Casey *et al.* (1965).
[1] Quantitative measurements made by the method of Swain and Self (1964) using the quantities shown in Table 58.
[2] In all cases the volatile components were produced linearly with time, after an initial lag period. The rates are given in nano (10^{-9}) moles per hour for the straight-line portion of the graphs (usually 15 to 60-min. boiling time).
[3] Propenal is a secondary product of methionine (see note (4) in Table 58).

et al. 1965). It was thought possible that propenal would polymerize under these conditions and methanethiol was certainly oxidized to dimethyl disulfide. These were the main reaction products in aqueous solution at 100°C., but the equilibrium between methional and its decomposition products would undoubtedly be disturbed by changing conditions of temperature, pH, and nature of reactant.

Dry heating of methionine produced mainly methanethiol and dimethyl disulfide, a reaction which might be of interest in connection with the flavor of dried potato products. Dimethyl sulfide has been shown to be produced by the action of heat on methionine (Obata and Mizutani 1961; Casey *et al.* 1963), either alone or in the presence of sugars and other natural reactants, but the amounts were usually small. In the presence of a methyl donor such as pectin, dimethyl sulfide was produced in larger quantities, probably by the mechanisms of Lavine *et al.* (1953) according to which a reaction occurs in acid solution between methanol, produced by the demethylation of pectin, and methionine. However, the use of methanol alone, methanol and galacturonic acid, or methyl esters of simple carboxylic acids instead of pectin failed to increase the amount of dimethyl sulfide produced over that obtained from methionine alone.

That pectin was acting as a methyl donor was shown by an examination of the decomposition of ethionine. When heated with ninhydrin this compound gave mainly ethanethiol, but when pectin was present, ethyl methyl sulfide was also produced. Ethionine has not yet been isolated from potatoes but ethanethiol has been found (Self *et. al.* 1963B; Gumbmann and Burr 1964). The work of Goheen (1962) on the production of dimethyl sulfide from lignin demonstrated a similar demethylation reaction to that of Lavine *et al.* (1953) without the methanol intermediate. There was however, the possibility that, as in asparagus (Challenger and Haywood 1954), methionine itself might be methylated to give *s*-methyl methionine, which would subsequently decompose to give dimethyl sulfide and propenal.

In our own laboratories, we have carried out a gas chromatographic investigation of the low boiling volatile substances produced after boiling for ten minutes at 100°C., from a solution of methionine with the addition of Cu^{++} ions or Fe^{++} ions (Mazelis 1961) and ascorbic or dehydroascorbic acid (AA or DHA) at pH 7.5, (Lieberman and Mapson 1964). With 3.0 mM methionine, 0.3 mM AA and 0.03 mM copper sulfate, relatively large quantities of dimethyl sulfide and propenal were produced, together with moderate amounts of methanethiol and ethanal (acetaldehyde), whereas if 0.3 mM DHA was used in place of AA then large amounts of dimethyl disulfide, moderate amounts of methanethiol and propenal, but only trace amounts of dimethyl sulfide and ethanal were produced. If on the other hand, 7.0 mM ethylenediaminetetraacetic acid was added to the methionine-copper-ascorbate system, methanethiol, and ethanal became major headspace components, together with moderate amounts of propenal and dimethyl disulfide.

The above examples serve to show how varied are the pathways available in the tuber for the selective production of volatile substances at certain times of the year, or under particular environmental or storage conditions. The results are difficult to evaluate, but there may perhaps be a connection between the high dimethyl sulfide content of the cooking odors of stored potatoes and the fact that DHA has been found to decrease during storage (Leichsenring *et al.* 1957).

The studies of Lieberman and Mapson (1964) in which ethylene was produced from both linolenic acid and methionine in model systems, by the addition of a copper-ascorbate solution, were not directly related to potato flavor production, although this reaction is competitive with the others so far discussed. Ethylene might also react with other precursors or volatiles to produce odorous substances, e.g., ethylene sulfide (Strausz and Gunning 1962; Wiebe *et al.* 1965).

Finally, the hydrolysis of amino acid model systems has been shown to produce methanol, ethanol, and 2-propanone all of which have been identified from potatoes (Swain and Self 1941). The fermentation of potatoes by micro-organisms to produce ethanol is of commercial interest (Jackson 1961 and 1962), and ethanol production was quite noticeable in our own work when quantitative experiments were being designed. The longer a piece of cut tuber spent in water before heating, the higher was the ethanol content of the headspace vapor, the rate of production being approximately one nanomole of ethanol per minute. The production of ten nanomoles of ethanol from potatoes during the preparation period was negligible as compared with the 2μ moles resulting from 30 minutes boiling, but if the tubers were left in water overnight the 800 nanomoles produced would seriously upset the estimation.

Sugars and Related Compounds

A considerable literature relating to the sugar content of potatoes has accumulated because a high reducing sugar content adversely affects the suitability of potatoes for making chips (Burton 1948), and the quality of stored potatoes in general (van Vliet and Schriemer 1960; Kröner 1944). The sugars, when heated, may act as precursors of volatile ketones, etc. (Table 58), some of which will be Strecker reagents.

It has been shown in model systems that sugars and associated compounds are capable of producing widely different amounts of volatile material from a given precursor (Tables 59 and 60), according to type of sugar, concentration, temperature, and pH of the system. In par-

TABLE 60

AMOUNTS OF 2-METHYLPROPANAL PRODUCED FROM VALINE BY BOILING WITH DIFFERENT REAGENTS[1]

Reagent	Amount Produced (nM Total)
Butane-2,3-dione (diacetyl)	18
Sorbose	12
Arabinose	7.5
Xylose	6.2
Fructose	3.7
Glucose	1.7
Sucrose	0.88
Rhamnose	0.55

[1] 1.0 ml. of 0.1 M sugar solution boiled with 1.0 ml. of 0.01 M valine for 15 min., using quantitative methods of Swain and Self (1964).

ticular, the ascorbic acid-dehydroascorbic acid balance in the tuber before and after cooking (Hansen et al. 1957) will probably affect the rate of the production of volatiles, e.g., of 2-methylpropanal, because the activity of dehydroascorbic acid is higher even than that of butane-2,3-dione (diacetyl), as shown in Table 60. Not only do sugars affect flavor by acting as "Strecker" reagents (Table 58), but also by the effect of their own volatile degradation products, evolved during these processes. The chemistry of the degradation of sugars is not well established, but butane-2,3-dione, methanol and 2-propanone have been identified in model systems of boiling sugars (Casey et al. 1965).

Some Recent Experiments Using Amino Acid/Sugar Model Systems.— A more intensive study of amino acid-sugar model systems was designed to show the effect on the rate of production of volatile degradation products; by changing the pH of the solution, and the concentration of the reactant and the concentration of the precursor (Table 61). Figs.

TABLE 61

THE EFFECT OF ADDED BUFFER ON THE PRODUCTION OF VOLATILES FROM MIXTURES OF 0.01 M AMINO ACIDS AND 0.1 M GLUCOSE SOLUTIONS[1]

Amino Acid and Volatile Produced	Amount Produced in Nanomoles		
	Water	0.01M Phosphate pH 6.5	0.01M Phosphate pH 7.5
Valine (2-methylpropanal)	1.7	5.1	*
Methionine (propenal)	0.13	0.23	12.0
α-aminobutyric acid (propanal)	5.5	11.6	19.5
Alanine (ethanal)	5.0	8.6	25.0
Leucine (3-methylbutanal)	3.0	12.6	35.5

[1] The mixtures (1.0-ml. samples of all reagents) were boiled for 30 min.
* Not analyzed.

81 and 82 show the effect on the production of volatiles of changing either the amino acid concentration or that of the sugar. It is interesting to note that at the concentrations of sugar commonly found in potatoes, that is, a 1 to 10% dry weight basis (Schwimmer and Burr 1959) (10^{-2} to 10^{-1} M), there was the most rapid change in production efficiency of propanal, whereas at the usual amino acid concentration (in this case α-amino n-butyric acid, which was not found among the major amino acids (Talley et al. 1964) and therefore would be present in less than 0.001% dry weight basis, i.e., less than 10^{-5} M) there is relatively little change, suggesting that sugar concentration may be more important in controlling cooked potato flavor changes than amino acid concentration. In Table 60 the variation in the production of 2-methylpropanal arising from the use of different sugars as reagents, and of different pH values

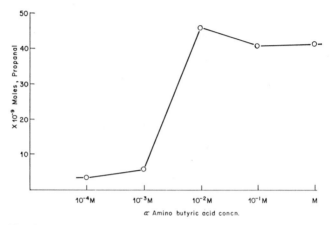

FIG. 81. PROPANAL PRODUCED BY BOILING DIFFERENT CONCEN-
TRATIONS OF α-AMINOBUTYRIC ACID WITH 0.1M FRUCTOSE FOR
30 MINUTES

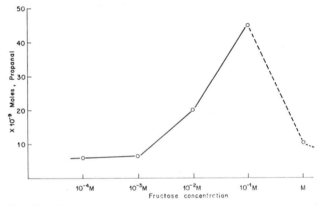

FIG. 82. PROPANAL PRODUCED BY BOILING 0.1M α-AMINOBU-
TYRIC ACID WITH DIFFERENT CONCENTRATIONS OF FRUCTOSE FOR
30 MINUTES

(Table 61), covers a wide range and, furthermore, the addition of 0.01 M solutions of salts such as sodium chloride and sodium phosphate causes the quantity of volatile substances to vary markedly.

Lipids and Fatty Acids

Linolenic and linoleic acids were identified in the lipids of raw tubers by Kröner and Völksen (1942) and Völksen (1950) as isolated palmitic acid. These substances were not related to potato flavor until Buttery et al. (1961) suggested a correlation between the degree of autoxidation and the development of off-flavor in dehydrated potato granules, held in air at 75°F. Twelve fatty acids including four major ones, linoleic, linolenic, palmitic, and oleic, were determined in dehydrated potatoes by gas chromatography of their methyl esters. Changes in the fatty acid composition of the granules during storage at 24°C. for up to 140 days in air and 115 days in oxygen were tabulated. The unsaturation ratio (linoleic + linolenic)/(palmitic + stearic) was found to fall steadily during this time. In Part II of the paper, the volatile carbonyl oxidation products of dehydrated potato granules were studied and found to contain mainly low boiling aldehydes and ketones and the C_1 to C_5 paraffins. Ellis (1950) had identified a range of alkanals and alkenals among the degradation products from the autoxidation of linoleate and linolenate and a similar pattern of volatiles might have been expected from potato granules. In fact, further decomposition appeared to occur, possibly because of the highly dispersed nature of the fat in the dehydrated granules, and the C_1 to C_5 saturated paraffins were detected in the headspace volatiles. The origin of these hydrocarbons was discussed in relation to the work of Kerr and Trotman-Dickenson (1960) in which the peroxide-catalyzed free radical degradation of, e.g., pentanal was found to give products such as propane, carbon monoxide, and butane. Buttery et al. (1961) suggested that hexanal might degrade in a similar manner to produce a range of saturated and unsaturated hydrocarbons. Further speculation as to the ultimate fate of hydrocarbons resulting from the degradation of aldehydes can be made based on the work of Strausz and Gunning (1962), in which the cyclic sulfides, ethylene and propylene sulfide were produced from the respective olefins when gaseous carbonyl sulfide was photolyzed in the system to give a metastable sulfide atom. It is known that a metastable sulfur atom can be inserted into the carbon hydrogen bonds of a paraffin (Knight et al. 1963) to produce, for example, methanethiol from methane. A moderate amount of ultraviolet light was necessary to make these reactions proceed but a philosophy which has to be adopted by gas chromatography flavor research workers is that most of these reactions can obtain sufficient thermal energy to produce 20 nanomoles of volatile material. Contributors to the Symposium on Foods in 1962 tabulated the theoretically derived aldehydes from the C_{18}—unsaturated fatty acid hydroperoxides (Hoffmann 1962; Keeney 1962). The list includes the alkanals, 2-alkenals, dienals, and trienals. Similar volatiles have been identified in the flavor volatiles of chips by Dornseifer and Powers (1963) and Mookherjee et al. (1965) (Table 62) and from autoxidized potato granules by Buttery et al. (1961) and all suggest that the unsaturated fatty acids are likely precursors for these carbonyls. Table 63 contains a list of carbonyl com-

TABLE 62

TABLE 62

MONOCARBONYL COMPOUNDS IDENTIFIED IN POTATO CHIPS

	Fresh, n Mole/100 Gm.	Stale, n Mole/100 Gm.
Pentanal	100	180
Hexanal	100	340
Heptanal	30	50
Octanal	10	20
Nonanal	20	10
2-Propanone	190	440
2-Butanone	180	220
2-Pentanone	80	400
2-Hexanone	40	90
2-Heptanone	10	30
2-Octanone	20	30
2-Nonanone	10	10
2-Hexenal	. . .	20
2-Heptenal	10	90
2-Octenal	10	80
2-Nonenal	10	30
2-Decenal	10	20
2-Undecenal	10	20
Deca-2,4-dienal	1010	160
Total	1840	2240

From Mookherjee et al. (1965).

TABLE 63

SUGGESTED FATTY ACID PRECURSORS FOR SOME CARBONYLS IN THE FLAVOR OF POTATO PRODUCTS[1]

Volatile Carbonyl Compounds	Theoretical Precursor Acid
Ethanal	Linolenic[2]
Propanal	Linolenic[3]
Pentanal	Linoleic[2]
Hexanal	Linoleic[3]
Octanal	Oleic[2]
Nonanal	Oleic[2,3]
2-Pentenal	Linolenic[2,3]
2-Heptenal	Linoleic[2]
2-Octenal	Linoleic[2,3]
2-Decenal	Oleic[2,3]
2-Undecenal	Oleic[2,3]
Deca-2,4-dienal	Linoleic[2,3]

[1] The carbonyls have been identified in volatiles from potato products by Buttery et al. (1961), Dornseifer and Powers (1963), and Mookherjee et al. (1965).
[2] Hoffmann (1962).
[3] Keeney (1962).

pounds identified in the volatile compounds from potato products which have also been described as theoretical autoxidation products of oleic, linoleic, and linolenic acids. There are other volatile autoxidation products which could theoretically be derivable from these acids but have not yet been isolated from potatoes, e.g., 2-butenal from linolenate. In addition, 2-alkanones were also found in the volatiles of chips by

Mookherjee *et al.* (1965) (Table 62) and although the dairy flavor workers have studied several mechanisms for the production of 2-alkanones, e.g., from β-keto acids (Wong *et al.* 1958) and other precursors, these authors thought that the high yield of 2-alkanones (two thirds of which was 2-propanone) from chips at room temperature would require a different explanation. They suggested that acyl radicals resulting from the autoxidation of aldehydes, which proceeds easily at room temperature (Gould 1959), would react with other compounds to produce the ketones (*cf.* Chapter 23).

Other Precursors

Twelve sulfur containing volatiles produced by potatoes during cooking were studied by Gumbmann and Burr (1964) and were thought to originate primarily from the sulfur-containing amino acids, although other substances such as protein, thiamin, biotin, co-enzyme A, and glutathione were also listed as possible precursors. Doubts were expressed as to whether the thiol content was an artifact resulting from the method of collection of the volatile compounds in mercuric chloride and their subsequent regeneration. From the chemistry of model systems of methionine and ethionine (Casey *et al.* 1963) it would seem that the thiols were produced first and subsequently oxidized to disulfide. Thus methane and ethane thiols would give rise to dimethyl disulfide and diethyl disulfide respectively.

The most exciting paper on potato flavor to be published recently must surely be that of Deck and Chang (1965) in which they described the isolation, from potato chips, of a single volatile substance having the odor of raw potatoes at a concentration of 10 p.p.m. in oil. Its structure was established as 2,5-dimethyl pyrazine by gas chromatography, mass spectrometry, and infrared spectrophotometry, but no origin for the substance was proposed by the authors. If it is assumed that a substance with a raw potato odor is not likely to originate from the cooking fat, then one can speculate about the possible precursors for this compound in the potato. Pyrazines are known to form readily from unstable α-amino ketones by condensation to the dihydropyrazine derivative. The precursor of 2,5-dimethyl pyrazine by this route would be aminoacetone, and Green and Elliott (1964) have demonstrated the formation of this material in bacteria from threonine. Threonine dehydrogenase would oxidize threonine to 2-amino acetoacetate, the free acid of which spontaneously decarboxylates to aminoacetone. Threonine dehydrogenase from *Staphylococcus aureus* was found to be protected against thermal inactivation by both potassium chloride and NAD^+, both of which are present in the tuber. One might postulate a potential supply of aminoacetone and hence of 2,5-dimethyl pyrazine from threonine decomposition if there existed a specific dehydrogenase or a chemical equivalent in the raw tuber. However, it should be noted that 2,5-dimethyl pyrazine has not yet been detected in the raw tuber.

EXPERIMENTAL DETAILS OF THE ANALYSIS OF POTATO FLAVOR

The almost universal application of gas chromatography to the analysis of potato flavor is evident in the literature of the last five years. In most cases some preliminary separation and concentration of volatiles was effected by chemical means prior to gas-chromatographic analysis, and further confirmation of the identity of individual substances was usually obtained by infrared and mass spectrometry.

Sample Separation and Concentration

Chemical trapping techniques of group separation have been particularly useful for carbonyls and sulfur containing volatile compounds. The carbonyls were converted to the 2,4-dinitrophenylhydrazones (Mookherjee et al. 1965) and recovery from these derivatives was usually achieved by fusion with α-ketoglutaric acid (Dornseifer and Powers 1963) (Buttery et al. 1961) using modifications of the method of Ralls (1960). Hydrogen sulfide, organic sulfides, and thiols were selectively absorbed in lead acetate, mercuric chloride, and mercuric cyanide traps respectively (Self et al. 1963A; Gumbmann and Burr 1964). Acid regeneration was used by the latter authors in a closed system and the volatiles formed were removed for gas chromatography. Self et al. (1963A) measured the melting points of the derivatives after recrystallization, and confirmed by mixing melting points with authentic 2,4-dinitrophenylhydrazones.

Physical trapping techniques which employ cold surfaces for condensation of volatile material have been widely used. Many different designs to avoid losses by e.g., fogging (Teranishi et al. 1965) have been examined to find a truly quantitative method of recovery of samples, e.g., the total trapping technique of Swoboda (1963). Perhaps the most usual method of analysis is to employ a combination of chemical and physical traps, although there are good reasons (e.g., surface absorption effects) for passing the headspace odors directly into a gas chromatograph whenever possible, e.g., in analysis of the headspace volatiles above dehydrated potato granules (Teranishi et al. 1962).

Gas Chromatography and Subsequent Confirmatory Identification

The use of dual column temperature-programmed gas chromatography units (Teranishi et al. 1962) has enabled a wide range of volatile substances to be identified rapidly, particularly now that rapid scanning mass spectrometers can be coupled directly to the gas chromatographs (McFadden *et al.* 1963; McFadden and Day 1964; Watson and Biemann 1965). Capillary columns (Self *et al.* 1963B; Self 1963) and both capillary and packed columns (Buttery *et al.* 1961; Gumbmann and Burr 1964) have been employed, and their merits have been discussed by the authors. A great many stationary phases and operating conditions have been necessary to separate particular compounds or groups of compounds but for total analysis of potato volatiles, the intermediate polarity of $\beta\beta'$-oxydipropionitrile phase has been very successful for volatiles with boiling points below 120°C. (Swain and Self 1964). The programming of this phase from $+10°$ to $+50°$C. provides adequate preliminary separation of the sulfides, thiols, aldehydes, alcohols, and ketones in this group.

Sample Preparation, Calibration, and Quantitative Gas-Chromatographic Analysis of Low-Boiling Volatiles

The odor concentration above boiling potatoes is usually very low, though water vapor and carbon dioxide are present in abundance. Large quantities (0.5 to 2.5 kg.) of potatoes have been boiled (Gumbmann and Burr 1964; Self *et al.* 1963A) in order to obtain sufficient sample for gas chromatography. Alternatively, methods for the volume concentration of the headspace vapors using low temperature ($-183°$C.) condensation traps have been designed (Self 1961). As already mentioned, Buttery *et al.* (1961) were able to make direct injections of the headspace volatiles above autoxidized potato granules. Lengthy boiling and collection times and large amounts of potato, however, were not convenient for quantitative comparison studies of the rate of production of volatiles from potatoes grown under different physiological conditions, nor for comparative studies of different parts of the same tuber. For this type of work a technique was devised whereby quantitative analyses could be carried out by boiling small samples (1 gm.) of potato contained in a 10-ml. boiling tube (Self and Swain 1963; Swain and Self 1964). Five such tubes could easily be mounted in the same oil bath and their contents treated similarly during the heating process. The volatiles released during boiling were refluxed in a 2-ml. internal volume water-cooled condenser and only the condenser headspace vapor sampled into a cold trap ($-183°$C.) (Fig. 83). Calibration curves were prepared (Fig. 84) using different concentrations of authentic organic liquids in 0.8 ml. boiled-out distilled water. Five sets of apparatus were calibrated in this way, using a selection of 12 easily resolved low-boiling volatiles and the quantitative results given later in the paper were obtained by this method.

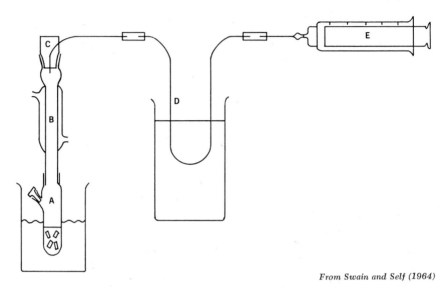

From Swain and Self (1964)

FIG. 83. SCHEMATIC DIAGRAM OF THE SAMPLE COLLECTION APPARATUS

(A) Boiling tube with stoppered side arm. (B) Cold water reflux condenser of small internal capacity. (C) Stopper pierced by a length of stainless steel capillary tubing. (D) Stainless steel capillary tube dipping into liquid oxygen (−183°C.). (E) Motor operated plunger in a 5 ml syringe.

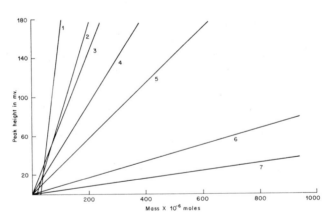

FIG. 84. CALIBRATION FOR SOME VOLATILES FOUND IN COOKED FOOD AROMA

(1) acetaldehyde; (2) ethanethiol; (3) 3-methylbutanal; (4) dimethyl sulfide; (5) acrolein; (6) ethanol; and (7) methanol.

THE FLAVOR OF COOKED POTATOES AND POTATO PRODUCTS

In a concise review of potato varieties Salaman (1926) suggested that the strength of potato flavor was a varietal characteristic, whereas Rathsack (1935) considered that the strength of potato flavor was related to the mineral content of the soil and particularly to the ratio of potassium to nitrogen content. Some of the first work on the chemistry of fresh potato flavor was carried out in Germany and this was later extended to include dehydrated products vital to the wartime economy.

Kröner and Wegner (1942) utilized experience gained from studies of other aspects of potato quality in turning their attention toward a chemical analysis of the steam volatile constituents of potatoes. An ether extract of the steam distillate from 100 kg. fresh potatoes yielded 0.6 to 1.0 gm. oil, in which pentanol, esters, fatty acids, and a high-boiling sulfur compound were detected. Wegner (1949) suggested that a phenolic compound was also present in the oil extracted from potatoes in this way. Work of this kind marked the beginning of a new approach to potato flavor but, although these chemical studies continued, it was not until the advent of gas chromatography that more significant advances were made toward the identification of volatile substances produced by the cooking or processing of potatoes.

The Taste of Potatoes

There are several references to the taste of potatoes but most of them would be better dealt with under flavor. Among papers dealing specifically with taste, Hilton (1951) described bitterness due to solanine, and Kröner (1944) suggested that the excess sugars accumulated in badly stored tubers resulted in an inferior taste. The alteration of taste (e.g., by the addition of salt during cooking) will be dealt with later in relation to the sensory assessment of flavor.

The Flavor of Potato Chips

Using the experimental methods outlined above and based on information gained from fundamental studies of flavor precursor chemistry, the flavor of potato chips, until recently, has been attributed largely to autoxidation products of the frying oils employed; these compounds being mainly aldehydes, ketones, and hydrocarbons (Dornseifer and Powers 1963; Mookherjee et al. 1965). The identification of a substance like 2,5-dimethyl pyrazine from potato chips (Deck and Chang 1965), however, would suggest that perhaps the generation of characteristic flavor in the potato is enhanced by controlled production of carbonyls from the cooking fat. The fact that these same carbonyls in larger concentrations are responsible for off-flavors in fats means that, with a fat content of 30 to 35% of their total weight, chips are vulnerable to fat autoxidation induced off-flavors. A delicate balance between the natural potato volatile substances, which also contain a similar group of saturated aldehydes, etc., and the autoxidized fat odors would be required to produce an acceptable stored commodity. The large decrease in the amount of deca-2,4- dienal, which has been described as having a "deep fried" odor, in stored chips (Mookherjee et al. 1965) (Table 62), coupled with the fact that its odor threshold in water is 0.5 p.p.b. has stimulated these authors to predict its importance in potato chip flavor. The present situation therefore suggests that the correlation should be explored, between the concentrations of the increasing, unpleasant staling and "browning" carbonyls, and the decreasing, pleasant, fresh-fried odors of the dienals. Furthermore, changes in the concentration of the intrinsic raw and fresh cooked potato odors, such as the pyrazine derivatives and possibly the methionine decomposition products, can be considered independently of the volatiles derived from the fat, and will be dependent upon the variety of potato used and its storage history.

The Flavor and Off-Flavor of Potato Granules

It would appear that all the problems of the various subdivisions of potato flavor converge when discussing the flavor of dehydrated potato products. The off-flavor of dried potatoes was studied by Burton (1949) and he discriminated between a charred taste due to high temperature storage and an off-flavor probably due to oxidative rancidity of the fat (Highlands et al. 1954). The flavor of dehydrated potato granules was also thought by Buttery and co-workers (Buttery et al. 1961; Buttery and Teranishi 1963) to be dependent, to some extent, on the autoxidation of fat. Although the natural fat concentration of potatoes is rather low (1 to 2% dry basis), dried potato flakes or granules expose a very large surface to oxidation and decomposition of the unsaturated fatty acids present could proceed rapidly and their degradation products, if above their respective threshold levels, would contribute largely to the change from fresh to stale flavor.

The amino acid-initiated odors of cooked potatoes will also be present to some extent and Buttery and Teranishi (1963) suggested that liberal production of the branched aldehydes, 2- and 3-methylbutanal and 2-methylpropanal from isoleucine, leucine, and valine respectively, probably contributes largely to the "browning" flavor of aging dried potato products. Three comments relating to these findings can be made: (a) when potatoes were steamed at 150°C. rather than boiled at 100°C. these "browning" aldehydes were considerably increased; (b) when potatoes were boiled with ninhydrin this was again the case; (c) when model systems of valine and leucine were examined, leucine gave a high rate of production of alkanal with both glucose and fructose (Table 59) and it is likely that isoleucine would behave similarly, but valine did not produce 2-methylpropanal so quickly.

None of these observations are strictly relevant to dehydrated granules, except that they demonstrate the relative ease with which these three amino acids can be degraded by heat and/or the presence of a suitable reactant. A further observation with regard to the dried product was that dry heating of methionine produced methanethiol and dimethyl disulfide in quantities relatively large when compared with other known methionine degradation products. It was evident, for example, that the molecule was not deaminated or decarboxylated to any extent in the dry state. This reaction would soon unbalance the odor of the dried product in respect to the thiol and sulfide components but perhaps the stability of methionine is not comparable with that of valine, leucine, etc. In contrast to this personal observation, Buttery et al. (1961) has commented that samples of granules stored in air did not give off any major concentration of odorous substances into their headspace, but upon reconstitution with hot water large quantities of carbonyls were released. This suggests a possible hydrolytic cleavage of peroxides and hydroperoxides.

The Flavor Volatiles of Fresh Cooked Potatoes

Gumbmann and Burr (1964) (Table 64) considerably extended the short list of sulfur compounds identified earlier by Self et al. (1963A) in the volatiles of cooked potato and confirmed that methanethiol and dimethyl disulfide together constituted 90% of the total sulfide, with di-

TABLE 64

VOLATILE SULFUR COMPOUNDS FROM POTATOES[1]

Reference Compound	Relative Retention Times on Silicone (Capillary)	% by Weight Organic Sulfides[2]
Methanethiol	0.472	45
Ethanethiol	0.506	5
Dimethyl sulfide	0.515	2
2-Propanethiol	0.543	0.5
n-Propanethiol	0.613	0.2
Methyl ethyl sulfide	0.625	0.2
Diethyl sulfide	0.839	0.05
Methyl n-propyl sulfide	0.885	...
Dimethyl disulfide	1.00	45
Methyl ethyl disulfide	1.70	0.7
Methyl isopropyl disulfide	2.55	1

[1] From Gumbmann and Burr (1964).
[2] This does not include the quantity of inorganic hydrogen sulfide produced which was estimated separately.

methyl sulfide and ethanethiol making up a further 7% by weight. Both groups agreed upon the importance of volatile sulfur containing substances in potato flavor.

It has been suggested that low-boiling volatile substances such as hydrogen sulfide and ethanal, produced during the heating of potatoes, might play an important part in the overall cooking odor (Self *et al.* 1963C) whereas the higher boiling compounds e.g., methional might perhaps be more important in the mouth sensation of flavor. Our interest initially was therefore concentrated on the lower boiling volatile compounds, using the methods already described for sampling and quantitative estimation.

Analyses of the low-boiling volatile compounds produced from four different varieties of potatoes during cooking are shown in Table 65.

TABLE 65

COMPARISON OF FOUR VARIETIES OF POTATOES GROWN AT TWO DIFFERENT CENTERS

	Dr. McIntosh		Ulster Beacon		Majestic		King Edward	
	A	B	A	B	A	B	A	B
Methanethiol	135	167	192	84	188	188	67	188
Dimethyl sulfide	19	74	64	71	16	56	97	48
Ethanal	295	910	930	295	341	295	455	409
Propanal	330	569	603	69	86	51.7	276	36
2-Methyl propanal	49	250	104	22	34	17	22	44
Propenal	679	196	250	21	18	21	134	9
Methanol	498,000	375,000	52,200	119,000	36,500	113,000	112,000	56,200
2-Propanone	207	569	708	190	224	483	1,156	535
Ethanol	1,087	1,300	660	261	0	521	1,740	521
3-Methylbutanal	14	163	102	24	28	18	28	18
2-Methylbutanal	6	58	58	12	14	18	6	24
Dimethyl disulfide	0	0	70	0	47	0	0	0

A = Plant Breeding Institute (Cambridge).   Measured in nM per 100 gm. fresh weight.
B = Gleadthorpe (Nottingham).   Lifted and analyzed October 1963 as mature tubers.

"Expert" taste panels have suggested that these four varieties, Dr. McIntosh, Ulster Beacon, King Edward, and Majestic, produce noticeably different aromas when cooked and in certain cases (e.g., potatoes grown at the Plant Breeding Institute, Cambridge) the overall strength of the sulfury component as assessed by the panel was in agreement with the total sulfur content indicated by these figures (i.e. methanethiol + dimethyl sulfide + dimethyl disulfide).

Finally, Table 66 shows that after six months storage under normal agricultural conditions the amount of volatile material produced during cooking had significantly increased for both Golden Wonder and Kerr's Pink varieties. These increases may simply reflect the increased reducing sugar content of the tubers after storage, but many other factors might be involved, such as texture and its effect on the availability of the flavor precursors, the concentration of pectin in the cell walls (which would affect the degree of methylation of the flavor metabolites), and the pH

of the cell liquid. All these are examples of other parameters important
in controlling the flavor quality of potatoes, which have not been discussed. These examples of the influence of the variety, center and storage

TABLE 66

THE EFFECTS OF STORAGE UNDER AGRICULTURAL CONDITIONS ON THE VOLATILES PRODUCED
BY TWO VARIETIES OF POTATOES

(Values given in nanomoles/100 gm. fresh weight)

Analysis Date	Golden Wonder		Kerr's Pink	
	11/21/63	5/7/64	11/21/63	5/7/64
Volatile				
Hydrogen sulfide	+[1]	++[1]	+	+++[1]
Methanethiol	104	188	83	271
Ethanethiol	<16[2]	<16	<16	<16
Dimethyl sulfide	80	158	32	339
Ethanal	637	1820	455	977
1-Propanethiol	<13	<13	<13	<13
Propanal	483	586	310	449
2-Methylpropanal	83	153	28	667
Propenal	71	322	36	178
Methanol	194,000	234,000	178,000	156,000
2-Propanone	+	+	172	775
Ethanol	1,740	2,180	1,740	5,440
3-Methylbutanal	58	116	23	23
2-Methylbutanal	58	139	23	23
Dimethyl disulfide	+	0[3]	+	+

[1] +, ++, +++, small, medium, and large peaks produced, but not measured quantitatively.
[2] <, accuracy is lost at and below this value on the calibration curves.
[3] 0, no detectable amount of the particular volatile was present.
    The potatoes were grown in the Northeast of Scotland and lifted in early November 1963. The first analysis
was completed on November 15, while the remainder of the tubers were stored in a clamp through the winter
and analyzed early in May 1964.

on the farm, on the quantities of the various flavor volatile components
produced on boiling indicate the order of magnitude of the differences attributable to such factors. But before these differences can be claimed to
be significant in odor assessment, the olfactory threshold values for each
individual substance (Guadagni et al. 1963A) and for the combined
group (Guadagni et al. 1963B) must be ascertained. Without such
information all quantitative variation has to be studied, and only a few
very tentative conclusions can yet be reached.

Sensory Testing: The Cooking and Seasoning of Potatoes

In a review of the effect of monosodium glutamate (MSG) on food
flavors Caincross (1948) noticed that MSG, when added to potatoes,
suppressed the flavor of peel and earthy flavor, and Smith (1950) found
a preference for MSG treated chips.

Recently, from the Arthur D. Little organization, Neilson and Caul
(1965) have commented that the flavor sensations of mashed potatoes
might be described as sweet, earthy, raw, starchy and sour. They go

on to observe that when salt was added to potatoes before mashing both odor and flavor were changed. Also, in low concentrations, the addition of salt may not affect the taste, but it may affect the flavor. This problem has been investigated chemically (Self 1963) and the suppression of the flavor volatile pattern of cooking potatoes produced by the addition of salt is shown in Table 67. That salt suppresses the amount of volatile

TABLE 67

CHANGES IN THE VOLATILES OF BOILING POTATOES CAUSED BY THE ADDITION OF SALT

Volatile	No Salt	0.06% Salt	3.6% Salt
Hydrogen sulfide	$++$[1]	$++$	$+$[1]
Methanethiol	45	18	18
Dimethyl sulfide	438	192	118
Ethanal	546	536	419
Propanal	262	220	179
2-Methylpropanal	167	67	44
Propenal	405	90	45
Methanol	342,000	167,000	9,000
2-Propanone	207	110	41
Ethanol	7,730	2,580	1,720
2-Methylbutanal	37	19	9
3-Methylbutanal	56	37	19

Measured in nanomoles/100 gm. 1 gm. of potato was boiled for 30 min. in: (i) 0.8 ml. boiled out distilled water; (ii) 0.6 mg. sodium chloride dissolved in 0.8 ml. boiled out distilled water; (iii) 36 mg. sodium chloride dissolved in 0.8 ml. boiled out distilled water.
[1] $+$, $++$, small and medium-sized peaks on the gas chromatogram not measured quantitatively.

material produced in the headspace above cooking potatoes caused some concern. Whatever the reason for this phenomenon, the effect on the flavor would appear to be that either the precursor substances are not degraded to smaller molecules, and are therefore still present to be appreciated in the mouth flavor, or that the evolution of volatile components is suppressed and they remain in the cooking water, thus increasing the concentration absorbed in the tuber tissues until the potatoes are eventually removed from the water. The effect of MSG on the volatile pattern of cooking potatoes has not yet been determined, but such a test could be performed quantitatively by use of the method already described (Swain and Self 1964).

As a footnote to this section on sensory testing, mention might be made of a simple but interesting exploratory experiment recently performed in our laboratory. When a normal domestic aluminum saucepan, with lid, was used to boil gently a 0.01 M solution of methionine in water, unbiased staff members who had recently joined us commented upon the pleasant potato smell in the laboratory, whereas, on a later occasion, when asked to compare the odors issuing from two identical unlabeled saucepans, one containing boiling potatoes and the other boiling methionine, they quickly and easily identified the genuine product.

Here perhaps we have a demonstration of one of the many psychological variables in sensory testing. In this case, the odor complex of the model system (in the saucepan) was sufficiently close to that of the genuine article to evoke the perception of "potato," whereas direct comparison between the model system and the real thing left no room for doubt as to which was which.

Future Trends

In common with the present situation in many other flavor fields, that of potato flavor now awaits the accurate assessment of the importance of the volatile substances identified, in relation to the combined effects they induce at the receptor sites in the mouth and nose. The work of Lea and Swoboda (1958) and Lea (1962) on variation in threshold with medium of presentation, and more recently that of Guadagni et al. (1963A and B) on the measurement of odor thresholds and the interactions existing in complex odor systems indicate the enormous complexity of the task ahead. It may transpire that the major volatile substances now identified are not the most important ones in relation to the mouth sensation of flavor (e.g., methanol in boiled potatoes), and that the minor components with high intensity of odor as yet only just perceivable by our instruments may make more significant impressions on and through the human receptors. It is evident that the present stage of instrumental measurements in flavor research must give way to sensory instrumental correlation of the type envisaged by von Sydow (1964). The gas-chromatographic pattern must be adjusted for the human olfactory sensitivity to the volatiles as well as for that of the flame ionization detector, and the question of interaction within the total blend of odorous substances remains a further appalling complication.

DISCUSSION

R. W. Moncrieff.—One point that occurred to me that seems to have some practical significance, is that in some of the tests you described the volatile compounds were collected after boiling the potato in small quantities of water for 20 minutes. All the volatile substances that were collected and identified were lost from the potato. I am wondering if an experiment has been made in which the volatile substances were collected after 40 minutes boiling? Also, are the compounds that remain in the potato of any interest?

R. Self.—Yes, we have continued the boiling time up to several hours and collected the volatile components. All we do is increase the quantities of the various components. We don't seem to get any qualitative change. It is just a quantitative change. We have also examined the volatiles from the cooked potato and we again get a similar pattern, but it is less concentrated.

E. A. Day.—Have you found methional as a degradation product of methionine?

R. Self.—No, we tried, but again the concentration that our gas chromatography unit could pick up was about 0.01%. We added methional to cooked potato and presented it to a panel and they were able to detect it at 0.0000001%. The panel said that it was objectionable and nauseating. However, people say that methional is potato-like at low concentrations. It is interesting that when we added it to potatoes they said it was onion-like.

E. L. Pippen.—I would like to ask if you have considered the possibility that heavy metal impurities in the salt might have had some effect on the relative amount of volatile components you obtained when you added salt to the potatoes?

R. Self.—I have not considered this one.

E. L. Pippen.—We have used salt sometimes to salt out materials in distillates of poultry and we obtain a black precipitate due to the impurities in the salt.

R. Self.—It is common to add various salts to concentrate volatiles in headspace analysis and we have information that sodium chloride in model systems increases the amount of volatile components produced in the headspace. So why should it decrease the amount from the potatoes?

J. E. Hodge.—A possible origin for the 2,5-dimethyl pyrazine is that this compound has been formed in ammoniated molasses through browning reactions. Wiggins showed that it was present in animal feeds and was a toxic substance that had adverse effects on cattle. He isolated 2-methyl pyrazine, 2,5-dimethyl pyrazine, and 2,6-dimethyl pyrazine. It probably comes from pyruvaldehyde reacting with ammonia.

R. Self.—An interesting note about the odor of this substance—we had it in the laboratory at fairly high concentrations on the order of 10 to 100 times the concentrations that Deck and Chang said it smelled like raw potatoes. We thought that the smell was like stale tobacco fumes.

J. Kintner.—Have you done any rate studies in the decomposition of carbonyls to the saturated hydrocarbons? Could there be a spontaneous regression of an off-flavor in dehydrated potatoes due to a saturated hydrocarbon which could become volatile and then lost when they are reconstituted?

R. Self.—We have not done any rate studies on this system at all. The recent work of Gunning and co-workers is worth investigating on this subject.

J. Kintner.—Have you tested the potatoes that were boiled with salt? Was the flavor retained in the potato any more intense than normal?

R. Self.—Yes, with the 0.06% concentration of salt you get an improvement in flavor, but with the higher concentration of salt the aroma is masked.

W. F. Wilkens.—Did I understand you to say that the 2,4-dienals or the dienals as such in potato chips tend to have a quality which enhances the flavor or the desirability of these products?

R. Self.—This is the work of Mookherjee, Deck, and Chang and that I think, is what they found.

M. E. Mason.—What was the source of the 2,5-dimethyl pyrazine?

R. Self.—They identified it in fried potato chips.

M. E. Mason.—Another mechanism for its formation was pointed out by Hodge in his 1953 review of browning. The heating of an amino acid with acetol will produce 2,5-dimethyl pyrazine. I do not know that acetol is particularly important in any food product, but I would like to suggest that it could arise from threose or perhaps glycerol losing one molecule of water upon heating, then an ene-diol rearrangement would give acetol. This may be important in browning and perhaps you should look for glycerol and smaller sugars.

P. Muneta.—In certain cases there is a considerable difference in the flavor of fresh potato chips versus those potato chips which have been stored. I think this may be due to the browning reaction.

R. Self.—I am in agreement. Probably the methionine decomposition products are as important as the fat decomposition products here.

BIBLIOGRAPHY

Bailey, S. D., Mitchell, D. G., Bazinet, M. L., and Weurman, C. 1962. Studies on the volatile components of different varieties of cocoa beans. J. Food Sci. 27, 165–170.

Ballance, P. E. 1961. Production of volatile compounds related to the flavour of foods from the Strecker degradation of DL-methionine. J. Sci. Food Agr. 12, 532–536.

Burton, W. G. 1948. In The Potato. Chapman and Hall, London.

Burton, W. G. 1949. Mashed potato powder. IV. Deterioration due to oxidative changes. J. Soc. Chem. Ind. 68, 149–151.

Buttery, R. G., Hendel, C. E., and Boggs, M. M. 1961. Autoxidation of potato granules. J. Agr. Food Chem. 9, 245–252.

Buttery, R. G., and Teranishi, R. 1963. Measurement of fat autoxidation and browning aldehydes in food vapors by direct vapor injection gas-liquid chromatography. J. Agr. Food Chem. 11, 504–507.

Caincross, S. E. 1948. Effect of monosodium glutamate on food flavor. Symposium on monosodium glutamate. 1, 32–38.

Casey, J. C., Self, R., and Swain, T. 1963. Origin of methanol and dimethyl sulphide from cooked foods. Nature 200, 885.

Casey, J. C., Self, R., and Swain, T. 1965. Factors influencing the production of low boiling volatiles from foods. J. Food Sci. 30, 33–34.

Challenger, F., and Haywood, B. J. 1954. The occurrence of a methylsulfonium derivative of methionine (α-aminodimethyl-γ-butyrothetin) in asparagus. Chem. and Ind. 729.

Chick, H., and Slack, E. B. 1949. Distribution and nutritive value of the nitrogenous substances in the potato. Biochem. J. 45, 211–221.

Day, E. A., Keeney, M., and Stahl, W. M. 1958. The role of methional as a flavor compound. Food Research 23, 130–132.

Deck, R. E., and Chang, S. S. 1965. Identification of 2,5-dimethylpyrazine in the volatile flavor compounds of potato chips. Chem. and Ind. 1343–1344.

Deininger, N., and Sullivan, F. 1954. Study and evaluation of the odour properties of surfaces. Ann. New York Acad. of Sci. 58, Art. 2, 215–224.

Dornseifer, T. P., and Powers, J. J. 1963. Changes in the volatile carbonyls of potato chips during storage. Food Technol. 17, 118–120.

Ellis, G. W. 1950. Autoxidation of the fatty acids. III. Oily products from elaidic and oleic acid. The formation of monoacyl derivatives of dihydroxystearic acid and of α,β-unsaturated keto acids. Biochem. J. 46, 129–141.

Goheen, D. W. 1962. Chemicals from lignin by nucleophilic demethylation. Forest Prod. J. 12, 471–473.

GOULD, E. S. 1959. Mechanism and Structure in Organic Chemistry. Holt, Rinehart and Winston. New York.

GREEN, M. L., and ELLIOTT, W. H. 1964. The enzymic formation of amino-acetone from threonine and its further metabolism. Biochem. J. 92, 537–549.

GUADAGNI, D. G., BUTTERY, R. G., and OKANO, S. 1963A. Odor thresholds of some organic compounds associated with food flavors. J. Sci. Food Agr. 14, 761–765.

GUADAGNI, D. G., BUTTERY, R. G., OKANO, S., and BURR, H. K. 1963B. Additive effect of sub-threshold concentrations of some organic compounds associated with food aromas. Nature 200, 1288–1289.

GUMBMANN, M. R., and BURR, H. K. 1964. Volatile sulphur compounds in potatoes. J. Agr. Food Chem. 12, 404–408.

HAMPSON, C. F. 1965. Current trends in potato consumption. European Assoc. for Potato Research, Utilization Section Meeting. London.

HANSEN, F., BRANDT, E., and HOFF-JORGENSEN, E. 1957. Investigations about the composition and food value of Danish potatoes. Tidsskr. Planteavl 61, 292–376.

HARPER, R. 1963. Some attitudes to vegetables and their implication. Nature 200, 14–18.

HERZ, W. J., and SHALLENBERGER, R. S. 1960. Some aromas produced by simple amino acid sugar reactions. Food Research 25, 491–494.

HIGHLANDS, M. E., LICCIARDELLO, J. J., and HERB, S. F. 1954. Observations on the lipid constituents of white potatoes. Am. Pot. J. 31, 353–357.

HILTON, R. J. 1951. Factors in relation to tuber quality in potatoes. II. Preliminary trials on bitterness in Netted Gem potatoes. Sci. Agr. 31, 61–70.

HODGE, J. E. 1953. Chemistry of browning reactions in model systems. J. Agr. Food Chem. 1, 928–943.

HOFFMANN, G. 1962. Vegetable oils. In Symposium on Foods: Lipids and Their Oxidation. H. W. Schultz, E. A. Day, R. O. Sinnhuber (Editors). Avi Publishing Co., Westport, Conn.

HUNTER, I. R., and POTTER, E. F. 1958. Microdetermination of volatile aldehydes. Anal. Chem. 30, 293–295.

JACKSON, M. L. 1961. Industrial products from potatoes and potato processing wastes. University of Idaho, Bull. 12.

JACKSON, M. L. 1962. Utilizing the potato industrially. Ind. Eng. Chem. 54, 50–56.

KEENEY, M. 1962. Secondary degradation products. In Symposium on Foods: Lipids and Their Oxidation. H. W. Schultz, E. A. Day and R. O. Sinnhuber (Editors). Avi Publishing Co., Westport, Conn.

KEENEY, M., and DAY, E. A. 1957. Probable role of the Strecker degradation of amino acids in development of cheese flavor. J. Dairy Sci. 40, 874–876.

KERR, J. A., and TROTMAN-DICKENSON, A. F. 1960. The reactions of alkyl radicals. III. n-Butyl radicals from the photolysis of n-valeraldehyde. J. Chem. Soc. 1960, 1602–1608.

KNIGHT, A. R., STRAUSZ, O. P., and GUNNING, H. E. 1963. The reaction of sulfur atoms. III. The insertion in carbon-hydrogen bonds of paraffinic hydrocarbons. J. Am. Chem. Soc. 85, 2349–2355.

KRÖNER, W. 1944. The problem of the taste of potatoes. Gemeinschaftsverpflegung. 8, Suppl. 49–51.

KRÖNER, W., and VÖLKSEN, W. 1942. Potato Fat. Naturwissenschaften *30*, 473.

KRÖNER, W., and WEGNER, H. 1942. On the odour and taste (flavor) of potatoes. Naturwissenschaften *30*, 586–587.

KUPIECKI, F. P., and VIRTANEN, A. I. 1960. Cleavage of alkyl cysteine sulphoxides by an enzyme in onion (*allium cepa*). Acta Chem. Scand. *14*, 1913–1918.

LAVINE, T. F., FLOYD, N. F., and CAMMAROTI, M. S. 1953. The formation of sulfonium salts from alcohols and methionine in sulfuric acid. J. Biol. Chem. *207*, 107–117.

LEA, C. H. 1962. The oxidative deterioration of food lipids. *In* Symposium on Foods: Lipids and Their Oxidation. H. W. Schultz, E. A. Day, and R. O. Sinnhuber (Editors). Avi Publishing Co., Westport, Conn.

LEA, C. H., and SWOBODA, P. A. T. 1958. The flavor of aliphatic aldehydes. Chem. and Ind. 1289–1290.

LEICHSENRING, J. M., NORRIS, L. M., and PILCHER, H. L. 1957. Effect of storage and of boiling on the ascorbic, dehydroascorbic and diketo-gulonic acid content of potatoes. Food Research *22*, 37–43.

LIEBERMAN, M., and MAPSON, L. W. 1964. Genesis and biogenesis of ethylene. Nature *204*, 343–345.

LUGT, C., GOODIJK, G., and GLASTRA-UBBELS, D. 1962. Assessment of the eating quality of potato varieties. *In* Potato News from the Netherlands, Dutch Government Publications, The Hague.

MAZELIS, M. 1961. Non-enzymic decarboxylation of methionine by ferrous ion. Nature *189*, 305–306.

McFADDEN, W. H., and DAY, E. A. 1964. Scan rate considerations in combined gas chromatography-mass spectrometry. Anal. Chem. *36*, 2362–2363.

McFADDEN, W. H., TERANSHI, R., BLACK, D. R., and DAY, J. C. 1963. Use of capillary gas chromatography with a time of flight mass spectrometer. J. Food Sci. *28*, 316–319.

MIZUTANI, J., OBATA, Y., and ISHIKAWA, Y. 1960. Studies on the degradation mechanisms of proteins and their derivatives in the foods. III. The decomposition of several cysteine aldehyde compounds in aqueous solutions. Bull. Agr. Chem. Soc. (Japan) *24*, Suppl. 382–385.

MOOKHERJEE, B. D., DECK, R. E., and CHANG, S. S. 1965. Relationship between monocarbonyl compounds and flavor of potato chips. J. Agr. Food Chem. *13*, 131–134.

MULDER, E. G., and BAKEMA, K. 1956. Effect of the nitrogen, phosphorus, potassium and magnesium nutrition of potato plants on the content of free amino-acids and on the amino-acid composition of the protein of the tubers. Plant and Soil *7*, 135–166.

NEILSON, A. J., and CAUL, J. F. 1965. Minor constituents as major flavoring agents. Perf. Essent. Oil Rec. *56*, 321–324.

OBATA, Y., and MIZUTANI, J. 1961. Studies on the degradation mechanisms of proteins and their derivatives in foods. V. Volatile sulphur compounds in the soybean meal hydrolysates and the development of dimethyl sulphide. Agr. Biol. Chem. (Tokyo) *25*, 36–38.

PATTON, S. 1956. The broth-like flavor of methional. Food Technol. *10*, 60.

PATTON, S., and BARNES, I. J.   1958.   The odor and flavor of methional. Food Research 23, 221–223.

PATTON, S., BARNES, I. J., and EVANS, L. E.   1959.   n-Deca-2,4-dienal, its origin from linoleate and flavor significance in fats.   J. Am. Oil Chemists' Soc. 36, 280–283.

PERYAM, D. R., POLENUS, B. W., KAMEN, J. M., EINDHOVEN, J., and PILGRIM, F. J.   1960.   Food preferences of men in the U.S. Armed Forces.   U.S. Dept. Army Quartermaster Res. and Eng. Command. Quartermaster Food and Container Institute for the Armed Forces, Chicago, Ill.

PICKARD, D., and CORI, R.   1964.   Report on a consumer survey carried out for the Potato Marketing Board (U. K.) and National Farmers Union of England and Wales and of Scotland.   Publ. by Potato Marketing Board, 50 Hans Crescent, Knightsbridge, London.

RALLS, J. W.   1960.   Rapid method for semiquantitative determination of volatile aldehydes, ketones and acids.   Anal. Chem. 32, 332–336.

RATHSACK, D.   1935.   Der Speisewert der Kartoffel.   Verlagsgesellschaft für Ackerbau.   Berlin.

ROHAN, T. A., and STEWART, T.   1965.   The precursors of chocolate aroma: The distribution of free amino acids in different commercial varieties of cocoa beans.   J. Food Sci. 30, 416–419.

SALAMAN, R. N.   1926.   In Potato Varieties.   Cambridge University Press, Cambridge, England.

SCHONBERG, A., and MOUBACHER, R.   1952.   The Strecker degradation of α-amino acids.   Chem. Revs. 50, 261–277.

SCHWIMMER, S.   1963.   Alteration of the flavor of processed vegetables by enzymic preparations.   J. Food Sci. 28, 460–466.

SCHWIMMER, S., and BURR, H. K.   1959.   Structure and chemical composition of the potato tuber.   In Potato Processing.   W. F. Talburt and O. Smith (Editors).   Avi Publishing Co., Westport, Conn.

SELF. R.   1961.   An enrichment trap for use with capillary columns.   Nature 189, 223.

SELF, R.   1963.   The use of capillary column gas chromatography for the analysis of the odour of cooked potatoes.   In Recent Advances in Food Science 3.   Biochemistry and Biophysics.   J. M. Leitch and D. N. Rhodes (Editors).   Butterworths, London.

SELF, R.   1965.   Unpublished results.   Earlham Food Research Laboratory, Norwich, England.

SELF, R., CASEY, J. C., and SWAIN, T.   1963C.   The low-boiling volatiles of cooked foods.   Chem. and Ind. 863–864.

SELF, R., LAND, D. G., and CASEY, J. C.   1963B.   Gas chromatography using capillary column units for flavor investigations.   J. Sci. Food Agr. 14, 209–220.

SELF, R., ROLLEY, H. L. J., and JOYCE, A. E.   1963A.   Some volatile compounds from cooked potatoes.   J. Sci. Food Agr. 14, 8–14.

SELF, R., and SWAIN, T.   1963.   Flavor in potatoes.   Proc. Nutr. Soc. 22, 176–182.

SMITH, O.   1950.   Improving flavor of chips with monosodium glutamate. Natl. Potato Chip Inst., General, Article 3, 1–2.

STRAUSZ, O. P., and GUNNING, H. E.   1962.   The reaction of sulfur atoms. I. The addition to ethylene and propylene.   J. Am. Chem. Soc. 84, 4080–4083.

SWAIN, T., and SELF, R. 1964. Studies on potato flavor. Europ. Potato J. 7, 228–237.

SWOBODA, P. A. T. 1963. Total trapping of chromatographic effluent in argon carrier gas. Nature 199, 31–32.

TALLEY, E. A., FITZPATRICK, T. J., and PORTER, W. L. 1964. Chemical composition of potatoes. IV. Relationship of the free amino acid concentration to specific gravity and storage time. Am. Pot. J. 41, 357–366.

TERANISHI, R., BUTTERY, R. G., and LUNDIN, R. E. 1962. Gas chromatography. Direct vapor analyses of food products with programmed temperature control and dual columns with dual flame ionization detectors. Anal. Chem. 34, 1033–1035.

TERANISHI, R., FLATH, R. A., MON, T. R., and STEVENS, K. L. 1965. Collection of gas chromatographically purified samples. J. Gas Chromatography 206–207.

VLIET, W. F. VAN, and SCHRIEMER, W. H. 1960. The sugar accumulation in potatoes kept at low temperature, as studied in a small selection of samples of Dutch varieties. European Potato J. 3, 263–271.

VÖLKSEN, W. 1950. Constituents of the potato. II. Potato fat. Arch. Pharm. 238, 203–207.

VON SYDOW, E. 1964. Private communication. Swedish Institute for Food Preservation Research (SIK), Göteborg, Sweden.

WATSON, J. T., and BIEMANN, K. 1965. Direct recording of high resolution mass spectra of gas chromatographic effluents. Anal. Chem. 37, 844–851.

WEDEMEYER, G. A., and DOLLAR, A. M. 1963. Co-oxidation of the sulfur-containing amino acids in an autoxidizing lipid system. J. Food Sci. 28, 537–540.

WEGNER, H. 1949. Steam-volatile flavor (odor and taste) materials of potatoes. Z. Lebensm. u. Forschung 89, 140–148.

WIEBE, H. A., KNIGHT, A. R., STRAUSZ, O. P., and GUNNING, H. E. 1965. The reaction of sulfur atoms. V. Further studies on the reaction with olefins. J. Am. Chem. Soc. 87, 1443–1449.

WONG, N. P., PATTON, S., and FORSS, D. A. 1958. Methyl ketones in evaporated milk. J. Dairy Sci 41, 1699–1705.

CHAPTER 17

J. F. Carson | Onion Flavor

INTRODUCTION

A study of the chemistry of flavor development in the onion (*Allium cepa*) should include some discussion of the closely related garlic (*Allium sativum*). Historically, the knowledge of the chemistry of flavor precursors and enzymes in garlic suggested the possibility of related reactions in the onion and many of the techniques developed in investigations of garlic were later applied to onion studies. Both of these vegetables are now classic examples of enzymatic development of flavor in which the initial products of reaction are highly unstable and undergo further changes. The flavor precursors or substrates for enzymatic action are sulfoxide amino acids. The most important volatile flavor compounds obtained from the onion contain sulfur and include hydrogen sulfide, thiols, disulfides, trisulfides, thiosulfinates, and the elusive lachrymatory factor.

VOLATILE FLAVOR COMPONENTS OF THE ONION

Semmler (1892B) first established that onion oil on vacuum distillation yields disulfides and polysulfides. One fraction was obtained with an analysis agreeing with that of allyl propyl disulfide. Other fractions isolated were found to contain polysulfides and a material thought to be the same as that obtained from asafetida oil. For many years allyl propyl disulfide was considered to be the major flavor component in the onion, but it is now known that this is not present in significant amounts in the volatile flavor of commercial American onions.

Kohman (1947) isolated propionaldehyde from onion vapors. Although its contribution to flavor is probably not important, the compound is important in connection with the chemistry of the lachrymatory factor. Challenger and Greenwood (1949) first isolated 1-propanethiol from onion vapor. Carson and Wong (1961A) showed the presence of acetaldehyde, propionaldehyde, *n*-butyraldehyde, acetone, and methyl ethyl ketone by aspirating chopped onions and trapping the volatiles as 2,4-dinitrophenylhydrazones. Spåre and Virtanen (1961) isolated the interesting aldehyde, 2-methyl-2-pentenal which they considered as probably formed by an aldol condensation from propionaldehyde. Bernhard *et al.* (1964) have reported the presence of allyl monosulfide in the volatiles of some cultivars of *Allium cepa*.

TABLE 68

DISULFIDES AND TRISULFIDES FROM ONIONS

CH_3SSCH_3	CH_3SSSCH_3
$C_3H_7SSC_3H_7$	$C_3H_7SSSC_3H_7$
$CH_3SSC_3H_7$	$CH_3SSSC_3H_7$

Carson and Wong (1961C) isolated a series of disulfides and trisulfides containing methyl and n-propyl groups as shown in Table 68. Onions were steam distilled under reduced pressure and the vapors adsorbed on carbon. The volatiles were extracted from the carbon with ether, the ether removed by vacuum distillation, and the resulting oil separated by gas-liquid partition chromatography. Because of the danger of chemical rearrangements and the production of artifacts accompanying the use of activated carbon, an alternate procedure was used. Onions were steam distilled, the distillate extracted continuously with isopentane and the fractions isolated as before. In both methods, the same disulfides and trisulfides containing methyl and n-propyl groups were found to be the major components of the oil. In addition, ethyl, n-propyl, and isopropyl alcohols were found. No disulfides containing allyl groups could be detected by gas chromatography.

The onion isolates obtained obviously were not representative of fresh onion flavor since no lachrymatory effect was present. As a consequence of mercaptan disulfide interchange and the thermal instability of aliphatic trisulfides, the actual proportions of these compounds obtained in an experiment will depend on conditions of isolation, and in particular on the solvent used and temperature of extraction and distillation.

Thiolsulfinates from Garlic and Onion

Although the thiosulfinates are volatile components of flavor they are of sufficent importance to be treated separately. Because of their thermal instability, they can be isolated in pure form only with great difficulty. Cavallito and Bailey (1944), while studying the antibacterial properties of garlic, discovered allicin, the most important flavor component in fresh garlic oil. This compound was shown to be 2-propenyl-2-propenethiolsulfinate $CH_2 = CH—CH_2—S(O)—S—CH_2—CH = CH_2$). The compound was isolated as an oil with a fresh garlic odor by co-distillation with water under reduced pressure followed by extraction of the allicin in the distillate into ether and removal of the ether *in vacuo.* Approximately 6 gm. of oil was obtained from 4 kg. of garlic cloves. Cavallito and Bailey reported that the compound could not be distilled dry *in vacuo* without decomposition. Allicin and several alkyl alkanethiol sulfinates were synthesized by oxidation of the corresponding disulfides with per acids. These compounds can be characterized by reaction with cysteine to yield crystalline disulfides.

$$RS(O)SR + 2HSCH_2CH(NH_2)COOH \rightarrow 2RSSCH_2CH(NH_2)COOH + H_2O$$

The facile disproportionation of thiolsulfinates to thiolsulfonates and disulfides has been shown by Barnard (1957C) to occur spontaneously

$$2RS(O)SR \rightarrow RSO_2SR + RSSR$$

at room temperature. This reaction explains the isolation of disulfides from garlic and onion.

Thiolsulfinates can be readily distinguished from thiolsulfonates by infrared spectra. The former have strong absorption in the sulfoxide region near 1093 cm.$^{-1}$ and the latter have strong sulfone absorption at 1141 and 1343 cm.$^{-1}$ (Barnard 1957A, B; Carson and Wong 1961C). Trace amounts of thiolsulfinates can be distinguished from thiolsulfonates and disulfides by the N-ethylmaleimide reagent (Carson and Wong 1959A). The test requires anhydrous conditions. Thiols and thiolesters interfere (Benesch et al. 1956).

Matsukawa and Yurugi (1952), while investigating the chemistry of vitamin B_1, discovered a reaction that is useful for identifying small quantities of thiolsulfinates. It was found that thiamin I at pH 8 reacts with thiolsulfinates to yield a "thiamin disulfide" II according to the equation which appears at the top of page 393.

The thiamin disulfides are crystalline compounds which are soluble in organic solvents with characteristic absorption in the ultraviolet. Reaction of these compounds with cysteine regenerates thiamin and gives alkylthiocysteines III. The thiamin is thus a trapping reagent for thiolsulfinates. The reaction is not completely unequivocal for thiolsulfinates because it is given by thiosulfonates, Bunte salts ($NaRS_2O_3$), and sulfenyl thiocyanates (RSSCN).

To identify thiolsulfinates in plant extracts, a garlic enzyme is added, the pH adjusted to 8, thiamin is added and the mixture heated. The thiamin disulfide derivatives are then extracted into an organic solvent. The mixture may be chromatographed on paper and after treatment with cysteine to regenerate thiamine, the spots may be located by the thiochrome reaction. In an alternate procedure, the extract of thiamin disulfides is first reacted with cysteine and the mixture of alkylthiocysteines chromatographed directly on paper and visualized with ninhydrin. In still a different method, thiolsulfinates are first chromatographed on paper, the spots excised, reacted with cysteine and the alkylthiocysteines chromatographed as before. This latter procedure will distinguish mixed thiolsulfinates RS(O)SR' from mixtures of RS(O)SR and R'S(O)SR'.

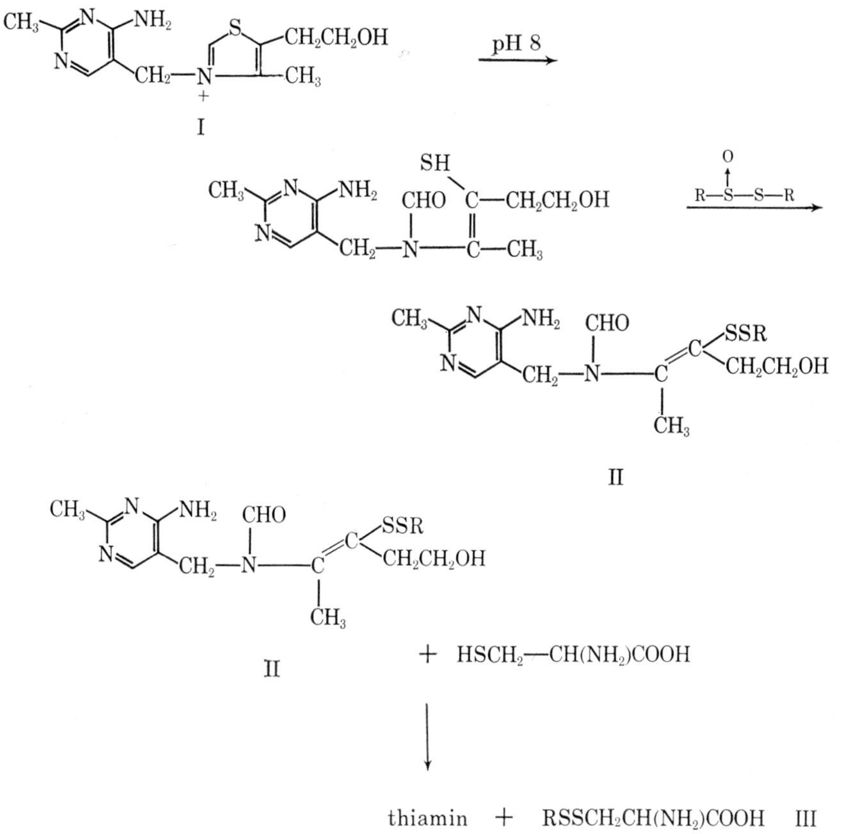

$$\text{(I)} \quad \xrightarrow{\text{pH 8}}$$

I

$$\xrightarrow{\text{R—S—S—R}}$$

II

II

$$+ \ \text{HSCH}_2\text{—CH(NH}_2\text{)COOH}$$

$$\downarrow$$

$$\text{thiamin} \ + \ \text{RSSCH}_2\text{CH(NH}_2\text{)COOH} \quad \text{III}$$

By the application of these techniques (Fujiwara *et al.* 1955; Matsukawa *et al.* 1953A, B; and Yurugi 1954), evidence was obtained for the presence of methyl and propyl thiolsulfinates (no allyl) in onion. From garlic, methyl, propyl, and allyl derivatives were found and the plant *Ipheion uniforum* of *Lilliacea* yielded thiolsulfinates with methyl, ethyl, and propyl groups.

THE FLAVOR PRECURSOR OF GARLIC

The brilliant discoveries of Stoll and Seebeck (1948) established the chemical and enzymological basis for the flavor of garlic which showed the way for later research in onion flavor precursors. These investigators isolated from garlic the crystalline amino acid, (+) S-allyl-L-cysteine sulfoxide to which they gave the trivial name alliin. The structure was unequivocally established by classical methods of degradation and by synthesis. In the course of this work, Stoll and Seebeck (1951) synthesized all four isomers, the dextro-and levorotatory sulfoxides from L-cysteine and the corresponding isomers from D-cysteine. They also prepared the dextro- and levorotatory S-propyl-L-cysteine sulfoxides one of which has since been found in onion.

The enzyme alliinase was also isolated from garlic cloves and it was shown that it catalyzes the decomposition of sulfoxide amino acids to thiolsulfinate, ammonia, and pyruvic acid.

$$2R\overset{\overset{O}{\uparrow}}{S}CH_2\underset{\underset{H}{|}}{\overset{\overset{NH_2}{|}}{C}}—COOH + H_2O \xrightarrow{\text{Alliinase}} R\overset{\overset{O}{\uparrow}}{S}SR + 2NH_3 + 2CH_3COCOOH$$

Where R = CH_2=CH—CH_2—

The enzyme (Stoll and Seebeck 1949A, B) has a maximum activity in the range pH 5 to 8. For activity, the substrate must have an aliphatic substituent on the sulfur of an L-cysteine sulfoxide. The amino group must be free and unsubstituted. The naturally occurring (+) isomer alliin reacts faster enzymatically than the (−) isomer.

The Absolute Configuration of S-Substituted Cysteine Sulfoxides

Hine and Rogers (1956) have established by X-ray analysis that the absolute configuration at the asymmetric sulfur of (+) S-methyl-L-cysteine sulfoxide is (S) according to the Cahn-Prelog-Ingold convention (Cahn 1964). Since the sulfoxide chromophore exerts a dominant influence on the specific rotation (Hine and Rogers 1956, Gaffield et al. 1965), both the (+) propyl- and (+) allyl-L-cysteine sulfoxides undoubtedly also have an (S) configuration about sulfur.

Amino Acid Flavor Precursors of the Onion

The isolation of methyl and propyl disulfides and trisulfides, the evidence for the corresponding thiolsulfinates, and the enzymic production of ammonia and pyruvic acid from onions (Vilkki 1954) suggested an amino acid-enzyme system similar to that of garlic. Matsukawa et al. (1953A, B) predicted that sulfoxide amino acids containing methyl and propyl groups would be found in the onion. Virtanen and Matikkala (1959B) isolated from onions, under conditions of enzyme inactivation, (+) S-methyl-L-cysteine sulfoxide ($CH_3S(O)CH_2CH(NH_2)COOH$) and the (+) S-n-propyl derivative ($C_3H_7S(O)CH_2CH(NH_2)COOH$). The amino acids were isolated by chromatography on ion exchangers and cellulose powder. The structure of the methyl derivative was established by reduction with hydriodic acid to S-methyl-L-cysteine followed by reaction with ninhydrin to yield methylthioacetaldehyde isolated as the dimedon condensation product. The structure of the propyl derivative was established by hydriodic acid reduction to S-propyl-L-cysteine.

Carson and Wong (1961C) isolated the same sulfoxide amino acids from onions as the N:2,4-dinitrophenyl derivatives and showed that they were the dextrorotatory isomers by comparison of specific rotations and infrared spectra with previously synthesized compounds. An onion extract was dinitrophenylated and the mixture was separated by partition chromatography on silicic acid. The 2,4-dinitrophenyl derivatives are convenient for this purpose because of their ease of crystallization and their very high negative molecular rotations in acetic acid.

Virtanen and Matikkala (1958, 1959A) isolated a new cyclic sulfoxide amino acid, 3-methyl-1,4-thiazane-5-carboxylic acid S-oxide (cycloalliin) IV from onions. The compound was isolated as the crystalline hydrochloride hydrate in yields of 1.4 to 3.2 gm./kg. fresh weight. The structure was established by degradation with boiling 6 N hydrochloric acid. Under these conditions, the compound is partly reduced to a thioether V and partly split to 2-methyltaurine VI and cysteic acid VII. Carson and Wong (unpublished) established the structure by a different method.

Desulfurization with Raney nickel yielded N-isopropyl L-alanine—a procedure which also established the L configuration at the carbon α to the carboxyl. Virtanen and Matikkala (1961A) later showed that the compound exists in the intact onion but that it is also produced as an artifact, during isolation, resulting from a very labile precursor. The amino acid is inert to onion enzymes and presumably makes no contribution to onion flavor. Palmer and Lee (1966), by X-ray examination of the crystalline hydrochloride hydrate, established the chair conformation

for the compound in the crystalline state with the sulfoxide oxygen axial
and the methyl group equatorial as shown in VIII.

VIII

   Although the discovery of S-methyl- and S-propyl-L-cysteine sulfoxides
in onion provided an explanation for the formation of thiosulfinates and
disulfides by the Stoll enzyme reaction, certain discrepancies became
apparent. In particular, the lachrymatory effect is not explained and the
amount of pyruvic acid produced by onion is far in excess of the quantity
calculated for the amount of the two amino acids present (Schwimmer
and Weston 1961). Moreover, the formation of cycloalliin is not explained. In a series of papers, Virtanen and Spåre (1961, 1962), and
Spåre and Virtanen (1963) described the isolation of a new and unusual
sulfoxide amino acid which produces the lachrymatory effect by enzyme
action.

   These investigators isolated from onion the very reactive amino acid,
S-(1-propenyl)-L-cysteine sulfoxide IX. The high reactivity of this compound as a consequence of the vinylic double bond, is such that in
the presence of base it cyclizes to cycloalliin IV and in the presence of
mineral acid, a carbon sulfur linkage is broken with the formation of
propionaldehyde. Much of the cycloalliin isolated from onion is an
artifact resulting from the action of ammonium hydroxide solution on the
sulfoxide amino acid when amino acids are eluted from a cation exchanger
with ammonia.

   Virtanen and co-workers established that the propenyl cysteine
sulfoxide in the presence of onion enzyme reacts to yield the lachrymatory
factor X, ammonia, and pyruvic acid. The reaction differs from the
Stoll reaction of alkyl and allyl cysteine sulfoxides in that a sulfenic acid
X rather than a thiolsulfinate is produced.

   Lukes (unpublished) has developed an improved procedure for isolating propenyl cysteine sulfoxide from commercial dehydrated onions. Carson et al. (1966) from nuclear magnetic resonance spectroscopy of the
free amino acid and of the N:2,4-dinitrophenyl- and N:2,4,6-trinitro-
phenyl derivatives have shown that the vinylic double bond of the natural
product IX has a trans configuration.

$$CH_3CH=CH-\overset{O\uparrow}{S}-CH_2\overset{NH_2}{\underset{H}{C\cdot}}COOH + H_2O \xrightarrow{\text{Enzyme}}$$

$$\overset{IX}{}\quad\overset{II}{}$$

$$CH_3CH=CH\overset{H}{\underset{|}{S}} \to O + NH_3 + CH_3-\overset{O}{\overset{\|}{C}}-COOH$$

$$X$$

$$CH_3CH_2CHO + S$$

$$CH_3CH_2CH=C-CHO$$
$$\underset{CH_3}{|}$$

Base

$$\overset{O}{\overset{\uparrow}{S}}$$
$$H_2C \diagup \quad \diagdown CH_2$$
$$H_3C\text{-}CH \quad H\overset{\diagdown}{C}COOH$$
$$\underset{\underset{H}{|}}{N} \quad IV$$

The Structure of the Lachrymatory Factor

Evidence for the structure of compound X rests mainly on mass spectrometry (Moisio *et al.* 1962). A solution of the propenyl cysteine sulfoxide and onion enzyme after a reaction time of one minute gave a strong peak of mass 90 in the mass spectrometer with nothing of greater mass except for the peaks at 91 and 92 representing the same molecule with heavier sulfur isotopes. This agrees with the suggested formula $CH_3CH=CHSHO$. The extreme instability of the compound is shown by the fact that after an hour, the mass 90 peak was much weaker and a peak of mass 58 corresponding to propionaldehyde and a peak of mass 98 corresponding to 2-methyl-2-pentenal appeared. After two hours, the mass 90 peak corresponding to the lachrymator had disappeared. This explains the formation of propionaldehyde and of 2-methyl-2-pentenal presumably formed by an aldol condensation of the former.

The question remains as to the linkage of sulfur, oxygen, and hydrogen in the molecule ($-SOH$ versus $-\overset{H}{\underset{|}{S}} \to O$). The only sulfenic acids isolated in pure form are derivatives of anthraquinone (Fries 1912; Jenny 1958) and these are considered to have the $-SOH$ structure. This problem was investigated by Moisio *et al.* (1962) by conducting the enzyme reaction in D_2O. In ordinary water in addition to the parent peak of mass 90, a peak at 73 was observed corresponding to an ion which has lost OH (90–17). In heavy water, the parent peak of 90 became 91 showing that deuterium was exchanged for hydrogen. However, the mass 73 fragment now appeared at 74 just 17 units less than 91 corresponding again to loss of hydroxyl. A sulfenic acid of structure RSOH would be expected to exchange the hydroxyl hydrogen for deuterium and OD (18 units) rather than OH would be lost. It was therefore concluded

$$CH_3CH{=}CH{-}\overset{\overset{\textstyle O}{\diagup}}{S}{-}H.$$

that the structure was $CH_3CH{=}CH{-}S{-}H$.

Niegisch and Stahl (1956) had earlier obtained the same peak of mass 90 in mass spectrometric studies of onion volatiles but the highly unusual structure as X would scarcely be suspected without prior knowledge of the precursor. Wilkens (1961) from infrared evidence has suggested an isomeric structure $CH_3CH_2CH{=}S{=}O$ for the lachrymator. Unfortunately pure model compounds are not available for a chemical study of these unusual structures.

Attempted Synthesis of the Lachrymatory Precursor

Attempts to synthesize the natural (+) S-(1-propenyl)-L-cysteine sulfoxide have so far been abortive (Spåre and Virtanen 1963). Carson (in press) has recently synthesized (+) and (−) cis-S-(1-propenyl)-L-cysteine sulfoxide. The compounds differ from the naturally occurring material thereby furnishing independent evidence of the trans nature of the latter. Cis-S-(1-propenyl)-L-cysteine was first synthesized by isomerization of S-(2-propenyl)-L-cysteine (Carson and Wong 1963).

$$CH_2{=}CHCH_2SCH_2CH(NH_2)COOH \xrightarrow[\substack{\text{Dimethyl Sulfoxide}\\ \text{or}\\ \text{Dimethyl Formamide}}]{\text{KOtBu}}$$

(+) and (−) isomers

Rather surprisingly, only the cis isomer was obtained. Oxidation of the product with hydrogen peroxide yielded a mixture of diastereomeric sulfoxides from which the (+) and (−) isomers were obtained by fractional crystallization. Both of these compounds produce the lachrymatory effect and characteristic onion odor when treated with onion enzyme. They differ from the naturally occurring amino acid in specific rotation and by the fact that cyclization in dilute ammonium hydroxide produces a mixture of cycloalliin and a stereoisomer of this compound. (Carson and Boggs 1966).

Peptides in Onion

Virtanen and Matikkala (1960A, B; 1961 A, B, C) have isolated several γ-glutamyl peptides of sulfur-containing amino acids as shown in Table 69. The first one is the lachrymatory precursor bound in peptide linkage with glutamic acid and the last one is a derivative of glutathione, S-(2-carboxyl-1-propyl)-glutathione. None of these compounds is susceptible to action by onion enzymes and therefore probably contribute nothing to the volatile flavor of fresh onion. Their possible contribution to the flavor of cooked onion products has not been determined.

TABLE 69

SULFUR-CONTAINING PEPTIDES IN ALLIUM CEPA

γ-L-Glutamyl (+)-S-propenyl-L-cysteine sulfoxide
γ-L-Glutamyl-S-methyl-L-cysteine
γ-L-Glutamyl-L-methionine
γ-L-Glutamyl-S-(β-carboxy-n-propyl)-L-cysteinyl glycine

Onion Alliinase

Schwimmer et al. (1960) and Kupiecki and Virtanen (1960) have obtained enzyme preparations from onion which catalyze the decomposition of S-alkyl-L-cysteine sulfoxide to thiolsulfinates, ammonia and pyruvic acid. Conventional methods of isolation were used including precipitation from ammonium sulfate solutions followed by solution in water and lyophilization or precipitation with acetone. The different preparations are stable at $0°C$. from 1 to 2 weeks. The maximum activity in phosphate buffer is at pH 7.4. The enzyme is stimulated by the addition of pyridoxal phosphate to the extent of 50%. Schwimmer and Mazelis (1963) observed that the pH for maximum activity depended on the specific buffer used. The pH maximum at 7.4 to 7.6 with acetate or phosphate increased to 8.5 to 8.8 in the presence of pyrophosphate and the total activity was increased. Onion enzyme differs from garlic alliinase in the sharp pH maximum in contrast to the broad optimum at pH 5 to 8 exhibited by the garlic enzyme. Although the garlic enzyme can be precipitated at pH 4, the onion enzyme is inactivated by this treatment. In specificity, the two enzymes are very similar.

Mazelis (1963) has obtained a similar enzyme from Brassica spp. This alliinase or cysteine sulfoxide lyase has a pH optimum at 8.4 to 8.6 in a borate buffer and pyridoxal phosphate is a coenzyme. Although many Brassica vegetables contain S-methyl-L-cysteine sulfoxide (Morris and Thompson 1956; Synge and Wood 1956), the enzyme is apparently not active at the pH of normal vegetable usage.

The Measurement of Onion Flavor

Volatile sulfur has been used as a measure of onion flavor by Platenius (1935) who determined sulfur (as barium sulfate after oxidation with bromine) in a distillate after acid hydrolysis of the onion. Currier (1945) modified the procedure by converting sulfur to methylene blue. Platenius and Knott (1941) showed that a high correlation existed between total solids and pungency.

If one assumes that pungency arises from the enzymatic decomposition of S-substituted cysteine sulfoxides according to the Stoll equation, an analysis of any of the products should give a measure of pungency. Schwimmer and Weston (1961) have developed a procedure for the measurement of the increase in pyruvic acid in onion tissue disintegrated by comminution. Analyses of pyruvic acid as a measure of flavor have been applied to garlic by Jäger (1955) and Alfonso and Lopez (1960). Onion juice, after comminution and filtration, is reacted with 2,4-dinitro-phenylhydrazine and the resulting dinitrophenylhydrazones are estimated colorimetrically. Since the procedure actually measures total carbonyl content, the results were compared with those of a method specific for pyruvic acid. In this method, reduced diphosphopyridine nucleotide is oxidized by pyruvic acid in the presence of excess lactic dehydrogenase and the decrease of reduced nucleotide is a measure of pyruvic acid. The two methods yielded approximately the same values from which it can be concluded that the enzymatic increase in 2,4-dinitrophenylhydrazine reacting carbonyl can be largely attributed to pyruvic acid.

The enzymatic reaction is rapid, over 95% of the maximum amount of pyruvic acid is produced within six minutes. The total amount produced roughly paralleled the generally accepted degree of pungency. Weak onions yielded 2 to 4 μ moles, those of intermediate strength 8 to 10 μ moles, and strong onions 15 to 20 μ moles of pyruvic acid per gram of onion.

Schwimmer and Guadagni (1962) compared pyruvic acid content of onion juice with an organoleptic evaluation of the olfactory threshold by a panel of judges and obtained a good correlation ($r = -0.97$). Schwimmer et al. (1964) showed that the procedure is also useful for dehydrated onion powders. In general, the method has the distinct advantage over most other methods in that it is rapid and small samples of onion tissue (1 gm.) may be used.

Spåre and Virtanen (1963) used an interesting procedure for detecting the persence of the lachrymatory precursor in onions. A few drops of the aqueous solution to be tested were placed in a small weighing vial and the pH adjusted to 6 to 7. A small amount of enzyme powder was added to the solution and the vial held firmly against the eye. Depending on the concentration, the lachrymatory effect was perceived after 15 to 45 seconds. This procedure was used to screen fractions obtained in the chromatographic isolation of propenyl cysteine sulfoxide.

Of the various gas chromatographic procedures for determining volatile flavor of onions or garlic, the electron capture hydrogen flame dual channel method is very promising. The electron capture detector has the great advantage of selectivity toward certain classes of compounds including sulfur-containing materials, and in many cases, it exhibits a higher sensitivity than other detectors. By this procedure, Oaks *et al.* (1964) have analyzed the head space above a macerated garlic clove.

Eighteen compounds were detected by electron capture, nine of which were found to be mono-, di-, and trisulfides containing methyl-methyl, methyl-allyl, and allyl-allyl groups with traces of methyl propyl trisulfides.

DISCUSSION

W. F. Wilkens.—In relation to your electron-capture work, where you are using a ϕ value between your flame ionization and electron-capture detector. We ran some preliminary studies on freshly crushed onion tissue in a closed vial and injected the headspace, and came up with a ϕ value of 30 for one of the compounds present, which differs considerably from the typical classification of sulfur compounds and the unsaturated compounds that have been found to date.

BIBLIOGRAPHY

ALFONSO, N., and LOPEZ, H. 1960. Flavor value of Mexican garlic. Z. Lebensm.-Untersuch. u-Forsch. *111*, 410–413.

BARNARD, D. 1957A. Oxidation of organic sulfides. Part IX. The reaction of ozone with organic sulfur compounds. J. Chem. Soc. 4547–4555.

BARNARD, D. 1957B. The reaction of sulfinyl chlorides with zinc. J. Chem. Soc. 4673–4674.

BARNARD, D. 1957C. The spontaneous decomposition of aryl thiolsulfinates. J. Chem. Soc. 4675–4676.

BENESCH, R., BENESCH, R. E., GUTCHO, M., and LAUFER, L. 1956. New color test for thiols and thiolesters. Science *123*, 981.

BERNHARD, R. A., SAGHIR, A. R., JACOBSEN, J. V., and MANN, L. K. 1964. Isolation and identification of allyl monosulfide and allyl alcohol from Allium. Arch. Biochem. and Biophys. *107*, 137–140.

CAHN, R. S. 1964. An introduction to the sequence rule. A system for the specification of absolute configuration. J. Chem. Ed. *41*, 116–125.

CARSON, J. F., and WONG, F. F. 1959A. A color reaction for thiolsulfinates. Nature *183*, 1673.

CARSON, J. F., and WONG, F. F. 1959B. Separation of aliphatic disulfides and trisulfides by gas-liquid partition chromatography. J. Org. Chem. *24*, 175–179.

CARSON, J. F., and WONG, F. F. 1961A. The volatile flavor components of onions. J. Agr. and Food Chem. *9*, 140–143.

CARSON, J. F., and WONG, F. F. 1961B. The reactions of thiosulfinates with triphenylphosphine, triphenylarsine and triphenylstibine. J. Org. Chem. 26, 1467–1470.

CARSON, J. F., and WONG, F. F. 1961C. Isolation of (+)S-methyl-L-cysteine sulfoxide and of (+)S-n-propyl-L-cysteine sulfoxide from onions as their N:2,4-dinitrophenyl derivatives. J. Org. Chem. 26, 4997–5000.

CARSON, J. F., and WONG, F. F. 1963. Synthesis of cis-S-(prop-1-enyl)-L-cysteine. Chem. and Ind. 1764–1765.

CARSON, J. F., and BOGGS, L. E. 1966. The synthesis and base-catalyzed cyclization of (+)- and (−)-cis-S-(1-propenyl)-L-cysteine sulfoxides. J. Org. Chem. 31, 2862–2864.

CARSON, J. F., LUNDIN, R. E., and LUKES, T. M. 1966. The configuration of (+)-S-(1-propenyl)-L-cysteine S-oxide from Allium cepa. J. Org. Chem. 31, 1634–5.

CAVALLITO, C. J., and BAILEY, J. H. 1944. Allicin, the antibacterial principal of Allium sativum. I. Isolation, physical properties and antibacterial action. J. Am. Chem. Soc. 66, 1950–1951.

CAVALLITO, C. J., BUCK, J. S., and SUTER, C. M. 1944. Allicin, the antibacterial principle of Allium sativum. II. Determination of the chemical structure. J. Am. Chem. Soc. 66, 1952–1954.

CAVALLITO, C. J., BAILEY, J. H., and BUCK, J. S. 1945. The antibacterial principle of Allium sativum. III. Its precursor and essential oil of garlic. J. Am. Chem. Soc. 67, 1032–1033.

CHALLENGER, F., and GREENWOOD, D. 1949. Sulfur compounds of the genus Allium. Detection of propylthiol in the onion. The fission and methylation of diallyl disulfide in cultures of Scopulariopsis brevicaulis. Biochem. J. 44, 87–91.

CURRIER, H. B. 1945. Photometric estimation of volatile sulfur in onions as a criterion of pungency. Food Research 10, 177.

DÄBRITZ, E., and VIRTANEN, A. I. 1964. S-vinyl-cysteine-S-oxide, precursor of a new lachrymatory substance, vinylsulfenic acid. Acta Chem. Scand. 18, 837–838.

FRIES, K. 1912. On α-anthraquinone sulfenic acid. Ber. 45, 2965–2973.

FULLER, J. E., and HIGGINS, E. R. 1940. Onion juice and bacterial growth. Food Research 5, 503–507.

FUJIWARA, M., YOSHIMUSA, M., and TSUNO S. 1955. Allithiamine, a newly found derivative of vitamin B. III. On the allicin homologues in the plants of the Allium species. J. Biochem (Japan) 42, 591–601.

GAFFIELD, W., WONG, F. F., and CARSON, J. F. 1965. Configurational relationships among sulfinyl amino acids. J. Org. Chem. 30, 951–952.

HINE, R., and ROGERS, D. 1956. Absolute configuration of (+)S-methyl-L-cysteine sulfoxide. Chem. and Ind. (London) 1428.

JÄGER, H. 1955. Determination of allicin in fresh garlic. Arch. Pharm. 288, 145–148.

JENNY, W. 1958. Anthraquinone-1,4-disulfenic acid and anthraquinone-1,4-diselenenic acid. Helv. Chim. Acta 41, 317–321.

KOHMAN, E. F. 1947. The chemical components of onion vapors responsible for wound-healing properties. Science 106, 625.

KOHMAN, E. F. 1952. Onion pungency and onion flavor; their chemical determination. Food Technol. 6, 288–290.

Kuon, J., and Bernhard, R. A. 1963. Free amino acids of the common onion. J. Food Sci. 28, 298–304.

Kupiecki, F. P., and Virtanen, A. I. 1960. Cleavage of alkyl cysteine sulfoxides by an enzyme in onion (Allium cepa). Acta Chem. Scand. 14, 1913–1918.

Matikkala, E. J., and Virtanen, A. I. 1957. A new sulfur-containing amino acid in onion. II. Suomen Kemistilehti B., 30, 219.

Matikkala, E. J., and Virtanen, A. I. 1962. A new γ-glutamyl peptide, γ-L-glutamyl-S-(prop-l-enyl)-L-cysteine, in the seeds of chives (Allium schoenoprasum). Acta Chem. Scand. 16, 2461–2462.

Matsukawa, T., Iwatsu, T., and Kawasaki, H. 1953A. Studies on vitamin B₁ and related compounds. XLIII. Synthesis of allithiamine homologues. J. Pharm. Soc. of Japan 73, 497–501.

Matsukawa, T., and Kawasaki, H. 1953. Studies on vitamin B₁ and related compounds. XLI. Synthesis of allithiamine homologues. J. Pharm. Soc. of Japan 73, 216–219.

Matsukawa, T., and Yurugi, S. 1952. Studies on vitamin B₁ and related compounds. XXXIX. Structure of allithiamine. J. Pharm. Soc. (Japan) 72, 1616–1619.

Matsukawa, T., Yurugi, S., and Matsuoka, T. 1953B. Products of the reactions between thiamine and ingredients of Allium genus. Detection of allithiamine and its homologues. Science 118, 325–327.

Mazelis, M. 1963. Demonstration and characterization of cysteine sulfoxide lyase in the cruciferae. Phytochemistry 2, 5–22.

Moisio, T., Spåre, C. G., and Virtanen, A. I. 1962. Mass spectral studies of the chemical nature of the lachrymatory factor formed enzymically from S-(1-propenyl)-cysteine sulfoxide isolated from onion (Allium cepa). Suomen Kemistilehti B, 35, 29.

Morris, C. J., and Thompson, J. F. 1956. The identification of (+)S-methyl-L-cysteine sulfoxide in plants. J. Am. Chem. Soc. 78, 1605–1608.

Niegisch, W. D., and Stahl, W. H. 1956. The onion-gaseous emanation products. Food Research 21, 657–665.

Oaks, D. M., Hartmann, H., and Dimick, K. P. 1964. Analysis of sulfur compounds with electron capture hydrogen flame dual channel chromatography. Anal. Chem. 36, 1560–1565.

Ostermayer, F., and Tarbell, D. S. 1960. Products of acid hydrolysis of S-methyl-L-cysteine sulfoxide, the isolation of methyl methanethiolsulfonate, and mechanism of the hydrolysis. J. Am. Chem. Soc. 82, 3752.

Palmer, K. J., and Lee, K. S. 1966. The structure of cycloalliin hydrochloride monohydrate. Acta Crystallog. 20, 790–795.

Platenius, H. 1935. A method for estimating the volatile sulfur content and pungency of onions. J. Agric. Res. 51, 847–853.

Platenius, H., and Knott, J. E. 1941. Factors affecting onion pungency. J. Agric. Res. 62, 371–379.

Renis, H. E., and Henze, R. E. 1958. Cysteine derivatives in mature onion bulbs. Food Research 23, 345–350.

Schwimmer, S., Carson, J. F., Makower, R. U., Mazelis, M., and Wong, F. F. 1960. Demonstration of alliinase in protein preparation in onions. Experimentia 16, 449–450.

SCHWIMMER, S., and GUADAGNI, D. G. 1962. Relation between olfactory threshold concentration and pyruvic acid content of onion juice. J. Food Sci. 27, 94–97.

SCHWIMMER, S., and MAZELIS, M. 1963. Characterization of alliinase of Allium cepa. Arch. Biochem. Biophys. 100, 66–73.

SCHWIMMER, S., VENSTROM, D. W., and GUADAGNI, D. G. 1964. Relation between pyruvate content and odor strength of reconstituted onion powder. Food Technol. 18, 121–124.

SCHWIMMER, S., and WESTON, W. J. 1961. Enzymatic development of pyruvic acid in onion as a measure of pungency. J. Agr. Food Chem. 9, 301–304.

SEMMLER, F. W. 1892A. The essential oil of garlic (Allium sativum). Arch. der Pharm. 230, 434–443.

SEMMLER, F. W. 1892B. The essential oil of onion (Allium cepa L). Arch. der Pharm. 230, 443–448.

SMALL, L. D., BAILEY, J. H., and CAVALLITO, C. J. 1947. Alkyl thiolsulfinates. J. Am. Chem. Soc. 69, 1710–1713.

SPÅRE, C. G., and VIRTANEN, A. I. 1961. The volatile carbonyls and alcohols in the flavor substances of onion (Allium cepa). Acta Chem. Scand. 15, 1280–1284.

SPÅRE, C. G., and VIRTANEN, A. I. 1963. On the lachrymatory factor in onion (Allium cepa) vapors and its precurser. Acta Chem. Scand. 17, 641–650.

STOLL, A., and SEEBECK, E. 1948. Allium compounds I. Alliin, the true mother compound of garlic oil. Helv. Chim. Acta 31, 189–210.

STOLL, A., and SEEBECK, E. 1949A. Allium compounds II. Enzymic degradation of alliine and the properties of alliinase. Helv. Chim. Acta 32, 197–205.

STOLL, A., and SEEBECK, E. 1949B. Allium compounds III. Specificity of alliinase and synthesis of compounds related to alliin. Helv. Chim. Acta 32, 866–876.

STOLL, A., and SEEBECK, E. 1951. Synthesis of natural alliin and its three optically active isomers. Helv. Chim. Acta. 34, 481–487.

SYNGE, R. L. M., and WOOD, J. C. 1956. (+)S-methyl-L-cysteine S-oxide in cabbage. Biochem. J. 64, 252–259.

VILKKI, P. 1954. Chromatographic studies on the formation of pyruvic acid in onion juice. Suomen Kemistilehti 27B, 21–24.

VIRTANEN, A. I. 1962A. On enzymic and chemical reactions in crushed plants. Arch. Biochem. Biophys., Supplement 1, 200–208.

VIRTANEN, A. I. 1962B. Some organic sulfur compounds in vegetables and fodder plants and their significance in human nutrition. Angew. Chem. Internat. Ed. I. 299–306.

VIRTANEN, A. I. 1965. Studies on organic sulfur compounds and other labile substances in plants. Phytochemistry 4, 207–228.

VIRTANEN, A. I., and MATIKKALA, E. J. 1956. A new sulfur-containing amino acid in the onion. Suomen Kemistilehti B, 29, 134–135.

VIRTANEN, A. I., and MATIKKALA, E. J. 1958. A new sulfur-containing amino acid in onion III. Suomen Kemistilehti B, 31, 191.

VIRTANEN, A. I., and MATIKKALA, E. J. 1959A. The structure and synthesis of cycloalliin isolated from Allium cepa. Acta Chem. Scand. 13, 623–626.

VIRTANEN, A. I., and MATIKKALA, E. J. 1959B. The isolation of S-methyl-cysteine sulfoxide and S-*n*-propylcysteinesulfoxide from onion (*Allium cepa*) and the antibiotic activity of crushed onion. Acta Chem. Scand. *13*, 1898–1900.

VIRTANEN, A. I., and MATIKKALA, E. J. 1960A. New γ-glutamyl peptides in onion (*Allium cepa*) I. γ-Glutamyl-phenylalanine and γ-glutamyl-S-β-carboxy-β-methyl-ethyl-cysteinyl glycine. Suomen Kemistilehti B, *33*, 83–84.

VIRTANEN, A. I., and MATIKKALA, E. J. 1960B. New γ-glutamylpeptides in the onion (*Allium cepa*). Hoppe-Seyler's Zeit. für physiol. chem. *322*, 8–20.

VIRTANEN, A. I. and MATIKKALA, E. J. 1961A. Proofs of the presence of γ-L-glutamyl-S-(1-propenyl)-cysteine sulfoxide and cycloalliin as original compounds in onion (*Allium cepa*). Suomen Kemistilehti B, *34*, 114.

VIRTANEN, A. I., and MATIKKALA, E. J. 1961B. New γ-glutamyl peptides in onion (*Allium cepa*) III. Suomen Kemistilehti B, *34*, 53–54.

VIRTANEN, A. I., and MATIKKALA, E. J. 1961C. The structure of the γ-glutamylpeptide isolated from onion (*Allium cepa*) IV. γ-L-glutamyl-S-(1-propenyl)-cysteine-sulfoxide. Suomen Kemistilehti B, *34*, 84.

VIRTANEN, A. I., and SPÅRE, C. G. 1961. Isolation of the precursor of the lachrymatory factor in onion (*Allium cepa*). Suomen Kemistilehti B, *34*, 72.

VIRTANEN, A. I., and C. G. SPÅRE. 1962. On the enzymic splitting of S-(1-propenyl)-cysteine sulfoxide and the formation of the lachrymatory factor. Suomen Kemistilehti B, *35*, 28–29.

WILKENS, W. F. 1961. The isolation and identification of the lachrymogenic compound of onion. Cornell University, Ph.D. Thesis. University Microfilms, Inc., Ann Arbor, Michigan.

YURUGI, S. 1954. Studies on vitamin B_1 and related compounds LIX. Reaction between thiamine and ingredients of Allium genus plants V. On the sulfur-containing ingredients of Allium genus plants. J. Pharm. Soc. of Japan. *74*, 519–524.

CHAPTER 18

Ron G. Buttery | Hop Flavor

INTRODUCTION

The principal use of hops is in brewing beer. Hops are also used to a much smaller extent in formulation of some other beverages, in perfumery, and in preparation of certain yeasts.

There are two main groups of chemical compounds in hops which are important to their flavor and taste. These are (1) hop oil (0.2 to 4% of the dry hops) which gives hops their aroma, and (2) the bitter resin (10 to 20% of the dry hops) which is the source of the desirable bitter taste of beer. Both groups are very complex mixtures of different compounds. As this symposium is principally concerned with aroma, this chapter will be confined to recent work on hop oil. Several reviews published within the last few years cover work on the bitter resins (Hudson *et al.* 1962; Whitear and Hudson 1964; Clarke *et al.* 1964).

The knowledge of hop oil composition has been reviewed by Bullis and Likens (1962); Howard (1963); Lawrence (1964); and Hildebrand and Clarke (1965).

The application of gas-liquid chromatography (GLC) has contributed most to the identification of hop oil constituents. Early GLC studies of hop volatiles were carried out by Howard (1956, 1957); Howard and Slater (1957); and Howard and Stevens (1959A, B), and by Rigby (1956, 1958), and Rigby and Bethune (1957). These studies have been continued by Roberts (1962, 1963); Roberts and Stevens (1965); Jahnsen (1962), and Buttery *et al.* (1963A, B, 1964, 1965A, B).

Complexity of Hop Oil

Hop oil, as the brewing industry knows it, is usually obtained by a six-h steam distillation of hops in a standard apparatus. This apparatus recirculates condensed water back into the still so that there is a minimum of loss of water-soluble constituents (Wright and Connery 1951).

Figure 85 shows a capillary GLC analysis of hop oil from Bullion variety of hops grown in Oregon. As can be seen, it is a very complex mixture of compounds. We can consider hop oil as consisting of two main types of compounds, hydrocarbons, and compounds containing oxygen. The compounds present in largest concentration are terpenoid hydrocarbons. Peak 6 is myrcene, a C_{10} terpene hydrocarbon, and peaks 47 and 50 are caryophyllene and humulene, C_{15} sesquiterpene hydro-

406

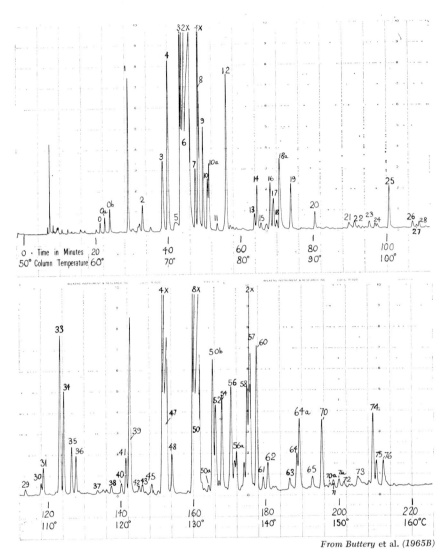

From *Buttery* et al. (1965B)

FIG. 85. TEMPERATURE-PROGRAMMED CAPILLARY COLUMN GAS CHROMATOGRAPHY
ANALYSIS OF "BULLION" HOP OIL

Column 150 ft. long by 0.01 in., internal diameter, coated with silicone SF 96 (100).

carbons. The hydrocarbon constituents can be readily separated from
the oxygenated constituents by selective adsorption on silica gel according
to the method of Kirchner and Miller (1952), which was first applied to
hop oil by Rigby and Bethune (1955) and Howard (1957). Table 70

TABLE 70

TABLE 70

HYDROCARBON AND OXYGENATED FRACTIONS IN HOP OILS FROM A NUMBER OF HOP VARIETIES

Type of Hop	Hydrocarbon Fraction, %	Oxygenated Fraction, %
California Cluster	63	33
Idaho Cluster	68	31
Fuggle	71	29
Bullion	78	18
Brewers Gold	76	19
Hallertau	78	17

shows the percentages of these fractions found in oils from different types of hops. The hydrocarbon fraction is usually 2 to 5 times the oxygenated fraction.

IDENTIFICATION OF HYDROCARBON CONSTITUENTS

Figure 86 shows capillary GLC analyses of the hydrocarbon fractions from several varieties of hops. Peaks 2 to 12 are C_{10} terpene hydrocarbons; peaks 40 to 62 are C_{15} sesquiterpene hydrocarbons. These are listed in Table 71. Humulene and caryophyllene are normally present in 5 to 10 times the concentration of any other sesquiterpene in most varieties. However, in some unusual varieties such as the English

TABLE 71

TERPENOID HYDROCARBONS OF HOPS

Peak	Identity	Usual Range of Concentration in Whole Oil of Different Varieties (%)
2	α-Pinene[1, 3]	0.04–0.2
4	β-Pinene[1, 3]	0.4–1.4
6	Myrcene[2]	20–70
10	Limonene[3]	0.04–0.3
12	Ocimene[3, 4]	0.04–1.1
40	. . .	0.04–0.1
41	Copaene (tentative)[5]	0.1–0.7
47	Caryophyllene[6]	8–13
50	Humulene[6]	13–50
50a	Farnesene[6]	0–17
52	. . .	0.4–1.5
54	β-Selinene[7]	0.3–2
56	α-Selinene (tentative)[3, 5]	0.3–2
58	γ-Cadinene[5]	0.4–1.5
60	δ-Cadinene[5]	0.7–1.7
61	Selinadiene (possibly -4(14), 7(11)-)[5]	0.06–1.6
62	Selinadiene (possibly -3,7(11)-)[5]	0.1–1.6

[1] Shigematsu and Kitazawa (1962).
[2] Chapman (1903).
[3] Buttery et al. (1963A, 1964).
[4] Howard and Slater (1957).
Buttery et al. (1965B).
Sorm et al. (1949).
[7] Stevens (1964).

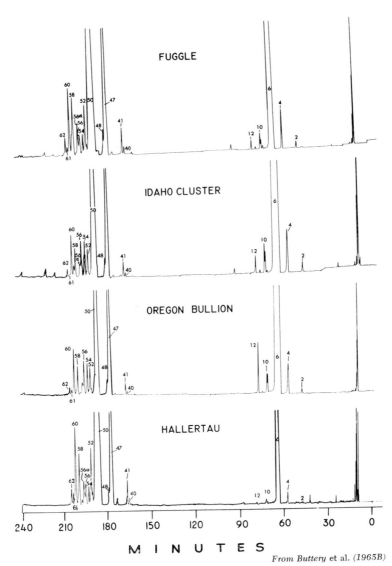

FUGGLE

IDAHO CLUSTER

OREGON BULLION

HALLERTAU

240   210   180   150   120   90   60   30   0

M I N U T E S

From Buttery et al. (1965B)

FIG. 86. TEMPERATURE-PROGRAMMED CAPILLARY COLUMN GAS CHROMATOGRAPHY OF THE HYDROCARBON FRACTIONS FROM DIFFERENT VARIETIES OF HOPS

Column 150 ft. long by 0.01 in., internal diameter, coated with silicone SF 96 (100).

OW-153 and the American OB-852, the selinenes predominate (Stevens 1964). In other unusual varieties such as Shinshuwasi the cadinenes appear to predominate (Shigematsu and Kitazawa 1962). In some European varieties such as Tettnang, Spalt, and Styrian, farnesene is about 10% of the oil but in most varieties it is less than 1%.

Despite the high concentration of the hydrocarbons in hop oil, except for myrcene they do not seem to be very important to aroma, especially in beer. The reasons for this are pointed out later in the chapter under the section on flavor and odor contribution of hop oil constituents.

IDENTIFICATION OF OXYGENATED CONSTITUENTS

Figure 87 shows a capillary GLC analysis of the oxygenated fraction of hop oil from Bullion variety hops. Over 87 different compounds can

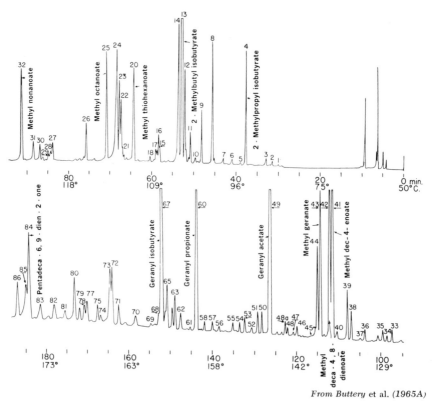

From *Buttery* et al. (1965A)

Fig. 87.   Temperature-Programmed Capillary Column Gas Chromatography Analysis of the Oxygenated Fraction of "Bullion" Variety Hop Oil

Column 192 ft. long by 0.01 in. I.D., coated with silicone SF 96 (50).

be detected. Many of these compounds are completely covered by the much larger hydrocarbon peaks in the analysis of the whole oil. The oxygenated constituents can be divided up into a number of groups based on their chemical similarities. The first and largest of these groups is the methyl esters. These are listed in Table 72. Major constituents are italicized. In the column on the left are listed methyl esters of a series of straight chain saturated acids. In the center column is a related series of methyl esters of unsaturated straight chain acids. The methyl esters of the unsaturated C_{10} acids were first detected in hop oil by Roberts (1962) and Jahnsen (1962) who suggested that they might be the isomeric methyl geranates. It was found later, however (Buttery et al. 1963B), that they were methyl esters of dec-4-enoic and deca-4,8-dienoic acids. Smaller amounts of methyl geranate also were later shown to be present by Roberts and Stevens (1965), and Buttery et al.

TABLE 72

ESTER CONSTITUENTS OF HOP OIL[1]

Of Straight Chain Acids		Of Branched Chain Acids
Methyl Esters		
Saturated	Unsaturated	Saturated, Unsaturated
Hexanoate	Octenoate[6]	and Terpenoid
Heptanoate	Nonenoate[6]	*4-Methylhex-2-enoate*
Octanoate	*Dec-4-enoate*	5-Methylhexanoate
Nonanoate[2]	*Deca-4,8-dienoate*	Methylheptanoate[6]
Decanoate[2]	Undecenoate[6]	*Methyloctanoate*[6]
Undecanoate	Undecadienoate[6]	Methylnonanoate[6]
Dodecanoate	*Dodec-8-enoate*[6]	*Geranate*[3]
	Dodecadienoate[6]	*Methyldecanoate*[6]
	Tridecenoate[6]	
Isobutyrates, 2-Methylbutyrates and 3-Methylbutyrates		
Isobutyrates	2-Methylbutyrates	3-Methylbutyrates
2-Methylpropyl	*2-Methylpropyl*	*2-Methylbutyl*
Butyl	*2-Methylbutyl*	
Pentyl		
2-Methylbutyl[4]		
3-Methylbutyl		
Hexyl		
Heptyl		
Geranyl[5]		
Neryl		
Acetates and Propionates		
Acetates	Propionates	
Octyl	*2-Methylbutyl*[5]	
Geranyl	*Hexyl*	
Neryl	Heptyl	
	Geranyl	
	Neryl	

[1] Buttery et al. (1965A).
[2] Roberts (1962).
[3] Roberts and Stevens (1965).
[4] Howard and Stevens (1959B).
[5] Shigematsu and Kitazawa (1962).
[6] Exact identity tentative.

(1965A). The amount of methyl geranate varies considerably with different hop varieties; it is almost absent in oil from Washington state grown, Cluster variety (0.1%) but as much as one per cent is found in Oregon Brewers Gold variety.

Nickerson and Likens (1966) have shown that the methyl esters of the C_{10} unsaturated acids are converted into ethyl esters by the fermentation during the processing of beer. This probably also is true of the other hop oil methyl esters.

A second group of compounds in hop oil which are related to the methyl esters are the methyl thioesters (Buttery et al. 1965A). They have the general formula ($CH_3-S-\overset{\overset{\displaystyle O}{\|}}{C}-R$). A number of these esters have been detected in hop oil, but only methyl thiohexanoate and methyl thioheptanoate have been identified with any certainty. The two thioesters occur only at small concentrations in the oil, usually about 0.1%, but they are important to hop oil aroma because they have potent odors. It is not certain whether these compounds occur in hops as they are picked from the vine, or whether they form in the normal treatment of the hops with SO_2 (sulfuring) during drying.

A third group of esters occurring in hop oil is shown in Table 72. These are esters of the branched chain acids, isobutyric, 2-methylbutyric, and 3-methylbutyric. 2-Methylbutyl isobutyrate was first shown to occur in hop oil by Howard and Stevens (1959B). It is the main oxygenated constituent in most American hop varieties and occurs at a concentration of about two per cent in hop oil from California Cluster hops. However, it can be almost completely absent from some European varieties. Hop oil from the European variety, Tettnang, contains only 0.02%.

A fourth group of esters, acetates and propionates, is also shown in Table 72. Geranyl acetate is the only acetate that occurs in any appreciable amount in hop oil and it only occurs in more than trace concentration (>0.1%) in the oil from two varieties of hops, Bullion and Brewers Gold, where it can be as much as one per cent.

Methyl Ketones

This is a fifth group of oxygenated compounds which occur in hop oil. Only methyl ketones have been found up to this time. These are shown in Table 73. There is some analogy between the methyl ketones and the methyl esters.

2-Undecanone has been known to occur in hop oil for some time. It was first detected with some certainty by Sorm et al. (1949). 2-Undec-

TABLE 73

METHYL KETONES OF HOP OIL[1]

Straight Chain Saturated	Straight Chain Unsaturated	Branched Chain Saturated
Nonan-2-one	Tetradeca-9-en-2-one[5]	3-Methylbutan-2-one[2]
Decan-2-one	Pentadeca-12-en-2-one[5]	4-Methylpentan-2-one[2]
Undecan-2-one[3]	Pentadeca-6,9-dien-2-one	Methyldecan-2-one[5]
Tridecan-2-one[4]	Pentadeca-6,9,13-trien-2-one[5]	Methylundecan-2-one[5]
Tetradecan-2-one		Methyldodecan-2-one[5]
Pentadecan-2-one		Methyltridecan-2-one[5]

[1] Buttery et al. (1965A).
[2] Shigematsu and Kitazawa (1962).
[3] Sorm et al. (1949).
[4] Roberts (1963).
[5] Exact identity tentative.

anone and other saturated ketones usually occur at a considerably higher concentration in oil from European hop varieties than in oil from American varieties.

Pentadeca-6,9-dien-2-one seems common to all varieties at about the 0.5 to 1% level except in Brewers Gold, where it is usually only about 0.1%.

It might be useful to take this compound as an example and describe its identification. Mass spectrometry indicated a C_{15} ketone with two double bonds and the empirical formula $C_{15}H_{26}O$. Infrared absorption spectrometry (I.R.) confirmed that the compound was a ketone (absorption maximum at 1720 cm.$^{-1}$) with cis-double bonds (no absorption at 965 cm.$^{-1}$). Proton magnetic resonance spectra (PMR) showed particularly that the two double bonds were separated by only one CH_2 group and confirmed that the compound was a straight chain, di-unsaturated methyl ketone. The evidence up to this point showed that the compound had the structure $CH_3CH_2 \ldots -CH=CH-CH_2-CH=CH- \ldots CH_2-COCH_3$ with five other $-CH_2-$ groups. Ozonolysis and reduction of the ozonide gave hexanal, which showed that one double bond was six carbon atoms from the saturated end. This fixed the position of the double bonds and showed that our structure was $CH_3(CH_2)_4CH=CH-CH_2-CH=CH-(CH_2)_3COCH_3$ with both double bonds cis.

Oxygenated Terpenoids and Sesquiterpenoids

This is a sixth group of compounds which occur in the oxygenated fraction of hop oil. It is made up primarily of terpene alcohols, sesquiterpene epoxides, and sesquiterpene alcohols. Only two free terpene alcohols have been detected in hop oil. These are linalool (Chapman 1903) and α-terpineol (Buttery et al. 1964).

Both humulene and caryophyllene form epoxides on exposure to air. Roberts (1963) detected both humulene and caryophyllene epoxides in hop oil from their GLC retention properties. These epoxides might be formed from humulene and caryophyllene while the hops are still on the vine. Freshly distilled hop oil, however, usually contains only very small quantities of these epoxides. They are usually associated with hop oil samples that have been stored for some time under air. Isolation of the GLC peaks that occur at the retention times of humulene and caryophyllene epoxides in freshly distilled oil has shown that the peaks are composed of a mixture of different compounds of which the epoxides are only a minor part. However, isolation from old samples of hop oil has given humulene epoxide with an infrared spectrum identical with that of authentic humulene epoxide prepared according to Ramaswami and Bhattacharyya (1962).

Capillary GLC combined with mass spectrometry has indicated the presence of 11 oxygenated sesquiterpenes in hop oil (Buttery *et al.* 1963A). Most of these appeared to be alcohols. They only occur in relatively small amounts and none has been identified with any degree of certainty. Humulene epoxide and other epoxides can be converted to alcohols under relatively mild conditions (Damodaran and Dev 1963) and at least some of the hop oil sesquiterpene alcohols may be formed in this way.

Chapman (1928) isolated an alcohol from hop oil which he showed to have the formula $C_{15}H_{24}O$ with only one double bond. He called this alcohol "luparenol." We (Buttery *et al.* 1964) also isolated a similar alcohol. Its PMR analysis indicates that it has one double bond of the type $>C=C\overset{\diagup CH_3}{\diagdown}$ and three tertiary methyl groups, probably all near the —OH. This would have to be a sesquiterpenoid with three rings. It is unlikely that this compound is formed from rearrangement of an epoxide because there is only one tricyclic sesquiterpene in hop oil, copaene, and it occurs at only a small concentration. An alcohol derived from copaene epoxide would not fit the I.R. and PMR information.

FLAVOR AND ODOR CONTRIBUTION OF THE HOP OIL CONSTITUENTS

Howard and Stevens (1959A) and Rigby (1958) carried out some studies on the odor and flavor strengths of hop oil components. These authors found that the oxygenated fraction was several-fold more potent than the hydrocarbon fraction. Guadagni *et al.* (1966) have extended this earlier work to a study of the odor thresholds of 25 of the main chemical components of hop oil. They have drawn some interesting conclusions by applying the apparent additive property of odor intensities (Guadagni *et al.* 1963). These additive odor intensity calculations are based on the olfactory threshold and the concentration of each particular hop constituent. With oil of Bullion variety hops in dilute water solution, it was found that myrcene accounted for 58% of the total odor intensity. Methyl thiohexanoate, the next most important constituent, accounted for 4.8% of the total. Methyl dec-4-enoate accounted for 3.0%, caryophyllene for 1.6%, humulene for 1.5%, 2-methylbutyl isobutyrate for 1.2%, geranyl acetate for 1%, and all others studied for less than 1% each. Only 20 main oxygenated constituents were studied out of a total of about 87. The sum of the odor intensities of these 20 compounds was approximately one-half of the total odor intensity of the oxygenated fraction. It is quite possible that the other 67 constituents could have only moderate odor thresholds but collectively add up to give half of the total odor intensity of the oxygenated fraction. Although certain oxygenated constituents have high odor intensities, it seems that the combination of many compounds is necessary for the characteristic hop aroma.

The study of Guadagni *et al.* (1966) considered only solutions of hop oil in water. When we come to consider hop oil constituents as they affect beer flavor and aroma we usually have quite a different set of circumstances. Some brewers actually add hop oil to the finished beer. In this case we have the same proportion of constituents in the beer that occurs in hop oil and the odor intensities may follow those found for hop oil in water. However in most beers, hop oil is not added as such but is extracted from the hops into the aqueous mixture called "wort" when the hops are boiled with it in the normal processing of beer. In this case we have at least three phases: (1) the vapor which is continually being removed, (2) the aqueous wort, which is mostly water, and (3) the hops, which contain water-insoluble fat and wax. The volatile constituents least soluble in water would tend to be more readily lost by steam distillation or more readily remain in the fat and wax of the hops, and would not be concentrated in the water phase. Conversely, the more water-soluble a constituent, the more it would tend to favor the water phase over the vapor or hop phases. The oxygenated constituents, being more water-soluble, would be expected to get into the water phase much more efficiently than the hydrocarbons.

Analysis of the wort after it has been boiled with hops has shown that this does seem to take place. Likens and Nickerson (1964) have shown the wort after boiling with hops actually contains a higher concentration of the oxygenated constituents methyl dec-4-enoate and methyl deca-4,8-dienoate, than the hydrocarbons humulene and caryophyllene, even though the hydrocarbons occur in the oil at a concentration ten times that of the esters. Recent work by the author has confirmed this. Likens

(1962) has also shown that the spent hops after boiling with the wort still contain more than 50% of their original caryophyllene and humulene.

Most U.S. brewers filter or centrifuge the hopped wort very efficiently after the boiling. In some brewing processes, where possibly a greater hop character is desired, the hopped wort may not be filtered as efficiently, and some sesquiterpene hydrocarbons may be carried over in the form of a suspension or emulsion in hop fat and wax globules. This carry-over could lead to a higher concentration of hydrocarbons in the final beer. Harold *et al.* (1961) detected much higher concentrations of hop sesquiterpene hydrocarbons in an Australian beer than Likens and Nickerson (1964) could find in American beers.

It seems very likely from the work of Nordström (1964) that many of the hop constituents that get into the wort would be chemically modified by the enzyme systems present during fermentation. One of the most likely changes is replacement of the alcohol parts of the hop oil esters with ethanol, as was shown to be the case with methyl dec-4-enoate and methyl deca-4,8-dienoate (Nickerson and Likens 1966). A second expected change is the formation of acetate esters from the hop esters and the free hop alcohols such as linalool, α-terpineol, and the sesquiterpene alcohols.

In summary, we can say that a considerable amount is known about the volatile flavor constituents of hops. However, it appears from recent work that many of the major flavor constituents in the steam volatile oil of hops are not the ones important in the hop flavor imparted to beer. Future work on this subject will probably concentrate on those volatile hop constituents which have the greatest affinity for water and which therefore are most efficiently extracted from the hops into the wort in the processing of beer.

DISCUSSION

D. A. Kendall.—Were the odor thresholds on the hop oil constituents done on chromatographically purified materials, particularly the myrcene?

R. G. Buttery.—Yes, they were purified by gas chromatography and the myrcene was purified by separation on two different columns of different polarities.

D. A. Kendall.—Have you determined the thresholds in beer? In our experience it is substantially different than the thresholds in water. It would be interesting to compare the relative thresholds in beer of the compounds you identified from hop oil and see if you come out with the same contribution factor. Do you have any estimate of the per cent of hop oil recovered or collected in the wort? In other words, you have 1.2% hop oil from the hops themselves, how much of this total oil is retained in the wort which is not just a water solution, but is a 10% sugar solution?

R. G. Buttery.—Sam Likens has calculated this; I think it is about 20%.

D. A. Forss.—Were all of the double bonds cis in the unsaturated esters?

R. G. Buttery.—All the unsaturated esters we have found have been cis. This is also true with ketones, except for the one with three double bonds in which it has at least one trans.

D. A. Forss.—Would you care to expand on your methods for determining the contribution of myrcene and the other components in the odor threshold determination. In other words, did you consider the possibilities of interactions?

R. G. Buttery.—No, we were looking at it on a purely quantitative basis. We found that most of the compounds have additive properties as far as odor is concerned. We would take ten compounds, each at one-tenth of the threshold, and obtain a positive threshold value for that mixture.

BIBLIOGRAPHY

BULLIS, D. E., and LIKENS, S. T. 1962. Hop oil past and present. Brewers Digest, April 1962, 54–59.

BUTTERY, R. G., BLACK, D. R., and KEALY, M. P. 1965A. Volatile oxygenated constituents of hops. Identification by combined gas chromatography and mass spectrometry. J. Chromatog. *18*, 399–402.

BUTTERY, R. G., BLACK, D. R., and LING, L. 1965B. Unpublished work.

BUTTERY, R. G., LUNDIN, R. E., McFADDEN, W. H., JAHNSEN, V. J., and KEALY, M. P. 1963B. Volatile hop constituents: Identification of methyl dec-4-enoate and methyl deca-4,8-dienoate. Chem. and Ind. *51*, 1981–1982.

BUTTERY, R. G., McFADDEN, W. H., LUNDIN, R. E., and KEALY, M. P. 1964. Volatile hop constituents: Conventional and capillary gas-chromatographic separation with characterization by physical methods. J. Inst. Brewing *70*, 396–401.

BUTTERY, R. G., McFADDEN, W. H., TERANISHI, R., KEALY, M. P., and MON, T. R. 1963A. Constituents of hop oil. Nature *200*, 435–436.

CHAPMAN, A. C. 1903. The essential oil of hops. J. Chem. Soc. Trans. *67*, 505–518.

CHAPMAN, A. C. 1928. The higher-boiling constituents of the essential oil of hops. J. Chem. Soc. (London), 1303.

CLARKE, B. J., GARRICK, C. C., HAROLD, F. V., HILDEBRAND, R. P., MORIESON, A. S., and MURRAY, P. J. 1964. Hop extract—a new approach. Mast. Brewers Assoc. Am., Tech. Proc. Oct., 1–29.

DAMODARAN, N. P., and DEV, S. 1963. Some new humulene-based sesquiterpenoids. Tetrahedron Letters, No. 28, 1941–1948.

GUADAGNI, D. G., BUTTERY, R. G., and HARRIS, J. 1966. Odour intensities of hop oil components. J. Sci. Food Agr. *17*, 142–144.

GUADAGNI, D. G., BUTTERY, R. G., OKANO, S., and BURR, H. K. 1963. Additive effect of subthreshold concentrations of some organic compounds associated with food aromas. Nature *200*, 1288–1289.

HAROLD, F. V., HILDEBRAND, R. P., MORIESON, A. S., and MURRAY, P. J. 1961. Trace volatile constituents of beer. Part I. J. Inst. Brewing *67*, 160–172.

HILDEBRAND, R. P., and CLARKE, B. J. 1965. Hops and the brewing process. Brewers Digest, June, 58–67.

HOWARD, G. A. 1956. New approach to the analysis of hop oil. J. Inst. Brewing *62*, 158–159.

HOWARD, G. A. 1957. Evaluation of hops. V. The essential oil of hops. J. Inst. Brewing *63*, 126–138.

HOWARD, G. A. 1963. The composition and brewing value of hop oil. Brewers Digest, Sept., 50–53.

HOWARD, G. A., and SLATER, C. A. 1957. Evaluation of hops. VII. Composition of the essential oil of hops. J. Inst. Brewing 63, 491.

HOWARD, G. A., and STEVENS, R. 1959A. Evaluation of hops. IX. Flavour of hop oil constituents. J. Inst. Brewing 65, 494–496.

HOWARD, G. A., and STEVENS, R. 1959B. The occurrence of 2-methylbutyl esters in hop oil. Chem. and Ind., 1518–1519.

HUDSON, J. R., STEVENS, R., and WHITEAR, A. L. 1962. Hop resins and beer flavor. J. Inst. Brewing 68, 431–437.

JAHNSEN, V. J. 1962. Complexity of hop oil. Nature 196, 474–475.

KIRCHNER, J. G., and MILLER, J. M. 1952. Preparation of terpeneless essential oils. Ind. Eng. Chem. 44, 318–321.

LAWRENCE, W. C. 1964. Volatile compounds affecting beer flavor. Wallerstein Lab. Comm. 27, 123–153.

LIKENS, S. T. 1962. Development and fate of hop oils. Mast. Brewers Assoc. Am., Tech. Proc. Oct., 10–16.

LIKENS, S. T., and NICKERSON, G. B. 1964. Detection of certain hop oil constituents in brewing products. Am. Soc. Brewing Chem. Proc., 5–13.

NICKERSON, G. B., and LIKENS, S. T. 1966. Evidence for the occurrence of hop oil components in beer. J. Chromatog. 21, 1–5.

NORDSTRÖM, K. 1964. Formation of ethyl acetate in fermentation with Brewers yeast. J. Inst. Brewing 70, 209–221.

RAMASWAMI, S. K., and BHATTACHARYYA, S. C. 1962. Terpenoids. XXXI. Isolation of humulene monoxide and humulene dioxide. Tetrahedron 18, 575–579.

RIGBY, F. L. 1956. The estimation of the brewing value of hops by chemical analyses. Proc. Amer. Soc. Brewing Chem. 156–164.

RIGBY, F. L. 1958. Chemical analysis of hops. Brewers Digest, October, 50–56.

RIGBY, F. L., and BETHUNE, J. L. 1955. Separation of the aromatic constituents of hops. Proc. Amer. Soc. Brewing Chem. 174–183.

RIGBY, F. L., and BETHUNE, J. L. 1957. Analysis of hop oil by gas-liquid partition chromatography. J. Inst. Brewing 63, 154–161.

ROBERTS, J. B. 1962. Hop oil. I. Preliminary investigations of the oxygenated fraction. J. Inst. Brewing 68, 197–200.

ROBERTS, J. B. 1963. Hop oil. II. The major constituents of the non-saponifiable fraction. J. Inst. Brewing 69, 343–346.

ROBERTS, J. B., and STEVENS, R. 1965. Hop oil. III. Characterization of esters. J. Inst. Brewing 71, 45.

SHIGEMATSU, N., and KITAZAWA, Y. 1962. On the composition of the oil of hops. Bull. Brewing Sci. (Japan) 8, 23–33.

SORM, F., MLEZIVA, J., ARNOLD, Z., and PLIVA, J. 1949. Sesquiterpenes from the essential oil of hops. Collection Czech. Chem. Commun. 14, 699–715.

STEVENS, R. 1964. Chemistry of hop constituents. Part XIX. The essential oil of the variety OW-153. J. Chem. Soc. (London), 956–958.

WHITEAR, A. L., and HUDSON, J. R. 1964. Hop resins and beer flavor. III. Hop resins in beer. J. Inst. Brewing 70, 24–30.

WRIGHT, R. G., and CONNERY, F. E. 1951. Studies of hop quality. Am. Soc. Brewing Chem. Proc., 87–101.

CHAPTER 19

Walter G. Jennings | Peaches and Pears

To the consumer, flavor is the composite sensation perceived when a food placed in the mouth stimulates the olfactory receptors as well as the taste, tactile, kinesthetic, and thermal receptors in the oral cavity. Technically we define flavor as a combination of taste and odor stimuli (Amerine *et al.* 1965). Since taste contributes only qualities of sweetness, sourness, saltiness, and bitterness, it is obvious that the characteristic differentiating flavors of foods are attributable primarily to volatile constituents. This is particularly true for fruits with pronounced characteristic bouquet and aroma, and this discussion of the flavor of peaches and pears will be specifically directed to their volatile constituents.

Several workers (e.g., Wick 1965) have pointed out that not all volatiles contribute to flavor, and the contribution of any one volatile may be entirely out of proportion to its concentration in the mixture. A gas chromatogram of an essence constitutes at best a graph of the individual volatiles, whose relationship to flavor remains to be established.

Early investigators studying flavor components were seriously handicapped because the methodology then available was not readily adaptable to the isolation and identification of the extremely small amounts of volatile compounds with which they had to deal. Harley and Fisher (1927) were able to demonstrate the presence of acetaldehyde among pear volatiles, and Tindale *et al.* (1938) followed the alcohol and acetaldehyde content of Bartlett pear during ripening. They observed a continuous increase in the alcohol content, and reported that acetaldehyde increased during cold storage and subsequent ripening, and reached a maximum at the onset of core breakdown. Antoniani *et al.* (1954), Antoniani and Serini (1955), and Serini (1956) conducted maturity studies on both pears and apples, and reported that the amounts and ratios of 2,3-butylene glycol and acetoin varied during the ripening process. Gerhardt (1954) studied the rates of emanation of volatile reducing compounds from pears and apples, and Luh *et al.* (1955) conducted a similar study on pears. The latter authors reported that as pears ripened at 20°C., methyl alcohol, total carbonyl compounds, acetyl methyl carbinol, diacetyl, and ester content gradually increased. Formic and acetic acids were identified by paper chromatographic studies of the volatile acids of several pear varieties, not including the Bartlett, by Mehlitz and Matzik (1956).

Jennings *et al.* (1960) separated essences obtained from fresh, ripe Bartlett pears into 32 fractions by gas chromatography. Each of the fractions was submitted to a trained aroma panel, and five of the fractions appeared to contribute to the desirable pear aroma, while four were classed as atypical and undesirable. Drawert (1962) on the basis of matching gas chromatographic retentions, tentatively identified ethyl formate, methyl acetate, ethyl acetate, ethanol, isopropanol, 2-butanol, 2-methyl propanol, *n*-butanol, pentanol, 3-methyl butanol, *n*-hexanol, and another ester in pears. In studies of the lower boiling volatiles from Bartlett pears, Lim (1963) utilized matching retentions on gas chromatography and tentatively identified ethylene, acetaldehyde, and the six normal acetates from methyl to hexyl acetate. Jennings (1961), Jennings (1965), and Jennings and Creveling (1963) established that the typical aroma of Bartlett pears was due to esters and studied the hydrolysis products of pear essence by gas chromatographic separations and infrared and ultraviolet spectroscopy of the individual fractions. They reported these consisted of acetic, propionic, butyric, caproic, caprylic, nonanoic, and 2,4-decadienoic acids, and ethyl, *n*-propyl, *n*-butyl, *n*-amyl, and *n*-hexyl alcohols. Jennings and Sevenants (1964A) were able to chromatograph and recover Bartlett pear essence without losing the desirable aroma characteristics. By infrared spectroscopy, they identified hexyl acetate as a "contributory flavor compound," and methyl *trans*:2-*cis*:4 decadienoate as a "character impact compound" of Bartlett pear. Heinz *et al.* (1964) and Jennings (1965) established that the level of decadienoate esters, as estimated by ultraviolet spectroscopy, correlated well with sensory evaluations of pear essence.

By comparison, the characterization of peach volatiles has received very little attention. Power and Chesnut (1921) reported that the hydrolysis products of peach essence included methyl alcohol, linalool, furfural, acetaldehyde, and formic, acetic, valeric, and caprylic acids. Traces of a higher aldehyde were found, and they concluded that neither hydrogen cyanide nor benzaldehyde was present in peach pulp. They surmised that the methyl alcohol could have been produced by pectin hydrolysis. From their findings, they postulated that the odorous constituents of peaches were primarily linalyl esters of formic, acetic, valeric, and caprylic acids. Daghetta *et al.* (1956) studied volatiles of the Hale peach, and reported that these included ethyl alcohol, acetic acid, acetaldehyde, and ethyl acetate. Lim (1963) reported the Red Globe peach to be the richest source of volatiles, and on the basis of matching gas chromatographic retentions postulated that these included ethylene, acetaldehyde, ethyl alcohol, and ethyl and hexyl acetate. Jennings and Sevenants (1964B), using gas chromatography and infrared spectroscopy, established the presence of benzaldehyde, benzyl alcohol, γ-caprolactone, γ-octalactone, γ-decalactone, and δ-decalactone in freestone peaches.

While the advent of gas chromatography has given the flavor chemist a powerful tool, the technique has been abused, and the results are not infrequently over-interpreted. Gas chromatography is really nothing more than a method for achieving separation of a volatile mixture into individual fractions. Experience indicates that it is the exception rather than the rule when a single chromatographic separation of a complex natural mixture results in fractions composed of single molecular species. Experienced investigators are loathe to depend on retention data as the sole criterion for identification. Dissimilar retentions can establish that two compounds are not identical, but similar retentions indicate only that a difference between two compounds has not yet been demonstrated. For definitive characterization studies, it is highly desirable to collect and rechromatograph on several dissimilar substrates each individual chromatographic fraction, before finally subjecting these individual components to mass, infrared, or N.M.R. spectrometry. Because the amount of an individual fraction may be 0.1 µl. or less, this demands rather special techniques of collecting and re-injecting. Those developed by Sevenants (1965) appear most promising.

A major problem in investigations of this type is the preparation of an essence material suitable for gas chromatographic separations. Concentrated extracts of steam distillates are frequently satisfactory. Our studies have utilized a deaerator effluent from a large commercial cannery that processes fresh fruit to purées. A large scale continuous liquid-liquid extractor (Fig. 88, from Heinz 1965) has been used with both pears and peaches, and charcoal adsorption of the volatiles directly from the deaerator effluent has proved most successful with pears (Fig. 88). In this latter case, the activated charcoal is immersed in the flowing effluent from the vacuum deaerator for a period of time, drained, freeze-dried, and the adsorbed volatiles recovered in a Soxhlet extractor. Although minor differences have been observed between the adsorption essence and the extraction essence, these do not include massive rearrangements as might be expected. Both types of essence possess the desirable aroma, and their chromatograms are almost identical.

Ten per cent Triton X-305 on Gas Chrom Q, 10% Carbowax 20M on Gas Pack F, or 20% Apiezon L on Chromosorb W have proved most satisfactory for separating the volatiles comprising pear essence, but none of these completely resolve this complex mixture. Fig. 89 shows a typical chromatogram of pear essence on Triton X-305. When these individual fractions are collected and rechromatographed on one of the other substrates, most of these fractions turn out to be composed

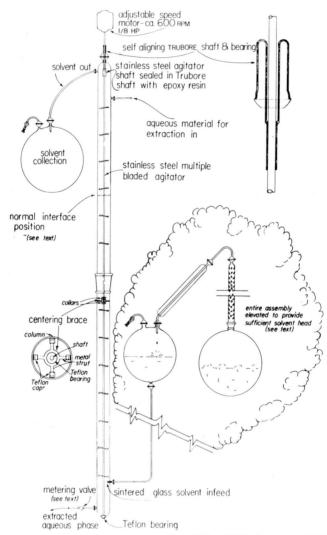

adjustable speed
motor- ca. 600 RPM
1/8 HP

self aligning TRUBORE shaft & bearing

solvent out

stainless steel agitator
shaft sealed in Trubore
shaft with epoxy resin

aqueous material for
extraction in

solvent
collection

stainless steel multiple
bladed agitator

normal interface
position
"(see text)

collars

centering brace

column

shaft

metal
strut

Teflon
bearing

Teflon
cap

entire assembly
elevated to provide
sufficient solvent head
(see text)

metering valve
(see text)

sintered glass solvent infeed

extracted
aqueous phase

Teflon bearing

From Heinz (1965); Sevenants (1965)

FIG. 88.   CONTINUOUS LIQUID-LIQUID EXTRACTOR

The unit is designed to reuse the extracting solvent, and at a
throughput of 40 liters of aqueous essence per hour achieves an
extraction efficiency of ca. 90%, as estimated by ultraviolet
measurements of the decadienoate moiety.

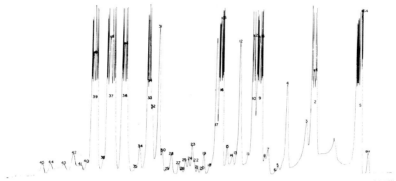

From Heinz (1965)

FIG. 89.   CHROMATOGRAM OF BARTLETT PEAR ADSORPTION ESSENCE

10% Triton X-305 on Gas Pack F, temperature programmed.

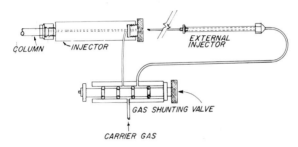

FIG. 90.   DIAGRAM OF EXTERNAL INJECTOR

By inserting the glass capillary collecting tube(s) directly into
the external injector, essentially complete reinjection is achieved
with no loss due to syringe hold-up. The unit is also adaptable
to micro-hydrogenation.

of at least two, and occasionally as many as six components. To handle
the vanishingly small samples that result from the repeated refractiona-
tion, special techniques of injection, collection, and infrared analysis have
been required (Jennings 1965; Sevenants 1965). Collections are accomplished in thin-walled glass capillaries, and reinjection is achieved by
inserting the capillary in an external injector (Fig. 90) inserted through
the regular injector. The external injector is heated, and the carrier gas
shunted from its normal path through the external injector. Essentially
complete recoveries and reinjections have been achieved with this
technique. The external injector can also be packed with a catalyst-
impregnated bed to achieve very efficient microhydrogenation.

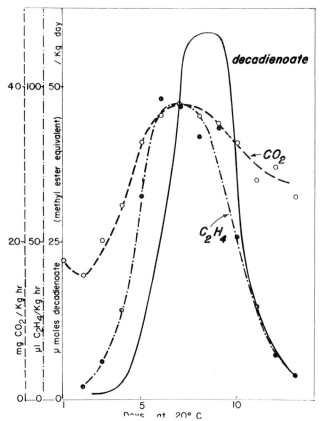

From Heinz et al. (1965) and reproduced by permission of the Institute of
Food Technologists

Fig. 91. Production of Ethylene, Carbon Dioxide, and
Decadienoate Esters in the Ripening Bartlett Pear

The ester curve represents a first derivative of ester production
making it comparable to the ethylene and carbon dioxide curves,
i.e. a daily incremental production.

Components of Bartlett pear essence so far identified are listed in Table
74. The inter-relationship among many of these compounds is immediately evident, and at least three are artifacts. The 4-oxy *trans*
butenoate esters, as an example, result from hydrolytic cleavage of the
cis bonds of the *trans*:2-*cis*:4-decadienoate esters. Similarly, the hexanal
is produced by this same cleavage. This occurs only in the isolated
essence, and requires light and oxygen. Even this essence, however, still
possessed a typical desirable aroma. The decadienoate esters are of
particular interest, because these have been shown to be important to the

TABLE 74

VOLATILE COMPONENTS OF BARTLETT PEAR

Methyl acetate[1]

Ethyl acetate[1, 2]

Ethanol[1]

Propyl acetate[1]

Propanol[1]

Butyl acetate[1, 2]

Hexanol[1, 6]

Butanol[1, 2]

Amyl acetate[1, 2]

Pentanol[1, 2]

Hexyl acetate[1, 2]

Hexanol[1, 2]

Cis-hexenyl acetate[2]

Heptyl acetate[1, 2]

Methyl octanoate[1]

Methyl 4-oxy trans butenoate[2, 4, 5, 6]

n-Heptanol[1]

Ethyl octanoate[1, 2]

Ethyl 4-oxy trans butenoate[2, 4, 6]

Octyl acetate[1, 2]

Methyl trans: 2-octenoate[2]

n-octanol[1, 2]

Ethyl trans: 2-octenoate[1, 2]

Methyl decanoate[1, 2]

Methyl cis: 4-decenoate[1, 2, 6, 7]

Ethyl decanoate[1, 2]

Ethyl cis: 4-decenoate[2, 3, 6]

Methyl trans: 2-cis: 4-decadienoate[1, 2, 4]

Methyl 3-hydroxy octanoate[2, 3, 6]

Ethyl trans: 2-decenoate[1, 2]

Sesquiterpene, triunsaturated with moieties

Methyl cis: 2-trans: 4-decadienoate[2, 7]

Methyl trans: 2-trans: 4-decadienoate[2, 7]

Ethyl trans: 2-cis: 4-decadienoate[1, 2, 4, 7]

Ethyl 3-hydroxy octanoate[2, 3]

Ethyl dodecanoate[1]

Ethyl cis: 6-dodecenoate

Ethyl trans: 2-trans: 4-decadienoate[2, 7]

Propyl trans: 2-trans: 4-decadienoate[2, 7]

Ethyl trans: 2-dodecenoate[1, 2]

Ethyl trans: 2-cis: 6-dodecadienoate[1, 2]

Butyl trans: 2-cis: 4-decadienoate[2, 7]

Methyl cis: 8-tetradecenoate[2]

Ethyl tetradecenoate[1]

Ethyl cis: 8-tetradecenoate[2]

[1] Retention data.
[2] Infrared spectral data.
[3] Mass spectral data.
[4] Ultraviolet spectral data.
[5] Melting points.
[6] Derivatives.
[7] Synthesis.

TABLE 75

VOLATILE COMPONENTS OF RED GLOBE PEACHES

Acetaldehyde[1]

Methyl acetate[1]

Ethyl acetate[1]

Ethyl alcohol

Hexyl formate[2]

Hexyl acetate[2]

Trans-2-hexenyl acetate[2, 4, 5]

Hexyl alcohol[2]

Acetic acid[2]

Trans-2-hexene-1-ol[2, 5]

Benzaldehyde[2]

Iso-valeric acid[2]

Ethyl benzoate[2]

Gamma-caprolactone[2]

Benzyl acetate[2]

Gamma-heptalactone[2]

Caproic acid[2]

Benzyl alcohol[2]

Gamma-octalactone[2]

Gamma-nonalactone[2]

Hexyl benzoate[2]

Gamma decalactone[2]

Alpha-pyrone[2,3,4]

Delta-decalactone[2]

[1] Retention data.
[2] Infrared spectral data.
[3] Mass spectral data.
[4] Derivative.
[5] Synthesis.

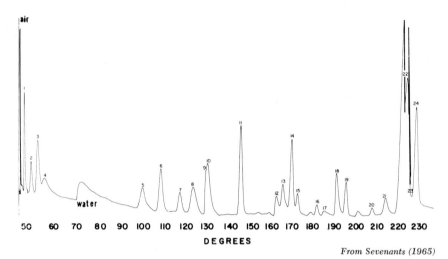

From Sevenants (1965)

FIG. 92.   CHROMATOGRAM OF PEACH ESSENCE

10% Carbowax 20 *M* on Gas Pack F, programmed as indicated.   The essence was extracted from commercial deaerator effluent, and is quite comparable to essences obtained by extracting laboratory steam distillates.

typical aroma of Bartlett pear (Heinz *et al.* 1964).   Because of their triconjugate system, these possess high extinction coefficients and their concentration can be readily estimated by ultraviolet spectroscopy. Fig. 91 illustrates that their production is closely related to the maturation of the fruit, and that the incremental increase of these esters achieves a maximum shortly after the climacteric point, when the fruit possesses optimum flavor.

Fig. 92 shows a typical chromatogram of a freestone peach essence on 10% Carbowax 20M on Gas Pack F.   Again, most of these fractions consist of more than one component, and each individual fraction was collected and refractionated several times on dissimilar columns.   Table 75 lists the compounds so far identified in peach essence.

None of these compounds, as they emerge from a chromatograph, possess aromas that could be described as peach-like.   A synthetic mixture containing all these volatiles does have an aroma which, while criticized as synthetic, does resemble peaches.   When the amounts of isovaleric acid were increased to concentrations somewhat greater than those found in the chromatograms, the peach-like character was enhanced.   The flavor panel could easily distinguish this essence from a fresh peach aroma, but found it definitely superior to those commercial synthetic essences available for comparison.   These results indicate that none of these compounds, individually, are responsible for the typical peach aroma, that peach aroma is due to an integrated response to a whole series of compounds, and that the relative concentrations of individual components may be quite important to this aroma.

Tables 74 and 75 show that both pears and peaches contain a number of low-molecular weight volatiles that are widely and indiscriminately distributed among most fruits. Some of their constituents, however, would appear to be unique to the fruit investigated, e.g., the decadienoates to pear, and the lactones and pyrone to peach.

Due to the continuing efforts of a large number of investigators, we now know that in the process of maturation fruits produce an abundance of compounds, many of which are probably related to flavor. It is vaguely disturbing that relatively few of these compounds (e.g., acetic, propionic, and higher fatty acids) occupy positions in recognized biochemical pathways, and that the majority are frequently assumed to have no biochemical significance. It is entirely possible that these compounds do play a role in the biology and physiology of the fruit, and some efforts to ascertain the origin and purpose of volatile aroma compounds in fruit would appear to be long overdue. Certain constituents, such as hormones, auxins, or pigments, may be degraded as the fruit attains maturity, halting processes such as cell expansion, elongation, or photosynthesis. The resulting fragments may contribute to our spectrum of volatile compounds. Or some of these volatile compounds may be produced to serve certain specific functions, such as growth regulation, color formation, softening, or some other manifestation of the ripening process. Ethylene has been studied at great length, and its effect on many fruits is well known, but its origin and purpose remain to be elucidated. The decadienoates, important to pear flavor and produced only in the ripening fruit (Heinz et al. 1965), bear a close structural relationship to sorbic acid and have been shown to act as powerful fungistatic agents (Moustafa 1965); there are indications that they are closely related to certain plant auxins (Crosby 1964).

It is possible that the volatiles are produced, at least in part, from the decomposition of cellular constituents, e.g., oxidation of unsaturated fatty acids. As the fruit attains maturity and becomes senescent, its high energy biochemical equilibria shift, the integrity of separate systems is lessened, and various reactions should be able to occur more freely. Weakened cell walls may allow the passage of some constituents, which may mix with other constituents once involved in vital processes. Unsaturated compounds that are now no longer protected may combine with oxygen to produce aldehydes, alcohols, and ketones. Acids and alcohols may combine to produce esters.

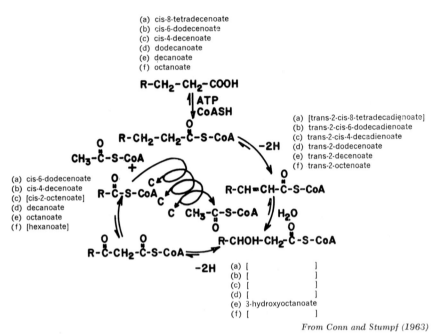

FIG. 93.   SCHEME FOR β-OXIDATION AND PEAR VOLATILES POSSIBLY INVOLVED

Or, as the fruit attains a certain state of maturity, certain normal biochemical pathways may be disrupted, and new compounds may be produced. It is interesting to note that many of the compounds found in Bartlett pear are the methyl and ethyl esters of reactants that can be fitted into the scheme of β-oxidation (Fig. 93). Undoubtedly there are other reaction mechanisms that could also account for these compounds, but the interesting point is that it is possible to account for their production through established biochemical pathways.

It is becoming increasingly evident that combined research efforts of scientists in all phases of research, without respect to commodity or disciplinary lines, would seem to offer the best promise of someday fitting these many compounds into a probable biological and biochemical scheme.

DISCUSSION

D. A. Forss.—The dienoic acids could, of course, come from decadienal and subsequent oxidation. Lipoxygenases are widely distributed and if there is linoleic acid present, it would be a fairly simple breakdown to the aldehyde and then this of course could go very quickly to the acid.

W. G. Jennings.—There is a lipoxygenase in pears. However, the only aldehyde we find is acetaldehyde. We were very cognizant of the fact that when we prepared these essences, that it is very difficult to relate the composition of an essence to how the components exist in the fruit. You want to make sure that the material you chromatograph reflects, as closely as possible, the relationship in the fruit. We routinely go through several techniques of extraction, or collection by steam distillation. Then as a final check, we sacrifice a column. Lately we have been taking a single fruit, mascerating it with ether in a Waring blendor, evaporating the ether and injecting this material directly onto the column to make sure that the volatile compounds we are looking at are present in the fruit. There were no dienals present at this point, however, the decadienoates were present.

BIBLIOGRAPHY

AMERINE, M. A., PANGBORN, R. M., and ROESSLER, E. B. 1965. Principles of Sensory Evaluation of Food. Academic Press, New York and London.

ANTONIANI, C., FEDERICO, L., and SERINI, G. 1954. Correlation between content of 2,3-butylene glycol and acetyl methyl carbinol and the state of maturity of fruit. Chimica (Milan) 9, 84–85.

ANTONIANI, C., and SERINI, G. 1955. Correlation between content of 2,3-butylene glycol and acetyl methyl carbinol and the state of maturity of fruit. L. Pyrus malus. Ann. Sper. Agr. (Rome) 9, 1167–1173.

CONN, E. E., and STUMPF, P. K. 1963. Outlines of Biochemistry. John Wiley and Sons, New York.

CROSBY, D. G. 1964. Personal communication.

DAGHETTA, A., FORTI, C., and MONZINI, A. 1956. The question of the volatile organic compounds produced by fruit in cold storage. III. Ann. Sper. Agr. (Rome) 10, 321–327.

DRAWERT, F. 1962. Concerning aroma and fragrant substances. Gas chromatographic investigation of aroma concentrates from apples and pears. (in German) . Vitis 3, 115–116.

GERHARDT, F. 1954. Rate of emanation of volatiles from pears and apples. Proc. Am. Soc. Hort. Sci. 64, 248–254.

HARLEY, C. P., and FISHER, D. F. 1927. The occurrence of acetaldehyde in Bartlett pears and its relation to pear scald and breakdown. J. Agr. Res. 35, 983–993.

HEINZ, D. E. 1965. Studies on the volatile components of Bartlett pears. Ph.D. Thesis, University of California, Davis.

HEINZ, D. E., CREVELING, R. K., and JENNINGS, W. G. 1965. Direct determination of aroma compounds as an index of pear maturity. J. Food Sci. 30, 641–643.

HEINZ, D. E., PANGBORN, R. M., and JENNINGS, W. G. 1964. Pear aroma: relation of instrumental and sensory techniques. J. Food Sci. 29, 756–761.

JENNINGS, W. G. 1961. Volatile esters of Bartlett pears. J. Food Sci. 26, 564–568.

JENNINGS, W. G. 1965. New fruit esters and the flavor of Bartlett pears. Proc. 6th International Symposium on Volatile Fruit Flavors, Lucerne (In press).

JENNINGS, W. G., and CREVELING, R. K. 1963. Volatile esters of Bartlett pears. II. J. Food Sci. 28, 91–94.

JENNINGS, W. G., LEONARD, S., and PANGBORN, R. M. 1960. Volatiles contributing to the flavor of Bartlett pears. Food Technol. 14, 587–590.

JENNINGS, W. G., and SEVENANTS, M. R.   1964A.   Volatile esters of Bartlett pears.   III.   J. Food Sci. *29*, 158–163.

JENNINGS, W. G., and SEVENANTS, M. R.   1964B.   Volatile components of peach.   J. Food Sci. *29*, 796–801.

LIM, L. S.   1963.   Studies on the relationship between the production of volatiles and the maturity of peaches and pears.   M.S. Thesis, University of California, Davis, Calif.

LIM, L., and ROMANI, R. J.   1963.   Volatiles and the harvest maturity of peaches and nectarines.   J. Food Sci. *29*, 246–253.

LUH, B. S., LEONARD, S. J., PATEL, D. S., and CLAYPOOL, L. L.   1955.   Volatile reducing substances in canned Bartlett pears.   Food Technol. *9*, 639–642.

MEHLITZ, A., and MATZIK, B.   1956.   Volatile acids in fruit juices.   Fruchtsaft-Ind. *1*, 130–146.

MOUSTAFA, H. H.   1965.   Unpublished data.

POWER, F. B., and CHESNUT, V. K.   1921.   Odorous constituents of peaches.   J. Am. Chem. Soc. *43*, 1725–1739.

SERINI, G.   1956.   Correlation between content of 2,3-butylene glycol and acetyl methyl carbinol and the state of maturity of fruit.   II.   Ann. Sper. Agr. (Rome) *10*, 857–863.

SEVENANTS, M. R.   1965.   Studies on the volatile components of peach.   Ph.D. Thesis, University of California, Davis.

TINDALE, G. B., TROUT, S. A., and HEULIN, F. E.   1938.   Investigations on the storage, ripening, and respiration of pears.   J. Dept. Agr., Victoria. *36*, 34–52, 90.

WICK, E. L.   1965.   Chemical and sensory aspects of the identification of odor constituents in foods.   Food Technol. *19*, 145–151.

CHAPTER 20

M. A. Gianturco | Coffee Flavor

INTRODUCTION

Coffee has been consumed by man for many centuries and this commodity has gradually become one of the most important articles of international trade. For instance, the world production of green coffee for the year 1962 has exceeded three billion kilograms, a crop with a value of almost two billion dollars (Pan-American Coffee Bureau 1963).

Its distinctive flavor is certainly the principal reason for the high acceptability enjoyed throughout the world by the beverage prepared from roasted coffee beans; in particular, the aroma of coffee seems to have an appeal all of its own for a large number of people.

The problem of establishing the nature of this flavor has understandably intrigued chemists for a long time; but their efforts have generally been frustrated by the complexity of the problem, which has not yielded even to the attack of some very eminent scientists. Outstanding among these, are Reichstein and Staudinger (1926, 1955), the Swiss chemists who eventually became Nobel laureates for their contributions to various fields of chemistry.

Of course, the tools available to Reichstein and Saudinger, who worked on the coffee problem in the 1920's, appear almost primitive to the instrument-minded researcher of the 1960's; a fact that only augments our respect for these pioneers of flavor chemistry. But, at any rate, they failed; and this explains why only a few other major investigations on the flavor of coffee were launched (Hughes and Smith 1949; Johnson and Frey 1938; Prescott et al. 1937A, B) until the advent of vapor phase chromatography (VPC) and of the spectral methods of structural elucidation suggested that the time had come for a new attack on the old problem.

The literature on the chemistry of coffee has been very competently reviewed by Kirchner in 1949 and, again, by Lockhart in 1957, in the early days of gas chromatography. The present review aims to cover the subsequent eight-year period and to illustrate how the results obtained may help to put coffee technology on a scientific basis.

DEVELOPMENT OF VOLATILE CONSTITUENTS

The flavor of green coffee is not very appealing. The desirable taste and aroma are only developed, in fact, during roasting, a process that can

431

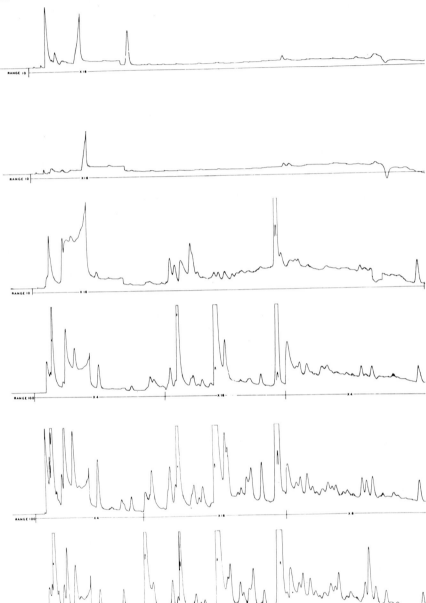

FIG. 94.   DEVELOPMENT OF VOLATILE CONSTITUENTS DURING ROASTING OF COFFEE

From top to bottom: green coffee, 2, 6, 8, 11 and 15 min. roasts.   4 m × 0.25 in.
15% Triton 305 packed column (60–80 mesh Diatoport S), programmed from 50° to
210°C. at the rate of 2°/min, with a flow of 75 ml He/min: detection by flame
ionization.

be considered as a mild pyrolysis of the constituents of the bean (the final temperature reached by the beans varies between 200° and 230°C., depending on the blend or variety).

The gradual formation of volatile substances as roasting progresses is illustrated by the vapor phase chromatograms of Fig. 94.

A more detailed study of this type has permitted us to determine the rate at which the concentration of various volatile constituents changes during the roasting process. Naturally, these rates represent the difference between the rate of formation in the system and that of elimination from it (by volatilization or reaction).

A few typical examples, illustrated in Fig. 95, show that some compounds reach their peak during the interval of time corresponding to a commercial roast, while others do so outside this interval. Particularly noteworthy is that, while many of the volatile constituents decrease when roasting is continued beyond the usual (North-American) commercial limits, the rates of formation of a few compounds greatly exceed, in the over-roast area, their rates of elimination.

These different behaviors are certainly related to the vast differences existing between the aroma of a light American roast, for instance, and that of an "espresso" or a French roast. Finally, the fact that the concentration of some volatiles, after an initial decrease, rapidly increases again, can be rationalized by considering that a given volatile substance could be derived from two or more precursors of different thermal stability; for instance, even if acetaldehyde originated exclusively from interaction of amino acids with carbohydrates or with oxidation products of polyphenols, its precursors could equally well be alanine, cysteine, cystine, threonine, or asparagine (Self 1963). Alternatively, it may be possible for a given precursor to give origin to a certain volatile substance by two or more different pathways of different energy requirements.

It is suggested that a careful study of the type illustrated in Fig. 95, if conducted on a statistical basis and correlated with analytical organoleptic evaluations, could open one path to the understanding of which of the numerous volatile constituents of coffee are truly essential to its flavor.

The construction of "aromagrams," proposed by Reymond et al. (1966), is clearly based on a similar concept.

CHROMATOGRAPHIC COMPARISON OF VARIOUS TYPES OF COFFEE

After having observed that the volatile composition of a given coffee changes continuously during the roasting process, it may be of interest to compare the chromatographic profiles of different types of coffee, each roasted to the peak of flavor (Fig. 96).

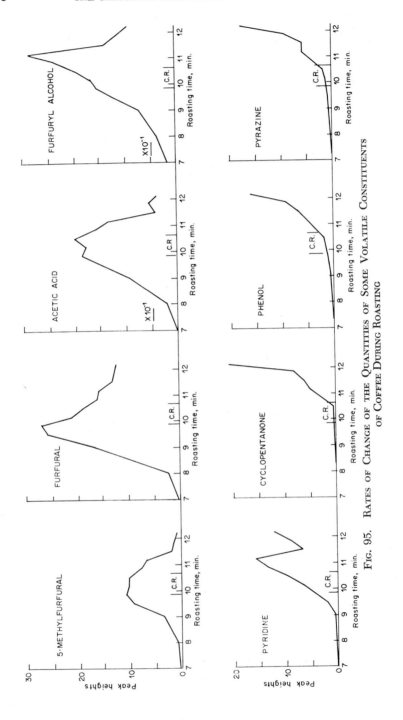

FIG. 95. RATES OF CHANGE OF THE QUANTITIES OF SOME VOLATILE CONSTITUENTS OF COFFEE DURING ROASTING

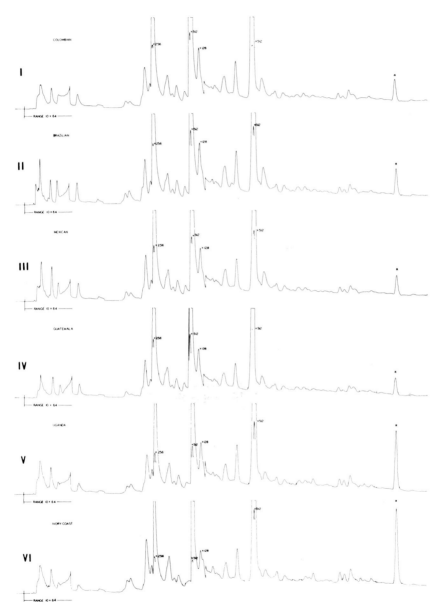

Fig. 96. Comparison of the Volatile Compositions of Six Varieties of Roasted
Coffee

4 m × 0.25 in. 15% Triton 305 packed column (60–80 mesh Diatoport S), programmed from 50° to 210°C. at the rate of 2°/min, with a flow of 75 ml He/min;
detection by flame ionization.

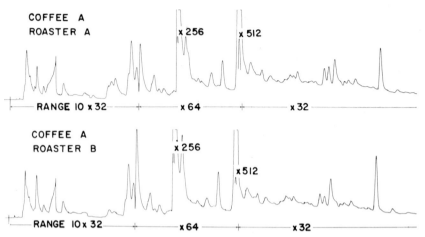

FIG. 97. COMPARISON OF THE VOLATILE COMPOSITION OF A GIVEN COFFEE ROASTED
IN TWO DIFFERENT MACHINES

4 m × 0.25 in. 15% Triton 305 packed column (60–80 mesh Diatoport S), programmed from 50° to 210°C. at the rate of 2°/min, with a flow of 75 ml He/min: detection by flame ionization.

Without further comments on this point, the attention of the reader is called—in particular—to the proportionally high amount of 4-vinylguaiacol (peak marked with an asterisk) in the two Robusta coffees investigated, namely the Uganda and the Ivory Coast samples. One wonders if this could contribute to the undesirable notes that characterize some coffees of the Robusta variety, even though one does not fail to realize that differences in less prominent or less defined peaks could be just as important, or even more so. In fact, improved chromatographic resolution might eventually reveal more significant patterns, and show the above view to be rather myopic.

It is, however, a matter of some practical importance that a fuller understanding of the chemical differences existing between various types of coffee could, perhaps, be used to improve certain types. Attempts to do this have actually been going on for some time, both in Europe and in the United States, by means of roasting equipment of new design. These new roasters permit a more efficient heat transfer, with consequent changes in the times and air temperatures necessary to achieve roasting. Moreover, some new machines operate under pressure.

From the chemist's standpoint, some of the changes in roasting parameters should be viewed as changes in reaction conditions, which can alter the rates, and supposedly even the paths, of some of the reactions leading from precursors to constituents of the aroma complex.

Figure 97 represents the chromatograms of a given coffee roasted, to the same color, in a conventional roaster (A) and in a machine of new design (B). It appears that the use of the unconventional roaster (B) does, indeed, favor the formation of some volatile constituents, and hinder that of others. This would seem to present some interesting possibilities for applied research.

METHODS OF ISOLATION OF THE AROMA COMPLEX

The chromatograms of Figs. 94, 96, and 97 were run on samples obtained by steam distillation of roasted coffee, in a small analytical unit that enables quite reproducible results. This simple apparatus, employed in our laboratory for some time to rapidly isolate samples of volatile constituents of coffee and other foodstuffs, has been recently described in some detail by Reymond *et al.* (1966).

However, steam distillation, while useful for orientative studies of the type described above, is not a particularly suitable method of obtaining samples for identification work. To this end, it is preferred in our laboratory to strip the volatile fraction, at low temperature and very low pressure, from the mixture of glycerides (the so-called coffee oil) that can be obtained by extrusion-pressing of the roasted beans.

The resulting volatile mixture, called the "aroma complex," is highly unstable and can be kept relatively unchanged only at very low temperatures. A change in color from yellow to orange to dark brown was observed when the "aroma complexes" of three different coffees were kept at room temperature. While the stabilities of the volatile fractions obtained from different coffees may differ, VPC has, so far, indicated only quantitative differences between various "aroma complexes."

The great instability of the "aroma complex" should, perhaps, discourage the use of VPC for the separation of the components of this complicated volatile mixture. However, if proper precautions are observed, the sample obtained by "total trapping" of the effluent from a VPC column has organoleptic properties that approximate fairly closely even though not exactly, those of the sample of "aroma complex" initially injected into the instrument. This fortunate circumstance is probably related to the fact that some experiments of isothermal fractional distillation—in which crude fractionation was achieved by gradually lowering the pressure of the system—have shown that substances which act as deterioration promoters of the "aroma complex" can be easily confined to a few distillation cuts (Gianturco 1965). In other words, it is conceivable that, once the sample is injected into a VPC column and its components begin to separate from one another, the material may actually become more stable than the intact sample.

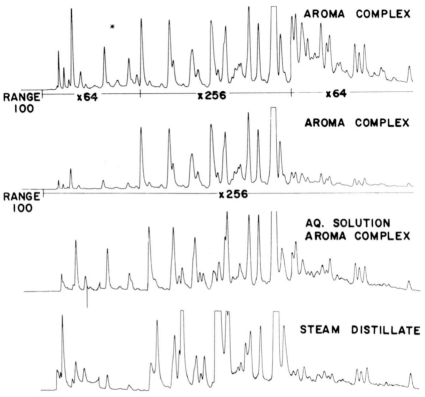

FIG. 98.   COMPARISON OF THE AROMA COMPLEX STRIPPED FROM COFFEE OIL WITH A
STEAM DISTILLATE OF THE SAME COFFEE

4 m × 0.25 in. 15% Triton 305 packed column (60–80 mesh Diatoport S), programmed from 50° to 210°C. at the rate of 2°/min, with a flow of 75 ml He/min:
detection by flame ionization.

Figure 98 will serve to illustrate the complicated nature of the "aroma
complex" obtained from coffee oil and its relationship to the volatile
fraction which results from steam distillation of roasted coffee.   In particular, the two top chromatograms—run at different attenuation settings—
show that the "aroma complex" contains a large number of components
and that the great majority of them are present at very low concentrations.   A comparison of the third and fourth curve shows, instead, the
qualitative similarity existing between an aqueous solution of the
"aroma complex" from coffee oil and a steam distillate of the same coffee.
The quantitative differences, however, are also quite evident, in accord
with the different organoleptic properties of the two samples.

The relationship observed between the headspace of the "aroma

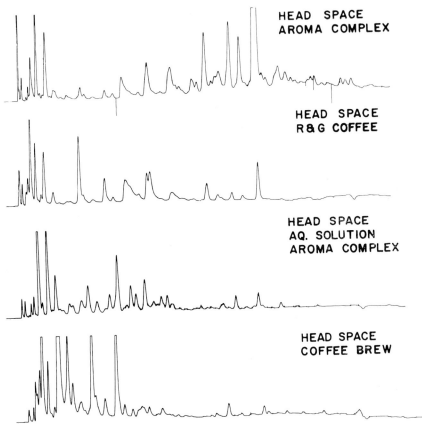

Fig. 99.   Comparison of the Head Spaces of the Aroma Complex, Its Aqueous
Solution, R & G Coffee and Coffee Brew

4 m × 0.25 in. 15% Triton 305 packed column (60–80 mesh Diatoport S), programmed from 50° to 210°C. at the rate of 2°/min, with a flow of 75 ml He/min:
detection by flame ionization.

complex" and that of roasted and ground coffee is illustrated in Fig. 99,
from which it appears that, while the low-boiling constituents are likely
to be the same in the two samples, the concentration of some high-
boiling substances is so low in the headspace of roast and ground coffee
that a visual comparison of the two samples in this region of the
chromatogram becomes, in fact, quite difficult.   Basically, the same
considerations apply when one compares the headspace of an aqueous
solution of the "aroma complex" from coffee oil with the headspace of
a coffee brew.

One should not ignore, however, the differences existing between the sensitivity of the human olfactory system and that of the gas chromatographic detectors; i.e., the fact that the chromatographic detectors cannot pick up some high-boiling components in the headspace of roasted coffee or in that of a dilute brew does not constitute proof that these components are not present in these samples. In fact, it is conceivable that some highly odoriferous compounds of low volatility, which have been shown to be present in the "aroma complex" isolated from coffee oil, might be important contributors to the overall aroma of ground coffee or of a coffee brew. Problems of this type have been discussed by Weurman (1963). Interesting comments on the importance of high boiling compounds for the aroma of coffee have also been made, earlier, by Moncrieff (1951).

Another observation suggested by the chromatograms of Fig. 99 is that the headspace of the "aroma complex" changes very considerably when the material is dissolved in water. Were the material dissolved in an oil or in another vehicle, the headspace would yield a still different chromatogram. This is an indication of the fact that compounding of a synthetic mixture smelling like coffee, when incorporated into a given substrate, would require practically tailor-making the mixture to fit the particular substrate.

Leaving such futuristic considerations aside, it seems to be safe to assume, on the basis of the chromatograms of Figs. 98 and 99, that the "aroma complex" stripped from coffee oil is an adequate sample for the identification of the aromatic constituents of coffee, since it appears to contain the bulk of the compounds which can be obtained by other isolation procedures (however, should a few exceptions be found, one would not be too surprised).

The use of the essentially water-free "aroma complex" presents also great advantages from the point of view of convenience of analysis and, consequently, this is the material that has been used almost exclusively for our identification work.

The methods employed by some of the other investigators to isolate the volatile fraction have generally been variations of the process of steam distillation, eventually followed by solvent extraction and removal of the solvent. The difficulties encountered with this kind of isolation procedure are well known, and have been previously discussed (Gianturco and Giammarino 1966; Weurman 1963).

IDENTIFICATION OF THE VOLATILE CONSTITUENTS, METHODS AND RESULTS

The early investigations on the nature of the flavor of coffee were carried out, of course, by classical methods. These have proven to be

TABLE 76

RESULTS OF PRINCIPAL INVESTIGATIONS ON THE AROMA OF COFFEE—CLASSICAL METHODS

Compounds	Reichstein and Staudinger, 1926	Prescott et al. 1937A, B	Johnson and Frey, 1938
Hydrogen sulfide	X		X
Methyl mercaptan	X		
Acetaldehyde	X		X
Furan			X
Dimethyl sulfide	X		
Acetone	X		
Methanol	X		
Diacetyl	X	X	X
2-Methylbutanal	X		
Formic acid		X	
Diethyl ketone		X	
Acetylpropionyl	X		
N-Methylpyrrole	X		
Pyridine	X		X
Pyrazine	X		
Acetic acid	X	X	
Acetol	X		
Acetoin			X
2,5-Dimethylpyrazine	X		
2,6-Dimethylpyrazine	X		
Furfuryl mercaptan	X		
Furfural	X	X	X
Furfuryl formate	X		
Furfuryl alcohol	X	X	X
Furfuryl acetate	X		
Sylvestrene		X	
iso-Valeric acid	X		
Phenol	X		
5-Methylfurfural	X		
2-Acetylfuran	X		
Guaiacol	X	X	
Naphthalene	X		
4-Vinylguaiacol	X	X	
N-Furfuryl-2-pyrrole	X		
Catechol	X		
Eugenol	X	X	
Maltol	X		
2,3-Dihydroxyacetophenone	X		
Acetovanillone		X	
n-Heptacosane		X	
Palmitic acid	X		

inadequate to the solution of complex flavor problems and need not be discussed.

Most of the recent investigators have relied upon VPC, as a separating technique, and upon infrared, ultraviolet—when applicable—and/or mass spectrometry for the identification of the compounds isolated. Of considerable interest is the technique of cryogenic VPC, pioneered by Merritt and Walsh (1963). The widespread use of these techniques of isolation and identification renders unnecessary any further comment on these matters.

Formula	Compound	Rhoades, 1960	Zlatkis and Sivetz, 1960	Sullivan, et al. 1959; Merritt[1] et al. 1963	Reymond et al. 1963	Gianturco and Friedel, 1963; Gianturco et al. 1963, 1964A, B, 1966
H_2S	Hydrogen sulfide	X				X
CH_2O	Formaldehyde					X
CH_2O_2	Formic acid		X			X
CH_4O	Methanol	X	X	X	X	X
CH_4S	Methyl mercaptan	X	X			X
CS_2	Carbon disulfide		X	X		
C_2H_4O	Acetaldehyde	X	X	X	X	X
$C_2H_4O_2$	Acetic acid					X
$C_2H_4O_2$	Methyl formate	X	X	X	X	X
C_2H_6O	Ethanol	X	X	X		X
C_2H_6S	Dimethyl sulfide	X	X	X		X
$C_2H_6S_2$	Dimethyl disulfide			X		
C_3H_3N	Acrylonitrile			X		
C_3H_4O	Acrolein			X		
C_3H_6O	Propanal	X	X	X		
C_3H_6O	Acetone	X	X	X	X	X
$C_3H_6O_2$	Propionic acid					X
$C_3H_6O_2$	Acetol					X
$C_3H_6O_2$	Methyl acetate		X	X	X	X
$C_3H_6O_2$	Ethyl formate		X			
C_3H_8S	Methyl ethyl sulfide			X		
$C_3H_8S_2$	Methyl ethyl disulfide			T		
C_4H_4O	Furan	X	X	X		X
C_4H_4S	Thiophene		X			X
$C_4H_4O_2$	Crotonolactone					X
$C_4H_4N_2$	Pyrazine					X
C_4H_5N	3-Butene nitrile			X		
C_4H_5N	Pyrrole			X		X
C_4H_6O	Methyl vinyl ketone			X		
$C_4H_6O_2$	Diacetyl	X	X	X	X	X
$C_4H_6O_2$	Butyrolactone					X
$C_4H_6O_2$	Crotonic acid					X
C_4H_8O	i-Butanal	X	X		X	X
C_4H_8O	Butanal	X	X			
C_4H_8O	Butanone	X	X	X	X	X
$C_4H_8O_2$	i-Butyric acid					X
$C_4H_8O_2$	Acetoin					X
$C_4H_8O_2$	Ethyl acetate				X	X
$C_4H_{10}O_2$	Dimethyl acetal				X	
$C_5H_4O_2$	Furfural		X			X
C_5H_5N	Pyridine					X
C_5H_5NO	2-Pyrrolaldehyde					X
C_5H_6O	2-Methylfuran	X	X	X	X	X
$C_5H_6O_2$	Furfuryl alcohol					X
$C_5H_6N_2$	2-Methylpyrazine					X
C_5H_7N	N-Methylpyrrole			T		X
C_5H_8	Isoprene	X	X			X
C_5H_8	Pentadiene		X			
C_5H_8O	Cyclopentanone					X
$C_5H_8O_2$	Pentane-2,3-dione	X				X
$C_5H_8O_2$	2-Methyltetrahydrofuran-3-one					X
$C_5H_8O_2$	Senecioic acid					X
$C_5H_8O_2$	Acetylacetone			X		
$C_5H_8O_3$	Acetol acetate					X
$C_5H_{10}O$	2-Methylbutanal		X			X
$C_5H_{10}O$	3-Methylbutanal	X	X	X	X	
$C_5H_{10}O$	Valeraldehyde		X			
$C_5H_{10}O_2$	2-Hydroxy-3-pentanone					X
$C_5H_{10}O_2$	3-Hydroxy-2-pentanone					X
$C_5H_{10}O_2$	i-Valeric acid					X
$C_5H_{10}O_2$	2-Methylbutyric acid					X
C_6H_6O	Phenol					X
$C_6H_6O_2$	5-Methylfurfural					X
$C_6H_6O_2$	2-Acetylfuran					X
$C_6H_6O_3$	Furfuryl formate					X
$C_6H_6O_3$	Dimethylmaleic anhydride					X
$C_6H_6O_3$	2-Methyl-3-hydroxy-γ-pyrone					X
C_6H_6SO	2-Acetylthiophene					X
C_6H_7N	3-Methylpyridine					X
C_6H_7NO	2-Acetylpyrrole					X
C_6H_7NO	N-Methylpyrrole-2-aldehyde					X
C_6H_7NO	5-Methylpyrrole-2-aldehyde					X
C_6H_8O	2,5-Dimethylfuran			X		X
$C_6H_8O_2$	3-Methylcyclopentane-1,2-dione					X

TABLE 77 (Continued)

Formula	Compound	Rhoades, 1960	Zlatkis and Sivetz 1960	Sullivan, et al. 1959; Merritt[1] et al. 1963	Reymond et al. 1963	Gianturco and Friedel, 1963; Gianturco et al. 1963, 1964A, B, 1966
$C_6H_8N_2$	2,3-Dimethylpyrazine					X
$C_6H_8N_2$	2,5-Dimethylpyrazine					X
$C_6H_8N_2$	2,6-Dimethylpyrazine					X
C_6H_8OS	Furfuryl methyl sulfide					X
$C_6H_{10}O$	2-Methyl-3-ethylacrolein			X		
$C_7H_6O_3$	1-(2'-furyl)-propane-1,2-dione					X
$C_7H_7NO_2$	Methyl nicotinate					X
C_7H_8	Toluene					X
C_7H_8O	m-Cresol					X
$C_7H_8O_2$	Guaiacol					X
$C_7H_8O_2$	5-Methyl-2-acetylfuran					X
$C_7H_8O_3$	Furfuryl acetate					X
$C_7H_8O_3$	Methyl ethyl maleic anhydride					X
C_7H_9NO	2-Propionylpyrrole					X
C_7H_9NO	N-Methyl-2-acetylpyrrole					X
C_7H_9NO	N-Methyl-5-methylpyrrole-2-aldehyde					X
$C_7H_{10}O$	2-Propylfuran			T		
$C_7H_{10}O_2$	3,4-Dimethylcyclopentane-1,2-dione					X
$C_7H_{10}O_2$	3,5-Dimethylcyclopentane-1,2-dione					X
$C_7H_{10}O_2$	3-Ethylcyclopentane-1,2-dione					X
$C_7H_{10}O_2$	3-Methylcyclohexane-1,2-dione					X
$C_8H_8O_3$	2,3-Dihydroxyacetophenone					X
$C_8H_8O_3$	1-(2'-Furyl)-butane-1,2-dione					X
$C_8H_8O_3$	1-[(5'-Methyl)-2'-furyl]-propane-1,2-dione					X
$C_8H_{12}O$	2-Butylfuran			T		
$C_9H_8O_2$	2,2'-Difurylmethane					X
C_9H_9NO	N-Furfuryl-2-pyrrole					X
$C_9H_{10}O_2$	4-Vinylguaiacol					X
$C_9H_{12}O_2$	4-Ethylguaiacol					X

[1] Compounds marked with a "T" were reported by the original authors as tentatively identified.

The results obtained by the early investigators are reported in Table 76, and the published results of recent studies are given in Table 77.

A total of one hundred and three volatile constituents of coffee has been reported in one or another of the recent studies; however, no one has claimed, so far, to have identified all the constituents of the "aroma complex," or—at least—all the essential constituents. Indeed, a high-resolution chromatogram recently obtained in our laboratory (Fig. 100) clearly shows that considerable work remains to be done.*

Even a cursory examination of the formulae of the substances listed in Table 77 will reveal that the pyrolytic decomposition of carbohydrates into 2, 3, 4 or 5-carbon units, with eventual recombination of the fragments, is probably directly responsible for the formation of several constituents of the "aroma complex" of coffee. The 16 furanic compounds firmly identified, the cyclic diketones and maltol are also clearly of carbohydratic origin. In fact, by simply heating glucose in the presence of base it has been possible to obtain (Robinson and Fray 1964)

* For some important recent contributions to this field, see: 1) Viani, R., Müggler-Chavan, F., Reymond, D. and Egli, R. H. 1965, Helv. Chim. Acta, 48, 1809–1815; and Gautschi, F., Winter, M., Flament, Y., Willhalm, B., and Stoll, M. 1966. Abstracts of the 152nd meeting of the American Chemical Society, New York, 1966, 3A.

3-methylcyclopentane-1,2-dione, one of the five cyclic diketones isolated from the "aroma complex" (Gianturco and Friedel 1963; Gianturco *et al.* 1963). The same result has been observed by heating with base a mixture of acetone and glyceraldehyde, two supposed degradation products of glucose. Finally, low yields of two of the other cyclic diketones have resulted (Gianturco 1965) by heating with base glyceraldehyde and butanone, another constituent of the "aroma complex" (Table 78). Moreover, a simple experiment of the pyrolysis of sucrose, conducted directly in the injection block of a gas chromatograph, has revealed the formation of many of the compounds present in coffee.

Roasting of the proteins of the coffee bean must yield several products of low molecular weight—such as amino acids, ammonia, amines, hydrogen sulfide, methyl mercaptan, dimethyl sulfide, dimethyl disulfide, etc.—some of which either appear as such in the "aroma complex" or react

TABLE 78

FORMATION OF SOME CYCLIC DIKETONES ISOLATED FROM COFFEE

GLUCOSE $\xrightarrow[\text{OH}^-]{\Delta}$ [Various Degradation Products + glyceraldehyde + acetone] $\longrightarrow$

$$\begin{array}{cc} CH_3 & CH_2OH \\ | & | \\ CO & + & CHOH \\ | & | \\ CH_3 & OHC \end{array} \xrightarrow{OH^-} \begin{array}{cc} CH_3 & CH_2OH \\ \diagdown & \diagdown \\ CO & CHOH \\ | & | \\ CH=CH \end{array} \rightleftharpoons \begin{array}{cc} CH_3 & CH_2OH \\ \diagdown & \diagdown \\ COH & COH \\ \| & \| \\ CH——CH \end{array} \rightleftharpoons$$

Glyceraldehyde + Butanone $\xrightarrow{OH^-}$

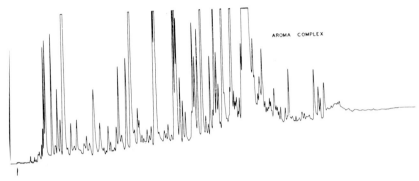

AROMA COMPLEX

Fɪɢ. 100. Hɪɢʜ-Rᴇsᴏʟᴜᴛɪᴏɴ Gᴀs Cʜʀᴏᴍᴀᴛᴏɢʀᴀᴍ ᴏғ ᴛʜᴇ Aʀᴏᴍᴀ Cᴏᴍᴘʟᴇx ᴏғ
Cᴏғғᴇᴇ

50 ft × 0.125 in. 1% Triton 305 packed column (F & M Hi Pak), programmed from
50° to 220°C. at the rate of 2°/min, with a flow of 40 ml He/min: detection by flame
ionization.

with carbohydrates and their degradation products (formation of
aliphatic aldehydes, furfuryl methyl sulfide, pyrazines, pyrroles, and
thiophenes).

A few substances, instead, such as pyridine, 3-methylpyridine, and
methyl nicotinate could derive from trigonelline, while phenol, guaiacol,
4-vinylguaiacol, and 4-ethylguaiacol must originate from chlorogenic
and ferulic acid. The formation of 4-ethylguaiacol from ferulic acid
obviously involves a reduction, and this implies that some other component of the system must be oxidized at the same time. Pyrolytic
experiments have shown (Gianturco 1965) that thermal decomposition
of sucrose, for instance, generates substances which can act as the reducing agent in this reaction.

Table 79 shows that a certain order and systematicity are beginning to
emerge, and this might facilitate the remaining identifications. For
instance, the isolations of furan, furfural, acetylfuran were followed by
those of 5-methylfuran, 5-methylfurfural, 5-methyl-2-acetylfuran, and
then by those of pyrrole, 2-pyrrolaldehyde and 2-acetylpyrrole, until the
series of 12 compounds was completed with the identifications of N-
methylpyrrole, N-methyl-2-pyrrolaldehyde and N-methyl-2-acetylpyrrole.
In the furan series, some products were also formed of higher oxidation
state, such as 1-(2′-furyl)-propane-1,2-dione, 1-(2′-furyl)-butane-1,2-dione
and 1-[(5′-methyl)-2′-furyl]-propane-1,2-dione; it would be at least
esthetically pleasing if this series should be completed with the identification of 1-[(5′-methyl)-2′-furyl]-butane-1,2-dione and, perhaps with that
of some of the corresponding compounds in the pyrrole and N-methyl-
pyrrole series.

TABLE 79

SOME FURANIC AND PYRROLIC COMPOUNDS ISOLATED FROM COFFEE

The question marks in Table 79 are to suggest some other possibilities. Analogously, the fact that only three pyridinic substances have been found so far in the "aroma complex" is somewhat odd, if one considers that an experiment of the pyrolysis of trigonelline (at roasting temperatures) has shown that several substances are generated in this process (Gianturco 1965). The pyrazine series has also been shown to be incomplete (Gianturco 1965).

While considerations of the type described are largely speculative in nature, so far it has been found very fruitful, indeed, to synthesize some of the substances whose presence in coffee could be reasonably predicted, and to keep on file the appropriate spectral information.

To summarize, it can be said that some progress has been made, in the last few years, toward the goal of reaching a chemical definition of coffee flavor. Further progress should be facilitated by the coupled use of VPC and mass spectrometry. One substantial obstacle that still remains is the difficulty encountered when trying to obtain complete chromatographic resolution of the "aroma complex"; but developments in this area allow some optimism.

A very fundamental question that needs to be answered pertains to the role played by the various constituents of the "aroma complex" in determining the flavor of coffee. A similar question must certainly loom large in the minds of many flavor chemists.

A field that seems to have been largely neglected concerns the study of flavor precursors and nonvolatile constitutents of flavor. The latter certainly play an important role in determining some of the organoleptic properties of the beverage.

In reference to applied research, it can be said that the methods developed for the basic studies could be profitably put to good use by technologists. To mention a few examples, detailed gas chromatographic investigations of the roasting process could be of help in the design of new roasting machines, and lead to the choice of the optimal conditions of roasting for each type of coffee. These studies could also be profitable as a guide to ways of improving the volatile character of some low-grade coffees. Fairly conclusive studies of the phenomenon of staling should now, also, be feasible. Finally, many of the unit operations performed during the manufacture of soluble coffee are susceptible to gas chromatographic analysis and control, and this might prove to be particularly helpful in the design of new processes.

DISCUSSION

R. Self.—Are there qualitative differences as well as quantitative differences in coffee volatiles?

M. Gianturco.—Clearly there are many quantitative differences, but I cannot say whether there are qualitative differences. A few years ago we had a chromatogram with 50 peaks. We identified 60 compounds and we were forced to conclude that some of the peaks were mixed. Then, a little later, we came up with 100 compounds; now, the chromatograms show 150. I am sure if Dr. Teranishi worked on this for a month he would show 300. It seems foolish to start making comparisons between various coffees, if you only go by what you see now. We might be very shortsighted right now. What is under the peaks?

A. M. Swanson.—How do the chromatograms of instant coffee compare with those from the roasted beans?

M. Gianturco.—Basically, you find the same compounds in fresh coffee as in instant coffee; however, the ratios and amounts are completely different. Soluble coffee is made from an extract of coffee, from which the water is removed. When you remove the water, you lose a large quantity of the volatiles; you lose more or less depending upon the process.

BIBLIOGRAPHY

GIANTURCO, M. A. 1965. Unpublished.

GIANTURCO, M. A., and FRIEDEL, P. 1963. The synthesis of some cyclic diketones isolated from coffee. Tetrahedron *19*, 2039–2049.

GIANTURCO, M. A., FRIEDEL, P., and GIAMMARINO, A. S. 1964A. The volatile constituents of coffee. III. The structures of two heterocyclic compounds and the synthesis of tetrahydrofuranones. Tetrahedron *20*, 1763–1772.

GIANTURCO, M. A., and GIAMMARINO, A. S. 1966. Considerations on the study of the aromatic constituents of roasted coffee. Proc. 2nd Colloque International sur la Chimie des Cafes Verts, Torrefies et Leurs Derives, Paris, (in press).

GIANTURCO, M. A., GIAMMARINO, A. S., and FRIEDEL, P. 1966. The volatile constituents of coffee. V. Further identifications. Nature *210*, 1358.

GIANTURCO, M. A., GIAMMARINO, A. S., FRIEDEL, P., and FLANAGAN, V. 1964B. The volatile constituents of coffee. IV. Furanic and pyrrolic compounds. Tetrahedron *20*, 2951–2961.

GIANTURCO, M. A., GIAMMARINO, A. S., and PITCHER, R. G. 1963. The structures of five cyclic diketones isolated from coffee. Tetrahedron *19*, 2051–2059.

HUGHES, E. B., and SMITH, R. F. 1949. The volatile constituents of roasted coffee. J. Soc. Chem. Ind. *68*, 322–327.

JOHNSON, W. R., and FREY, C. N. 1938. The volatile constituents of roasted coffee. J. Am. Chem. Soc. *60*, 1624–1627.

KIRCHNER, J. G. 1949. The chemistry of fruit and vegetable flavors. *In* Advances in Food Research *2*, pp. 259–296. Academic Press, New York.

LOCKHART, E. E. 1957. Chemistry of coffee. *In* Chemistry of Natural Food Flavors. J. H. Mitchell, *et al.*, (Editors) U. S. Government Printing Office: 0-436956.

MACKAY, D. A. M., LANG, D. A., and BERDICK, M. 1961. Objective measurement of odor. Anal. Chem. *33*, 1369–1374.

MERRITT, C., BAZINET, M. L., SULLIVAN, J. H., and ROBERTSON, D. H. 1963. Mass spectrometric determination of volatile components from ground coffee. J. Agr. Food Chem. *11*, 152–155.

MERRITT, C., and WALSH, J. 1963. Programmed cryogenic temperature gas chromatography applied to the separation of complex mixtures. Anal. Chem. *35*, 110–113.

MONCRIEFF, R. W. 1951. Coffee. Coffee Tea Ind. *74*, No. 2, 11, 39, 40, 42.

PAN-AMERICAN COFFEE BUREAU. 1963. Annual Coffee Statistics 1962, Publication No. 26. Pan-American Coffee Bureau. New York.

PRESCOTT, S. C., EMERSON, R. L., and PEAKES, L. V. 1937A. The staling of coffee. Food Res. *2*, 1–20.

PRESCOTT, S. C., EMERSON, R. L., WOODWARD, R. B., and HEGGIE, R. 1937B. The staling of coffee. II. Food Res. *2*, 165–173.

RADTKE, R., SPRINGER, R., MOHR, W., and HEISS, R. 1963. The staling of coffee. Z. Lebensm. Untersuch. Forsch. *119*, 293–302.

REICHSTEIN, T., and STAUDINGER, H. 1926. Improvements in a method for isolating the aromatic principle contained in roasted coffee. Brit. Pats. 246,-454 and 260,960.

REICHSTEIN, T., and STAUDINGER, H. 1955. The aroma of coffee. Perf. and Ess. Oil Record *46*, 86–88.

REYMOND, D., CHAVAN, F., and EGLI, R. H. 1963. Gas chromatographic analysis of the highly volatile constituents of roasted coffee. *In* Recent Advances in Food Science *3*, J. M. Leitch and D. N. Rhodes (Editors) pp. 151–157. Butterworths, London.

REYMOND, D., PICTET, C., and EGLI, R. M. 1966. Analytical characteristics of the aroma of coffee. Proc. 2nd Colloque International sur la Chimie des Cafes Verts, Torrefies et Leurs Derives, Paris, (in press).

RHOADES, J. W. 1958. Sampling method for the analysis of coffee volatiles by gas chromatography. Food Res. *23*, 254–261.

RHOADES, J. W. 1960. Analysis of the volatile constituents of coffee. J. Agr. Food Chem. *8*, 136–141.

ROBINSON, R., and FRAY, G. J. 1964. Cyclic diketones. Brit. Pat. 979,295.

SELF, R. 1963. The use of capillary columns for the analysis of the odor of cooked potatoes. *In* Recent Advances in Food Science 3. J. M. Leitch and D. N. Rhodes (Editors) pp. 170–179. Butterworths, London.

SULLIVAN, J. H., ROBERTSON, D. H., and MERRITT, C. 1959. Chemical components of coffee aroma. Abstracts 135th Meeting Am. Chem. Soc., Boston, Mass. April 5–10, No. 14A.

WEURMAN, C. 1963. Recent developments in food odor research methods. *In* Recent Advances in Food Science 3. J. M. Leitch and D. N. Rhodes (Editors) pp. 137–150. Butterworths, London.

ZLATKIS, A., and SIVETZ, M. 1960. Analysis of coffee volatiles by gas chromatography. Food Res. *25*, 395–398.

CHAPTER 21

R. M. Silverstein | Pineapple Flavor

INTRODUCTION

The bulk of the volatile compounds of most fruit flavors consists of homologous series of esters, acids, alcohols, aldehydes, and ketones. Flavor differences can be attributed to varying proportions of these widely distributed materials, and to trace amounts of unique components. Jennings and Sevenants (1964) termed the former "contributing flavor compounds," and the latter "character-impact compounds."

To date, relatively few "character-impact compounds" have been identified, principally because many investigators in this field use gas chromatography for both isolation and identification. But matching of retention times against arbitrary reference compounds does not really constitute identification. The unique, the unexpected will not be discovered; the trivial will be sought and found.

The methodology used in these laboratories involves isolation of pure components by repetitive chromatography, and identification by a combination of whatever techniques are required. For most compounds that can be put through a gas chromatographic column, a combination of four spectra suffices: mass, infrared, NMR, and ultraviolet. For compounds of greater complexity, such information will permit intelligent selection of chemical procedures, and the resulting products can be identified from their spectra.

There are obvious disadvantages to this methodology. There are practical difficulties in trying to work with less than milligram samples: poor quality of the spectra; high losses on trapping, on extraction, and on solvent removal; decomposition of unstable components (frequently by air oxidation); and contamination (frequently by water, lubricants, and column substrates). On the other hand, no *a priori* assumptions as to possible components are necessary. Reference compounds are used for confirmation only after a tentative identification has been established.

It is now feasible to connect a gas chromatographic instrument directly to a mass spectrometer (Day and Libbey 1964; Anderson and von Sydow 1964). It may one day be feasible to obtain the other spectra in a similar fashion.

Application of our methodology to the problem of pineapple flavor resulted in identification of a major component that not only had not previously been found in pineapple, but had not been reported in the

450

literature to our knowledge. The identification of several other unique compounds will also be described.

ISOLATION OF FLAVOR COMPONENTS

Work was started in this laboratory in the summer of 1963 on the flavor concentrate from 250 freshly-picked pineapples which were pressed to give 25 gallons of juice. The pineapples were a Smooth Cayenne, winter harvest, grown in the Waipio region, Oahu, Hawaii. The juice was saturated with sodium chloride and extracted once, volume for volume, with peroxide-free ethyl ether. The ether solution was dried, and the ether was removed at 40°C. The residual oil (18 gm.) was subjected to short-path distillation. The pressure was slowly re-

TABLE 80

VOLATILE CONSTITUENTS OF PINEAPPLE FLAVOR

Esters	Acids
Methyl acetate	Acetic
Ethyl acetate	
Ethyl acrylate	Alcohols
Methyl n-butyrate	Methanol
Ethyl n-butyrate	Ethanol
Methyl n-valerate	n-Propanol
Methyl isovalerate	Isobutanol
Ethyl lactate	n-Pentanol
Ethyl isovalerate	
Methyl n-caproate	Carbonyl compounds
Methyl isocaproate	Acetone
Ethyl n-caproate	Formaldehyde
Methyl n-caprylate	Acetaldehyde
Ethyl n-caprylate	Diacetyl
n-Amyl n-caproate	Furfural
Methyl β-methylthiopropionate	Methyl-n-propylketone
Ethyl β-methylthiopropionate	5-Hydroxy-2-methylfurfural

(From Haagen-Smit et al. 1945; Gawler 1962; and Connell 1964).

duced to 0.1 mm. Hg, and then the bath temperature was slowly raised from 25° to 120°C. Four crude fractions were collected. Each of these fractions was fractionated by repetitive gas chromatography until pure compounds were isolated.

Table 80 lists the compounds that have been identified by previous investigators of pineapple flavor (Haagen-Smit et al. 1945; Gawler 1962; and Connell 1964). With the exception of the two sulfur-containing compounds, these components are unexceptional. Some of these identifications must still be considered tentative.

TABLE 81

NEW PINEAPPLE FLAVOR COMPONENTS

Name	Formula	Ppm (Approximate)
2,5-Dimethyl-4-hydroxy-3-(2H)-furanone	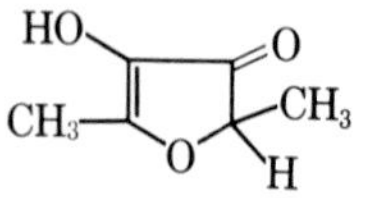	4
p-Allylphenol	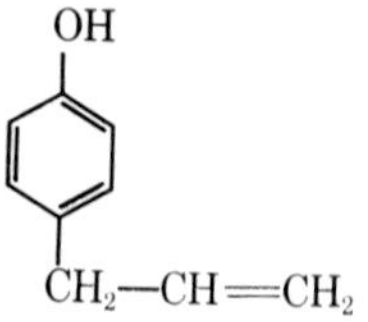	0.5
γ-Caprolactone	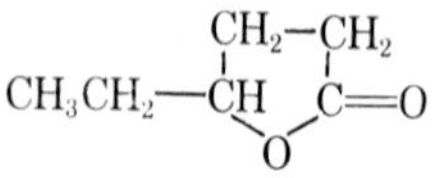	0.3
Methyl-β-methylthiopropionate	$CH_3SCH_2CH_2COOCH_3$	0.2
Ethyl-β-methylthiopropionate	$CH_3SCH_2CH_2COOCH_2CH_3$	0.1
Methyl-β-hydroxycaproate (Tentative)	$CH_3CH_2CH_2CHCH_2COOCH_3$ with OH	0.1
Methyl-β-acetoxycaproate (Tentative)	$CH_3CH_2CH_2CHCH_2COOCH_3$ with $OCCH_3$, $\overset{\parallel}{O}$	0.1

IDENTIFICATION

Table 81 lists the compounds identified to date in this laboratory. These are major components, and they seem different enough from the common fruit components to warrant comment.

Identification of the Furanone Component

The first compound in Table 81, 2,5-dimethyl-4-hydroxy-3(2H)-furanone (I) (Rodin *et al.* 1965) is of particular interest:

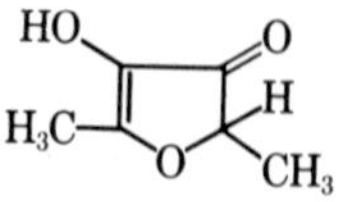

This compound was present in large amounts; 100 mg. had been isolated as a colorless solid, m.p. 70°C. It had a most intense odor best described as "burnt pineapple" or "pineapple upside-down cake." Its other outstanding characteristic was its instability in air. Tentative identification

INFRARED SPECTRUM

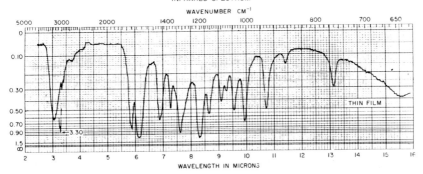

MASS SPECTRAL DATA (RELATIVE INTENSITIES)

m/e	% OF BASE PEAK	m/e	% OF BASE PEAK
14	5	44	8
15	16	45	11
17	3	53	4
18	11	55	18
26	4	56	10
27	28	57	61
28	16	58	3
29	35	72	4
31	7	85	21
39	5	128	95
41	4	129	6.82
42	5	130	1.12
43	100		

ISOTOPE ABUNDANCE

m/e	% OF P
128 (P)	100
129 (P+1)	7.18
130 (P+2)	1.18

ULTRAVIOLET SPECTRUM

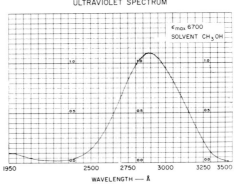

ϵ_{max} 6700
SOLVENT CH_3OH

NMR SPECTRUM

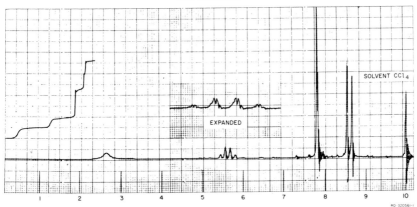

SOLVENT CCl_4

EXPANDED

RD-520561-1

FIG. 101. DATA FOR COMPOUND I

followed from consideration of the four spectra shown in Fig. 101. It may be instructive to work through the interpretation of the spectra.

The first step in translating the four spectra of Fig. 101 into a molecular structure is to establish a molecular weight and an empirical formula from the mass spectrum. The parent peak (P) was found to be 128; thus, the exact molecular weight was obtained. Since this is an even number the molecule contains either no nitrogen or an even number of nitrogen atoms. Absence of nitrogen was confirmed by a sodium fusion test. The P + 2 peak is too small to allow for the presence of sulfur or halogen atoms. From the calculated contributions of isotopes to the P + 1 and P + 2 peaks, we select $C_6H_8O_3$ as the best fit to our P + 1 peak of 7.18% and P + 2 peak of 1.18% (Silverstein and Bassler 1963).

Turn now to the infrared spectrum and pick out the prominent features. A strong, broad hydroxyl band at 3.06 μ was noted, also a strong carbonyl band at 5.88 μ, and a very strong broad band at 6.16 μ; the positions and relative intensities of the latter two bands suggest a conjugated carbonyl group, C=C—C=O. A 2,4-dinitrophenylhydrazone test was positive. The shape and breadth of the hydroxyl absorption indicate that the hydroxyl group is strongly hydrogen-bonded. The initial impression is that of a carboxylic hydroxyl group. However, that is quite firmly ruled out by the absence of absorption peaks below 1 τ in the NMR spectrum. Absence of aromatic peaks in the NMR spectrum rules out the possibility of phenolic hydroxyl groups. This effectively limits the compounds to alcohols and enols.

Consider the NMR spectrum in some detail. From low field to high field we note: a broad absorption at 2.66 τ, a quartet at 5.62 τ, a singlet at 7.80 τ, and a doublet at 8.62 τ. The ratios are respectively 1:1:3:3. We make the following assignments in the same sequence: OH, CH, CH_3, CH_3. We note that the CH quartet at 5.62 τ and the CH_3 doublet at 8.62 τ are coupled; therefore these groups are vicinal. Futhermore, the strong downfield shift of the quartet suggests that the carbon atom to which the proton is attached may in turn be attached to an oxygen atom. The strong downfield shift of the OH peak (outside the usual range of about 4.5 to 9.3 τ for alcohols) can be justified by assigning it to an enolic proton. A strongly positive ferric chloride test (green) afforded confirmation. The CH_3 group represented by the peak at 7.80 τ is attached to a carbon atom that does not carry a proton. There are no olefinic protons. From the infrared and NMR data, the following fragments are indicated:

$$\underset{}{\text{C=C—OH}} \quad \text{C=C—C=O} \quad \overset{\displaystyle CH_3}{\underset{}{\text{O—CH}}} \quad \text{C—CH}_3$$

There is one additional and, as it turns out, crucial bit of information. The UV absorption peak is at 289 mμ; ϵ is 6700 (the molar absorptivity may be low because of decomposition of the solution on standing).

An acyclic structure cannot be written which would satisfy all the spectral data. A number of unsaturated five-membered ring lactones were considered, and discarded because of discrepancies between predicted spectra and the evidence at hand; the requirement of absorption at 289 mμ, in particular, could not be satisfied. The only structure consonant with the spectral data is:

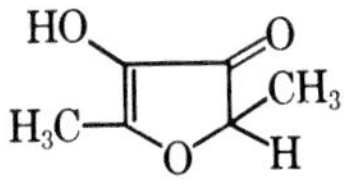

2,5-dimethyl-4-hydroxy-3(2H)-furanone

I

This compound, of course, can be written in either of two other tautomeric forms.

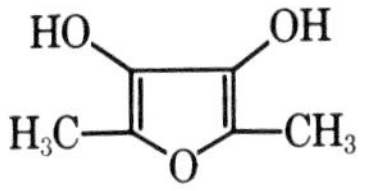

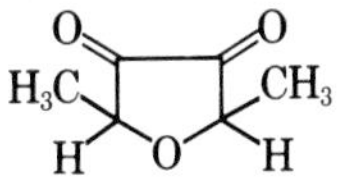

The lower homolog, tetrahydro-3,4-furandione, has been reported (Kendall and Hajos 1960) to exist exclusively in the diketo form. However, the spectral evidence indicates that I exists exclusively as the monoenol. The 2,5-dimethyl compound I has not been reported in the literature.

Confirmatory evidence for the structure of I can be derived from the reported IR and UV values for a related compound, 2,5-dimethyl-3(2H)-furanone (II) (Eugster et al. 1961).

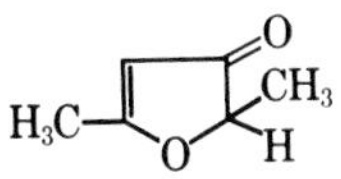

II

The carbonyl absorption in the IR spectrum was 5.84 μ, and the UV absorption peak was 260 mμ ($\epsilon = 12{,}200$). The bathochromic shift proposed (Jaffé and Orchin 1962) for an α-hydroxy substituent in an acyclic conjugated ketone is 35 mμ; the calculated value of 295 mμ is thus in fair agreement with our value of 289 mμ.

The shift position, in the NMR spectrum, of the methine proton of I (5.62 τ) is in good agreement with that reported (5.5 τ) for the methine proton of the related compound III (Rosenkranz et al. 1963):

$$CH_3CH_2OOC$$

III

Although attempts to carry out chemical transformations on I were unsuccessful, a "derivative" was obtained inadvertently from a solution of I in a mixture of methanol and chloroform which had been stored

INFRARED SPECTRUM

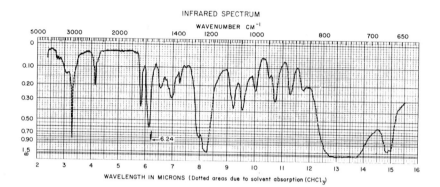

MASS SPECTRAL DATA (RELATIVE INTENSITIES)

m/e	% OF BASE PEAK	m/e	% OF BASE PEAK	ISOTOPE ABUNDANCE	
13	3	42	7	m/e	% OF P
14	9	43	100		
15	31	44	11	158 (P)	100
17	6	45	5	159 (P+1)	8.2
18	21	86	5	160 (P+2)	TOO SMALL TO MEASURE
27	3	93	3		
28	7	157	0.72		
29	9	158 (P)	0.24		
31	7	159	0.020		
32	3				

NMR SPECTRUM

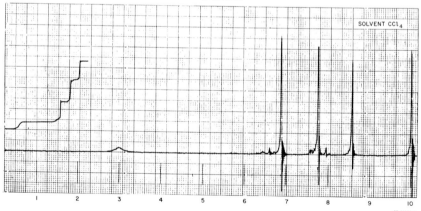

SOLVENT CCl₄

FIG. 102.   DATA FOR COMPOUND IV

for a week in the refrigerator. This derivative was identified from spectral data (Fig. 102) as 2,5-dimethyl-4-hydroxy-2-methoxy-3(2H)-furanone (IV). The mass spectral data show the molecular weight to be 158 (loss of one hydrogen, gain of methoxy group). The P + 1 peak allows for 8 carbon atoms; the P + 2 peak was too small to measure accurately. Loss of the methine proton in I is indicated by the absence of the quartet from the NMR spectrum of IV. The shift position of the new peak at 6.88 τ is reasonable for a methoxy group. The informative peaks of the IR spectrum are largely unchanged from those of the IR spectrum of I.

Two plausible mechanisms can be written to rationalize the transformation I → IV. These both invoke air oxidation to hydroperoxides, usually postulated in air oxidation of furans (Dunlop and Peters 1953) and acid catalysis from degradation of chloroform.

The first sequence depicts oxidation to a hemiketal type of hydroperoxide. Protonation of the hydroperoxide oxygen is followed by nucleophilic displacement of hydrogen peroxide by methanol, and loss of a proton. The second sequence assumes a nucleophilic attack by methanol at the β-carbon of a conjugated ketone. This is followed by air oxidation and protonation. Ketonization with loss of a proton displaces hydrogen peroxide.

Synthesis of IV has been reported (Steinbauer and Waldmann 1958), but no spectral data were presented.

Identification of the Other Components

The other components of Table 81 were tentatively identified from their spectra. The identifications were confirmed (except for the last two components) by comparison with spectra of authentic samples (Silverstein *et al.* 1965).

SYNTHESIS OF THE FURANONE

A literature search for 2,5-dimethyl-4-hydroxy-3(2H)-furanone was negative. A rational synthesis was therefore required for proof of structure. The following sequences gave a product whose properties (including aroma) were identical with those of the isolated compound I.

BIOGENESIS OF THE FURANONE

After this work had been completed, the studies carried out by J. E. Hodge of Northern Utilization Laboratories, U.S. Dept. Agr., Peoria, Illinois were noted. In the course of his extensive studies of the "browning reaction," Hodge had isolated the same furanone by heating rhamnose with pyridine acetate (Hodge *et al.* 1963). This work raises some interesting questions as to the origin of the furanone in our pineapple flavor concentrate. The nagging possibility that it may be an artifact cannot be dismissed. It may have been formed during the short-path distillation. However, the presence of sugars in the ether extract seems unlikely. In this connection, the principal anthocyanin of pineapple plant has been identified as cyanidin 3-rhamnoglucosido-5-glucoside. (Leeper 1965).*

TASTE TESTS

Some preliminary taste evaluations have been run by adding various concentrations of the components of Table 81 to "stripped" pineapple juice. p-Allylphenol was found to be objectionable at all detectable concentrations. This information should be of immediate concern to agronomists and plant geneticists. γ-Caprolactone was not detectable at the levels tested. The sulfur-containing esters gave mixed responses of "like" and "dislike." At higher levels, they imparted an "overripe" taste. It should prove interesting to try to correlate the levels of these esters with the levels of methionine which only appears during the ripening stage (Gortner and Singleton 1965).

A preliminary taste evaluation of furanone proved disappointing. Although the aroma was impressive, none of the tasters could detect any enhanced "pineapple" flavor when the furanone was added to the "stripped" juice. Further studies are obviously needed.

ACKNOWLEDGMENTS

The flavor concentrate was prepared by Dr. W. A. Gortner (present address, Human Nutrition Research Division, U.S. Dept. Agr., Beltsville, Maryland) and Dr. R. W. Leeper, Pineapple Research Institute. Dr. Leeper also carried out the taste evaluation studies. Isolation and identification studies were carried out at Stanford Research Institute by Mr. J. O. Rodin, Dr. C. M. Himel, and Dr. R. M. Silverstein. The synthesis of the furanone compound was performed by Dr. D. W. Henry, Stanford Research Institute.

DISCUSSION

G. F. Russell.—Did you do any decoupling experiments on the furanone you identified from the pineapple extract?

R. M. Silverstein.—No, we felt we did not have to. That second order coupling that I mentioned, of course, is a CH_3 coupled to a proton. The CH_3 peak was really a closely-spaced doublet and the quartet was really a quartet of quartets from this long range coupling.

---

* Note added in proof: The same amount of the furanone was found when the maximum bath temperature reached in the short-path distillation was 50°C.

M. E. Mason.—Your mass spectra are very clean and you were able to use isotope abundance in the analysis of your compounds. Would you comment on your technique?

R. M. Silverstein.—The mass spectrum was run on approximately 0.5 milligram. I should mention it looks cleaner than it should because we discarded all the minor peaks, anything less than three per cent was not shown. The P + 1 and the P + 2 are useful if you are dealing with aromatic compounds, cyclic compounds, or polyunsaturated compounds; it is useful about 90% of the time. If you are dealing with alcohols, amines, or branch-chain compounds the parent peak is so weak that usually you can not measure the P + 1 or P + 2, in fact you may not even be able to decide what your parent peak is. If you have a large parent peak, you are in good shape. You can usually limit yourself to maybe 2, 3, 4, or 5 possibilities that really fit, depending on the molecular weight and complexity of your compound.

M. E. Mason.—It looks like you have a chance for stereoisomerism around the double bond? If this enol exists, could not you have a dl-cis or dl-trans? This would account for maybe your melting point differences?

R. M. Silverstein.—I do not think there would be any stereoisomerism around the double bond. The furanone exists as shown or it could be written as a diketone or a dienol. The spectra shows that it is completely in the enol form. An interesting thing is that the lower homolog without the methyl groups has been reported to exist completely as the diketone.

BIBLIOGRAPHY

ANDERSON, J., and VON SYDOW, E. 1964. The aromas of black currants. Acta Chem. Scand. *18*, 1105.

CONNELL, D. W. 1964. Volatile flavoring constituents of the pineapple. Australian J. Chem. *17*, 130–140.

DAY, E. A., and LIBBEY, L. M. 1964. Cheddar cheese flavor. J. Food Sci. *29*, 583–589.

DUNLOP, A. P., and PETERS, F. N. 1953. The Furans. Reinhold Publishing Corp., New York.

EUGSTER, C. H., ALLNER, K., and ROSENKRANZ, R. E. 1961. Knowledge of the chemistry of monomeric β-hydroxyfurans. Chimia *15*, 516–517.

GAWLER, J. H. 1962. Constituent of canned Malayan pineapple juice. J. Sci. Food Agr. *13*, 57–62.

GORTNER, W. A., and SINGLETON, V. L. 1965. Chemical and physical development of pineapple fruit III. Nitrogenous and enzyme constituents. J. Food Sci. *30*, 24–29.

HAAGEN-SMIT, A. J., KIRCHNER, J. G., PRATER, A. N., and DEASY, C. L. 1945. Chemical studies of pineapple. J. Am. Chem. Soc. *67*, 1646–1650, and 1651–1652.

HODGE, J. E., FISHER, B. E., and NELSON, E. C. 1963. Dicarbonyls, reductones, and heterocyclics produced by reactions of reducing sugars with secondary amine salts. Proc. Am. Soc. of Brewing Chemists. *1963*, 84–92.

JAFFÉ, H. H., and ORCHIN, M. 1962. Theory and Application of Ultraviolet Spectroscopy. John Wiley and Sons, New York.

JENNINGS, W. G., and SEVENANTS, M. R. 1964. Volatile esters of Bartlett pear. J. Food Sci. *29*, 158–163.

KENDALL, E. C., and HAJOS, Z. G. 1960. Tetrahydro-3, 4-furandione. J. Am. Chem. Soc. *82*, 3219–3220.

LEEPER, R. W. 1965. Private communication.

RODIN, J. O., HIMEL, C. M., SILVERSTEIN, R. M., LEEPER, R. W., and GORTNER, W. A. 1965. Volatile flavor and aroma components of pineapple. I. Isolation and tentative identification of 2,5-dimethyl-4-hydroxy-3(2H)-furanone. J. Food Sci. *30*, 280–285.

ROSENKRANZ, R. E., ALLNER, K., GOOD, R., VON PHILLIPSBORN, W., and EUGSTER, C. H. 1963. Knowledge of the chemistry of monomeric furenidone. Helv. Chim. Acta. *46*, 1259–1285.

SILVERSTEIN, R. M., and BASSLER, G. C. 1963. Spectrometric Identification of Organic Compounds. John Wiley and Sons, New York. 9.

SILVERSTEIN, R. M., RODIN, J. O., HIMEL, C. M., and LEEPER, R. W. 1965. Volatile flavor and aroma components of pineapple II. Isolation and identification of chavicol and γ-caprolactone. J. Food Sci. *30*, 668–672.

STEINBAUER, E., and WALDMANN, E. 1958. Knowledge concerning acetylformoin. Monatsh. Chem. *89*, 570–576.

Origin of Flavor in Foods

| John E. Hodge | Origin of Flavor in Foods |
| | Nonenzymatic Browning Reactions |

INTRODUCTION

Between natural and synthetic flavors are the flavors produced by the artificial drying, processing, and cooking of harvested foodstuffs. The best of these flavors are universally known and widely appreciated. They enhance the value of food and feed to both man and his domesticated animals.

Some of the most popular confection flavors the world around (vanilla, chocolate, caramel, butterscotch) contain products of nonenzymatic browning reactions. The appetizing aromas of fresh bread, coffee, roasting nuts, pralines, and barbecue depend largely on sugar-derived browning products. It takes no food scientist to appreciate the art of the chef and his masterful control over induced browning reactions, but it does take one to determine exactly what compounds are being appreciated so that the flavor of less appetizing processed foods might be enhanced by their use.

The elements of browning flavors are presented in this chapter from studies of simple model systems that are related to foods. Several preceding chapters have discussed browning reactions in particular foods in relation to their flavor. Since a general review of this subject will be published soon (Reynolds 1965), the browning reactions of foods will not be covered.

The chemistry of browning reactions in model systems has been advanced considerably since the review of Hodge (1953) in later reviews by Ellis (1959), Heyns and Paulsen (1960), Anet (1964), and Reynolds (1963, 1965). Of this chemistry, only that pertaining to the production of flavor compounds will be discussed.

MODEL SYSTEMS OF INTEREST

A look at the food flavor components presented in the preceding chapters reveals hundreds of compounds that have arisen from carbohydrate, protein, lipid, and flavonoid components, separately and in combinations. Flavor production is complex chemistry indeed; so we turn to simpler systems to learn about the underlying chemical reactions and their products.

The heat-induced caramelization of isolated sugars produces both desirable and undesirable flavor compounds. If amino compounds are present, some of the same compounds produced by caramelization are also produced from sugars but at much lower temperatures. The decomposition of sugars needs to be investigated more closely however, especially with regard to the nonvolatile sweet, bitter, and flavor-fixing components of the derived caramel and melanoidins. For example, Herz and Shallenberger (1960) and Kamada and Nakano (1961) indicate that a sweeter, "superior" caramel is produced from glucose by the addition of alanine, but not by the addition of glycine or some other amino acids. The question arises, How does alanine (or the acetaldehyde generated from it) alter the flavor of glucose decomposition products in a favorable way? What different compounds are thereby produced?

Analyses of the volatile components of baked goods have proceeded apparently without reference to fundamental knowledge on the flavorful compounds that arise by heat caramelization of the sugars of bread. Baker et al. (1953) and Wiseblatt (1957) cite the maximum crust temperature of about 150°C. and conclude that the heat caramelization of sugars (unaffected by amino compounds) should have little effect on bread flavor. Linko and Johnson (1963) do not support this view. Regardless of this uncertain situation in bread making, the caramelization of naturally occurring sugars by heat alone is such a basic phenomenon for food science that it should not be bypassed. It is the simplest flavorful model browning system to study.

Of the several types of food components that interact to form carbonylic flavor compounds (and reactive carbonylic intermediates before the final flavor production), the reducing sugars on one hand and the amino acids and peptides of proteins on the other comprise the most important model system. Food browning flavors are most likely to arise here, from the Maillard reaction (Maillard 1912; Ellis 1959). Both the degradation of amino acids and the degradation of sugars must be examined, because both contribute carbonyl flavor compounds.

Many animal and vegetable proteins contain carbohydrate prosthetic groups. The mucoids and glycoproteins might decompose with browning differently from the separate sugar and amino acid components. Here the decomposition of 2-amino-2-deoxy sugars and non nitrogenous deoxysugars also should be considered. How does the carbohydrate already combined with protein decompose to yield flavor?

Lipids, by their oxidation (Schultz et al. 1962), yield flavorful carbonyl compounds. In addition, the aldehydes and α,β-unsaturated ketones from lipids may participate in browning reactions to produce other flavors (Montgomery and Day 1965). Polyunsaturated fatty acids yield malonaldehyde and other substances that react with 2-thiobarbituric acid and correlate with the rancidity of animal foods (Zipser et al. 1964).

These substances react with amino acids, proteins, glycogen, and other food constituents (Kwon et al. 1965) and probably are reactive browning intermediates (cf. Kato 1962). Acrolein from pyrolyzed fats or sugars is another aldehyde that would immediately react with other unsaturated compounds generated from carbohydrates, lipids, or proteins. The cross-reaction of such unsaturated carbonyl compounds should be studied in model systems to indicate reactions that can occur to alter the flavor of foods.

Just as glycoproteins should be considered separately from sugar and amino acid components, so should lipid-carbohydrate combinations be investigated separately. These preexist in the phosphatides that show browning reactions.

Neukom (1963) cited for flavor considerations condensed tannins, polyphenols, and flavonoids of bitter and astringent taste. These phenolics are likely substrates for nonenzymatic browning reactions (Burton et al. 1963). Rohan (1963, 1964) showed that reducing sugars, amino acids, and flavonoids are the main precursors of chocolate aroma. Browning reactions are involved after fermentation of the condensed tannins to yield sugars and reactive intermediate compounds, as in producing tea and cacao flavors (Purr et al. 1963; Rohan 1963, 1964; Rohan and Stewart 1965). Reductones produced by Maillard reactions and sugar caramelizations tend to inhibit lipid and oxidative browning reactions of the polyphenol type and possibly reduce off-flavors from these sources (Hodge 1953; Evans et al. 1958; Hodge et al. 1963).

The effect of some inorganic ions on promoting and inhibiting Maillard and ascorbic acid browning reactions is known (Bohart and Carson 1955; Jackson et al. 1960; Markuze 1963), and of course, the catalytic effects of heavy metal ions on lipid oxidations and subsequent browning are recognized. When added to maltose or sucrose caramelization mixtures, some inorganic salts intensify the flavor (Diemar and Hala 1959) and red color (Ikeda and Shimomiya 1963).

These are systems worthy of closer examination in the future. Now let us turn to what is known about sugar caramelization and the Maillard reaction in relation to food flavors.

NONENZYMATIC VS. ENZYMATIC FLAVORS

Flavors formerly considered of enzymatic origin now have been demonstrated to be wholly or partially nonenzymatic. Some common components in fermented foods are also nonenzymatic browning products; for example, pyruvaldehyde, acetol, acetoin, and diacetyl. Hanai (1956) showed that pyruvaldehyde and acetoin arise non-enzymatically upon cooking sweet potatoes, corn, molasses, sucrose, glucose, fructose, and maltose, but not starch. Lento *et al.* (1960) reported that acetol, pyruvaldehyde, and diacetyl were among the volatile products when glucose, fructose, or dihydroxyacetone solutions were heated in the pH range 4 to 12. Pyruvaldehyde was the predominant product at acidic pH, whereas the acetol and diacetyl yields increased with increasing pH. Yamada *et al.* (1957) showed that a disproportionation of pyruvaldehyde to acetic acid and acetoin occurred by the action of sunlight.

Vanilla and cacao beans need a heat-curing process to produce a full, characteristic flavor. Initial fermentations are conducted to release phenolics and nonenzymatic browning reactants, such as reducing sugars, amino acids, and flavonoids (Graves *et al.* 1958; Bailey *et al.* 1962; Rohan 1963, 1964; Dietrich *et al.* 1964). Fermentation also affects the flavor of maple syrup by the release of reducing sugars for caramelization reactions (Naghski *et al.* 1957). Filipic *et al.* (1965) found acetol as a major constituent in the flavor extract of maple syrup. Because the maple sap turns alkaline during boiling, at least part of the acetol is nonenzymatically formed.

Siefker and Pollack (1956) found that acetaldehyde and other aldehydes arise by the Maillard reaction in beer production. Bread flavor studies revealed the presence of some fermentation products in the volatiles (e.g., acetaldehyde, pyruvaldehyde, acetoin, and diacetyl) (Wiseblatt and Kohn 1960; Rothe and Thomas 1963; Wick *et al.* 1964). These should not be construed as necessarily arising from the dough fermentation, because they are also browning products.

SUGAR CARAMELIZATION

Sugars are colorless and generally sweet. As they are heated in the dry state to, at, and above, their melting points, they turn pale yellow, amber, orange brown, red brown, and finally to a very dark brown before foaming and carbonization yields a black residue. Flavor changes accompany the color changes. Burnt, bitter, and acrid flavors progressively overcome the sweet. But, between the bitter and the sweet, during the amber to medium brown stages, ethereal fragrances are detected that are universally appreciated. To capture the caramel aroma without the bitter, empyreumatic, and acrid notes has been a longstanding challenge to the cook and flavor technologist. Doubtless this problem could be solved more quickly if we knew what the compounds are. Fixatives might be found for the fleeting fragrant compounds, and the most important of them might be provided by synthesis.

The chemistry of sugar caramelization was reviewed by Zerban (1947) and Hodge (1953). Additional findings now can be recorded.

Flavoring caramel has long been made from sucrose or malt syrup. When sucrose is used, the dry crystals are melted slowly with stirring at about 160°C., a small volume of hot water is added to homogenize the melt, then the smooth syrup is reheated to drive off water and reach a desired degree of color and flavor. Small amounts of acidic substances are often added to hasten the inversion of sucrose to glucose and fructose. Also, small amounts of alkaline salts may be added to neutralize the sugar acids that are produced and to delay the dark color formation. An excess of alkali increases the caramelization rate (Hirschmüller and Eichorn 1958) and may change the nature of the products (Ramaiah et al. 1957A).

The question is: What are the flavor compounds that derive from caramelization processes?

Trillat (1905A, 1905B, 1906) reported that formaldehyde, methanol, acetone, acetic acid, phenolic substances, and benzaldehyde were formed by the caramelization of sucrose. Although his analytical methods were crude and are unacceptable today, his reported products have received some measure of confirmation.

Klein (1926) showed that heated solutions of the common sugars (glucose, fructose, galactose, maltose, lactose, sucrose) do yield formaldehyde. He isolated the dimedon derivative of formaldehyde from the distillates and determined its melting point. Trillat recognized that most of the formaldehyde would condense in the caramelized residue. In fact, he made a caramel from pure formalin by adding drops of strong alkali to it at elevated temperatures. Heating formalin with alkali gives a mixture of many aldo- and keto-hexoses (formose) by aldol condensation (Mariani and Torraca 1953; Ruckert et al. 1965). Trillat (1905C) claimed that the formalin (formose) caramel had the color, odor, and taste of sucrose caramel. This claim seems reasonable, since Ramaiah et al. (1957A, B) have reported that caramels prepared from the different sugars (crystalline D-glucose, commercial liquid glucose, fructose, and maltose), when heated in aqueous alkaline solution at 100°C., all gave the same pattern of four reducing spots on paper chromatograms. Upon heating these sugars as such, without added water or alkali, an additional common reducing spot was detected in each case along with the other four. They explained that after a Lobry de Bruyn-Alberda van Ekenstein transformation (Speck 1958), a single unknown compound of high molecular weight was formed (one of the four spots) which finally resulted in the production of coloring matter and appearance of the other unidentified spots (Ramaiah et al. 1957B, 1962). The contention that sucrose, glucose, fructose, maltose, and formose caramel are grossly similar is further supported by Bryce and Greenwood's findings (1963) that the 300°C. pyrolysis volatiles from sucrose, maltose, glucose, and starch, as determined by gas chromatography, are identical.

Puddington (1948) found, by measurements of activation energies during the thermal decompositions of sugars at 150° to 240°C. under high vacuum, that cellobiose (after the loss of two moles of water) decomposed in two distinct steps. Unlike cellobiose, maltose decomposed uniformly at a lower activation energy, with no change in the ratio of products as a function of temperature. D-Glucose first rapidly dimerized with the loss of five per cent water; then the further decomposition resembled that of cellobiose, not maltose.

The dimerization of glucose observed by Puddington (1948) can now be explained. Sugisawa and Edo (1964) showed that D-glucose, when heated at atmospheric pressure in a retort at 150°C. for 2.5 hr. until it became semiliquid and brown, gave the following compounds, in addition to ether-extracted 5-(hydroxymethyl)-2-furaldehyde:

glucose	sophorose
levoglucosan	cellobiose
isomaltose + kojibiose	laminaribiose
maltose + nigerose	isomaltotriose + panose
gentiobiose	higher oligosaccharides

These saccharide fractions were eluted from a carbon column and properly identified by derivatization. The gentiobiose (6-O-β-D-glucopyranosyl-D-glucopyranose) in this group is intensely bitter. Its presence, even in minor amounts, could lend bitterness to the entire glucose caramel. Also levoglucosan and mannose are both bitter and sweet.

Similarly, Diemar and Hala (1959) showed that maltose, when heated at 190°C. for about one hour, was split to glucosyl radicals which built up to disaccharides, trisaccharides, tetrasaccharides, and dextrins. Under these conditions, the flavor compound maltol (3-hydroxy-2-methyl-4H-pyran-4-one) was produced from maltose, but not from glucose. Mineral salts catalyzed the maltol formation.

Other research that revealed disaccharides and dimeric sugar anhydride formation in caramel is that of Müller and Täufel (1953) and Schneider (1958). Müller and Täufel showed that aqueous 40% invert sugar solutions, heated at 100°C., readily produce a number of difructose anhydrides (diheterolevulosan, McDonald 1946) in the absence of mineral acid catalysts, under conditions that produce no change in the 40% pure glucose solutions. Schneider also showed the more facile production of diheterolevulosan and difructosides under conditions where glucose did not react. According to Schneider, fructose is enolized 1,2- and 2,3- to glucose and psicose, respectively; then dihydroxyacetone is split out and rapidly converted to pyruvaldehyde, acetol, and lactic acid.

Hirschmüller (1958) reports the following sucrose caramelization products formed at 180°C.: carbon dioxide, carbon monoxide, methanol, acetaldehyde, benzaldehyde, acetone, acrolein, formic acid, acetic acid, furfural, and unidentified phenol derivatives. However, Rossi *et al.* (1962) could not find phenolic substances and benzaldehyde by chromatography of a distillate from dry-heated sucrose. In the solid melt Hirschmüller identified sucrose, glucose, fructose, glucosan, fructosan, glucosin (dextrin-like glucose polymers), fructosin, glyceraldehyde, dihydroxyacetone, pyruvic acid, 5-(hydroxymethyl)-2-furaldehyde, and humic substances. 5-(Hydroxymethyl)-2-furaldehyde has repeatedly been shown to be a hexose caramelization product, even in the pH range 6.0 to 6.7, but it is detected in lesser amounts in the more concentrated syrups (Sokolovskiĭ and Nikiforova 1957) where it is more likely to condense with other compounds.

Bollmann and Schmidt-Berg (1965) examined the first decomposition products of dry-heated sucrose and found glucose (at 130°C., 15 min.) reversion products (above 150°C.), fructose and its anhydrides (160°C.), and 5-(hydroxymethyl)-2-furaldehyde (above 170°C.). Among the di- and trisaccharides formed were 6-kestose and other fructosylsucroses.

Lukesch (1956) melted sucrose at 150°C. (the temperature of baking bread crusts), powdered the cooled melt, and extracted it with organic solvents. The solvent-free extracts when chromatographed on paper showed glucose, fructose, glyceraldehyde, dihydroxyacetone, pyruvic acid, pyruvaldehyde, and 5-(hydroxymethyl)-2-furaldehyde.

Table 82 lists some compounds that have been reported as carbohydrate caramelization and pyrolysis products. The flavors recorded are scattered through the literature and are by no means well substantiated. Most of the flavor entries probably represent casual observations at unstated concentrations. Therefore, Table 82 should be used only as a rought guide to the flavors of carbohydrate decomposition products.

At the much higher temperature of 300°C. in a nitrogen atmosphere, the following volatiles common to sucrose, glucose, maltose, isomaltose, starch, and cellulose were identified by gas chromatography (Bryce and Greenwood 1963):

Aldehydes	*Ketones*	*Furans*
acetaldehyde	acetone	furan
propionaldehyde	methyl ethyl ketone	2-methylfuran
n-butyraldehyde	methyl propyl ketone	2,5-dimethylfuran
valeraldehyde		
acrolein		

TABLE 82

FLAVORS OF CARBOHYDRATE CARAMELIZATION AND DEHYDRATION PRODUCTS

Compound	Formula	Color	Odor	Taste
Acyclics				
Carbon monoxide, dioxide	CO, CO_2	None	None	None
Formaldehyde	$H \cdot CHO$	None	Stinging, suffocating	...
Formic acid	$H \cdot COOH$	None	Painful	Sour
Acetaldehyde	$CH_3 \cdot CHO$	None	Penetrating, suffocating	...
Acetic acid	$CH_3 \cdot COOH$	None	Pungent, painful, vinegar, if dilute	Sour
Glycolaldehyde	$HO \cdot CH_2 \cdot CHO$	None	None	Sweet
Glyoxal	$CHO \cdot CHO$	Yellow	Pungent	Sweet
Glyoxylic acid	$CHO \cdot COOH$	...[1]	Suffocating	Sour
Lactic aldehyde	$CH_3 \cdot CHOH \cdot CHO$	None	None	Bitter
Lactic acid	$CH_3 \cdot CHOH \cdot COOH$	None	None	Sour
Acrolein	$CH_2 : CH \cdot CHO$	None	Acrid, scorched fat	...
Acrylic acid	$CH_2 : CH \cdot COOH$	None	Acrid	Sour
Pyruvaldehyde	$CH_3 \cdot CO \cdot CHO$	Yellow	Pungent, burning	...
Pyruvic acid	$CH_3 \cdot CO \cdot COOH$	Yellow	Acetic	Sour
Acetone	$CH_3 \cdot CO \cdot CH_3$	None	"Characteristic"	Sweet, burning
Acetol	$CH_3 \cdot CO \cdot CH_2 \cdot OH$	None	"Characteristic"	Sweet, burning
Dihydroxyacetone	$HO \cdot CH_2 \cdot CO \cdot CH_2 \cdot OH$	None	"Characteristic," pleasant	Sweet, cooling
Glyceraldehyde	$HO \cdot CH_2 \cdot CHOH \cdot CHO$	None	None	Sweet
Triose-reductone	$HO \cdot CH : C(OH) \cdot CHO$	None	None	Sour
Mesoxalic dialdehyde	$CHO \cdot C(OH)_2 \cdot CHO$	Yellow	Burnt sugar, when heated	...
Acetoin	$CH_3 \cdot CHOH \cdot CO \cdot CH_3$	None	Pleasant[2]	Sweetish[2]
Diacetyl	$CH_3 \cdot CO \cdot CO \cdot CH_3$	Green-yellow	Quinonic, buttery, chlorine-like	Sharp
Hydroxydiacetyl	$CH_3 \cdot CO \cdot CO \cdot CH_2 \cdot OH$	Orange-yellow	Sweetish	...
C-Methyl triose-reductone	$CH_3 \cdot CO \cdot C(OH) : CH \cdot OH$	None	...	...
Levulinic acid	$CH_3 \cdot CO \cdot (CH_2)_2 COOH$	None	None	Sour
Cyclics				
Furan	(furan ring)	None	Ethereal	...
2-Methyl furan	(furan ring)$-CH_3$	None	Ethereal	...
2,5-Dimethyl furan	CH_3-(furan ring)$-CH_3$	None	"Characteristic'	...
Furfuryl alcohol	(furan ring)$-CH_2 \cdot OH$	None	"Characteristic'	Bitter
2-Furoic acid	(furan ring)$-CO \cdot OH$	None	Stinging	Sour
2-Furaldehyde	(furan ring)$-CHO$	None	"Characteristic" (see text)	Sweet
5-Methyl-2-furaldehyde	CH_3-(furan ring)$-CHO$	None	Like 2-furaldehyde	...
5-(hydroxymethyl)-2-furaldehyde	$HO \cdot CH_2-$(furan ring)$-CHO$	None	None	Bitter, astringent
2-Furyl methyl ketone	(furan ring)$-CO \cdot CH_3$	None	Pleasant, ketonic	Burning, sweetish
2-Furyl hydroxymethyl ketone	(furan ring)$-CO \cdot CH_2OH$	None	None	Burning, sweetish
Isomaltol	(furan ring, $-OH$)$-CO \cdot CH_3$	None	Burnt, pungent, fruity see text)	Sour, sweet, fruity (see text)

TABLE 82 (*Continued*)

Compound	Formula	Color	Odor	Taste
4-Hydroxy-2,5-dimethyl-3(2 *H*)-furanone		None	Fragrant, fruity caramel, burnt pineapple	Burning, sweet
Reductic acid		None	None	Sour
1-Methylcyclo-pentenol(2)-one-(3)		None	Fragrant, burnt, licorice	Sweet
Maltol		None	Fragrant, caramel	Bitter, sweetish

[1] Colorless as the hydrated form.
[2] Traces of diacetyl usually interfere.

In addition, formaldehyde (by chromotropic acid reagent), formic acid, acetic acid, propionic acid, and a minute amount of methanol were detected. The yield of all volatiles was only about 0.2% of the carbohydrate pyrolyzed.

These compounds would lend flavor notes (Table 82), if they would be formed by local overheating during food processing. Reichstein and Beitter (1930) determined many of these compounds and others by classical methods in the distillates from dry-roasted, unfermented chicory. Gianturco *et al.* (1964) identified these and other furans in the aroma complex of coffee.

Without citation of all contributions in the latest literature, the progress made since 1953 on understanding the sugar caramelization process indicates the following as likely reaction steps: Enolization of aldoses with the production of the more reactive 2-ketoses; dehydration of ketohexoses, without fission, to 5-(hydroxymethyl)-2-furaldehyde, and dehydration of pentoses similarly to 2-furaldehyde; hydrolytic fission of furaldehydes or intermediates leading to furaldehydes to yield, for example, formic acid and levulinic acid from hexoses; fission of 2-ketoses to yield dihydroxyacetone and glyceraldehyde, glycolaldehyde and four-carbon carbonyl compounds; dehydration of the trioses to yield acetol and pyruvaldehyde; dismutation of biose, trioses, tetroses, and their dehydration products to yield lactic aldehyde, pyruvic aldehyde, lactic acid, glycolic acid, acetaldehyde, acetic acid, formaldehyde, formic acid, acetoin, and diacetyl; self- and cross-condensations of the aldehydes and ketones containing active hydrogen; reversion of aldoses and ketoses to di-, tri-, and higher oligosaccharides; dimerization of fructose to difructose anhydrides; cyclodehydration of aldoses to glycosans, and then polymerization; enolization and dehydration of the synthetic oligosaccharides. Evidence for most of these steps already has been given and more will appear under the Maillard reaction.

MAILLARD REACTION

Flavor production by nonenzymatic browning in foods proceeds mainly from reactions of reducing sugars with amines, amino acids, peptides, and proteins. Three pathways of the Maillard reaction are now clearly defined. From the main stem of sugar-amine condensation, enolization of the glycosylamines, and the Amadori transformation to 1-amino-1-deoxy-2-ketoses (Hodge 1953), two branches diverge (Fig. 103). In one branch, 3-deoxy hexosones are formed from the 1,2-eneaminol by elimination of the hydroxyl group on C-3 (Anet 1960, 1961, 1962A, 1962B, 1963A, 1963B, 1964; Kato 1962, 1963). In the other branch, the 1-amino-1-deoxy-2-ketose enolizes 2,3- irreversibly and eliminates the amine from C-1 to form a methyl α-dicarbonyl intermediate (Hodge 1953; Simon 1962; Hodge *et al.* 1963; Simon and Heubach 1965). Dehydration ocurs in both branches of Fig. 103, yielding α,β-unsaturated-α-dicarbonyl compounds (and their imino analogs) which presumably condense and polymerize to melanoidins (McWeeny and Burton 1963). 2-Furaldehydes are a distinctive end product of the first branch, whereas C-methyl aldehydes, keto-aldehydes, ketols, and reductones are products of the second.

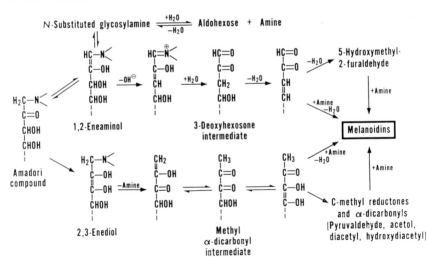

FIG. 103. TWO PATHWAYS OF REDUCING SUGARS TO MELANOIDINS IN THE MAILLARD REACTION

The 3-deoxyhexosones contain an α-dicarbonyl grouping on C-1 and C-2, whereas the methyl α-dicarbonyl intermediate contains it at C-2 and C-3. Both types of α-dicarbonyl intermediates would provide flavor compounds; e.g., furaldehydes from the 3-deoxyhexosones, and acetaldehyde, pyruvaldehyde, diacetyl, and acetic acid by hydrolytic fission of the methyl α-dicarbonyl intermediate and subsequent dehydration products. These compounds are already given as caramelization products of sugars. In the absence of amines, it can be assumed that 1,2-enolization of the sugar leads to the same transformations shown in Fig. 103. The hydroxyl group on C-3 and C-1 would be eliminated (at higher temperatures or under more acidic or alkaline reaction conditions) in the same way shown for glycosylamines and Amadori compounds. For example, maltol (with a C-methyl group) is formed from maltose by heat alone (Diemar and Hala 1959) and also in the presence of amino compounds (Patton 1950; Hodge et al. 1963); but the condensation with amino compounds allows the enolizations and eliminations to take place near neutral pH and at much lower temperatures.

Both branches of the reaction scheme provide active reagents for the degradation of α-amino acids to aldehydes and ketones of one less carbon atom (the Strecker degradation), which is the third pathway of the Maillard reaction that is well-defined and important for the origin of flavor in foods.

Practical Aspects of the Strecker Degradation

Patents have been granted to cover the production of food flavors via the Maillard reaction. For example, Kremers (1948) produced an imitation maple flavoring by heating sugars with α-aminobutyric acid, α-aminoisobutyric acid, serine, threonine, and other α-amino acids of three to six carbon atoms. Rusoff (1958) produced an artificial chocolate flavor by heating a reducing sugar with a glycyl or alanyl peptide at 130°C. for eight minutes. Bitterness was supplied by adding an alkaloid, such as theobromine or caffeine, and astringency was introduced by adding quebracho or chestnut tannins. General Foods Corporation (1963) made flavors resembling chocolate, coffee, or tea by autoclaving mixtures of wheat bran and peanut flour with sugar and water for only a few minutes near 200°C. Morton and Sharples (1959) made a honey-flavored syrup by refluxing glucose with β-phenylalanine in water. This reaction was known to give a floral scent, like wilted roses (Ruckdeschel 1914), but the inventors added invert sugar syrup containing citric and glutamic acids to enhance the honey flavor. Labahov and Kerebinski (1958) reported a mushroom-flavored mixture that was formed by heating glucose with sodium glutamate for 1.25 hr. at 195°C.

A yeast-free, chemically-leavened "Instant Bread Mix," developed by the Quartermaster Corps for use by the Armed Forces, gave a good-textured bread that had only a raw, starchy taste. Flavor for the bread was easily synthesized, however, by use of the Maillard reaction. Ruckdeschel (1914) had shown that glucose and leucine when heated together produced a bready aroma. Kiely *et al.* (1960) added only 0.05 to 0.10% leucine to the Instant Bread Mix, which already contained glucose, and thereby produced by baking a toasted bread-like aroma. The further addition of histidine or arginine added buttery notes and gave the finshed bread an acceptable flavor.

Keeney and Day (1957) incubated milk protein hydrolyzates with pyruvic acid, isatin, or ninhydrin for 18 hr. at room temperature and then distilled out cheese-like aromas. A small amount of such a distillate, when added to cottage cheese, produced a Cheddar-type flavor.

These practical accomplishments are based on a fundamental chemical reaction that is only one part of the total Maillard complex; namely, the Strecker degradation (Schönberg and Moubacher 1952; Hodge 1953).

Strecker Degradation

The so-called oxidative degradation of α-amino acids to aldehydes of one less carbon atom by compounds such as alloxan, ninhydrin, and 2-furaldehyde was more precisely defined by Schönberg *et al.* (1948). They demonstrated that the amino group must be α-to the carboxyl group and that the carbonyl compound must contain a $-C{:}O-C{:}O-$ or a $-C{:}O-$ $(CH{:}CH)_n$ $-C{:}O$-grouping. The reaction is illustrated by the following equation:

$$R\cdot CO\cdot CO\cdot R' + R''\cdot CH(NH_2)\cdot COOH \rightarrow R''\cdot CHO + CO_2 + R\cdot CH(NH_2)\cdot CO\cdot R$$

If the hydrogen on the α-carbon of the amino acid is substituted, a ketone is produced. For example, acetone is formed from α-aminoisobutyric acid, $CH_3\cdot C(CH_3)NH_2\cdot COOH$. 2-Furaldehyde is operative because it yields an α-diketone and a conjugated dicarbonyl compound by hydrolytic ring-opening. If the dicarbonyl compound is pyruvic acid, it would be converted to α-alanine during the reaction. Such transaminations incorporate nitrogen into the sugar-derived dicarbonyl compounds and eventually into the melanoidins (Fig. 103).

Table 82 shows several α-dicarbonyl compounds that are produced by simple heat treatment of carbohydrates. Each of these may react with protein hydrolysis products to produce flavorful aldehydes. Furthermore, sugar-derived, nonvolatile α-dicarbonyl compounds (Fig. 103) and dehydroascorbic acid are likely reagents for inducing the Strecker degradation. From Fig. 103 it is evident that the active dicarbonyl compounds can arise nonoxidatively from sugars.

The most reasonable mechanism for the Strecker degradation (Schönberg and Moubacher 1952) provides for Shiff base formation in the first step to form, for example, from pyruvaldehyde and α-alanine:

$$CH_3-\overset{\overset{O}{\parallel}}{C}-\overset{\overset{H}{|}}{C}=N-\overset{\overset{H}{|}}{\underset{\underset{CH_3}{|}}{C}}-\overset{\overset{O}{\parallel}}{C}-OH \rightleftarrows CH_3-\overset{\overset{OH}{|}}{C}=C-N=\overset{\overset{H}{|}}{\underset{\underset{CH_3}{|}}{C}}-\overset{\overset{O}{\parallel}}{C}-OH$$

The enolic tautomeric form is an α-imino acid, known to decarboxylate readily. Decarboxylation would yield:

$$CH_3-\overset{\overset{OH}{|}}{C}=C-\overset{H}{N}=\overset{H}{C}-CH_3 + CO_2$$

Now the eneaminol could self-condense to brown polymer or hydrolyze to aminoacetone, $CH_3 \cdot C:O \cdot CH_2 \cdot NH_2$, and acetaldehyde, $CH_3 \cdot CHO$.

TABLE 83

FLAVORS OF HEATED $1:1$ α-AMINO ACID-GLUCOSE MIXTURES

α-Amino Acid	Formula R·CH(NH₂)·COOH R=	Volatile Strecker Aldehyde RCHO	Aroma Noted by Panel 100°C.	180°C.	Reference[1]
None			None	Caramel	H-S
Glycine	H—	Formaldehyde	Caramel	Burnt sugar	H-S
			Caramel		K-N-M
α-Alanine	CH₃—	Acetaldehyde	Caramel, sweet	Burnt sugar	H-S
α-Aminobutyric	CH₃·CH₂—	Propionic	Caramel	Burnt sugar	H-S
			Maple syrup		B-K
Valine	(CH₃)₂CH—	Isobutyric	Rye bread	Penetrating chocolate	H-S
			Fruity aromatic		K-N-M
Leucine	(CH₃)₂CH·CH₂—	Isovaleric	Sweet, chocolate	Burnt cheese	H-S
			Toasted, bready		K-N-M
Isoleucine	CH₃·CH₂·CH(CH₃)—	2-Methyl-butanal-(1)	Musty	Burnt cheese	H-S
			Fruity aromatic		K-N-M
Serine	HO·CH₂—	Glycolic	Maple syrup		B-K
Threonine	CH₃·CHOH—	Lactic	Chocolate	Burnt	H-S
Methionine	CH₃·S·CH₂·CH₂—	Methional	Potato	Potato	H-S
Phenylglycine	C₆H₅—	Benzaldehyde	Bitter almond		B-K
Phenylalanine	C₆H₅·CH₂—	α-Toluic	Violets	Violets, lilac	H-S
			Rose perfume		K-N-M
Tyrosine	HO·C₆H₄·CH₂—		Caramel		H-S
Proline			Burnt protein	Pleasant, bakery aroma	H-S
Hydroxyproline			Potato		K-N-M
Histidine			None	Cornbread	H-S
				Buttery note	K-N-M
Arginine	H₂N·C:NH·NH·(CH₂)₃—			Burnt sugar	H-S
			Buttery note		K-N-M
Lysine·HCl	H₂N·(CH₂)₄—		None	Bread-like	H-S
Aspartic	HOOC·CH₂—		Rock candy	Caramel	H-S
Glutamic	HOOC·CH₂·CH₂—		Caramel	Burnt sugar	H-S
Glutamine	H₂N·CO·CH₂·CH₂—		Chocolate, pleasant	Butterscotch	H-S
Cysteine·HCl	HS·CH₂—		Sulfide		H-S
			Meaty		K-N-M
Cystine	—CH₂·S·S·CH₂—		Sulfide		H-S
			Burnt turkey skin		K-N-M

[1] B-K = Barnes and Kaufman 1947; H-S = Herz and Shallenberger 1960; K-N-M = Kiely et al. 1960.

Thus a small amount of aldehyde of one less carbon atom than the α-amino acid would be liberated to contribute to flavor, along with other carbonyl compounds that would be generated from the sugar.

Table 83 shows the volatile Strecker degradation aldehydes that are formed from common α-amino acids, and also aromas that have been reported by taste panels for the volatile browning products. The recorded aromas are generally more complex and different from those of the Strecker aldehydes. The fact that different aromas are produced by the same reaction mixtures heated to different temperatures shows that cross reactions between the sugar carbonyl compounds (or melanoidins) and the Strecker aldehydes will occur to produce new flavors. The opportunities for producing a wide variety of food flavors via the Maillard reaction are therefore broad.

Strecker degradations of α-amino acids performed with isatin as the α-dicarbonyl compound (instead of a sugar) gave some aromas different from those listed in Table 83 (Keeney and Day 1957). For example, from the acidified solutions heated 15 min. at 100°C., alanine gave a malty aroma; valine, apple; leucine, malty; isoleucine, malty apple; proline, mushroom; glutamic acid, bacterial agar; and methionine, cheesy-brothy. The aromas in Table 83 therefore probably contain a significant contribution from the sugar moiety.

Rothe and Voight (1963) reacted xylose with 21 different amino acids. They tasted the nonvolatile browning products and found that their flavor also depended on the α-amino acid involved.

Specific Flavor Compounds

If the question is asked, which of the compounds in Table 82 could be responsible for the fragrant caramel aroma that is so universally popular, only a few would attract attention. Most of the volatile acyclic sugar degradation products have a sharp, penetrating pungency that hinders an evaluation of their possible contribution to caramel flavor. At high dilutions of the vapor in air, burnt notes have been ascribed to the di- and tri-ketones (pyruvaldehyde, diacetyl, and mesoxalic dialdehyde). The cyclic compounds of Table 82 are much less pungent than the acyclic and lend themselves to more exact flavor descriptions.

The best-known browning products are furfurals. 2-Furaldehyde is said to have the odor of oil of cassia (like cinnamic aldehyde) mixed with oil of bitter almonds (like benzaldehyde), but not as fragrant as either (Fownes 1845). In high dilutions it is said to resemble the odor of fresh bread (Moncrieff 1944). Indeed, 2-furaldehyde and 5-(hydroxymethyl)-2-furaldehyde are found in bread volatiles, crust, and crumb and are the most stable of bread aldehydes (Collyer 1964; see also Chapter 8).

Whereas 2-furaldehyde could contribute largely to bread flavor, pure 5-(hydroxymethyl)-2-furaldehyde is lowly volatile and odorless; its taste is rather bitter and astringent.

Reichstein and Beitter (1930) dry-distilled fresh chicory that was free from enzymatic degradation and identified acetaldehyde, acetic acid, acetol, acetone, lactic acid, pyruvic acid, and diacetyl, along with large quantities of 2-furaldehyde, 5-(hydroxymethyl)-2-furaldehyde, furfuryl alcohol, and smaller amounts of 2-furoic acid 2-furyl methyl ketone, and maltol (I). Flavorful roasted chicory therefore yields many compounds common to bread, coffee (see also Chapter 20), and sugar caramelization products in general.

Maltol (I) is a trace end product of nonenzymatic browning reactions of the Maillard type (Patton 1950; Hodge and Nelson 1961; Hodge et al. 1963; Beitter 1963; Bohnsack 1964). These references document its occurrence in larch bark, in dry needles of coniferous trees, and in the distillates or roasted substance from soft woods, cellulose, chicory, cacao (Dietrich et al. 1964), coffee beans, soybeans, cereals, and diastatic flour doughs. It has been found in overheated skimmilk, condensed and dried milks, dried whey, malzkaffee, soy sauce, and bread crusts. Experimentally, maltol has been formed by the caramelization of maltose and certain maltooligosaccharides, but has not been formed in isolable amounts from glucose, sucrose, or pure starch (Backe 1910; Diemar and Hala 1959). From model Maillard-type browning reactions, maltol was isolated in up to 0.2% yields from autoclaved aqueous solutions of maltose or lactose with glycine (Patton 1950) and in up to two per cent yields from maltose in nearly dry reactions with piperidine salts (Hodge et al. 1963); however, no maltol was isolated from parallel reactions with glucose or galactose. Therefore, maltol is assumed to arise from 4-O-substituted glucose derivatives (e.g., maltose, lactose, cellobiose, maltooligosaccharides) by browning reactions with amino compounds.

Maltol itself gives a fragrant, caramel-like aroma, which resembles the burnt sugar of confections, such as pralines; its taste in dilute solutions gives burnt and fruity notes (Hodge and Moser 1961). At concentrations of only 5 to 250 p.p.m. (at which its own flavor can be neglected), maltol is said to enhance the flavor and sweetness of soft drinks, fruit juices, syrups, cakes, sweet rolls, ice cream, gelatin desserts, and other carbohydrate-rich foods (Anon. 1962A,B; Olsen 1964). It is "generally recognized as safe" as a food flavoring substance (Anon. 1962C; Olsen 1964; Bohnsack 1964).

Another compound with a fragrant burnt sugar odor is 1-methyl-cyclopentenol-2-one-3 (II). This compound, originally found in wood distillate (Meyerfeld 1912), also has been produced in small amounts by heating galactose in aqueous sodium hydroxide solution (Enkvist et al. 1954) and by refluxing glyceraldehyde or glucose with acetone in aqueous alkali (Fray 1961). Gianturco et al. (1963) isolated it from the aroma complex of coffee along with the enolic forms of 3,4-dimethyl-cyclopentane-1,2-dione, 3,5-dimethylcyclopentane-1,2-dione, 3-ethylcyclo-pentane-1,2-dione, and 3-methylcyclohexane-1,2-dione. Filipic et al. (1965) found methylcyclopentenolone in maple syrup. The structure II was fixed by Rojahn and Rühl (1926) and by Bredenberg (1959). Solutions of II are sweet and the flavor resembles licorice. It is used in walnut, maple, and butterscotch flavorings.

Compound III, 4-hydroxy-2,5-dimethyl-3(2H)-furanone, was prepared by reacting the 6-deoxyhexose, rhamnose, with piperidine acetate in ethanol at 75°C. (Hodge and Fisher 1963; Hodge et al. 1963). The structure shown, assigned from chemical, infrared, ultraviolet, and nuclear magnetic resonance data in 1963, has now been proven (Fisher and Hodge, 1965). The same compound was isolated from pineapples by preparative gas chromatography (Rodin et al. 1965) and was described as the major "character impact" component of pineapple flavor concentrate. Cystalline II is said to have an intense, fragrant, fruity-caramel odor resembling "burnt pineapple" or strawberry preserves. Nevertheless, the first and most frequent odor description among a dozen panelists was merely burnt sugar. Compound III is unstable in air at 25°C.; and, in water solution, it slowly hydrolyzes and reduces 2,6-dichloroindophenol solution as the ring opens by hydrolysis to form a reductone (Hodge et al. 1963).

A compound similar to III, with hydrogen in place of the enolic hydroxyl group; i.e. 2,5-dimethyl-3-(2H)-furanone, was synthesized as an unstable liquid with the odor of bread (Rosenkranz et al. 1963). However, this compound is not known as a sugar-amine reaction product.

The same reaction that produced the pseudo-reductone (III) from rhamnose, produced 2-(3-β-D-galactopyranosyloxy)furyl methyl ketone (i.e. isomaltol β-D-galactopyranoside) from lactose. Isomaltol (IV) was then produced from the galactoside by pyrolysis or hydrolysis (Hodge and Nelson 1961). The structure IV was proved by Fisher and Hodge (1964). This compound was isolated in trace amounts from bread crusts by Backe (1910) and was given the name isomaltol because it was thought to be a γ-pyrone like maltol (I). Traces of maltol also were found by Backe in the bread crusts.

The flavor of isomaltol in 0.2% aqueous solution neutralized to pH 6 with soda was recorded by a taste panel of 31 as like burnt sugar, but with many sweet and fruity responses (Hodge and Moser 1961). As the crystalline solid, isomaltol gives a fragrant, weakly pungent, burnt sugar odor.

Compounds I, II, III, and IV are grossly similar in aroma (caramel-like); also in chemical structure. The structure common to I, II, and III is $CH_3—\overset{|}{C}=C(OH)—\overset{|}{C}:O$, whereas IV contains $CH_3—\overset{|}{C}:O—\overset{|}{C}=$ $\overset{|}{C}—OH$. When enolic hydrogen-bonded chelate structures IVa ⇌ IVb are considered for isomaltol, which does show the characteristic reactions

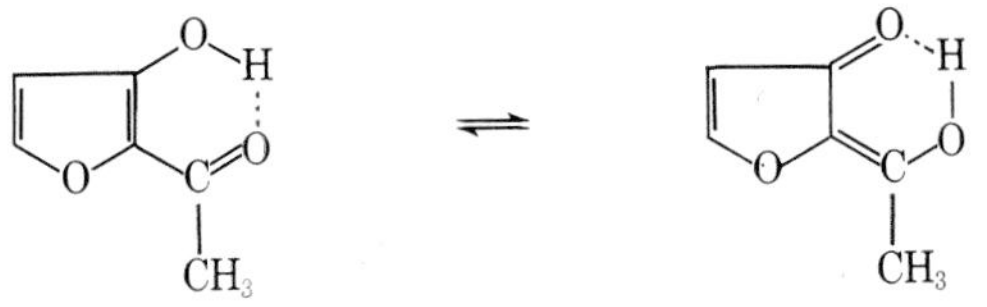

IVa   IVb

of a β-diketone, then the planarity of the molecule is evident. Also, resonance structures for the anion, vinylogous to a carboxylic acid, have been presented (Fisher and Hodge 1964).

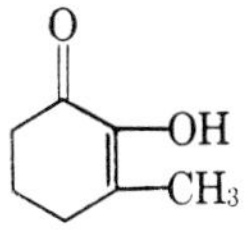

V

Compound V is the six-membered ring analog of II found among coffee aroma compounds (Gianturco *et al.* 1963). It also gives a burnt aroma, described as intense and quinone-like by Harries (1902).

If the methyl group of maltol (I) is not present, as in pyromeconic acid (VI), the pronounced caramel-like odor is lost (barely detectable in resublimed samples of VI), even though pyromeconic acid sublimes more readily than maltol. Rubiginol (VII) is odorless. If the methyl group

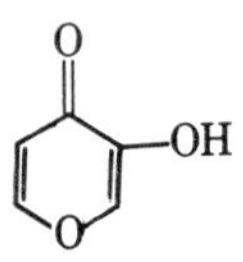

VI 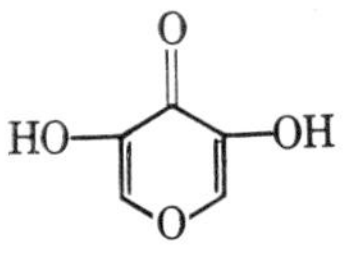   VII 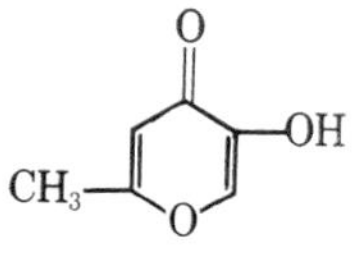   VIII

of maltol is moved away from the enolic hydroxyl group to the 6-position of the γ-pyrone ring, as in allomaltol (VIII), the prominent caramel odor is lost; also, if the enolic hydroxyl group is removed, as in 2,6-dimethyl-4*H*-pyran-4-one (IX).

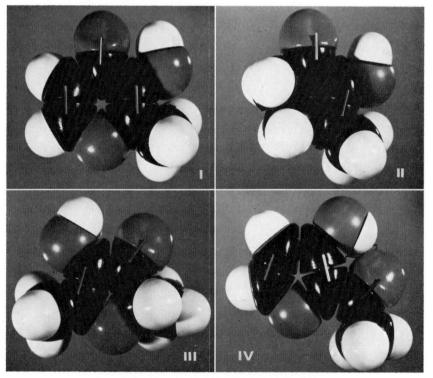

IX   X   XI

The maltol analog X, with an additional methyl group at the 6-position, was synthesized by Dashunin *et al.* (1963). It was said not to be a satisfactory replacement for maltol in raspberry flavorings. The isomer of X that has the methyl group of maltol replaced by an ethyl group [i.e.

FIG. 104.   STUART-BRIEGLEB MODELS

(I) Maltol; (II) methylcyclopentenolone; (III) 4-hydroxy-2,5-dimethyl-3(2*H*)furanone; and (IV) isomaltol.

the so-called ethyl maltol (XI)] is four to six times as powerful as maltol as a flavor enhancer and a sweetness synergist (Stevens and Rennhard 1965). Ethyl maltol is nine times more volatile from aqueous solution than maltol at room temperature. The increase in flavor intensity given by ethyl maltol over maltol, in going from the methyl to the ethyl group, is similar to the increase in vanilla-like flavor which is promoted by going from vanillin (XII) to ethyl vanillin (XIII).

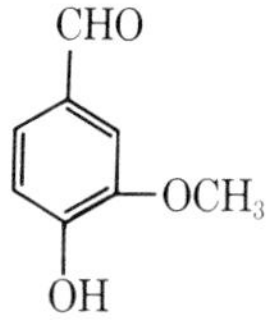

XII 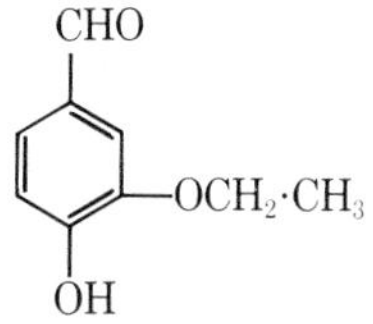   XIII

Ethyl vanillin (so-called) has 3.5 times the flavoring capacity of vanillin and gives a more pleasing aroma (Jacobs 1951).

Because it now appears that the methyl-enol-carbonyl grouping in I, II, III, and V (cf. XI), as well as the closely related grouping in IV, is productive of caramel flavor when these groups are located in planar or nearly planar rings (Fig. 104), it should be relevant to investigate the flavor of C-methyl triose-reductone (XIV) in neutralized solution. Compound XIV may exist in the planar, hydrogen-bonded, enol chelate structures XIVa and XIVb, which are analogous to the structures of isomaltol (IVa and IVb).

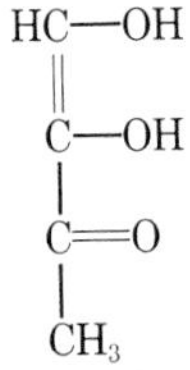

XIV 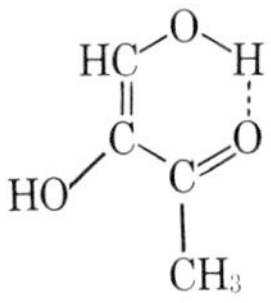   XIVa 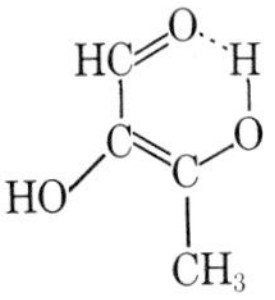   XIVb

The N-methylbenzylamino derivative of XIV (terminal enolic hydroxyl replaced by the secondary amino group) was isolated from a model glucose-amine salt browning reaction (Hodge et al. 1963).

This correlation of caramel-like flavor with chemical structure is presented to guide further research in this field and also the search for better flavoring compounds.

Formation of the Flavor Compounds

Steps for the formation of C-methyl flavor compounds, such as isomaltol and maltol from both lactose and maltose, 4-hydroxy-2,5-dimethyl-3(2H)-

furanone from rhamnose, and C-methyl triosereductone from glucose, are all explained through these initial steps (Hodge *et al.* 1963): (1) Condensation of the amino compound with aldose, followed by 1,2-enolization of the glycosylamine (in the Maillard reaction). In the absence of amine, 1,2-enolization of the aldehydo form of the aldose. (2) Ketonization of the 1,2-eneaminol or the 1,2-enediol to form 2-ketoses. (3) 2,3-Enolization of the 2-ketoses, with elimination of the amine (easy) or the C-1 hydroxyl (difficult) to produce $CH_2:C(OH)—C:O—CHOH—CHOH—CH_2OH$, which would ketonize to $CH_3—C:O—C:O—CHOH—CHOH—CH_2OH$. From this methyl-$\alpha$-dicarbonyl intermediate, further enolizations, dehydrations, and ring closures occur. After furanose ring closures and subsequent dehydration, isomaltol, and the pseudo-reductone from rhamnose are formed. After the pyranose ring closure, maltol may be formed. When the C-4 hydroxyl is unsubstituted, further enolizations and elimination of the terminal hydroxyl are promoted, although the sequences are not clear. A likely intermediate is diacetylformoin, $CH_3—C:O—C:O—CHOH—C:O—CH_3$, hydrolytic fission of which would yield pyruvaldehyde and acetoin, hydroxydiacetyl ($CH_3—C:O—C:O—CH_2OH$) and acetic acid, acetaldehyde and $CH_3—C:O—C:O—CHO$. From hydroxydiacetyl, C-methyl triose-reductone would form; and from the tricarbonyl C-methyl compound, acetic acid and glyoxal, acetaldehyde and glyoxylic acid, pyruvaldehyde and carbon monoxide, pyruvic acid and formaldehyde, and formic acid and pyruvaldehyde (all listed in Table 82) would form hydrolytically. Diacetylformoin, when self-condensed (aldol condensation) C-1 to C-5 carbonyl, and C-6 to C-2 carbonyl, would yield the cyclic hexose-reductones (Simon 1962; Hodge *et al.* 1963; Simon and Heubach 1965). When diacetylformoin is dehydrogenated in its reductone form, more of the C-methyl-α-dicarbonyl flavor compounds, including diacetyl, would arise from the polycarbonyl compound by loss of carbon monoxide.

The first reaction steps through Amadori compounds and the amine-elimination from C-1 are well-defined with secondary amine salt reagents but are not as well-defined with primary amine and amino acid reagents. Better defined with the primary amines is elimination of the hydroxyl on C-3 to form 3-deoxy hexosone intermediates which, with further dehydration, leads to furaldehydes (Anet 1964; Kato 1962, 1963). The extent to which each of the two main branches of the Maillard reaction (Fig 103) occurs in various foods remains to be determined.

CONCLUSION

The nonenzymatic browning reactions are not only a source of flavor (good and bad) in foods, they may be used also to synthesize some of the more desirable flavor compounds to add back to foods that are deficient in flavor. The Maillard reactions are the most important flavor-producing browning reactions that occur in foods on drying, processing, and cooking. For synthesizing the fragrant and more desirable browning products, the reactions of reducing sugars with basic secondary amine salts are productive. With secondary amines the amine-elimination step goes readily, with the eventual production of flavorful C-methyl-α-dicarbonyl compounds. Sugar caramelization in the absence of amino compounds is fundamentally important for the production of flavor compounds and, possibly, for forming flavor-fixing oligosaccharides; it should not be neglected in flavor studies.

DISCUSSION

E. A. Day.—Do you find much nitrogen in the polymers formed from the browning reaction?

J. E. Hodge.—Approximately three to four per cent. We do find C-methyl groups in the glucose-glycine model browning polymers. In our secondary amine salt reactions we can dilute with water, and get out a typical amorphous melanoidin which contains C-methyl groups. We have estimated for our secondary amine salts, 0.6 of a C-methyl per C_6 unit. In Wolfrom's glucose-glycine melanoidin he found about 0.3 of a C-methyl. Both of the arms, through Anet's mechanism and through our amine elimination, are operating and forming the melanoidin.

R. J. Bose.—Could you tell me if you tried any more sterically hindered amine salts like collidine hydrochlorides?

J. E. Hodge.—Yes, we tried for example 2-methylpiperidine and 2,6-dimethyl-piperidine. With 2,6-dimethylpiperidine, you can not get condensation with the glucose in the first place and consequently no following sequence of reactions. You can use di-isopropylamine which is strongly hindered and there will be little condensation with the sugar and consequently little browning, no more than what you would get from a tertiary amine.

K. Yoshikawa.—Could you tell me which compound had the strongest caramel flavor?

J. E. Hodge.—We will have to point to the pineapple-flavored compound as the strongest caramel flavored of this group because, when we took out a few milligrams to analyze in the microlab on the first floor, a few minutes later people all up and down the hall were looking out the doors wondering what was burning. Ethyl maltol also is quite flavorful, very volatile and has a very pleasant aroma.

BIBLIOGRAPHY

ANET, E. F. L. J. 1960. Degradation of carbohydrates. I. Isolation of 3-deoxyhexosones. Australian J. Chem. *13*, 396–403.

ANET, E. F. L. J. 1961. Degradation of carbohydrates. II. The action of acid and alkali on 3-deoxyhexosones. Australian J. Chem. *14*, 295–301.

ANET, E. F. L. J. 1962A. Formation of furan compounds from sugars. Chem. Ind. (London) *1962*, 262.

ANET, E. F. L. J. 1962B. Degradation of carbohydrates. III. Unsaturated hexosones. Australian J. Chem. 15, 503–509.

ANET, E. F. L. J. 1963A. Degradation of carbohydrates. IV. Formation of cis-unsaturated hexosones. Australian J. Chem. 16, 270–277.

ANET, E. F. L. J. 1963B. Unsaturated sugars: enols of 3-deoxy-D-"glucosone." Chem. Ind. (London) 1963, 1035–1036.

ANET, E. F. L. J. 1964. 3-Deoxyglycosuloses. Advan. Carbohydrate Chem. 19, 181–218.

ANON. 1962A. Pfizer flavor enhancer making its debut today. Oil Paint Drug Reptr. 181, No. 3, 7, 52.

ANON. 1962B. Flavor enhancers, with a heady aroma of growth, lure U.S. chemical producers. Oil Paint Drug Reptr. 181, No. 19, 3.

ANON. 1962C. Federal Register, December 29.

BACKE, A. 1910. On a new compound contained in food products. Compt. Rend. 150, 540–543; 151, 78–80.

BAILEY, S. D., MITCHELL, D. G., BAZINET, M. L., and WEURMAN, C. 1962. Volatile compounds of different varieties of cocoa beans. J. Food Sci. 27, 165–170.

BAKER, J. C., PARKER, H. K., and FORTMANN, K. L. 1953. Flavor of bread. Cereal Chem. 30, 22–30.

BARNES, H. M., and KAUFMAN, C. W. 1947. Industrial aspects of browning reaction. Ind. Eng. Chem. 39, 1167–1170.

BEITTER, H. 1963. Maltol. Ber. Getreidechemiker-Tagung, Detmold 1963, 69–75; Brot Gebaeck 17, No. 7, 132–134.

BOHART, G. S., and CARSON, J. F. 1955. Effects of trace metals, oxygen, and light on the glucose-glycine browning reaction. Nature (London) 175, 470–471.

BOHNSACK, H. 1964. Essential oil, perfumes, and flavor. IX. Maltol (2-methyl pyromeconic acid). Koerperpflegemittel 14, 33–34.

BOLLMANN, D., and SCHMIDT-BERG, S. 1965. The first decomposition products of dry-heated sucrose. Z. Zuckerind. 15, No. 4, 179–184; No. 5, 259–265.

BREDENBERG, J. B. 1959. The enol structure of 3-methylcyclopentane-1,2-dione. Acta Chem. Scand. 13, 1733–1766.

BRYCE, D. J., and GREENWOOD, C. T. 1963. The thermal degradation of starch. Part II. The identification by gas chromatography of the minor volatile products produced at 300°C. Die Stärke 15, 285–290.

BURTON, H. S., McWEENY, D. J., and PANDHI, P. N. 1963. Non-enzymatic browning: Browning of phenols and its inhibition by sulfur dioxide. Nature (London) 199, 659–661.

COLLYER, D. M. 1964. Bread flavor—a review of the literature to October 1963. Baker's Digest 38, No. 1, 43–46, 48, 50–54.

DASHUNIN, V. M., TOVBINA, M. S., FRIDMAN, S. A., and BELOV, V. N. 1963. Synthesis of perfumes. Derivatives of 3-hydroxy-γ-pyrone. Tr. Vses. Nauchm.-Issled. Inst. Sintetich. i Natural'n No. 6, 73–80; Chem. Abstr. 61, 11842f.

DIEMAR, W., and HALA, H. 1959. Contribution to the formation of 2-methyl-3-hydroxypyrone (maltol). Z. Lebensm.-Untersuch.-Forsch. 110, 161–168.

DIETRICH, P., LEDERER, E., WINTER, M., and STOLL, M. 1964. Flavors XI. Cocoa flavor. I. Helv. Chim. Acta 47, 1581–1590.

ELLIS, G. P. 1959. The Maillard reaction. Advan. Carbohydrate Chem. *14*, 63–134.

ENKVIST, T., ALFREDSSON, B., MERIKALLIO, M., PÄÄKKÖNEU, P., and JÄRVELLA, O. 1954. Formation of methylcyclopentenolone by digestion of spruce wood or galactose with sodium hydroxide solutions at 100°C. Acta Chem. Scand. *8*, 51–59.

EVANS, C. D., MOSER, H. A., COONEY, P. A., and HODGE, J. E. 1958. Amino-hexose-reductones as antioxidants. I. Vegetable Oils. J. Am. Oil Chemists' Soc. *35*, 84–88.

FILIPIC, V. J., UNDERWOOD, J. C., and WILLITS, C. O. 1965. The identification of methylcyclopentenolone and other compounds in maple sirup flavor extract. J. Food Sci. *30*, 1008–1015.

FISHER, B. E., and HODGE, J. E. 1964. The structure of isomaltol. J. Org. Chem. *29*, 776–781.

FISHER, B. E., and HODGE, J. E. 1965. Structure of a hydroxyfuranone from L-rhamnose. Abstracts of Papers, 150th Meeting, Am. Chem. Soc., September, p. 4D.

FOWNES, G. 1845. Synthetic formation of an organic base. Ann. *54*, 54.

FRAY, G. I. 1961. The formation of 3(or 5)-methylcyclopent-2-en-2-ol-1-one from acetone. Tetrahedron *14*, 161–163.

GENERAL FOODS CORPORATION. 1963. A method of manufacturing food flavors. Belgian Pat. 631,101. Nov. 4.

GIANTURCO, M. A., GIAMMARINO, A. S., FRIEDEL, P., and FLANAGAN, V. 1964. The volatile constituents of coffee. IV. Furanic and pyrrolic compounds. Tetrahedron *20*, 2951–2961.

GIANTURCO, M. A., GIAMMARINO, S., and PITCHER, R. G. 1963. Structures of five cyclic diketones isolated from coffee. Tetrahedron *19*, 2051–2059.

GRAVES, R. E., HALL, R. L., and KARAS, A. J. 1958. Cured vanilla extract from green vanilla beans. U.S. Pat. 2,835,591. May 20; Chem. Abstr. *52*, 18957e.

HANAI, S. 1956. Biacetyl. VI. Formation of methylglyoxal and acetoin by cooking of raw materials for fermentation, and detection of these compounds by paper chromatography. Nippon Jôzô Kyôkai Zasshi *51*, 892–896; Chem. Abstr. *51*, 17076i.

HARRIES, C. 1902. A cyclic ketotriose and its conversion to methyl-*o*-diketo-hexamethylene. Ber. *35*, 1176–1178.

HERZ, W. J., and SHALLENBERGER, R. S. 1960. Some aromas produced by simple amino acid, sugar reactions. Food Res. *25*, 491–494.

HEYNS, K., and PAULSEN, H. 1960. On the chemical basis of the Maillard reaction. Wiss. Veroeffentl. Deut. Ges. Ernaehrung *5*, 15–42.

HIRSCHMÜLLER, H. 1958. Dry thermal decomposition of sucrose. Intern. Sugar J. *60*, 51.

HIRSCHMÜLLER, H., and EICHORN, H. 1958. Relation between acid formation and color in the dry heating of sucrose. Z. Zuckerind. *8*, 111–114.

HODGE, J. E. 1953. Chemistry of browning reactions in model systems. J. Agr. Food Chem. *1*, 928–943.

HODGE, J. E., and FISHER, B. E. 1963. Structure of a pseudo-reductone from L-rhamnose. Abstracts of Papers, 145th Meeting, Am. Chem. Soc., September, p. 3D.

HODGE, J. E., FISHER, B. E., and NELSON, E. C. 1963. Dicarbonyls, reductones, and heterocyclics produced by the reactions of reducing sugars with secondary amine salts. Am. Soc. Brewing Chemists Proc. 1963, 84–92.

HODGE, J. E., and MOSER, H. A. 1961. Flavor of bread and pastry upon addition of maltol, isomaltol, and galactosylisomaltol. Cereal Chem. 38, 221–228.

HODGE, J. E., and NELSON, E. C. 1961. Preparation and properties of galactosylisomaltol and isomaltol. Cereal Chem. 38, 207–221.

IKEDA, I., and SHIMOMIYA, M. 1963. Caramel. Japanese Pat. 7079. May 25; Chem. Abstr. 60, 7374a.

JACKSON, S. F., CHICHESTER, C. O., and JOSLYN, M. A. 1960. The browning of ascorbic acid. Food Res. 25, 484–490.

JACOBS, M. B. (Editor). 1951. The Chemistry and Technology of Food and Food Products. 2nd Edition. Vol. II. p. 1653. Interscience Publishers New York.

KAMADA, H., and NAKANO, M. 1961. Production of caramel by the Maillard reaction. Nosan Kako Gijutsu Kenkyu Kaishi 8, 81–86; Chem Abstr. 59, 13275g.

KATO, H. 1962. Chemical studies on amino-carbonyl reaction. I. Isolation of 3-deoxypentosone and 3-deoxyhexosones formed by browning degradation of N-glycosides. Agr. Biol. Chem. (Tokyo) 26, 187–192.

KATO, H. 1963. Chemical studies on amino-carbonyl reaction. II. Identification of D-glucosone formed by oxidative browning degradation of N-D-glucoside. Agr. Biol. Chem. (Tokyo) 27, 461–466.

KEENEY, M., and DAY, E. A. 1957. Probable role of the Strecker degradation of amino acids in development of cheese flavor. J. Dairy Sci. 40, 874–876.

KIELY, P. J., NOWLIN, A. C., and MORIARTY, J. H. 1960. Bread aromatics from browning systems. Cereal Sci. Today 5, 273–274.

KLEIN, G. 1926. Splitting out of aldehydes from various sugars. Biochem. Z. 169, 132–138.

KREMERS, R. E. 1948. Imitation maple flavor. U.S. Pat. 2,446,478. Aug. 3; Chem. Abstr. 42, 8006f.

KWON, T-W., MENZEL, D. B., and OLCOTT, H. S. 1965. Reactivity of malonaldehyde with food constituents. J. Food Sci. 30, 808–813.

LABAHOV, D. I., and KEREBINSKI, C. 1958. Formation of melanoidins by heating a mixture of sodium glutamate and glucose. Izvest. Vysshikh Ucheb. Zavedenič Pishchevaya Tekhnol. 1958, No. 4, 123–130.

LENTO, A. G., UNDERWOOD, J. C., and WILLITS, C. O. 1960. The effect of pH on the volatile products of reducing sugars. Food Res. 25, 750–755.

LINKO, Y., and JOHNSON, J. A. 1963. Changes in amino acids and formation of carbonyl compounds during baking. J. Agr. Food Chem. 11, 150–152.

LUKESCH, H. 1956. Breakdown products of caramelized sucrose. Naturwissenschaften 43, 108–109.

MCDONALD, E. J. 1946. The polyfructosans and difructose anhydrides. Advan. Carbohydrate Chem. 2, 253–277.

MCWEENY, D. J., and BURTON, H. S. 1963. Some possible glucose/glycine browning intermediates and their reactions with sulphites. J. Sci. Food Agr. 14, 291–302.

MAILLARD, L. C. 1912. Action of amino acids on sugars; formation of melanoidins in a methodical way. Compt. Rend. 154, 66–68.

MARIANI, E., and TORRACA, G. 1953. The composition of formose. Intern. Sugar J. 55, 309–311.

MARKUZE, Z. 1963. Effects of trace metals on the browning of glucose-lysine solutions. Roczniki Panstwowego Zakladu Hig. 14, No. 1, 65–70; Chem. Abstr. 59, 4980h.

MEYERFELD, J. 1912. A new substance occurring in wood vinegar. Chem. Zeitung 36, 549–552; Chem. Zentr. 1912, II 117–118.

MONCRIEFF, R. W. 1944. Chemical Senses. L. Hill, London. pp. 206, 209.

MONTGOMERY, M. W., and DAY, E. A. 1965. Aldehyde-amine condensation reaction: A possible fate of carbonyls in foods. J. Food Sci. 30, 828–832.

MORTON, I. D., and SHARPLES, E. 1959. Honey flavoring. U.S. Pat. 2,916,-382. Dec. 8; Chem. Abstr. 54, 5981.

MÜLLER, K., and TÄUFEL, K. 1953. The changes in glucose and invert sugar on heating. Biochem. Z. 324, 221–227.

NAGHSKI, J., REED, L. L., and WILLITS, C. O. 1957. Maple syrup. X. Effect of controlled fermentation of maple sap on the color and flavor of maple syrup. Food Res. 22, 176–181.

NEUKOM, H. 1963. On chemical problems in food technology. Chimia (Aarau) 17, 225–232.

OLSEN, R. D. 1964. 15 ppm maltol replaces 5-15 per cent sugar in beverages. Food Processing 25, No. 1, 95.

PATTON, S. 1950. The formation of maltol in certain carbohydrate-glycine systems. J. Biol. Chem. 184, 131–134.

PUDDINGTON, I. E. 1948. The thermal decomposition of carbohydrates. Can. J. Res. 26B, 415–431.

PURR, A., SPRINGER, R., and MORCINEK, H. 1963. Enzymic changes in the cacao bean during fermentation. II. Occurrence and importance of hydrolases in resting and germinating beans. Z. Lebensm.-Untersuch.-Forsch. 123, 102–110.

RAMAIAH, N. A., AGARWAL, S. K. D., and AGARWAL, J. K. P. 1957A. Composition of caramel prepared by heating sugars. Current Sci. (India) 26, 81–82.

RAMAIAH, N. A., AGARWAL, S. K. D., and AGARWAL, J. K. P. 1957B. Chromatographic studies on the kinetics of the production of caramel. Indian Acad. Sci. 45A, 97–104.

RAMAIAH, N. A., AGARWAL, S. K. D., and KUMAR, M. B. 1962. Quantitative investigations on the production of organic acids during alkaline destruction of reducing sugars—a mechanism for caramelization. Proc. Intern. Soc. Sugar-Cane Technologists 11, 932–940.

REICHSTEIN, T., and BEITTER, H. 1930. The composition of the aroma substances of roasted chicory. Ber. 63, 816–826.

REYNOLDS, T. M. 1963. Chemistry of nonenzymic browning. I. The reaction between aldoses and amines. In Advances in Food Res. 12, 1–51, Academic Press Inc., New York.

REYNOLDS, T. M. 1965. Chemistry of nonenzymic browning. II. In Advances in Food Res. 14, 167–283. Academic Press Inc., New York.

RODIN, J. O., HIMEL, C. M., SILVERSTEIN, R. M., LEEPER, R. W., and GORTNER, W. A. 1965. Volatile flavor and aroma constituents of pineapple. I. Isolation and tentative identification of 2,5-dimethyl-4-hydroxy-3(2H)-furanone. J. Food Sci. 30, 280–285.

ROHAN, T. A. 1963. Precursors of chocolate aroma. J. Sci. Food Agr. *14*, 799–805.

ROHAN, T. A. 1964. The precursors of chocolate aroma: A comparative study of fermented and unfermented cocoa beans. J. Food Sci. *29*, 456–459.

ROHAN, T. A., and STEWART, T. 1965. The precursors of chocolate aroma: The distribution of free amino acids in different commercial varieties of cocoa beans. J. Food Sci. *30*, 416–419.

ROJAHN, C. A., and RÜHL, F. 1926. Clarification of the constitution of a methylcyclopentenolone occurring in wood vinegar distillate. Arch. Pharm. u. Ber Dtsch. Pharm. Ges. *264*, 211–227; Chem. Zentra. *1926*, I, 3319–3320.

ROSENKRANZ, R. E., ALLNER, K., GOOD, R., VON PHILLIPSBORN, W., and EUGSTER, C. H. 1963. The chemistry of simple furenidones (β-hydroxyfurans). Helv. Chim. Acta. *46*, 1259–1285.

ROSSI, P. F., GIOVENTU, L., and MASERA, F. 1962. Chromatographic studies of the products of sucrose pyrolysis. Ann. Chim. (Rome) *52*, 197–200.

ROTHE, M., and THOMAS, B. 1963. Aroma substances of bread. Z. Lebensm.-Untersuch.-Forsch. *119*, 302–309.

ROTHE, M., and VOIGHT, I. 1963. Browning and aroma production in the Maillard reaction. Naehrung 7, No. 1. 50–59.

RUCKDESCHEL, W. 1914. Melanoidins and their occurrence in kiln-dried malt. Z. Ges. Brauw. *37*, 430–432, 437–440.

RUCKERT, H., PFEIL, E., and SCHARF, G. 1965. Formaldehyde condensation. III. Steric course of sugar formation. Chem. Ber. 98, 2558–2565.

RUSOFF, I. I. 1958. Artificial chocolate flavor. U.S. Pat. 2,835,590. May 20; Chem. Abstr. *52*, 1895b.

SCHNEIDER, F. 1958. Reactions of glucose and frucose. Intern. Sugar J. *60*, No. 710 52.

SCHÖNBERG, A., and MOUBACHER, R. 1952. The Strecker degradation of α-amino acids. Chem. Rev. *50*, 261–277.

SCHÖNBERG, A., MOUBACHER, R., and MOSTOFA, A. 1948. Degradation of α-amino acids to aldehydes and ketones by interaction with carbonyl compounds J. Chem. Soc. *1948*, 176–182.

SCHULTZ, H. W., DAY, E. A., and SINNHUBER, R. O. (Editors) 1962. Symposium on Foods: Lipids and Their Oxidation. Avi Publishing Co., Westport, Conn.

SIEFKER, J. A., and POLLACK, G. E. 1956. Melanoidins in the brewing processes. I. Formation of aldehydes during wort boiling. Am. Soc. Brewing Chemists Proc. *1956*, 5–12.

SIMON, H. 1962. Mechanism of formation of piperidino-hexose-reductone. Ber. *95*, 1003–1008.

SIMON, H., and HEUBACH, G. 1965. Formation of alicyclic and open-chain nitrogenous reductones by reaction of secondary amine salts on monosaccharides. Chem. Ber. 98, 3703–3711.

SOKOLOVSKIĬ, A. L., and NIKIFOROVA, V. N. 1957. Products of sugar degradation and their effect on the properties of caramel. Zhur. Priklad. Khim. *30*, 1261–1263; Chem. Abstr. *52*, 2434–2435.

SPECK, J. C. 1958. The Lobry de Bruyn-Alberda van Ekenstein Transformation. Advan. Carbohydrate Chem. *13*, 63–103.

STEVENS, C., and RENNHARD, H. H. 1965. Personal communications and brochures of Chas. Pfizer and Co., New York, N. Y.

SUGISAWA, H., and EDO, H. 1964. Thermal polymerization of glucose. Chem. Ind. (London) 892–893 (May 23).

TRILLAT, A. 1905A. Antiseptic properties of smokes: attempts at disinfection with the vapors eliminated from sugar by heat. Compt. Rend. *141*, 215–217.

TRILLAT, A. 1905B. Formation of formaldehyde in the course of decomposition of sugar by heat. Bull. Assoc. Chim. Sucr. *23*, 249–652; Z. Ver. Rübenzuck.-Ind. *1906*, 95–103.

TRILLAT, A. 1905C. Observations on the role of formaldehyde in the caramelization of sugar. Bull. Assoc. Chim. Sucr. *23*, 652–655.

TRILLAT, A. 1906. On the presence of formaldehyde in caramelized substances. Compt. Rend. *142*, 454–456.

WICK, E., DE FIGUEIREDO, M., and WALLACE, D. H. 1964. The volatile components of white bread prepared by a pre-ferment method. Cereal Chem. *41*, 300–315.

WISEBLATT, L. 1957. The flavor of bread. Northwest Miller *258*, No. 11, 1a, 16a–17a.

WISEBLATT, L., and KOHN, F. E. 1960. Some volatile aromatic compounds in fresh bread. Cereal Chem. *37*, 55–56.

YAMADA, M., MASAI, S., YOSIZAWA, K., SASAKI, S., and HANAI, S. 1957. Biacetyl. VIII. Formation of acetoin from biacetyl. Nippon Jôzô Kyôkai Zasshi *52*, 59–60; Chem. Abstr. *51*, 17077d.

ZERBAN, F. W. 1947. The color problem in sugar manufacture. Sugar Research Foundation, Tech. Report Ser. *2*.

ZIPSER, M. W., KWON, T-W., and WATTS, B. M. 1964. Oxidative changes in cured and uncured frozen cooked pork. J. Agr. Food Chem. *12*, 105–109.

CHAPTER 23

David A. Forss | Origin of Flavors in Lipids

INTRODUCTION

Lipids are not only a major source of natural flavors in many foods, but they are also a repository for flavor compounds derived from changes in other constituents of foods. In addition lipids tend to undergo marked flavor changes on storage. A complete study of the origin of flavor in lipids would thus come close to being a study of the origin of flavor in foods in general.

Soon after I had agreed to participate in this symposium, I wrote to approximately 40 laboratories throughout the world which I knew were investigating food flavors and requested information about their research on the origin of flavors in lipids. This was done to obtain the latest information and to estimate how much of this type of research was being done. I received a great deal of very interesting literature on flavor research but little of it related to the origin of flavors.

On the other hand many laboratories not concerned with flavors are actually doing work closely related to their origin. Much can certainly be learned about the way flavor compounds are formed from research in apparently unrelated fields. One early example of this is Farmer's work on the oxidation of rubber which has contributed so greatly to our understanding of the pathways of oxidation in lipids.

Some general aspects of the study of food flavors will be considered first The origin of flavors in lipids will then be presented from two different aspects, first considering four ways in which flavor compounds arise, and second considering how four particular classes of flavor compounds are formed. There will be appreciable overlap between the two approaches which is intended to try and integrate them.

GENERAL CONSIDERATIONS

Before the origin of flavors is studied, we must know what compounds are responsible. The current concept is that a relatively small number of compounds is responsible for a wide range of food flavors and that it is the amounts and relative proportions which determine the characteristic flavor. This makes it imperative in laboratory investigations to obtain quantitative isolation of flavor compounds or at least an accurate knowledge of the recoveries which are being achieved. Particularly with foods containing a high proportion of lipid, we have been surprised

492

at the poor recoveries, e.g., less than five per cent of nonan-1-ol from butterfat (added to give 0.5 p.p.m.) by steam distillation at 20 torr and 45°C. Sometimes a compound isolated does not actually exist in the food but is formed during the isolation procedure, e.g., hex-*trans*-2-enal may have existed in the food as hex-*cis*-3-enal. Undoubtedly isolation is the most inefficient procedure in the study of volatile flavor compounds in lipids, and indeed in most food materials.

A complete study of the origin of flavors in lipids would include a consideration of volatile and nonvolatile taste compounds as well as compounds exerting other physiological effects in the mouth. The complexity of oral responses will be illustrated by the following few examples, and this paper will then be devoted to a study of the formation of volatile compounds. Moncrieff (1964) has suggested that in addition to the four accepted taste responses, there is a fifth, the metallic taste due to inorganic iron and copper salts. In many of the food systems he described the metallic taste could be caused by oct-1-en-3-one (Stark and Forss 1962) arising from oxidation of the unsaturated acids. Oral sensations apart from taste play an important part in the appreciation of food flavors. Lipids may confer the feelings of oiliness or smoothness to foods while melting butter exerts a pleasant cooling effect on the tongue. Miracle fruit (*Synsepalum dulcificum*) causes sour materials to taste sweet (Inglett *et al.* 1965) while erucic acid, a major component of rapeseed oil depresses the appetite (Boldingh 1964).

Flavor potentiators such as monosodium glutamate, maltol, and 5'-ribonucleotides as well as simple substances such as sodium chloride, glucose, or citric acid profoundly modify the flavors of many foods. Furthermore, many flavor compounds react together synergisticly, additively, or subtractively so the role of any compound can often only be ascertained by its removal from the system. It is surprising perhaps, in view of these complexities of taste response, that so many useful advances have been made in the study of flavor.

While, during the last ten years, new techniques have been responsible for much progress in the isolation and identification of volatile flavor compounds, the study of the flavor precursors has lagged behind. Many precursors are large involatile molecules the isolation and identification of which requires other techniques, and flavor chemists must learn to use these if progress is to be made.

MECHANISMS

In any attempt to deal with the origins of flavors in lipids there will inevitably be considerable speculation and argument by analogy, because often the actual parent compound is unknown and when it is, the intermediate reactions may not be known. Often a flavor compound can be formed by several different pathways: e.g., propanal may arise from: (1) decomposition of the 16-hydroperoxide of linolenate; (2) stepwise oxidation of n-nonanal through the $C_{8\ 4}$ alkanals to propanal (Loury et al. 1965); (3) oxidation of n-propanol with alcohol dehydrogenase; (4) deamination of n-propylamine with monoamine oxidase; (5) the action of pyruvate decarboxylase on 2-ketobutyric acid; (6) a Strecker degradation of 2-aminobutyric acid; etc.

Of the many ways in which flavor compounds may arise in lipids I shall consider four. I shall refer to these as physical transfer, the effects of heat, the role of enzymes and secondary reactions of flavor compounds. Let's discuss them in that order.

Physical Transfers

The transfer of unaltered chemical compounds into foods is receiving most attention at present in the field of pesticides. But flavors both desirable and undesirable may also originate in this way. The transfer may take place by direct absorption, or by indirect means through the bloodstream of the animal or the sap of the plant, or both. And more often than not the foreign flavoring compound goes into the lipid phase. Atmospheric contamination is becoming increasingly important but hydrocarbons, ozone, aldehydes, organic acids, sulfur dioxide, and oxides of nitrogen have mainly an indirect though frequently important effect on the flavor of foods. Many of the reactions occurring in the atmosphere involve free radicals and resemble those occurring in the oxidation of lipids. Day and Anderson (1965) suggested that the methyl chloride they isolated from blue cheese was derived from the fumigant used in the cheese storage room. Organic solvents used to extract oilseeds used in stock feeds may pass into dairy products. Wong and Patton (1962) pointed out that the chloroform, acetonitrile, and ethylene chloride isolated from milk and cream might have arisen in this way.

Odorous compounds derived from stock feed and weeds are chiefly of concern in the dairy and meat industries. Mustard oil glycosides occur in many plants eaten by cows and one, Coronopus didymus has caused much tainting of dairy products in Southern Queensland and in New Zealand. When such plants are crushed the enzyme myrosin is liberated and usually hydrolyzes the glycoside to glucose, phosphoric acid, and an isothiocyanate. Steam distillation of Coronopus didymus at atmospheric pressure yielded benzyl cyanide (Forss 1951) but Park (1965) showed that in the unheated plant benzyl isothiocyanate was produced for a short time but rapidly isomerized to the thiocyanate which passed into the milk. The scorched flavor which appeared in the butter was probably due to reduction of the thiocyanate to benzyl mercaptan during pasteurization of the cream.

Morgan and Pereira (1963) found that the grassy aroma of green forages, due mainly to hex-2-enal, was fortified by hex-3-enals and hex-3-enols. They also (1962) isolated C_{2-6} n-alkanoic acids, 2-methylpropanoic and 2- and 3-methylbutanoic acids, C_{2-6} n-alkanals, 2- and 3-methylbutanal, 2-methylpropanal, acetone, butanone, benzaldehyde, phenylacetaldehyde, and furfural from grass and corn silage. Shipe et al. (1962) using cows with ruminal and tracheal fistulas showed that the vapors of several of the above compounds passed into the milk, no doubt into the milkfat, and acetone, butanone, dimethyl sulfide, and hex-cis-3-enol conferred flavors most closely resembling those found in commercial feedy milk. Honkanen and Moisio (1963) isolated oct-1-en-3-ol from several clovers and studied (Honkanen et al. 1964) the transfer of several aliphatic compounds from the rumen of cows into their milk. n-Alkan-1-ols with an odd number of carbons, lower alkan-2-ones, and esters of even numbered fatty acids were able to enter the milkfat in quantities sufficient to taint the milk. n-Alkanals, some alkan-2-ones, and three alk-1-en-3-ols were transferred in only trace amounts. They suggested that oct-1-en-3-ol from clover might enter the milk and be oxidized to oct-1-en-3-one causing a metallic flavor. From their data this seems possible. Oct-1-en-3-one also found in clovers was sensitive to acids and was destroyed rapidly in the rumen. "Bovolide," an unsaturated 4-lactone with an odor like celery isolated from milkfat was presumed to come from the fodder (Boldingh and Taylor 1962).

A final example of the physical transfer of flavor compounds mainly into the lipid phase is the smoking of meats such as hams and of cheeses.

Effects of Heat

Study of chemical changes occurring in synthetic lipids heated at 180-260°C. might be expected to provide information on changes occurring during processing of and cooking with fats and oils. The effects of enzymes can be ignored in these circumstances, while polymerization is favored by temperatures above 250°C. and the absence of air. Hydrolysis of the ester linkages between glycerol and fatty acids may take place, and so may addition of oxygen to saturated acids as well as to unsaturated fatty acids containing an active methylene group. The use of model compounds to study the changes in lipids produced by heating gives results more amenable to interpretation even though the number and variety of compounds produced may still be very great. However, the application of the information obtained to the changes occurring in natural fats is not always obvious.

Heating lipids above 200°C. may lead to the formation of desirable flavor compounds. Patton *et al.* (1959) showed that the attractive "deep fried" flavor of heated cottonseed and soybean oils, and beef tallow was due to deca-2,4-dienal obtained from the 9-hydroperoxide of linoleic acid. Aliphatic lactones and ketones may also be produced by heat and contribute to desirable flavors.

Crossley *et al.* (1962) studied the effect of heat on tricaprin and 2-oleodipalmitin. In a nitrogen atmosphere at 240° to 260°C., decanoic acid was the only major volatile product obtained from tricaprin but at 300°C. propenal and nonadecan-10-one were also formed (compare with the preparation of ketones by the dry distillation of barium salts of fatty acids):

$$R\ CO\ O\ CH_2 \qquad R\ COOH + R\ CO\ O\ \overset{\overset{\displaystyle CH_2}{\|}}{C} \qquad (250°C.) \qquad (1)$$
$$R\ CO\ O\ \underset{|}{CH} \rightarrow \qquad\qquad R\ CO\ O\ CH_2$$
$$R\ CO\ O\ CH_2$$
$$\rightarrow R\ COOH + R\ CO\ R + CH_2{=}CH\ CHO \qquad (300°C.) \qquad (2)$$

2-Oleodipalmitin was more reactive and at 190°C. under nitrogen yielded oleic / palmitic acid (1:2). When tricaprin was heated in the presence of air at 190°C. appreciable amounts of the C_{5-10} *n*-alkanoic acids and nonan-2-one, moderate amounts of the C_{7-8} alkan-2-ones and undecan-6-one, and traces of lower acids and *n*-decanal were obtained. Crossley *et al.* (1962) suggested tricaprin may break down to a series of C_{5-10} *n*-alkanoic acids by preferential oxidation of the carbon α to the ester group:

$$R\ CH_2\ CO\ O\ CH_2 - \rightarrow R\ \underset{\underset{\displaystyle OOH}{|}}{CH}\ CO\ O\ CH_2 - \qquad (3)$$

$$\rightarrow R\ CO\ CO\ O\ CH_2 - + H_2O \qquad (4)$$

$$\rightarrow R\ CO\ COOH + HO\ CH_2 - \qquad (5)$$

$$\rightarrow R\ COOH + CO + HO\ CH_2 - \qquad etc. \quad (6)$$

The alkan-2-ones are thought to form by oxidative attack at the β-carbon:

$$R\ CH_2\ CH_2\ CO\ O\ CH_2 - \rightarrow R\ \underset{\underset{\displaystyle OOH}{|}}{CH}\ CH_2\ CO\ O\ CH_2 - \qquad (7)$$

$$\rightarrow R\ CO\ CH_2\ CO\ O\ CH_2 - + H_2O \qquad (8)$$

$$\rightarrow R\ CO\ CH_3 + CO_2 + HO\ CH_2 - \qquad (9)$$

Oxidative attack further along the chain produces thermostable carbonyl compounds not split off from the glycerol molecule. They are probably precursors of off-flavors generated during prolonged storage of fats since heat-degraded tricaprin and 2-oleodipalmitin could be refined to an acceptable standard by conventional means but their keeping times were considerably less than those of the original triglycerides.

2-Oleodipalmitin heated in air at 190°C. yielded appreciable amounts of the C_{7-9} n-alkanoic acids and two unidentified $C_{9\&10}$ unsaturated ketones, and moderate amounts of the $C_{6\&10}$ n-alkanoic acids, decanedioic acid and the $C_{9\&10}$ alkan-2-ones. Crossley et al. (1962) postulated that, for example, n-nonanal derived from the 10-hydroperoxide of oleic acid according to Farmer et al. (1943) is oxidized to n-nonanoic acid. Alternatively, the n-octyl radical may be oxidized to a primary (terminal) hydroperoxide and thence through n-octanal to n-octanoic acid or yield a heptyl radical, and so on (This mechanism was used to explain the formation of the mono- and dibasic acids.):

$$CH_3\ (CH_2)_6\ CH_2\ \overset{10}{CH}\ CH{=}CH\ (CH_2)_6\ COO- +\cdot OH \tag{10}$$
$$\underset{|}{\overset{}{\ }}\ O\cdot$$

$$\rightarrow CH_3\ (CH_2)_6\ CH_2\cdot + OCH\ CH{=}CH\ (CH_2)_6\ COO- \tag{11}$$

and

$$\rightarrow CH_3\ (CH_2)_6\ CH_2\ CHO +\cdot CH{=}CH\ (CH_2)_6\ COO- \tag{12}$$
$$CH_3\ (CH_2)_6\ CH_2\cdot \rightarrow CH_3\ (CH_2)_6\ CH_2\ OO\cdot \tag{13}$$
$$\rightarrow CH_3\ (CH_2)_6\ CH_2\ OOH \tag{14}$$
$$\rightarrow CH_3\ (CH_2)_6\ CHO + H_2O \tag{15}$$
$$or\quad CH_3\ (CH_2)_6\ CH_2\ O\cdot \rightarrow$$
$$CH_3\ (CH_2)_5\ CH_2\cdot + H\ CHO \tag{16}$$

While the acids were quantitatively more important, two monounsaturated ketones occurred in large amount in the carbonyl fraction and were postulated to form from oleic acid as follows:

$$CH_3\ (CH_2)_6\ CH_2\ CH{=}CH\ CH_2\ (CH_2)_6\ COO- \tag{17}$$
$$\rightarrow CH_3\ (CH_2)_6\ \underset{|}{CH}\ CH{=}CH\ CH_2\ (CH_2)_6\ COO- \tag{18}$$
$$OOH$$

$$\rightarrow CH_3\ (CH_2)_6\ CO\ CH{=}CH\ CH_2\ (CH_2)_6\ COO- + H_2O \tag{19}$$
$$\rightarrow CH_3\ (CH_2)_6\ CO\ CH{=}CH\ \underset{|}{CH}\ (CH_2)_6\ COO- \tag{20}$$
$$OOH$$

$$\rightarrow CH_3\ (CH_2)_6\ CO\ CH{=}CH\ CHO \tag{21}$$
$$\rightarrow CH_3\ (CH_2)_6\ CO\ CH{=}CH\ COOH \tag{22}$$
$$\rightarrow CH_3\ (CH_2)_6\ CO\ CH{=}CH_2 + CO_2 \tag{23}$$

From the experimental data presented on these two unsaturated ketones, it seems more likely that they were indeed identical with their two reference compounds, non-3-en-2-one and dec-3-en-2-one, and were not alk-1-en-3-ones (Forss *et al.* 1962B). The $C_{8\&9}$ alkan-2-ones were thought to arise from the two vinyl ketones with loss of CO_2. Crossley *et al.* (1962) explained the small quantities of aldehydes isolated as due to their oxidation to acids and other compounds, which to some extent decomposed to unsaturated and saturated ketones. However, other workers isolated appreciable quantities of aldehydes from similar systems.

Endres *et al.* (1962A, B) also studied the oxidation of synthetic triglycerides (tripalmitin, 1- and 2-lauryl dipalmitin and 1- and 2-oleyl dipalmitin) at 200°C. Appreciable amounts of carbon monoxide, carbon dioxide, and hydrogen were isolated, and the results indicated that long chain carbonyls were formed initially. Later C_{1-16} *n*-alkanals, methyl and other saturated ketones, and C_{4-16} *n*-alkanoic acids were isolated. The presence of dicarboxylic acids indicated that oxygen attacked the double bond of oleic acid in 1-oleyl dipalmitin but not when the oleic acid was in the 2-position. The mechanism postulated by Fritsch and Deatherage (1956) for the autoxidation of methyl oleate was used to explain the formation of acids, *n*-alkanals, water and hydrogen. It involved the formation of alkoxy radicals from the decomposition of a primary (terminal) hydroperoxide and was very similar to that proposed by Crossley *et al.* (1962) (Equations 14 to 16). Water was formed via the union of two hydroxyl radicals, and hydrogen from two hydrogen radicals. Hydrogen was also produced by dehydrogenation of saturated fatty acids during the early stages of oxidation. The carbon monoxide was thought to arise by either of the reactions:

$$\text{R CO CH}_2 \text{ CO COOR} \rightarrow \text{R CO CH}_2 \text{ COOR} + \text{CO} \qquad (24)$$

$$\text{R CO CO COR} \rightarrow \text{R CO COR} + \text{CO} \qquad (25)$$

Workers in the same laboratory (Ramanathan *et al.* 1959) studied the oxidation of methyl laurate, stearate and oleate at 200°C. and suggested a mechanism involving dehydrogenation of the saturated esters followed by hydroperoxide formation in a similar way to methyl oleate. Some polymerization also took place.

Hrdlička and Pokorný (1962) oxidized stearic, oleic, erucic and linoleic acids at 180°C. and studied the volatile carbonyl compounds produced which were mostly *n*-alkanals and alk-2-enals with large amounts of propenal. Contrary to earlier evidence in the literature, alka-2,4-dienals were isolated only from oleic acid. The absence of dienals from the oxidation of linoleic acid was thought to be due ot their greater rate of polymerization.

Toi *et al.* (1962) obtained water, *n*-octanal, *n*-nonanal, semialdehyde methyl esters, $C_{7 \& 8}$ hydrocarbons, methyl alkanoates, free alkanoic acids, mono-methyl esters of diabasic acids, and alcohols from methyl oleate oxidized at 200°C. Most of these compounds can be accounted for by the theory of Farmer *et al.* (1943).

Hrdlička and Pokorný (1963) heated ten natural fats at 180°C. in the presence of air. The presence of compounds with 1 to 4 carbons indicates that the attack of oxygen is not selectively concentrated at the double bond and neighboring methylene groups, but that it takes place according to the theory of multiple oxidation. This was more pronounced with the more saturated fats. The fats decomposed with the formation of mainly saturated compounds with ketones predominating while a greater number of conjugated dienals was produced from highly unsaturated fats. (Their behavior thus differed from that of free linoleic acid.) The structure of the most unsaturated acid in the fat did not substantially affect the results. Cocoa butter was an exception and several conjugated dienals and only few saturated and mono-unsaturated compounds were formed in spite of the low content of unsaturated fatty acids. More carbonyl compounds were produced from the saturated fats (e.g., tallow and palm oil). With multiple oxidation ketones and polar carbonyl compounds were also formed.

Role of Enzymes

Lipases which can give rise to marked flavor changes in fats containing short-chain fatty acids will be discussed elsewhere in this symposium.

It is interesting to compare reactions occurring in triglycerides and fatty acids at 200°C. in the presence and absence of oxygen with reactions occurring in higher plants and micro-organisms at 10° to 20°C. In the presence of oxygen, yeast and blue-green algae dehydrogenate stearic acid to oleic acid. James *et al.* (1965) using gas-liquid radiochromatography, showed that plant leaves and seeds cannot dehydrogenate stearic acid but convert *n*-dodecanoic acid to hexadec-7-enoic acid, and *n*-tetradecanoic acid to oleic acid and subsequently to linoleic and linolenic acids. The production of these unsaturated fatty acids provides a rich pool of substrate for enzymatic and nonenzymatic breakdowns to flavor compounds. Fatty acids in plant leaves are degraded by α-oxidation:

$$CH_3 (CH_2)_7 CH{=}CH (CH_2)_7 COOH \tag{26}$$

$$\rightarrow CH_3 (CH_2)_7 CH{=}CH (CH_2)_6 \underset{\underset{OH}{|}}{CH} COOH \tag{27}$$

$$\rightarrow CH_3 (CH_2)_7 CH{=}CH (CH_2)_6 CHO + CO_2 \tag{28}$$

$$\rightarrow CH_3 (CH_2)_7 CH=CH (CH_2)_6 COOH \tag{29}$$

$$\rightarrow CH_3 (CH_2)_7 CH=CH(CH_2)_5 \underset{\underset{OH}{|}}{CH} COOH \tag{30}$$

This scheme resembles that proposed by Crossley *et al.* (1962) for the oxidation of *n*-decanoic acid from tricaprin. Some of the lower alkenals formed in this breakdown might well contribute to food flavors, e.g., tridec-4-enal, dodec-3-enal, and undec-2-enal. Following the above changes a series of *n*-alkanals would be expected to form. Photosynthetic bacteria degrade oleic acid to hexadec-7-enoic acid by β-oxidation.

The above reactions are carried out in aqueous solution by enzymes and their cofactors, and in the biosyntheses of unsaturated fatty acids requiring oxygen, Coenzyme A is the co-factor. Another enzymatic reaction important in the formation of food flavors is:

Acetoin + NAD (nicotinamide-adenine dinucleotide)

$$\xrightarrow{\text{acetoin dehydrogenase}} Diacetyl + NADH_2 \text{ (reduced NAD)} \tag{31}$$

Lipoxygenase (formerly known as lipoxidase) catalyzes the peroxidation of methylene-interrupted polyunsaturated acids with *cis*-double bonds, e.g., linoleic acid, and the major products are the same as those obtained via autoxidation, except that the former are optically active indicating an orientated rather than a random attack by oxygen. Lipoxygenase occurs in many plants, is most abundant in legumes and the lipoxygenase from soybean has been most studied (Privett *et al.* 1955).

Enzymes are capable of carrying out many of the familiar reactions of organic chemistry, e.g., a reaction which resembles that of the Cannizzaro or Tischenko was thought to proceed as follows:

$$Aldehyde + H_2O + NAD \xrightarrow{\text{aldehyde dehydrogenase}} Acid + NADH_2 \tag{32}$$

$$Aldehyde + NADH_2 \xrightarrow{\text{alcohol dehydrogenase}} Alcohol + NAD + H_2O \tag{33}$$

Twenty years ago these reactions were thought to be catalyzed by a single enzyme, "aldehyde mutase" (Dixon and Webb 1964) and recent work by Dalziel and Dickinson (1965) supports this view, the enzyme being an alcohol dehydrogenase with aldehyde dehydrogenase activity.

Hewitt (1963) has studied the source, specificity, and properties of flavor enzymes in string beans. He found that only the enzyme from string beans enhanced the flavor of processed string beans. Part of the flavor was due to hex-2-enal which could be formed from hex-2-enol with string bean enzyme and nicotinamide-adenine dinucleotide phosphate (NADP), or from string bean homogenate or from commercial alcohol dehydrogenase prepared from yeast and NAD.

Harper (1959) observed 3-keto acids in cheeses dependent on lipase for their flavor e.g., Romano, Provolone, and Blue cheese. The 3-keto acids were thought to be formed by "beta-oxidase" action on fatty acids. Perhaps they also formed from 3-hydroxy acids by 3-hydroxybutyrate dehydrogenase

Some thousand enzymes have been characterized and as our knowledge of them increases it will become increasingly useful, in relation to food flavors, to determine the enzymes in a particular food and to investigate or even speculate on the reactions taking place and the compounds being formed.

Secondary Reactions of Flavor Compounds

Volatile flavor compounds may be changed with alteration of the overall flavor. Harper (1959) has discussed secondary degradations of this type occurring in several varieties of cheese and has stressed the "dynamic state" of foods containing enzymes. Table 84 lists some of the

TABLE 84

ENZYMES ACTING ON PRIMARY DEGRADATION PRODUCTS DURING CHEESE RIPENING

Enzymes	Substrates	Products
Decarboxylase	Amino acids	Amines
Amino acid oxidase	Amino acids	2-Keto acids
Aminotransferase	Amino acids	2-Keto acids
Pyruvate decarboxylase	2-Keto acids	Aldehydes
Aminotransferase	2-Keto acids	Amino acids
"Fatty acid oxidase"	Fatty acids	3-Keto acids
"Aminase"	Fatty acids	Amino acids

secondary enzymic changes. The enzymes are derived from the natural microflora of milk, starter bacteria, rennin, and molds, and in the maturing of cheese nonenzymatic changes are not regarded as important. Citric acid plays an important part in the formation of many of these compounds, initially through the formation of certain amino acids and then through their conversion to aldehydes and ketones. Harper (1959) has discussed the use of radioactive sodium citrate to follow these reactions.

Ten years ago Patton and Kurtz (1955) showed that hept-2-enal exposed to air for ten days at 25°C., then treated with thiobarbituric acid reagent (TBA) gave a similar absorption curve to autoxidized linoleic acid treated with TBA. The curves had light absorption maxima at 532 $m\mu$ probably due to reaction of malonaldehyde with TBA. Lillard and Day (1964) have shown that ten times as much malonaldehyde is formed from oxidizing hepta-2,4-dienal as from non-2-enal.

In an attempt to account for carbonyls found in oxidized lipids but not theoretically predicted from the decomposition of lipid hydroperoxides,

Lillard and Day (1964) investigated the oxidative degradation at 45°C. of n-nonanal, non-2-enal, hepta-2,4-dienal, and oct-1-en-3-one. n-Nonanal slowly oxidized to n-nonanoic acid, non-2-enal rapidly oxidized to non-2-enoic acid and hepta-2,4-dienal was polymerized at 0.5 mole of oxygen uptake. In fact the unsaturated aldehydes oxidized at a faster rate than methyl linoleate or linolenate. This explains why n-alkanals predominate in autoxidation although unsaturated aldehydes are formed simultaneously. Oct-1-en-3-one did not absorb oxygen during a 52-hr. period which Lillard and Day (1964) believe is consistent with its prominence during the early stages of oxidation. However, in view of the fate of the aldehydes, the metallic flavor of oct-1-en-3-one might be expected to become more dominant as oxidation proceeds. On the other hand oct-1-en-3-one is decomposed by acids. Small quantities of n-alkanals, glyoxal, 2-keto-alkanals, and malonaldehyde were isolated from the autoxidized non-2-enal and hepta-2,4-dienal, and mechanisms for their formation suggested. One is impressed by the enormous number of compounds which are formed from the oxidation of say methyl oleate while the number of compounds that can be formed in the oxidation of a natural fat must be at least several hundred.

Wilkinson (1964) has underlined the probable importance of the role of secondary oxidations in oxidative deterioration of lipids, in particular relation to oxidized flavors in dairy products. He discusses the role of dispersed or dissolved water in flavor changes taking place in lipids and shows that hydrogen and hydroxyl ions and radicals supplied from this source can control many reactions.

Burton et al. (1963) examined the browning potentialities of a number of carbonyl compounds and obtained most rapid browning with alk-2-enals. Furfurals, 2- and 3-substituted alk-2-enals, and alkanals were less reactive.

Carbonyl compounds may also react with other compounds in a food and improve its flavor by eliminating undesirable compounds. For example Batzer et al. (1957) suggested that carbonyl compounds produced during radiation of meat may react with amines and sulfhydryl compounds.

ORIGIN OF SOME CLASSES OF COMPOUNDS

Aldehydes

Aldehydes are important in desirable and undesirable flavors in the lipid constituents of foods and the full realization of this in the "fifties" was largely due to the availability of such a versatile reagent as 2,4-dinitrophenylhydrazine. It has already been shown how propanal can be formed in six different ways and how oxidation of fatty acids can produce complete series of n-alkanals and n-alk-2-enals. For example Loury et al. (1965) demonstrated how n-decanal obtained from oxidized oleic acid can be degraded through nonanal, octanal, heptanal, hexanal, pentanal, butanal, propanal, ethanal to methanal.

It is likely that many desirable flavors are produced by oxidation. In 1943, Nye and Spoehr showed that the amount of hex-2-enal, an important odorous component of green leaves, which was liberated was related to the degree of crushing and availability of oxygen. Addition of oleic acid increased the yield of hex-2-enal and an enzyme was believed responsible since the reaction was inhibited by heat. Hex-2-enal may be derived from the 13-hydroperoxide of linolenic acid via hex-3-enal, possibly by lipoxygenase action on linolenate (an abundant constituent of plant leaves). Hultin and Proctor (1961) reported that hex-2-enal was an important component of banana flavor, but they wondered whether it was formed only after exposure of the pulp to air. More recently, Winter and Willhalm (1964) have shown that hex-2-enal was the main carbonyl compound in crushed strawberries and that it did not exist in the uncrushed fruit, neither did diacetyl.

Van Duin (1958) isolated octadecanal and hexadecanal by acid hydrolysis of butter plasmalogens and Schogt et al. (1960) isolated tetradecanal and hexadecanal from phospholipid-free milkfat, beef tallow, and ox heart fat. Later (1961) they isolated some of the C_{13-18} n-alkanals and C_{13-17} branched alkanals from the phosphorus-free lipids of milkfat and ox heart as well as from phosphatides of butter and ox heart. Day and Papaioannou (1963) attributed the candle-like flavor component of irradiated milkfat to long chain aldehydes which were thought to arise by hydrolysis of their enol-ether linkage in the triglyceride. n-Alkanals and alk-2-enals above C_{12} which are not in themselves potent flavor compounds, may be broken down to smaller more potent compounds.

Aldehydes may be produced from amino acids and in many cases their structure is sufficiently characteristic to show that they were derived from natural amino acids. Nonenzymatic browning reactions and the Strecker degradation have rather a vogue at the moment and are threatening to displace lipid oxidation as the most popular mechanism to account for the origin of flavor compounds. In foods such as potato chips which are exposed to high temperatures for several minutes nonenzymatic mechanisms can be assumed to account for 2-methylbutanal and 2-methylpropanal. MacLeod and Morgan (1958) demonstrated that *Streptococcus lactis* var. *Maltigenes* degraded isoleucine, valine, methionine, and phenylalanine to 2-methylbutanal, 2-methylpropanal, 3-methylthiopropanal, and phenylacetaldehyde. They suggested that a transaminase converted the amino acids to 2-keto acids which were then acted upon by a decarboxylase.

Theory predicts that many of the unsaturated aldehydes formed from linoleic and linolenic acid should have *cis*-double bonds but the *cis*-double bond is reported to change to the more stable *trans*-double bond (this always happens in the 2-position in aliphatic aldehydes) so frequently mixtures of the two isomers are found. Alternatively, oxidation may cause rearrangement of the parent hydroperoxide with formation of the *trans*- instead of the *cis*-aldehyde. Thus, Hoffmann (1961) showed that hepta- and deca-*trans*-2,*cis*-4-dienals derived from oxidized linolenate and linoleate respectively can be isolated from soybean oil and have different flavors from the *trans*-2,*trans*-4-isomers. Forss *et al.* (1962A) showed that nona-*trans*-2,*cis*-6-dienal had a cucumber odor and the *trans*-2,*trans*-6-isomer had a tallowy odor. Hoffmann (1964) isolated both isomers from beef tallow and suggested they were derived from octadeca-11,15-dienoic acids. However, Hammond and Hill (1964) postulated that nona-*trans*-2,*cis*-6-dienal was formed from the 9-hydroperoxide of linolenic acid by a split producing a nona-1,3,6-triene radical which reacted with a hydroxyl radical to form a conjugated enol which rearranged to the aldehyde. Earlier, Hoffmann (1962A) had suggested that nona-*trans*-2,*cis*-6-dienal might arise in a similar way via nona-*cis*-3-*cis*-6-dienal obtained from oxidized linolenic acid. Keppler *et al.* (1965) have isolated non-*cis*-6-enal and non-*trans*-6-enal from hardened linseed and soybean oils derived from the hydroperoxides of octadeca-8,15- and 9,15-dienoic acids. Colleagues in the same laboratory (Haverkamp Begemann and Koster 1964) have isolated hept-*cis*-4-enal from butterfat and claimed that it confers a creamy flavor to cream fudge. De Jong and van der Wel (1964) isolated several non-conjugatable octadecadienoic acids from butterfat and suggested that hept-*cis*-4-enal was derived from the 11,15; 10,15; and 9,15-octadecadienoic acids. This is possible but these acids only occur in traces and Stark (1965) has postulated that hept-*cis*-4-enal might also be derived from the 11-hydroperoxide of linolenic acid:

$$CH_3\ CH_2\ CH{=}CH\ CH_2\ CH{=}CH\ \overset{11}{C}H{-} \qquad (34)$$

$$\rightarrow CH_3\ CH_2\ CH{=}CH\ CH_2\ CH{=}CH|CH{-} \qquad (35)$$
$$O\ \ OH$$

$$\rightarrow CH_3\ CH_2\ CH{=}CH\ CH_2\ CH{=}CH\cdot\ +\ \cdot OH \qquad (36)$$

$$\rightarrow [CH_3\ CH_2\ CH{=}CH\ CH_2\ CH{=}CH\ OH] \qquad (37)$$

$$\rightarrow CH_3\ CH_2\ CH{=}CH\ CH_2\ CH_2\ CHO \qquad (38)$$

The opinion in our laboratory was that concentrated solutions of hept-cis-4-enal smelled like boiled potatoes and frozen peas.

Ketones

Ketones, though not as ubiquitous as aldehydes in food lipids, play a very prominent part in the flavor of some of them. Alkan-2-ones contribute to the desirable flavor of cheeses and in 1950 Patton reported the presence of the $C_{5, 7 \& 9}$ alkan-2-ones in blue cheese. Later Patton and Tharp (1959) isolated six (C_{3-15}) alkan-2-ones with odd numbers of carbons from both the steam distillate and unsaponifiable matter from milkfat heated at 200°C. at 0.1–0.25 torr. They attributed the formation of the methyl ketones to the decarboxylation of 3-keto acids in the triglycerides, and regarded the keto acids as normal metabolic products of milkfat synthesis.

Van der Ven *et al.* (1963) used Girard T reagent to isolate the pyrazolones of six (C_{6-16}) even-numbered 3-keto acids from butterfat triglycerides. The Dutch workers showed that water was necessary for the reaction but Nawar *et al.* (1962) described experiments in which anhydrous milkfat was heated in the absence of oxygen at 130°C. for 3 hr. with the production of the $C_{3, 5, 7, 9 \& 11}$ alkan-2-ones and traces of the $C_{4, 6 \& 8}$ alkan-2-ones and the C_{1-9} *n*-alkanals.

Lawrence (1963) showed that alkan-2-ones were produced even at 40°C. during the steam distillation of butterfat and pointed out that on occasions alkan-2-ones reported in the literature were really artifacts.

A recent paper (Langler and Day 1964) has clarified the position. Maximum yield of methyl ketones was obtained by heating a degassed sample of milkfat at 140°C. for 3 hr.; heating an additional 15 hr. had no further effect. Milkfat degassed at $2\text{-}5 \times 10^{-3}$ torr for 1 hr. at 40°C. still contained sufficient water for maximum ketone production but drying over calcium hydride for 18 hr. inhibited ketone formation.

Gehrig and Knight (1961) investigated the formation of heptan-2-one, an important compound in the flavor of mold-ripened cheeses. They showed that the spores of several filamentous fungi, *Penicillium* sp. (9 out of 12) and *Aspergillus* sp. (9 out of 11) and some related molds including *Paecilomyces varioti* and *Scaputariopsis brevicqulis* (probably *Scopulariopsis brevicaulis* (DAF)) rapidly converted *n*-octanoate to heptan-2 one. The pathway was being investigated and it would seem to involve several steps. Later they (1963) showed that spores from *Penicillium roqueforti* converted 1 µM solutions of sodium *n*-octanoate to CO_2 but with 20 µM solutions some heptan-2-one was produced; oxygen was required. β-Oxidation was thought to be responsible but a carbon atom would have to be lost in the reaction.

Most ketones isolated from foods, apart from butanone, have odd numbers of carbons. However, Hrdlička and Janíček (1964) found that hexan-2-one was the predominant ketone in toasted oat flakes.

Lactones

The importance of lactones in the flavor of lipids has only been fully realized over the last decade or so. Aliphatic 5-lactones have been isolated from milkfat (Keeney and Patton 1956; Boldingh and Taylor 1962), peaches (Jennings and Sevenants 1964) and heated beef fat (Boldingh and Taylor 1962; Nakanishi and Watanabe 1965), and 4-lactones from milkfat (Boldingh and Taylor 1962; Muck et al. 1963; Forss et al. 1966) and peaches (Jennings and Sevenants 1964).

These lactones are formed from the corresponding hydroxyalkanoic acids by heat, e.g., 130°C. for 1 hr. in vacuo or by similar treatment of the appropriate triglycerides.

Dextrorotatory 5-lactones occur in milkfat and scientific interest and legal requirements have encouraged a study of their synthesis. Francke (1963) reduced 5-keto-decanoic acid with Saccharomyces cerevisiae to the optically active hydroxy acid. NADP, DL-isocitric acid and fumaric acid were required to give yields of the order of 20 per cent. Francke (1963) also reduced the keto acid with pigeon- and ox-liver preparations. His colleagues (Tuynenburg Muys et al. 1963) made a comprehensive study of the preparation of optically active 4- and 5-lactones by micro-biological reduction of the corresponding keto acids. They obtained conversions up to 80% and observed that several yeasts (Saccharomyces and Candida) produced dextrorotatory hydroxy acids while certain molds (Cladosporium) and certain bacteria (Sarcina) produced levorotatory hydroxy acids.

Boldingh and Taylor (1962) speculated that in the biosynthesis of fatty acids, 5-keto acids result from two consecutive additions of acetate, the first of which escapes reduction to 3-hydroxy acid-coenzyme A.

Recently, van der Ven (1964) isolated a mixture of medium chain length keto acids (other than 3-) in a yield of 100 p.p.m. from steam-deodorized milkfat by means of the Girard T reagent. Analysis showed the $C_{8, 10 \& 12}$ 5-keto acids and minor quantities of the C_{10-12} 4-keto acids. The ratios of 4- and 5-keto acids were of the same order of magnitude as the ratios of the corresponding lactones isolated from heated milkfat which van der Ven (1964) said supported the idea that in nature these lactones arose from the keto acids. On the other hand Ansell and Palmer (1963) have shown that 4-lactones and smaller amounts of 5-lactones are formed from olefinic acids treated with sulfuric or trifluoroacetic acids. Enzymes in foods may be capable of inducing similar reactions.

Forss *et al.* (1966) pointed out that much of the analytical data used to confirm the presence of 4-dodecalactone (4-octyl-4-butyrolactone) might possibly apply equally well to the isomers substututed in the 2- and 3-positions. Recent work in our laboratory on 2-octyl-4-butyrolactone has shown that its thin layer chromatographic behavior, and infrared and mass spectra are quite different from those of the 4-octyl-4-butyrolactone.

Other lactones, although not so far isolated from foods, may be expected, e.g., Elad and Youssefyeh (1965) have shown that olefins add to the 2-position of 4-butyrolactone in the presence of sunlight. Alk-1-enes have been isolated from oxidized fats and the above reaction might proceed in potato chips. 2-Octyl-4-butyrolactone had a tallowy odor.

Alcohols

Alkanols generally play a minor role in flavor. They may be derived from carbohydrates, amino acids, or oxidized unsaturated acids and in the last two cases may be produced by the formation and reduction of the corresponding aldehyde. Guymon (1964) showed how some of the fusel oil alcohols are produced from 2-keto acids, by decarboxylation to the aldehyde and reduction to the alcohol, thus leucine is the source of 3-methylbutan-1-ol. The *n*-hexanol component in fusel oil may arise from *n*-hexanal obtained from an *n*-alkanoic acid.

Schormüller and Grosh (1965) isolated the $C_{2, 4, 5 \& 6}$ *n*-alkan-1-ols, 2-methylpropan-1-ol, and 3-methylbutan-1-ol from tomatoes and suggested they were formed from the corresponding aldehydes by alcohol dehydrogenase and $NADH_2$.

Stark and Forss (1966) isolated the C_{1-8} *n*-alkan-1-ols from oxidized butter and discussed their formation from C_{14-20} unsaturated acid hydroperoxides.

Unsaturated aliphatic alcohols are much more potent flavor compounds. Hoffmann (1962B) isolated oct-1-en-3-ol from oxidized methyl linoleate and soybean oil, and postulated that it arose by the formation of a hemi-acetal from the unstable 11-linoleate free radical, which underwent an intramolecular cyclic rearrangement and was cleaved to oct-1-en-3-ol (by allylic rearrangement). However, Wilkinson (1964) has suggested that where linoleate is oxidized with free access to oxygen, oct-1-en-3-ol may be formed by a secondary oxidation of the C_{13}-hydroxy conjugated diene resulting from the corresponding hydroperoxide. Addition of a radical to the *cis*-double bond at the C_9-position followed by addition of molecular oxygen to the resulting radical would produce a hydroperoxide which, after-cleavage of the 10-11 bond and subsequent abstraction of hydrogen from the substrate by the resulting radical, would form oct-1-en-3-ol:

$$\underset{13}{CH_3} \ \underset{12}{(CH_2)_4} \ \underset{}{\underset{|}{\underset{OH}{CH}}} \ \underset{\overset{11}{trans}}{C} H = \underset{10}{CH} \ CH \overset{9}{\underset{cis}{=}} CH \ R' \tag{39}$$

$$\xrightarrow{\cdot OR \ (or \cdot OH) \ +O_2} CH_3 \ (CH_2)_4 \ \underset{|}{\underset{OH}{CH}} \ CH = CH \underset{\underset{O}{\overset{|}{\underset{O}{|}}}}{|} CH \ \underset{OR}{\underset{|}{CH}} \ R' \tag{40}$$

$$\xrightarrow{+ RH} CH_3 \ (CH_2)_4 \ \underset{|}{\underset{OH}{CH}} \ CH = CH_2 + \underset{\overset{||}{O}}{CH} \ \underset{OR}{\underset{|}{CH}} \ R' + R \cdot \tag{41}$$

Stark and Forss (1964) isolated oct-1-en-3-ol from a mushroom-flavored fraction from butter and suggested it was formed from oxidized arachidonate as well as linoleate. The latter involved cleavage of the non-conjugated 10-hydroperoxide of linoleate, and it is interesting to observe that Swoboda and Lea (1965) suggested a similar mechanism to account for the formation of n-pentanal and hept-2-enal. A lower homolog, pent-1-en-3-ol has been isolated from strawberries (Winter and Willhalm 1964). Alk-2-enols in the presence of mineral acid can undergo reversible oxytropic change, dehydration to a diene or prototropic change with the formation of a saturated aldehyde. The last reaction might occur during the preparation of 2,4-dinitrophenylhydrazones. The oxytropic rearrangement of alk-1-en-3-ols to alk-2-en-1-ols is well known (Green and Hickinbottom 1957) but the latter have not been isolated from oils or fats although hex-2-enol occurs in oil of black tea (Takei *et al.* 1938).

Leaf alcohol (hex-*cis*-3-enol) is widely distributed in green plants and together with hex-2-enal is mainly responsible for their odor. Hex-*cis*-3-enol is possibly formed from the 13-hydroperoxide of linolenic acid by formation of hex-*cis*-3-enal and its reduction to the alcohol. Bedoukian (1963), however, thought it might arise from a sugar. He remarked that the *cis*-structure is also found in jasmone, jasmine lactone, methyl jasmonate, and nona-*trans*-2,*cis*-6-dien-ol and -al.

Other Compounds

Of the fatty acids only the C_{1-10} (Patton 1964) play a major role in food flavors. They may be formed in many ways, several of which have already been discussed, and by the action of enzymes. For example, the action of carboxylesterase, lipase (A triglyceride + water = a diglyceride + fatty acid), phospholipase A (A lecithin + H_2O = a lysolecithin + an unsaturated fatty acid), lysophospholipase (A lysolecithin + H_2O = glycerolphosphocholine + a fatty acid), cholesterol esterase and amidase (A monocarboxylic acid amide + H_2O = a monocarboxylic acid + NH_3).

Esters occur widely and have been isolated from reverted soybean oil (Chang *et al.* 1961) and from many fruits, e.g., bananas (Hultin and Proctor 1961; Issenberg and Wick 1963) and from animals (An extract of an abdominal gland of the giant water bug is used as a flavoring in Thailand. The active ingredients are hex-2-enyl acetate and butyrate (Devakul and Maarse 1964)). Forss and Davies (1962) found that "fruity" Australian Cheddar cheese contained excessive quantities of heptan-2-one, ethyl butanoate and ethyl hexanoate, and attributed the flavor defect to the action of yeast enzymes. More recently, Day and Anderson (1965) isolated 16 methyl and ethyl *n*-alkanoates from blue cheese presumably formed by microbial esterases.

Aliphatic hydrocarbons are weak flavor compounds: flavors attributed to them have in some cases been due to mercaptans and in our studies of C_8 aliphatic hydrocarbons with unsaturation in the 1-position, to traces of oct-1-en-3-ol.

Amines, of which the longer chain ones at least will tend to be dissolved in the lipid phase of foods, are mostly derived from proteins and amino acids. However, Lea (1957) referred to a fishy flavor in evaporated milk caused by liberation by bacteria of trimethylamine probably from the lecithin.

Many other flavor compounds in foods, e.g., indole, skatole, dicarbonyls, sulfur-compounds, furfural, hydroxymethylfurfural, phenols, aromatics, and terpenes although they are derived from nonlipid material, occur predominantly in the lipid phase.

CONCLUSIONS

Even so incomplete a survey as this of the origin of flavors in lipids brings forcefully to mind more problems than it answers, and some of these apply to the general field of the scientific study of foods.

Techniques for the isolation and identification of flavor compounds are now very well advanced. It is no doubt largely for this reason that so many workers have been attracted to this field and that so much valuable knowledge has recently been accumulated. But to deal effectively with flavor problems in industry or agriculture, other than by the empirical methods used in the past, requires an equal advance in our knowledge of the sources of these compounds in foods, the mechanisms by which they are formed, and the means by which these mechanisms may be controlled. Our knowledge of these things must be factual, not speculative as it so often is at present. Labeled atoms are widely used in the study of reaction mechanisms. Their use could prove equally informative in elucidating the mechanism of autoxidation and other reactions producing flavors from precursors.

It may take us a little longer to get to grips with the final major problem which I would like to mention. In flavor work we constantly rub up against, but seem to avoid looking at, the difficult question of what makes a particular combination of compounds an attractive flavor. Much of it is obviously a matter of habit and of conditioning, but to what degree and in what way are absolutes involved in these human reactions? In dealing with this problem flavor chemistry may follow many other branches of science in moving into the metaphysical field.

DISCUSSION

L. Khatri.—You mentioned the hydrocarbons, especially oct-1-ene changing to the alcohol. The hydrocarbons we have used appear to be pure, gas chromatographically. There was only 1 peak on 2 or 3 different columns. However they smell metallic rather than mushroomy.

D. A. Forss.—Yes, I have done the same thing. You are quite right, they look very pure, but did you calculate where you would expect to get the alcohol? Sometimes they have extremely long retention times.

L. Khatri.—I actually did not expect the alcohol; I thought that this was the original odor of these compounds.

D. A. Forss.—Yes, so did I.

BIBLIOGRAPHY

ANSELL, M. F., and PALMER, M. H. 1963. The lactonisation of olefinic acids: the use of sulphuric and trifluoroacetic acids. J. Chem. Soc. 2640–2644.

BATZER, O. F., SRIBNEY, M., DOTY, D. M., and SCHWEIGERT, B. S. 1957. Production of carbonyl compounds during irradiation of meat and meat fats. J. Agr. Food. Chem. 5, 700–703.

BEDOUKIAN, P. 1963. Leaf alcohol (cis-3-hexen-1-ol). Am. Perfumer Cosmet. 78, No. 12, 31–35.

BOLDINGH, J. 1964. Oils and fats for the benefit of mankind: current problems with respect to production, processing and nutrition. Fette, Seifen, Anstrichmittel 66, 892–898.

BOLDINGH, J., and TAYLOR, R. J. 1962. Trace constituents of butterfat. Nature 194, 909–913.

BURTON, H. S., McWEENY, D. J., and BILTCLIFFE, D. O. 1963. Non-enzymic browning: the role of unsaturated carbonyl compounds as intermediates and of SO_2 as an inhibitor of browning. J. Sci. Food Agr. 14, 911–920.

CHANG, S. S., BROBST, K. M., TAI, H., and IRELAND, C. E. 1961. Characterization of the reversion flavor of soybean oil. J. Am. Oil Chemists' Soc. 38, 671–674.

CROSSLEY, A., HEYES, T. D., and HUDSON, B. J. F. 1962. The effect of heat on pure triglycerides. J. Am. Oil Chemists' Soc. 39, 9–14.

DALZIEL, K., and DICKINSON, F. M. 1965. Aldehyde mutase. Nature 206, 255–257.

DAY, E. A., and ANDERSON, D. F. 1965. Gas chromatographic and mass spectral identification of natural components of the aroma fraction of blue cheese. J. Agr. Food Chem. 13, 2–4.

DAY, E. A., and PAPAIOANNOU, S. E. 1963. Irradiation-induced changes in milk fat. J. Dairy Sci. *46*, 1201–1206.

DEVAKUL, V., and MAARSE, H. 1964. A second compound in the odorous gland liquid of the giant water bug *Lethocerus indicus* (Lep. and Serv.). Anal. Biochem. 7, 269–274.

DIXON, M., and WEBB, E. C. 1964. Enzymes. 2nd Edition. Longmans, Green and Co., London.

VAN DUIN, H. 1958. Investigation into the carbonyl compounds in butter. III. Phosphatide-bound aldehydes. Neth. Milk Dairy J. *12*, 90–95.

ELAD, D., and YOUSSEFYEH, R. D. 1965. The light-induced addition of γ-butyrolactone to olefins. Chemical Communications No. 1, 13 January p. 7.

ENDRES, J. G., BHALERA, V. R., and KUMMEROW, F. A. 1962A. Thermal oxidation of synthetic triglycerides. I. Composition of oxidized triglycerides. J. Am. Oil Chemists' Soc. 39, 118–121.

ENDRES, J. G., BHALERA, V. R., and KUMMEROW, F. A. 1962B. Thermal oxidation of synthetic triglycerides. II. Analysis of the volatile condensable and noncondensable phases. J. Am. Oil Chemists' Soc. 39, 159–162.

FARMER, E. H., KOCH, H. P., and SUTTON, D. A. 1943. The course of autoxidation reactions in polyisoprenes and allied compounds. VII. Rearrangement of double bonds during autoxidation. J. Chem. Soc. 541–547.

FORSS, D. A. 1951. An investigation of the relation of the essential oils of *Coronopus didymus* to the tainting of butter. Australian J. Appl. Sci. 2, 396–410.

FORSS, D. A., and DAVIES, E. 1962. Fruity flavor in Cheddar cheese. Unpublished work.

FORSS, D. A., DUNSTONE, E. A., RAMSHAW, E. H., and STARK, W. 1962A. The flavor of cucumbers. J. Food Sci. 27, 90–93.

FORSS, D. A., RAMSHAW, E. H., and STARK, W. 1962B. Vinyl ketones in oxidized fats. J. Am. Oil Chemists' Soc. 39, 308.

FORSS, D. A., URBACH, G., and STARK, W. 1966. γ-Dodecalactone and other γ- and δ-lactones in Australian butter oil. 17th. Intern. Dairy Congr. Proc. 211–214.

FRANCKE, A. 1963. Enzymatic reduction of δ-keto fatty acids to the corresponding optically active hydroxy acids. Nature *197*, 384–385.

FRITSCH, C. W., and DEATHERAGE, F. E. 1956. A study of the volatile compounds produced by the autoxidation of methyl oleate, oleic acid, and cis-9-octadecene. J. Am. Oil Chemists' Soc. *33*, 109–113.

GEHRIG, R. F., and KNIGHT, S. G. 1961. Formation of 2-heptanone from caprylic acid by spores of various filamentous fungi. Nature *192*, 1185.

GEHRIG, R. F., and KNIGHT, S. G. 1963. Fatty acid oxidation by spores of *Penicillium roqueforti*. Appl. Microbiol. *11*, 166–170.

GREEN, M. B., and HICKINBOTTOM, W. J. 1957. The rearrangement of α,β-unsaturated alcohols to saturated aldehydes and ketones. I. The preparation of α,β-unsaturated alcohols and 1:2-diols and their prototropic change. J. Chem. Soc. 3262–3269.

GUYMON, J. F. 1964. Studies of higher alcohol formation by yeasts through gas chromatography. Qualitas Plant. *11*, 194–201.

HAMMOND, E. G., and HILL, F. D. 1964. The oxidized-metallic and grassy flavor components of autoxidized milk fat. J. Am. Oil Chemists' Soc. *41*, 180–184.

Harper, W. J. 1959. Chemistry of cheese flavors. J. Dairy Sci. 42, 207–213.

Haverkamp Begemann, P., and Koster, J. C. 1964. 4-Cis-heptenal: a cream-flavoured component of butter. Nature 202, 552–553.

Hewitt, E. J. 1963. Enzymatic enhancement of flavor. J. Agr. Food Chem. 11, 14–19.

Hoffmann, G. 1961. Isolation of two pairs of isomeric 2,4-alkadienals from soybean oil-reversion flavor concentrate. J. Am. Oil Chemists' Soc. 38, 31–32.

Hoffmann, G. 1962A. Symposium on Foods: Lipids and Their Oxidation. H. W. Schultz, E. A. Day, and R. O. Sinnhuber, (Editors.) Avi Publishing Co., Inc., Westport, Conn.

Hoffmann, G. 1962B. 1-Octen-3-ol and its relation to other oxidative cleavage products from esters of linoleic acid. J. Am. Oil Chemists' Soc. 39, 439–444.

Hoffmann, G. 1964. Isolation of two isomeric 2,6-nonadienals and their precursor 11,15-octadecadienoic acids from beef tallow. I. S. F.—World Fat Congress, Hamburg 12–18 Oct. 148–149.

Honkanen, E., and Moisio, T. 1963. On the occurrence of oct-1-en-3-ol in clover plants. Acta Chem. Scand. 17, 858.

Honkanen, E., Karvonen, P., and Virtanen, A. I. 1964. Studies on the transfer of some flavour compounds to milk. Acta Chem. Scand. 18, 612–618.

Hrdlička, J., and Janíček, G. 1964. Study of changes during thermic and hydrothermic processes. IV. Formation of carbonyl compounds in toasting of oat flakes. Potravinářská Technologie 8, 101–105.

Hrdlička, J., and Pokorný, J. 1962. Formation of volatile compounds during the autoxidation of lipids. I. Volatile carbonyl compounds in autoxidized fatty acids. Potravinářská Technologie 6, 161–169.

Hrdlička, J., and Pokorný, J. 1963. Formation of volatile compounds during the autoxidation of lipids. II. Volatile carbonyl compounds in autoxidized fats. Potravinářská Technologie 7, 113–124.

Hultin, H. O., and Proctor, B. E. 1961. Changes in some volatile constituents of the banana during ripening, storage and processing. Food Technol. 15, 440–444.

Inglett, G. E., Dowling, B., Albrecht, J. J., and Hoglan, F. A. 1965. Taste-modifying properties of miracle fruit (Synsepalum dulcificum). J. Agr. Food Chem. 13, 284–287.

Issenberg, P., and Wick, E. L. 1963. Volatile components of bananas. J. Agr. Food Chem. 11, 2–8.

James, A. T., Harris, R. V., Hitchcock, C., Wood, B. J. B., and Nichols, B. W. 1965. Investigations of the biosynthesis and degradation of unsaturated fatty acids in higher plants and photosynthetic bacteria. Fette, Seifen, Anstrichmittel 67, 393–396.

Jennings, W. G., and Sevenants, M. R. 1964. Volatile components of peach. J. Food Sci. 29, 796–801.

de Jong, K., and Van der Wel, H. 1964. Identification of some iso-linoleic acids occurring in butterfat. Nature 202, 553–555.

Keeney, P. G., and Patton, S. 1956. The coconut-like flavor defect of milk-fat. I. Isolation of the flavor compound from butter oil and its identification as δ-decalactone. J. Dairy Sci. 39, 1104–1113.

KEPPLER, J. G., SCHOLS, J. A., FEENSTRA, W. H., and MEIJBOOM, P. W. 1965. Components of the hardening flavor present in hardened linseed oil and soybean oil. J. Am. Oil Chemists' Soc. 42, 246–249.

LANGLER, J. E., and DAY, E. A. 1964. Development and flavor properties of methyl ketones in milk fat. J. Dairy Sci. 47, 1291–1296.

LAWRENCE, R. C. 1963. Formation of methyl ketones as artifacts during steam distillation of Cheddar cheese and butter-oil. J. Dairy Res. 30, 161–170.

LEA, C. H. 1957. Deteriorative reactions involving phospholipids and lipoproteins. J. Sci. Food Agr. 8, 1–13.

LILLARD, D. A., and DAY, E. A. 1964. Degradation of monocarbonyls from autoxidizing lipids. J. Am. Oil Chemists' Soc. 41, 549–552.

LOURY, M., LECHARTIER, G., and FORNEY, M. 1965. Identification of volatile products resulting of autoxidation of oleic acid by thin layer and paper chromatography. Rev. Franc. Corps Gras. 12, 253–262.

MacLEOD, P., and MORGAN, M. E. 1958. Differences in the ability of lactic streptococci to form aldehydes from certain amino acids. J. Dairy Sci. 41, 908–913.

MONCRIEFF, R. W. 1964. The metallic taste. Perf. Ess. Oil Record 55, 205–207.

MORGAN, M. E., and PEREIRA, R. L. 1962. Volatile constituents of grass and corn silage. I. Steam distillates. J. Dairy Sci. 45, 457–466.

MORGAN, M. E., and PEREIRA, R. L. 1963. Identity of the grassy aroma constituents of green forages. J. Dairy Sci. 46, 1420–1422.

MUCK, G. A., TOBIAS, J., and WHITNEY, R. McL. 1963. Flavor of evaporated milk. I. Identification of some compounds obtained by the petroleum ether solvent partitioning technique from aged evaporated milk. J. Dairy Sci. 46, 774–779.

NAKANISHI, T., and WATANABE, K. 1965. Studies on the change of meat tissue lipids by various treatments. Part I. About the presence of lactones in beef fat. 36th Meeting of Agricultural and Biological Society of Japan, 4 April.

NAWAR, W. W., CANCEL, L. E., and FAGERSON, I. S. 1962. Heat-induced changes in milk fat. J. Dairy Sci. 45, 1172–1177.

NYE, W., and SPOEHR, H. A. 1943. The isolation of hexenal from leaves. Arch. Biochem. 2, 23–35.

PARK, R. J. 1965. Benzyl thiocyanate taint in the milk of dairy cattle ingesting Coronopus didymus Sm. Nature 207, 640.

PATTON, S. 1950. The methyl ketones of blue cheese and their relation to its flavor. J. Dairy Sci. 33, 680–684.

PATTON, S. 1964. Flavor thresholds of volatile fatty acids. J. Food Sci. 29, 679–680.

PATTON, S., BARNES, I. J., and EVANS, L. E. 1959. n-Deca-2,4-dienal, its origin from linoleate and flavor significance in fats. J. Am. Oil Chemists' Soc. 36, 280–283.

PATTON, S., and KURTZ, G. W. 1955. A note on the thiobarbituric acid test for milk lipid oxidation. J. Dairy Sci. 38, 901.

PATTON, S., and THARP, B. W. 1959. Formation of methyl ketones from milk fat during steam distillation or saponification. J. Dairy Sci. 42, 49–55.

PRIVETT, O. S., NICKELL, C., LUNDBERG, W. O., and BOYER, P. D. 1955. Products of the lipoxidase-catalyzed oxidation of sodium linoleate. J. Am. Oil Chemists' Soc. 32, 505–511.

RAMANATHAN, V., SAKURAGI, T., and KUMMEROW, F. A. 1959. Thermal oxidation of methyl esters of fatty acids. J. Am. Oil Chemists' Soc. 36, 244–248.

SCHOGT, J. C. M., HAVERKAMP BEGEMANN, P., and KOSTER, J. 1960. Nonphosphatide aldehydogenic lipids in milk fat, beef tallow, and ox heart. J. Lipid Res. 1, 446–449.

SCHOGT, J. C. M., HAVERKAMP BEGEMANN, P., and RECOURT, J. H. 1961. Composition of aldehydes derived from some bovine lipids. J. Lipid Res. 2, 142–147.

SCHORMÜLLER, J., and GROSCH, W. 1965. Investigations of food flavors. III. Further methods for analyzing the volatile alcohols in tomatoes. Z. Lebensm.-Untersuch. Forsch. 126, 188–193.

SHIPE, W. F., LEDFORD, R. A., PETERSON, R. D., SCANLAN, R. A., GEERKEN, H. F., DOUGHERTY, R. W., and MORGAN, M. E. 1962. Physiological mechanisms involved in transmitting flavors and odors to milk. II. Transmission of some flavor components of silage. J. Dairy Sci. 45, 477–480.

STARK, W. 1965. Private communication.

STARK, W., and FORSS, D. A. 1962. A compound responsible for metallic flavour in dairy products. I. Isolation and identification. J. Dairy Res. 29, 173–180.

STARK, W., and FORSS, D. A. 1964. A compound responsible for mushroom flavour in dairy products. J. Dairy Res. 31, 253–259.

STARK, W., and FORSS, D. A. 1966. n-Alkan-1-ols in oxidized butter. J. Dairy Res. 33, 31–36.

SWOBODA, P. A. T., and LEA, C. H. 1965. On the flavour volatiles of fats and fat-containing foods. II. A gas chromatographic investigation of volatile autoxidation products from sunflower oil. J. Sci. Food Agr. 16, 680–688.

TAKEI, S., SAKATO, Y., and ONO, M. 1938. Odoriferous principle of green tea. XI. Primary alcohols from the oil of black tea. Bull. Inst. Phys.-Chem. Research (Tokyo) 17, 871–879; Chem. Abstr. 34, 1809[9] (1940).

TOI. B., OTA, S., and IWATA, N. 1962. Volatile products obtained from edible oils by open-air heating. III. Decomposition products from methyl oleate. Yukagaku 11, 508–513.

TUYNENBURG MUYS, G., VAN DER VEN, B., and DE JONGE, A. P. 1963. Preparation of optically active γ- and δ-lactones by microbiological reduction of the corresponding keto acids. Appl. Microbiol. 11, 389–393.

VAN DER VEN, B. 1964. Detection of γ- and δ-keto acids in butterfat. Rec. Trav. Chim. 83, 976–982.

VAN DER VEN, B., HAVERKAMP BEGEMANN, P., and SCHOGT, J. C. M. 1963. Precursors of methyl ketones in butter. J. Lipid Res. 4, 91–95.

WILKINSON, R. A. 1964. Theories of the mechanisms of oxidized flavour development in dairy products. Internal Rept. 4, Division of Dairy Research, C.S.I.R.O., Melbourne, Australia.

WINTER, M., and WILLHALM, B. 1964. Flavors. Flavor of fresh strawberries. Analysis of the carbonyl compounds, esters and volatile alcohols. Helv. Chim. Acta 47, 1215–1227.

WONG, N. P., and PATTON, S. 1962. Identification of some volatile compounds related to the flavor of milk and cream. J. Dairy Sci. 45, 724–728.

CHAPTER 24

Akira Kuninaka | Flavor Potentiators

INTRODUCTION

Though the words potentiator and potentiation are well known to pharmacologists, flavor potentiation is a new term in the vocabulary of flavor research. It refers to the action of a compound which, in small quantities, has by itself no sensory effect, but exaggerates the effect of other agents on that system (Sjöström 1965).

There are two groups of known flavor potentiators: Certain L-amino acids containing five carbon atoms and certain 5'-nucleotides containing 6-hydroxypurine. L-Glutamate, ibotenic acid, and tricholomic acid belong to the first group, and 5'-guanylate or guanosine 5'-monophosphate (5'-GMP), 5'-inosinate or inosine 5'monophosphate (5'-IMP), and 5'-xanthylate or xanthosine 5'-monophosphate (5'-XMP) belong to the second group. There is a specific synergistic action in flavor between a compound of the first group and a compound of the second group. The synergistic action furnishes the most important key to the development of the flavor potentiators.

Monosodium L-glutamate (MSG) is the best known flavor potentiator and has been used widely to enhance or potentiate the flavor of natural food products. The 5'-nucleotides, especially 5'-IMP and 5'-GMP, which were introduced recently as flavor potentiators, are even more intriguing than MSG, because they have specific flavor activities which are not provided by MSG. Flavor activity of ibotenic acid and tricholomic acid which were isolated from Japanese fungi in 1964 are qualitatively similar to that of MSG, although these new amino acids have not yet been used commercially.

In this paper I would like to discuss the flavor potentiators from historical, chemical, and practical points of view, emphasizing the 5'-nucleotides.

HISTORY

The introduction of flavor potentiators arises from studies on Japanese foods. Since the early part of the present century, many Japanese food scientists have undertaken to isolate the flavor components from the natural foods peculiar to Japan, such as sea tangle, a kind of seaweed and dried bonito, a kind of fish. Both sea tangle and dried bonito have been used generally for seasoning Japanese meals, because they can be

515

well preserved for a long time and the extracts have characteristic flavor activities. It seems natural therefore that Japanese workers had special interests in these materials.

At first Ikeda (1909) chemically fractionated sea tangle extract, and isolated a crystalline flavor compound which was easily identified as MSG. As it was already known that L-glutamate was present in protein hydrolysates, economical production of MSG from plant proteins was not so difficult. In fact, immediately after Ikeda's discovery MSG started to be produced commercially as the first chemical seasoning. Since then more economical processes for producing MSG have been developed and the flavoring action of MSG has also been studied extensively. MSG is now accepted as an excellent flavor enhancer or potentiator by food technologists, food processors, and housewives, and is used in huge volumes throughout the world.

On the other hand, Kodama (1913) isolated a crystalline flavor component of dried bonito and reported that it was the histidine salt of inosinic acid. Unfortunately, this compound could not be produced economically and therefore was not used commercially. The use of IMP as a flavor potentiator was realized about fifty years later, when we found the relationship between chemical structure and flavor activity of nucleotides (Kuninaka 1960) and developed a process for preparing these compounds from ribonucleic acid (Kuninaka *et al.* 1959, 1961).

Why was the commercial use of 5'-nucleotides delayed so long? One of the reasons was the existence of three isomers of inosinic acid. It was not clear which isomer had flavor enhancing properties. To solve the problem, we prepared these isomers and checked their flavor effects. Inosine 2'-monophosphate (2'-IMP) and inosine 3'-monophosphate (3'-IMP) were prepared from ribonucleic acid, and 5'-IMP was isolated from animal muscle tissue.

The conclusion was that among the three isomers only 5'-IMP had flavor activity and histidine was found not to be necessary. We also confirmed that hypoxanthine, inosine, and ribose 5-phosphate had no flavor activity. So, both ribosidic and 5'-phosphomonoester linkages are essential for flavoring action. Furthermore, in the structure of 5'-IMP, the hydroxyl group at the 6-position was confirmed to be essential for flavor activity. If the hydroxyl group is replaced by an amino group, for example, flavor activity decreases sharply. On the other hand, hydrogen at the 2-position could be replaced by another group such as a hydroxyl or amino group, without much change in flavor activity. In other words, not only 5'-IMP but also 5'-GMP and 5'-XMP were found to have flavor activity. The general structure of the nucleotides which have flavor activity is given in Fig. 105.

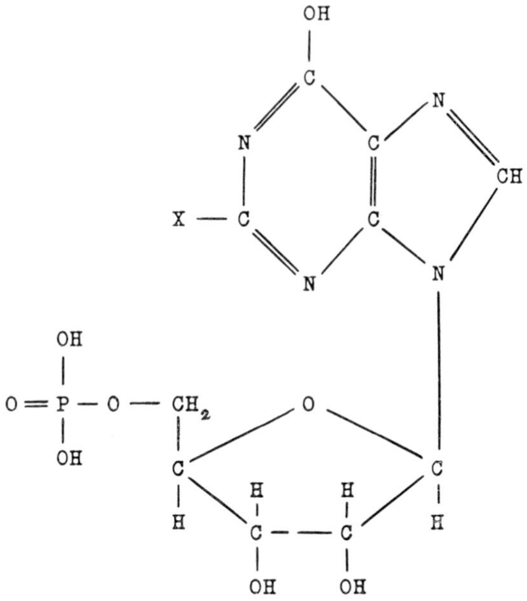

X = H, NH₂, (or OH)

FIG. 105. GENERAL STRUCTURE OF THE NUCLEOTIDES WHICH HAVE FLAVOR ACTIVITY

When "X" is substituted with simple hydrogen, the resulting compound is 5'-IMP. Substitution of an amino group or a hydroxyl group at this position creates 5'-GMP or 5'-XMP.

Aspergillus ribosidase specifically attacks the flavor nucleotides, 5'-IMP, 5'-GMP and 5'-XMP, as well as their nucleosides (Kuninaka 1956, 1957, 1959). It may be suggested that there is an analogy between sensory specificity and enzyme specificity. The fact is, our study of the specificity of the ribosidase enzyme action on the nucleotides, led us to the discovery of the specific flavor activities of 5'-GMP and 5'-XMP. According to Hosoi (1961), mosquitoes like neither MSG nor the flavor nucleotides, 5'-IMP and 5'-GMP, but specifically like adenosine 5'-monophosphate (5'-AMP) and its derivatives. It is interesting that 5'-AMP is not attacked by *Aspergillus* ribosidase which attacks the flavor nucleotides, but is specifically attacked by *Azotobacter* ribosidase (Hurwitz *et al.* 1957). Thus, 5'-IMP and 5'-GMP are preferred by *Aspergillus* enzyme as well as human, while 5'-AMP is preferred by *Azotobacter* enzyme as well as mosquito.

Among the three flavor nucleotides, 5′-XMP has not been produced commercially, because its flavor activity is weaker than that of 5′-GMP or 5′-IMP.

MSG and 5′-IMP were first reported as flavor components of natural foods, and then introduced as flavor potentiators. Actually, various foods contain them. On the other hand, the flavor activity of 5′-GMP was first assumed from the similarity in its chemical structure to 5′-IMP, and it was then actually proved when it was produced from ribonucleic acid as a by-product of 5′-IMP. Therefore, 5′-GMP may be thought to have been introduced as a nonnatural flavor potentiator. In fact 5′-GMP is found to be present only in a few natural foods, such as a kind of Japanese mushroom, *Cortinellus shittake*, which contains about 100 mg. of 5′-GMP per 100 gm. The 5′-GMP content of meats is usually only about 2 mg. per 100 gm. while the 5′-IMP content is about 100 mg. per 100 gm.

As will be discussed later, there is a synergistic relationship between 5′-nucleotides and MSG in flavor activity. The discovery of this relationship has accelerated the commercial development of 5′-IMP and 5′-GMP as flavor potentiators.

The history of 5′-nucleotides as flavor potentiators suggests that the following steps are necessary for development of a flavor potentiator: (1) isolation and identification of a flavor component of natural foods; (2) elucidation of its properties, especially the relationship between its chemical structure and flavor activity; (3) establishment of an economical process for producing it; and (4) recognition of its relationship with other flavor potentiators.

Recently Takemoto and Nakajima (1946A, B) and Takemoto *et al.* (1964A, B, C) isolated two new amino acids, tricholomic acid and ibotenic acid, from the Japanese mushrooms or fungi, belonging to *Tricholoma muscarium* and *Amanita strobiliformis*, respectively.

$$H_2C\!\!-\!\!CHCHCOOH \qquad\qquad HC\!\!=\!\!C\!\!-\!\!CHCOOH$$

Tricholomic acid   Ibotenic acid

It has been known in Japan that such fungi were effective in killing the common house fly and this work was undertaken in order to elucidate the specific insecticidal compounds in the fungi. Having isolated these two amino acids, these workers also reported that they had good flavor activity, and their threshold levels were lower than that of any known flavor potentiator (Table 85). Furthermore, it was clarified that there

TABLE 85

THRESHOLD LEVEL OF FLAVOR POTENTIATORS

Compound	Threshold Level in Per Cent
5'-IMP·Na$_2$	0.01–0.025 (0.00010)[1]
5'-GMP·Na$_2$	0.0035–0.02 (0.000030)[1]
MSG	0.014–0.03 (0.002)[2]
Tricholomic Acid	0.001–0.005
Ibotenic Acid	0.001–0.005

Compiled from Kuninaka (1960); Wagner *et al.* (1963); Fujita *et al.* (1964); Toi *et al.* (1964); Takemoto (1965); and Yoshino and Suzuki (1965).

[1] In 0.1% MSG solution (Fujita *et al.* 1964).

[2] In 0.01% 5'-IMP·Na$_2$ solution (Toi *et al.* 1964).

was a synergistic action between the 5'-nucleotides and them. In Japan, their stability and toxicity are now carefully studied, and a process for preparing them is now under study, too.

CHEMICAL STRUCTURE AND FLAVOR ACTIVITY

In general, the flavor activity of a compound specifically depends upon its chemical structure. To elucidate the relationship between chemical structure and flavor activity is interesting not only for systematization of flavor chemistry but also for the discovery of new flavor potentiators.

Amino Acids

Among the various amino acids, only L-glutamate had been known to have a characteristic activity as a flavor potentiator for a long time. Two new amino acids, ibotenic acid and tricholomic acid, were found recently to have the same kind of flavor potentiating activity as L-glutamate. Furthermore, both ibotenic acid and tricholomic acid, as well as glutamic acid, contain five carbon atoms. Ibotenic acid is readily decarboxylated in water by heating (Takemoto *et al.* 1964B), and the pyro-product of ibotenic acid has neither flavor activity nor insecticidal activity (Takemoto 1965). Thus, the flavor amino acids contain the following structure in common.

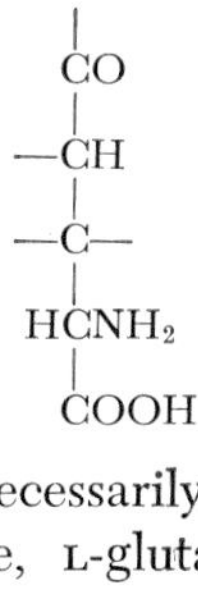

$$
\begin{array}{c}
| \\
\text{CO} \\
| \\
-\text{CH} \\
| \\
-\text{C}- \\
| \\
\text{H}\text{C}\text{NH}_2 \\
| \\
\text{COOH}
\end{array}
$$

The above structure is not necessarily enough for flavor potentiating activity. Because, for example, L-glutamine also contains the same structure, but it has no flavor activity. However, there is still a possibility that another derivative of the above structure has a flavor potentiating activity.

Nucleotides

Purine or pyrimidine bases, nucleosides, and 2'- or 3'-nucleotides have no flavor activity. Flavor compounds have been found only in 5'-nucleotides. It is interesting that flavor potentiators are not found in 2'- or 3'-nucleotides but in 5'-nucleotides which are much more important biochemically than 2'- or 3'-nucleotides. As shown in Fig. 105, the chemical structure necessary for the flavor potentiating activity is regarded as 6-hydroxypurine nucleoside 5'-phosphate. Typical flavor-potentiating nucleotides are 5'-IMP and 5'-GMP.

Several Japanese researchers have further studied the effects of chemical modifications of 5'-IMP or 5'-GMP on their activity. The first problem is whether the 2'- and 3'-hydroxyl groups of 5'-IMP or 5'-GMP are necessary for flavoring action. The second problem is how chemical modifications of the phosphate moiety affect the flavor activity. Regarding the first point, Nakao and Ogata (1963) disclosed that deoxyinosine 5'-monophosphate and deoxyguanosine 5'-monophosphate also had flavor activity. Therefore the 2'-OH of 5'-IMP or 5'-GMP can be replaced by H without the total loss of flavor activity.

Futhermore, Honjo et al. (1963) reported that flavor activity could be detected in 2', 3'-O-isopropylidene 5'-IMP(I),2'(3'), 5'-IDP(II), and 2'(3'), 5'-GDP(III), too, although the activity was weaker. In these cases the hydrogen of the 2' and/or 3'-OH groups was replaced by another group.

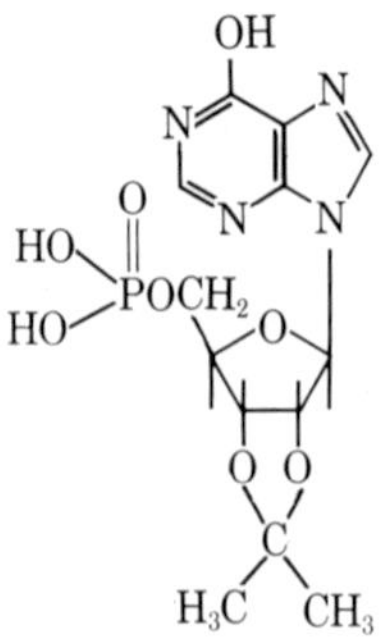

(I) 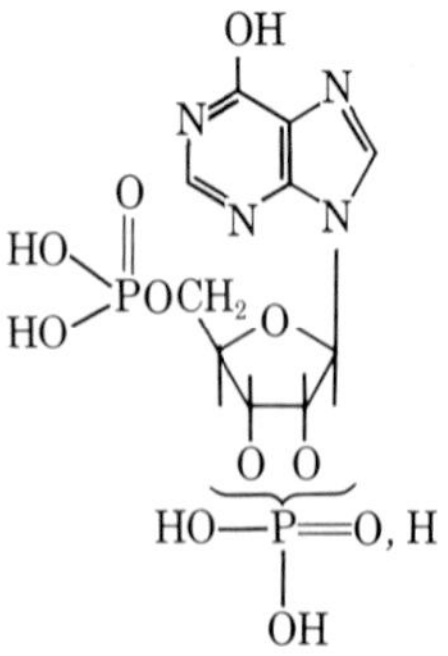   (II) 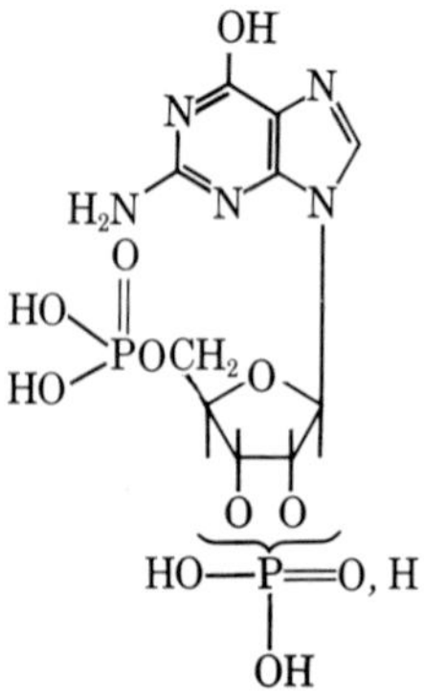   (III)

On the other hand, 9-(4'-hydroxybutyl)-6-hydroxypurine 4'-monophosphate (IV) had no flavor activity. In other words, when the ribose structure was replaced by an aliphatic alcohol structure, the flavor activity could not be detected.

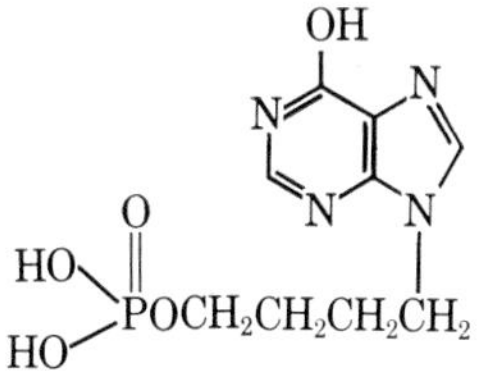

(IV)

The second point, namely the effect of modifications of the phosphate moiety was also studied by Honjo *et al.* (1963). The methylester(V) of 5′-IMP, the ethylesters(VI, VII) of 5′-IMP and 5′-GMP, the amidates (VIII, IX) of 5′-IMP and 5′-GMP, inosine monosulfate(X) and guanosine monosulfate (XI) had no flavor activity.

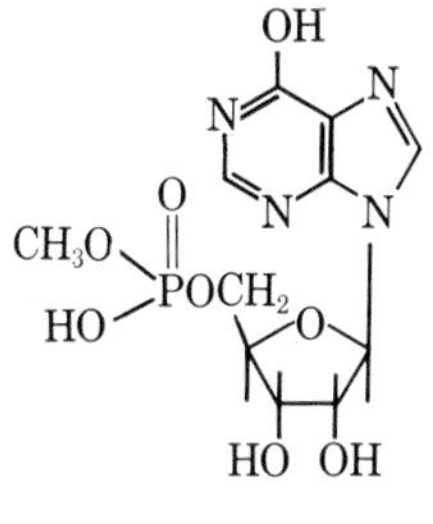

(V)

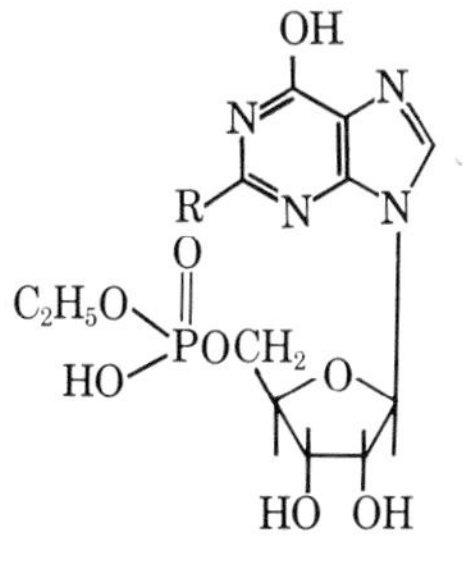

(VI) R=H
(VII) R=NH$_2$

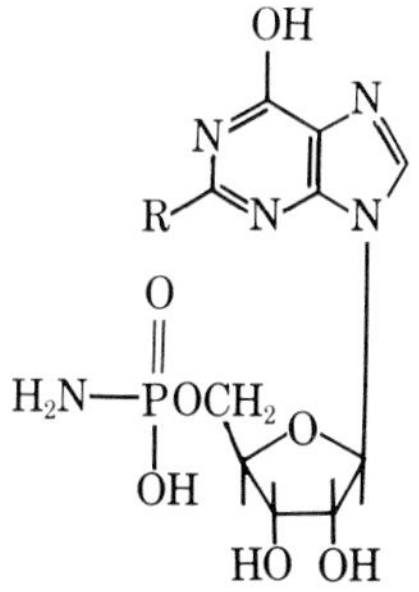

(VIII) R=H
(IX) R=NH$_2$

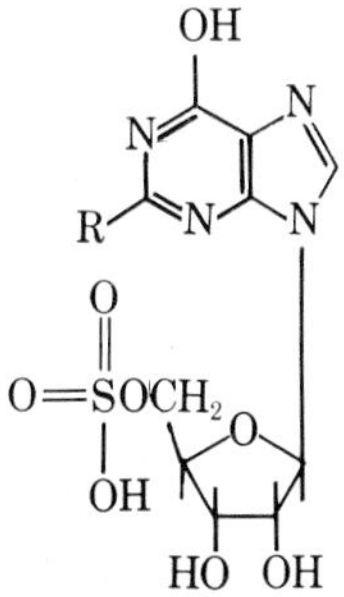

(X) R=H
(XI) R=NH$_2$

Thus, both hydroxyls of the phosphate group are essential for flavor activity and probably both primary and secondary dissociations are necessary for these compounds to have flavor activity.

The flavor activity was recognized in inosine 5'-diphosphate(XII), probably because two hydroxyl groups are present on the end phosphate group and primary and secondary dissociations are possible. The other four compounds, diinosine pyrophosphate(XIII), diguanosine pyrophosphate(XIV), 3', 5'-cyclic IMP(XV), and poly IMP(XVI), did not have any flavor activity.

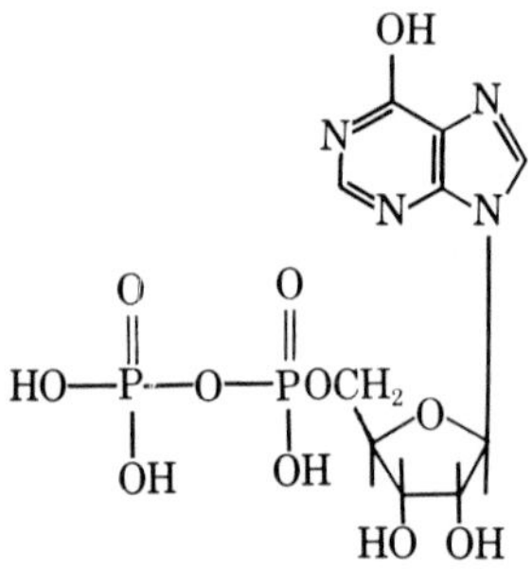

(XII)

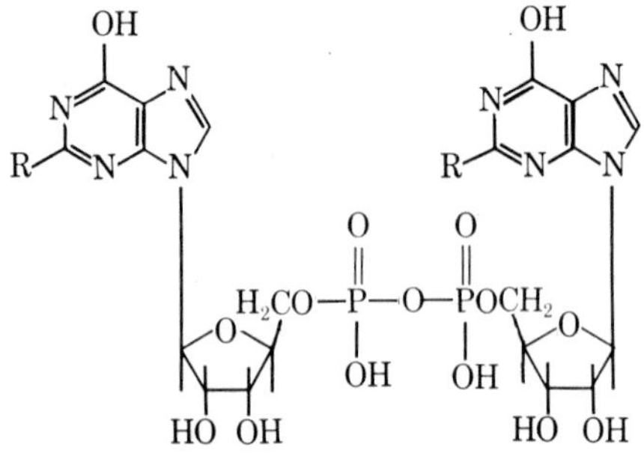

(XIII) R=H
(XIV) R=NH₂

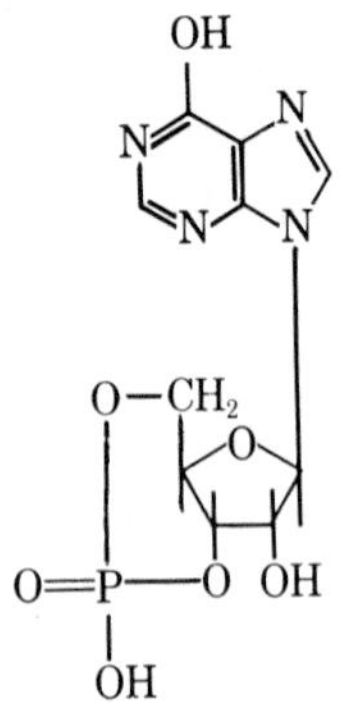

(XV)

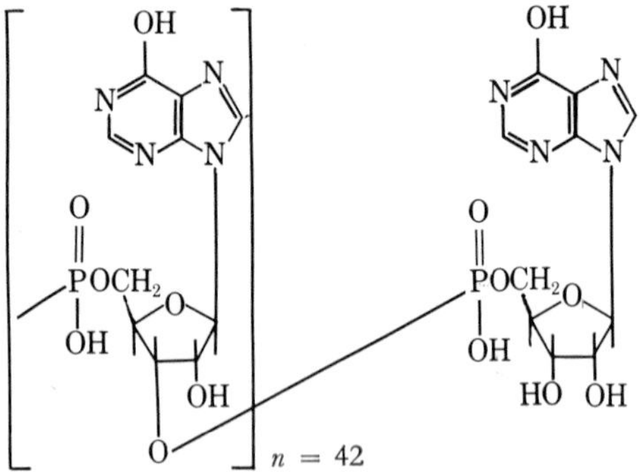

(XVI)

The above studies indicate that the structure of the nucleoside-5'-phosphate molecule must be quite specific in order for the compound to have flavor activity, although 2'-and 3'-hydroxyl groups are not necessarily essential.

Although none of the synthesized compounds shown above had stronger flavor activity than natural 5'-IMP or 5'-GMP, it is still possible that further research on the modification of the purine moiety will result in discovery of structures with high flavor activity.

SYNERGISTIC ACTION BETWEEN FLAVOR POTENTIATORS

There are many kinds of interactions in flavor between various components of foods. Among them, the synergistic action between an amino acid flavor potentiator and a 5'-nucleotide flavor potentiator is the most notable. If the synergistic action had not been discovered, the 5'-nucleotides would not have been used commercially.

At first, we found that the latent flavor level of 5'-IMP or 5'-GMP was markedly detectable when MSG solution was employed as its medium (Kuninaka 1960). For example, in the sensory tests, shown in Table 86,

TABLE 86

MUTUAL EFFECT BETWEEN MSG AND 5'-IMP (SCORING TESTS)

Test	Medium	Addition	Total Score[1]
I	Water	None	0
		0.01% 5'-IMP·Na$_2$	6
II	Water	None	0
		0.01% MSG	6
III	0.1% MSG	None	0
		0.01% 5'-IMP·Na$_2$	36
IV	0.1% 5'-IMP·Na$_2$	None	0
		0.01% MSG	38

From Kuninaka (1960).
[1] Scored by a Yamasa panel of twelve members as follows:
  0:0 = no difference
  0:1 = a slight difference
  0:2 = a significant difference
  0:3 = a large difference
  0:4 = a very remarkable difference

two samples of each were compared and scored. In water, the taste of 0.01% of 5'-IMP was faint, but in the presence of 0.1% MSG, the flavor effect caused by the same amount of 5'-IMP increased remarkably. The flavor strength of the mixture was almost equivalent to that of 0.5% MSG. This phenomenon could also be observed when 5'-IMP and MSG were exchanged.

Synergistic action also can be demonstrated by studying the mutual effects in reducing individual threshold levels. For example, the threshold level of 5'-IMP or 5'-GMP is reduced sharply in MSG solution, and the threshold level of MSG is reduced sharply in 5'-nucleotide solution (Table 85).

To evaluate the synergistic action in more detail, we prepared mixtures of MSG and nucleotide in various ratios, and dissolved them in 1.2% sodium chloride solution at various concentrations. The flavor activity of each solution was compared with that of 1.2% sodium chloride solution containing MSG alone. In the example, shown in Fig. 106, the ratio of MSG to 5'-IMP in the mixture is 20:1. Each solution was compared with 0.3% MSG solution. When the concentration of the mixture was

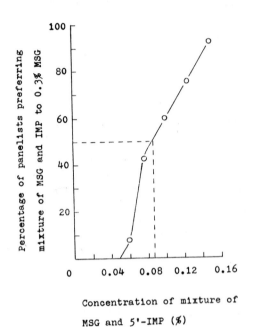

Concentration of mixture of

MSG and 5'-IMP (%)

Fig. 106. Comparison of 0.3% MSG Solution and the Solutions of 20:1 Mixture of MSG and 5'-IMP in Flavor Activity in the Presence of 1.2% of Sodium Chloride

Table 87

FLAVOR ACTIVITY OF MIXTURES OF MSG AND 5'-NUCLEOTIDE

Ratio of Mixing MSG:5'-IMP·Na$_2$[1] (5'-GMP·Na$_2$)[2]	Relative Flavor Activity per Unit Weight of Mixture
1:0	1
1:2	6.5 (13.3)
1:1	7.5 (30.0)
2:1	5.5 (22.0)
10:1	5.0 (19.0)
20:1	3.4 (12.4)
50:1	2.5 (6.4)
100:1	2.0 (5.5)

From Kuninaka *et al.* (1961).
[1] Loss on drying, 26.5%.
[2] Loss on drying, 8.0%.

less than 0.05%, all testers preferred the MSG solution. As the concentration of mixture increased, the preference of the testers shifted from MSG to the mxtiure. It was concluded that the flavor activity of 0.3% MSG solution was equivalent to that of 0.087% solution of the 20:1 mixture of MSG and 5'-IMP. In other words, the flavor activity of the mixture is 3.4 times as much as that of MSG.

We repeated the sensory tests in this manner changing the ratio of MSG to nucleotide. The data are summarized in Table 87. The relative flavor activity per unit weight of each mixture was calculated assuming that flavor activity per unit weight of MSG is 1. The values shown in parenthesis were obtained when 5'-GMP was employed in place of 5'-IMP. Table 87 shows that as the ratio of 5'-nucleotide to MSG is lowered, the flavor activity of the resulting mixture is reduced. However, this relationship is not linear. At a lower relative concentration the relative effectiveness of the nucleotide is much greater. For example:

$$\text{MSG} \quad 10 \text{ gm.} + 5'\text{-IMP} \cdot \text{Na}_2 \ 1 \text{ gm.} = \text{MSG } 5 \times 11 \text{ gm.}$$
$$\text{Thus, } 5'\text{-IMP} \cdot \text{Na}_2 \ 1 \text{ gm.} = \text{MSG } 45 \text{ gm.}$$

$$\text{MSG} \quad 10 \text{ gm.} + 5'\text{-GMP} \cdot \text{Na}_2 \ 1 \text{ gm.} = \text{MSG } 19 \times 11 \text{ gm.}$$
$$\text{Thus, } 5'\text{-GMP} \cdot \text{Na}_2 \ 1 \text{ gm.} = \text{MSG } 199 \text{ gm.}$$

$$\text{MSG } 100 \text{ gm.} + 5'\text{-IMP} \cdot \text{Na}_2 \ 1 \text{ gm.} = \text{MSG } 2 \times 101 \text{ gm.}$$
$$\text{Thus, } 5'\text{-IMP} \cdot \text{Na}_2 \ 1 \text{ gm.} = \text{MSG } 102 \text{ gm.}$$

$$\text{MSG } 100 \text{ gm.} + 5'\text{-GMP} \cdot \text{Na}_2 \ 1 \text{ gm.} = \text{MSG } 5.5 \times 101 \text{ gm.}$$
$$\text{Thus, } 5'\text{-GMP} \cdot \text{Na}_2 \ 1 \text{ gm.} = \text{MSG } 455.5 \text{ gm.}$$

The presence of the 5'-nucleotide in a smaller ratio can spare a larger amount of MSG. The sparing effect can be recognized not only in pure water or saline solution but also in actual foods or beverages. The sparing effect is an important aspect of 5'-nucleotides as flavor potentiators, particularly from the practical point of view.

The above data also illustrates that 5'-GMP has a greater efficiency than 5'-IMP. The relative weight efficacy of 5'-GMP to 5'-IMP is 3 - 4 to 1 (Kuninaka et al. 1964; Titus 1964; Connell 1965). This relationship between 5'-GMP and 5'-IMP was recognized not only in pure solution but also in actual food products. For example, Table 88 shows that 5'-GMP is about three times more effective than 5'-IMP in various soups. In addition, the flavor properties of 5'-GMP are qualitatively similar to that of 5'-IMP and there is no synergistic action between them.

Synergistic action is recognized not only between MSG and 5'-IMP or 5'-GMP but also between ibotenic or tricholomic acid and the 5'-nucleo-tides (Takemoto 1965; Yoshino and Suzuki 1965). For example, a mixed solution at the threshold level of tricholomic or ibotenic acid and at the threshold level of 5'-IMP or 5'-GMP has noticeable flavor activity. The flavor properties of tricholomic and ibotenic acid were qualitatively similar to that of MSG, and no synergistic action is recognized between them. It was concluded from repeated sensory tests that tricholomic acid and ibotenic acid were about five times more active than MSG in the synergistic action with 5'-nucleotides and that 5'-GMP was about four times more active than 5'-IMP in the synergistic action with tricholomic or ibotenic acid.

TABLE 88

EFFECT OF 5'- NUCLEOTIDES IN SOUP

Soup Variety	Per Cent Preference[1]	Treatment[2]
Clam chowder, cond.	65	0.06% Disodium inosinate
Beef noodle, dry	79	0.02% Disodium inosinate
Beef noodle, dry	92	0.007% Disodium guanylate
Chicken noodle, cond.	88	0.03% Disodium inosinate
Chicken noodle, cond.	90	0.01% Disodium guanylate
Chicken noodle, dry	78	0.03% Disodium inosinate
Chicken noodle, dry	87	0.01% Disodium guanylate
Mushroom, cond.	63	0.008% Disodium guanylate
Mushroom, cond.	67	0.025% Disodium inosinate
Mushroom, dry	86	0.03% Disodium inosinate
Mushroom, dry	86	0.01% Disodium guanylate
Vegetable beef, cond.	88	0.03% Disodium inosinate
Vegetable beef, cond.	82	0.01% Disodium guanylate
Beef bouillon	85	0.02% Disodium inosinate
Beef bouillon	71	0.007% Disodium guanylate

The above data are the results of three separate tests by a Merck preference panel of 19 members. Many of these results have been confirmed by other flavor testing groups in laboratories of the food processing industry. From Titus and Klis (1963) with permission,
[1] Percentage of panelists who preferred product containing 5'-nucleotides.
[2] All treatment levels expressed on an "as-served" basis.

It is now clear that 5'-IMP and 5'-GMP have the same kind of flavor potentiating activity, MSG, tricholomic acid and ibotenic acid have another kind of flavor potentiating activity, and synergistic action in regard to flavor exists between the above two groups.

The synergistic action between MSG and flavor 5'-nucleotides has also been demonstrated neurophysiologically by Kawamura et al. (1964), Sato and Akaike (1965), and Sato et al. (1965). Kawamura et al. (1964) placed a test solution on the dorsum of the tongue of a cat, analyzed the electrical response of the *chorda tympani* nerve, and found that the mixed solution of 5'-IMP and MSG induced more dominant responses than that

TABLE 89

INFLUENCE OF 5'-INOSINATE OR L-GLUTAMATE ON INTEGRATED RESPONSE OF WHOLE *Chorda Tympani* NERVE OF CAT TO TASTE COMPOUNDS

Compound	Pure Solution	Mixed Solution with 0.005M 5'-IMP·Na₂	Mixed Solution with 0.05M MSG
None	0	17	17
0.005M 5'-IMP·Na₂	17		45
0.05M MSG	17	45	
0.5M Sodium chloride	40	53	53
0.2M Acetic acid	100	100	100
0.005M Quinine	28	20	20
1M Sucrose	40	20	20

Based on results reported by Kawamura et al. (1964).

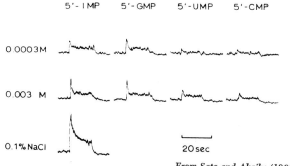

From Sato and Akaike (1965)

Fig. 107. The Integrated *Chorda Tympani* Response to Stimulation of the Rat Tongue by 5′-IMP, 5′-GMP, 5′-UMP and 5′-CMP Solutions, the Concentration of Which Is Indicated at the Left-Hand Side of Respective Records

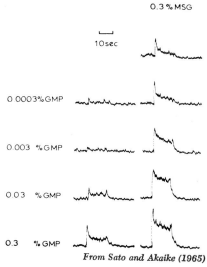

From Sato and Akaike (1965)

Fig. 108. The Integrated *Chorda Tympani* Response to Stimulation of the Rat Tongue By 0.3% MSG (Top Record), 0.0003–0.3% 5′-GMP (Records at the Left) and 0.3% MSG Solutions to Which 0.0003–0.3 gm./100 ml. 5′-GMP Was Added (Records at the Right)

of the pure solution either of 5′-IMP or MSG (Table 89). Even if the concentrations of 5′-IMP and MSG are less than threshold level, a mixture at these concentrations induces significant response.

Independently, Sato and Akaike (1965) compared the response of rat *chorda tympani* to four kinds of nucleotides (Fig. 107). The lowest concentration where the *chorda tympani* response could be recorded was about 0.001% or 0.000025M for 5'-IMP and 5'-GMP, about 0.003% or 0.00008M for uridine 5'-monophosphate (5'-UMP) and cytidine 5'-monophosphate (5'-CMP), and 0.02% for MSG. As the threshold concentrations of 5'-IMP and MSG for producing the response in a cat are 0.07 and 0.37%, respectively, rat taste receptors are extremely sensitive to 5'-nucleotides compared with those of a cat. The ratio of the magnitude of response for 0.1% solutions was 5'-GMP:5'-IMP:5'-UMP:5'-CMP = 1:0.87 : 0.55:0.44 in the sustained phase. The rat *chorda tympani* response to MSG was greatly enhanced when a very minute amount of 5'-GMP or 5'-IMP was added. For example, Fig. 108 shows that the response to 0.3% MSG was enhanced by an addition of 0.0003% 5'-GMP and that the enhancement is more marked in the sustained phase than in the initial rapid phase of the response. The enhancement of the response magnitude by 5'-nucleotides is not simply due to the addition of the responses to MSG and 5'-nucleotides, but the magnitude of response to the mixtures of MSG and of 5'-nucleotides is greater than the sum of the responses to either alone. A statistically significant enhancement or facilitation was obtained when 5'-GMP or 5'-IMP of a concentration of more than 0.003% was added to 0.3% MSG. Naturally the magnitude of response to MSG solution (0.3%) increases markedly by replacement of a part of MSG by an equal amount of 5'-GMP or 5'-IMP. It attains nearly a saturation level at 0.03% 5'-GMP or at 0.1% 5'-IMP. This fact means that in the synergistic action with MSG in rat *chorda tympani* 5'-GMP was about three times as active as 5'-IMP. When 5'-CMP or 5'-UMP was added to MSG, enhancement of the rat *chorda tympani* response was observed, but the enhancement was very small compared with that produced by 5'-IMP or 5'-GMP. No enhancement in the response magnitude was obtained either when 5'-GMP and 5'-IMP were mixed together or when 5'-IMP or 5'-GMP was mixed with 5'-UMP or 5'-CMP The results of the above neurophysiological studies are essentialy consistent with the results of our sensory tests.

In addition, the influence of temperature on response was also studied by Sato *et al.* (1965). The responses of rat *chorda tympani* to 0.03% 5'-GMP and 0.03% 5'-IMP were maximum at about 30°C., while those to 0.1% 5'-UMP, 0.1% 5'-CMP, 0.3% MSG and 0.1% sodium chloride decreased with a rise in temperature. The synergistic effect of 5'-nucleotide on the response to MSG was negligible at 10°C., but increased sharply with a rise in temperature.

OTHER FLAVOR PROPERTIES OF 5'-NUCLEOTIDES

The most important and the most basic flavor property of 5'-nucleotides is their synergistic action with MSG. Besides this, they have several specific flavor activities.

The 5'-nucleotides consistently alter certain flavor characteristics, regardless of the foods to which they are added (Titus 1964). The nucleotides enhance the following flavor notes; meaty, brothy, MSG, mouthfilling, dryness and astringency. Buttery and sweet flavors are usually not affected by the addition of nucleotides, but in some cases they are enhanced. On the other hand, the nucleotides suppress an HVP, or "hydrolyzed" flavor note and sulfury or "burnt cabbage" notes. Flavor notes such as sour, fatty and oily, starchy, burnt, and herb-spice complexes are not affected in most foods, but in those cases where these characteristics are changed by the nucleotides, they are suppressed.

Titus and Klis (1963) evaluated 5'-nucleotides as replacements for beef extract in bouillon. Replacement of beef extract by one-tenth as much 5'-IMP resulted in a product that was significantly more acceptable

TABLE 90

REPLACEMENT OF BEEF EXTRACT WITH 5'-NUCLEOTIDES IN BOUILLON

	Composition of Bouillon (Gm./4 l.)		
Ingredients	Standard	A	B
Beef extract[1]	10	7	7
5'-Nucleotides[2]	0	0.125	0.250
Other ingredients[3]	90	90	90
Preference tests[4] I	10 :	12	
II	4	:	18
III		5 :	17

Experiments by Yoshino and Suzuki (1965).
[1] Armour Brand.
[2] A 50–50 mixture of 5'-IMP·Na2 and 5'-GMP·Na2.
[3] HVP Powder distributed by Accent International 38.3 gm., yeast extract powder 9.3 gm, MSG 5.6 gm. sodium chloride 15.8 gm., cane sugar 20.2 gm., and shortening oil 0.8 gm.
[4] Three pairs of preference tests were carried out by a Yamasa panel of twenty-two members.
    Test I: No significant difference.
    Test II: B was preferred to Standard at 1% level of significance.
    Test III: B was preferred to A at 5% level of significance.
    The results indicate that 3 gm. (24 parts) of beef extract can be replaced satisfactorily by 0.125 gm. (1 part) of a 50-50 mixture of 5'-IMP·Na2 and 5'-GMP·Na2.

than the standard bouillon. We also confirmed that 24 gm. of beef extract could be replaced by 1 gm. of a 50-50 mixture of 5'-IMP and 5'-GMP in a bouillon as shown in Table 90. Thus, the flavor activity ratio in bouillon may be summarized as follows:

Beef extract:5'IMP:50—50 mixture of 5'-IMP and 5'-GMP = 1:10:24. Haldt (1965) reported that the combination of 5'-IMP, 5'-GMP and hydrolyzed plant proteins imparts a real beef flavor to gravies, sauces, soups, and other products.

According to Kawamura et al. (1964) the cat chorda tympani response to 0.5M sodium chloride solution increased slightly when 0.005M 5'-IMP or 0.05M MSG was added to the solution. The responses to 0.005M quinine and 1M sucrose solutions decreased by the addition of 0.005M

5'-IMP or 0.05M MSG. It is interesting that 0.005M 5'-IMP and 0.05M MSG gave similar effects on the responses to these compounds (Table 89).

STABILITY OF 5'-NUCLEOTIDES

Thermostability

The flavor 5'-nucleotide consists of a purine base, ribose, and phosphate. In other words, it contains a ribosidic linkage and a phosphomonoester linkage. The ribosidic linkage is more labile than the phosphomonoester linkage, and purine base is completely liberated from 5'-inosinate or 5'-guanylate by heating at 100°C. in $1N$ hydrochloric acid. Under usual cooking and storage conditions, however, 5'-IMP and 5'-GMP are rather stable (Table 91 and Fig. 109).

TABLE 91

RECOVERY OF 5'-NUCLEOTIDES AFTER STORAGE

	Recovery in Per Cent			
	One Month's Storage		Two Months' Storage	
Solvent	5'-IMP	5'-GMP	5'-IMP	5'-GMP
$N/100$ HCl	100	100	100	99.2
Water	100	100	100	100
$1N$ NaOH	100	100	100	100

Experiments by Yoshino and Suzuki (1965).
In 100 ml. of each solvent, 0.3 gm. of each 5'-nucleotide was dissolved and stored at 30°C.

Degradation of 5'-Nucleotides by Enzymes

Although the ribosidic linkage is split by nucleotide ribosidase, this enzyme has been found only in *Aspergillus* (Kuninaka 1956, 1959) and *Azotobacter* (Hurwitz *et al.* 1957). On the other hand, the phosphomonoester linkage is easily split by phosphomonoesterases. Phosphomonoesterases are distributed in various tissues of both animals and plants, and degrade 5'-IMP or 5'-GMP into inosine or guanosine and inorganic orthophosphate. Inosine or guanosine has no flavor activity even in the presence of equimolecular inorganic orthophosphate

The phosphomonoesterases do not attack 5'-nucleotides at 0°C. Therefore, it is possible to store natural food products, to which 5'-nucleotide is added, without loss of 5'-nucleotide at a temperature lower than 0°C. The phosphomonoesterases are easily inactivated by heating. Therefore, 5'-nucleotides added to heated food products are not destroyed enzymatically.

It was confirmed that 5'-GMP and 5'-IMP were stable in chicken soup

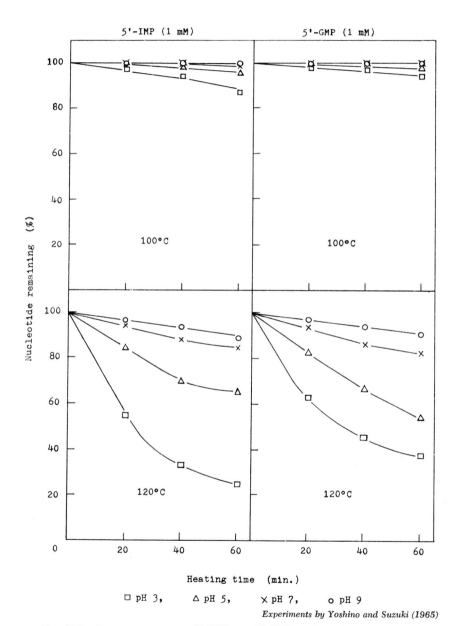

FIG. 109.   DECOMPOSITION OF 5'-IMP AND 5'-GMP AT VARIOUS PH VALUES

stocks of different water content: To 100 gm. of each powder soup (water content, 2.2%), cubic soup (water content, 12.5%) and canned soup (water content, 86%) 0.1 to 0.2 gm. of a 50-50 mixture of 5'-IMP and 5'-GMP was added. The soup stocks were stored at 20°C., and analyzed after 1, 2, and 3 months with the result that the nucleotides remained without significant loss in each soup stock after the storage.

In addition, 5'-nucleotides are less hygroscopic than MSG.

APPLICATION OF 5'-NUCLEOTIDES AS FLAVOR POTENTIATORS

As mentioned previously, there is a synergistic relationship between MSG and the flavor nucleotides, 5'-IMP and 5'-GMP. As a small amount of 5'-IMP and/or 5'-GMP markedly enhances the flavor activity of MSG, the 5'-nucleotides can greatly spare the MSG requirements of many foods. In general, a blend of 90 to 95 parts of MSG and 10 to 5 parts of 5'-nucleotides can be used effectively to potentiate the flavor of various kinds of food products, although the 5'-nucleotides alone can also be applied to foods which contain a rather large amount of L-glutamate.

In animal muscle tissues, 5'-IMP is formed from adenosine triphosphate. Thus, the 5'-IMP content of raw meats is usually rather high, and 5'-IMP is regarded as one of the most important flavor components in meats. This is the reason why 5'-nucleotides can be used to replace beef extract. However, the 5'-IMP content of processed meat products is usually rather low, because raw meats contain phosphomonoesterase and 5'-IMP present in meat originally is easily lost in several processing steps such as thawing, washing, and salting. The 5'-nucleotides added together with MSG after the above steps can be preserved without loss and improve the flavor of the meat products effectively, if the products are heated before or right after addition of the 5'-nucleotides.

According to Titus (1964), the profile panel recommended the use of the 5'-nucleotides in soups, gravies, bouillons, certain canned meats, fish, and vegetables, tomato juice, and instant coffee. The levels used in soups varied from product to product but usually fell in the range of 50 to 200 p.p.m. of 5'-IMP, or 25 to 100 p.p.m. of a mixture of 5'-IMP and 5'-GMP. The improvement of the flavor of dried noodle soup by the nucleotide was recognized actually in a consumer home-use test (Caul and Raymond 1964). Connell (1965) also reported that the effect of 5'-GMP and 5'-IMP was being proved in a wide range of North American foods.

The 5'-nucleotides, one of which was reported to be a flavor component of a special Japanese food 50 years ago, are now attaining world-wide recognition as unique flavor potentiators.

DISCUSSION

R. W. Moncrieff.—Can you describe the taste of MSG in terms of the four orthodox tastes. I have tasted MSG and have tried to assign it to one of the four orthodox tastes such as sour, salt, sweet, and bitter and have been quite unable to describe its taste adequately in those terms.

A. Kuninaka.—No I can not, only it tastes like MSG.

N. R. Jones.—I wonder could you comment on Hashimoto and Yunow's report last year that shellfish, which as you will recollect does not contain an adenosine monophosphate deaminase, tastes meaty. They find that deamination at the 6 position, that is the substitution of a hydroxyl for an amino in the 6 position, is not necessary. They find, in fact, that adenosine triphosphate, adenosine diphosphate, and adenosine monophosphate all act synergistically together with the glutamates of various fish extracts. The glutamate is presumably at the level of about 10 mg. per 100 gm. tissue. The nucleotide would be at the level of about 0.2% I would say.

A. Kuninaka.—Several fish do not have this enzyme. AMP accumulates after death. 5'-AMP has flavor activity, and there is a synergistic action between 5'-AMP and MSG. However, GMP and IMP are much more effective than AMP.

T. M. Lukes.—I am curious about the toxicity of the tricholomic acid and ibotenic acids isolated from a fungi?

A Kuninaka.—It is a very important problem. Tricholomic acid and ibotenic acid were isolated from the fungi that in Japanese means the fly-killing fungi. These compounds have strong fly-killing activity, and also they have flavor activity. In Japan, their toxicity is being very carefully studied.

M. Skellenger.—One of our more common therapeutic diets here is a low-sodium diet. Are these flavor potentiators low enough in sodium to be used, or has someone tried some of them made with another salt, perhaps a potassium salt instead of monosodium glutamate?

A. Kuninaka.—Monopotassium or monoammonium glutamate have almost the same flavor activity as monosodium glutamate.

S. Miladi.—Is glutamic acid itself, say at a low pH, a potentiator?

A. Kuninaka.—The flavor activity of glutamic acid is dependent on pH. Glutamic acid has little flavor activity.

BIBLIOGRAPHY

CAUL, J. F., and RAYMOND, S. A. 1964. Home-use test by consumers of the flavor effects of disodium inosinate in dried soup. Food Technol. *18,* 353–357.

CONNELL, J. E. 1965. Nucleotides pack a powerful punch as flavor enhancers. Food in Canada 25, No. 6, 30–32.

FUJITA, E., YASUMATSU, K., BICHU, S., and UDA, Y. 1964. *Cited by* A. Kuninaka, M. Kibi, and K. Sakaguchi. History and development of flavor nucleotides Food Technol. *18,* 287–293.

HALDT, H. P. 1965. Replaces beef extract economically. Food Proc. *26,* No. 6, 136–137.

HONJO, M., IMAI, K., FURUKAWA, Y., MORIYAMA, H., YASUMATSU, K., and IMADA, A. 1963. Synthesis of compounds related to inosine 5'-monophosphate and their flavor enhancing property. Ann. Rept. Takeda Res. Lab. *22,* 47–58.

Hosoi, T. 1961. Bloodsucking activity of mosquitoes and adenosine phosphate. Protein, Nucleic Acid, Enzyme (Tanpakushitsu, Kakusan, Koso) 6, 115–118.

Hurwitz, J., Heppel, L. A., and Horecker, B. L. 1957. The enzymatic cleavage of adenylic acid to adenine and ribose 5-phosphate. J. Biol. Chem. 226, 525–540.

Ikeda, K. 1909. On a new seasoning. J. Tokyo Chem. Soc. (Tokyo Kagaku Kaishi) 30, 820–836.

Kawamura, Y., Adachi, A., Ohara, M., and Ikeda, S. 1964. Neurophysiological studies on taste effectiveness of flavor enhancing substances. Symposium on Amino Acid and Nucleic Acid (Aminosan Kakusan) 10, 168–178.

Kodama, S. 1913. On a procedure for separating inosinic acid. J. Tokyo Chem. Soc. (Tokyo Kagaku Kaishi) 34, 751–757.

Kuninaka, A. 1956. Studies on the decomposition of nucleic acid by microorganisms. 5. On the enzymatic degradation of inosinic acid by Aspergillus oryzae. J. Agr. Chem. Soc. Japan (Nippon Nogeikagaku Kaishi) 30, 583–588.

Kuninaka, A. 1957. Enzymic degradation of yeast ribonucleic acid and its related compounds by Aspergillus oryzae. J. Gen. Appl. Microbiol. 3, 55–92.

Kuninaka, A. 1959. Studies on the decomposition of nucleic acid by microorganisms. 6. On the ribosidase of Aspergillus oryzae acting on 6-hydroxypurine ribonucleosides and their 5'-monophosphates. Bull. Agr. Chem. Soc. Japan 23, 281–288.

Kuninaka, A. 1960. Studies on taste of ribonucleic acid derivatives. J. Agr. Chem. Soc. Japan (Nippon Nogeikagaku Kaishi) 34, 489–492.

Kuninaka, A., Kibi, M., and Sakaguchi, K. 1964. History and development of flavor nucleotides. Food Technol. 18, 287–293.

Kuninaka, A., Kibi, M., Yoshino, H., and Sakaguchi, K. 1961. Studies on 5'-phosphodiesterases in microorganisms. 2. Properties and application of Penicillium citrinum 5'-phosphodiesterase. Agr. Biol Chem. 25, 693–701.

Kuninaka, A., Otsuka, S., Kobayashi, Y., and Sakaguchi, K. 1959. Studies on 5'-phosphodiesterases in microorganisms. 1. Formation of nucleoside 5'-monophosphates from yeast ribonucleic acid by Penicillium citrinum. Bull. Agr. Chem. Soc. Japan 23, 239–243.

Nakao, Y., and Ogata, K. 1963. Cited by Honjo, M., Imai K., Furukawa, Y., Moriyama, H., Yasumatsu, K., and Imada, A. 1963. Synthesis of compounds related to inosine 5'-monophosphate and their flavor enhancing property. Ann. Rept. Takeda Res. Lab. 22, 47–58.

Sato, M., and Akaike, N. 1965. 5'-Ribonucleotides as gustatory stimuli in rats, electrophysiological studies. Jap. J. Physiol. 15, 53–70.

Sato, M., Akaike, N., and Yamashita, S. 1965. Electrophysiological studies on the effects of ribonucleotides on taste receptors of rats. Effects of the addition of ribonucleotides to MSG and of temperature. Symposium on Amino Acids and Nucleic Acids (Aminosan Kakusan) 11, 53–61.

Sjöström, L. B. 1965. Potentiators and non-carbohydrates. Abstracts of Papers, 149th Meeting Am. Chem. Soc. 29C–30C.

Takemoto, T. 1965. Private communication.

Takemoto, T., and Nakajima, T. 1964A. Studies on the constituents of indigenous fungi. 1. Isolation of the flycidal constituent from Tricholoma muscarium. J. Pharm Soc. Japan (Yakugaku Zasshi) 84, 1183–1186.

TAKEMOTO, T., and NAKAJIMA, T. 1964B. Structure of tricholomic acid. J. Pharm. Soc. Japan (Yakugaku Zasshi) *84*, 1230–1232.

TAKEMOTO, T., NAKAJIMA, T., and SAKUMA, R. 1964A. Isolation of a flycidal constituent "ibotenic acid" from *Amanita muscaria* and *A. pantherina*. J. Pharm. Soc. Japan (Yakugaku Zasshi) *84*, 1233–1234.

TAKEMOTO, T., NAKAJIMA, T. and YOKOBE, T. 1964B. Structure of ibotenic acid. J. Pharm. Soc. Japan (Yakugaku Zasshi) *84*, 1232–1233.

TAKEMOTO, T., YOKOBE, T., and NAKAJIMA, T. 1964C. Studies on the constituents of indigenous fungi. 2. Isolation of the flycidal constituent from *Amanita strobiliformis*. J. Pharm. Soc. Japan (Yakugaku Zasshi) *84*, 1186–1188.

TITUS, D. S. 1964. The nucleotide story. *In* Symposium on Flavor Potentiation. Arthur D. Little, Inc., Cambridge, Mass.

TITUS, D. S., and KLIS, J. B. 1963. Product improvement with new flavor enhancers. Food Proc. *24*, No. 5, 150–152.

TOI, B., MAEDA, S., IKEDA, S., and FURUKAWA, H. 1964. *Cited by* A. Kuninaka, M. Kibi and K. Sakaguchi. History and development of flavor nucleotides. Food Technol. *18*, 287–293.

WAGNER, J. R., TITUS, D. S., and SCHADE, J. E. 1963. New opportunities for flavor modification. Food Technol. *17*, 730–735.

YOSHINO, H., and SUZUKI, M. 1965. Personal communication.

Summary of Symposium—
Panel Discussion

SUMMARY OF SYMPOSIUM—PANEL DISCUSSION

M. E. Stansby.—I would like to make a comment. A few years ago at a meeting on flavor, I think it would not have been surprising to have heard papers in which a lot of GLC curves would have been given, but with no mention of flavor, just the assumption that this must have something to do with flavor. I think we have progressed beyond this point to the stage where a lot of attention is being given to correlation between these substances and flavor. I think as some of the speakers have indicated, notably Mr. Forss, that this experimental work is getting almost out of hand, where we are just automatically collecting a lot of data. We need some fresh approaches to this matter, where more imagination is used. Now, one such approach which I was glad to see mentioned in Dr. Day's presentation deals with the effect of different dilutions of odors, where very often a very critical narrow range of odor will be found at a certain concentration, but below and above this, there is no such odor. It would appear that there might be, as Dr. Day pointed out, some kind of a tie-up between the particular odor that has been isolated by GLC and perhaps the protein or lipid in the material; there may be an equilibrium giving the desirable narrow range of odor. It seems to me this is the type of research that is needed. I wonder if the members of the panel might be able to suggest other areas along this line?

E. A. Day.—I think the absorption of these materials in the food would certainly have an effect upon the vapor pressure. I am not in a position to tell you how to set up good experiments to follow this.

H. W. Schultz.—Many of you, of course, know the classical experiment of quinine solution in gum arabic. In making prescriptions, a gum is used in the prescription along with some very flavorful or obnoxious material, so, for example, the level of quinine taste is lowered simply by this admixture without reducing the effectiveness of the quinine.

I. Hornstein.—There was some talk about the fact that so many people were finding the same compounds and there was a suggestion that perhaps what we needed was to determine the threshold values say in water, oil, and in various mixtures. The thought occurred to me that this was too big a job for any one person. Could this be done somehow on a group basis in some systematic fashion? Perhaps the committee would like to discuss that.

D. A. Forss.—Some very good work has been done at Albany on this sort of thing. If more of it could be done, it would be a great thing. It is helpful in making calculations but; of course, there is a limit to how far you can calculate.

E. A. Day.—This might be something that ASTM or IFT could organize by setting up standard methods that could be followed by all laboratories in accumulating data.

536

T. J. Siek.—Several groups of researchers have provided evidence that milk lipids contain glucose and galactose covalently bound to phospholipids. That is, they are reporting phosphatidyl choline galactoside and phosphatidyl serine galactoside. Do you have any opinions whether or not carbohydrates or sugars are covalently bound in phospholipids, or are the reports due to the contamination of carbohydrates with the phospholipids, which is what usually has been said about this. If sugars are bound covalently in the phospholipids, would this perhaps lead to some aldehyde through degradation of the sugars rather than by oxidative pathways?

J. E. Hodge.—I think carbohydrates have been shown to be covalently bound to the ethanolamine as N-glycosides in phosphatides. We had a lecture this spring on the subject and the lecturer indicated that the galactoside residues are bonded to the phosphatides.

E. A. Day.—I would like to ask Mr. Hodge, could this be responsible for the browning of phospholipids?

J. E. Hodge.—I do not know, but I would think so.

C. D. Evans.—Dr. Stansby called for more imagination in one respect, but I would like to see a little less imagination maybe in the description of flavors. Is there any possibility of setting up something as a standard, because I think the oil people are well aware of the various differences found in such a simple thing as an oil. I would like to see if any correlation could be made between size and shape as was mentioned in the discussion, and how this changes with either concentration or chain length.

R. W. Moncrieff.—I do not know if the question can be answered in the terms that you have suggested, but there is no doubt at all that you can define odors by their adsorption characteristics. If, for example, you have six films and you find the heat of adsorption on these separately, you then obtain six figures which give you perhaps a million possibilities. If you take different odorants and you take enough of these, perhaps 6, 8, or 10, then you can get unique sets of numbers for each odorant. Another possible approach to the problem, is that you can assess the likeness of two odors by a method that I described some years ago in the *Journal of Physiology* in a paper entitled "Adaptation and Odor Likeness." The basis of it is, if you have an odor A and another odor B, and if these two are similar to each other, the adaptation caused by B for A will be nearly as great as that caused by A for itself. That is, the cross-adaptation of two odorants that have similar odors will be nearly as great as the homogenous self-adaptation. So that it will be possible to arrive at a numerical assessment of the likeness of any two odors. If you take perhaps 10 or even 20 as standard odors then you can define the likeness of any given odor to these standards.

L. Calvin.—Does this assume that these odors are on a single or a multiple scale? If they are on a single scale it is fine, but what do you do on multiple scales?

R. W. Moncrieff.—I am afraid I do not understand the question. Perhaps if I say it again, it may clarify it. If, for example, you have ethyl alcohol, you can measure the likeness of it to methyl alcohol. If you have completely similar substances, that is identical substances, you have a likeness coefficient of unity; substances that are completely dissimilar will have a likeness coefficient of 0. The likeness of ethyl alcohol and methyl alcohol would probably be in the region of 0.40. If you consider the two esters, amyl acetate and butyl acetate, which are extremely similar, you would find that the likeness coefficient is 0.89. If, on the other hand, you take two substances which have no apparent similarity at all, they usually have little adaptation for each other, and the likeness coefficient will be around 0.05 or 0.03.

L. Calvin.—I am still a little concerned with the problem of unlikeness. Things can be alike in only one way, they can be unalike in many, many ways. I am a little concerned about how to measure this degree of dissimilarity rather than the degree of similarity.

R. W. Moncrieff.—If you say two odorants are quite similar then you have your cross-adaptation, which is the same as self-adaptation. If they are completely dissimilar then there is no cross-adaptation at all, although there will be self-adaptation. I do not quite see the difficulties.

D. A. Kendall.—Many of the papers have discussed flavor in regard to the volatile components. We have seen, at least in one instance, that salt can change the constitution of the volatile components in a vegetable. I think we are all familiar with some of the materials such as the potentiators that change flavor perception. Therefore, are not we missing something in relegating all of flavor to the aromatic constituents and the low boilers? Does not it make sense to pay some attention to the so-called nonvolatile residues that we leave behind in the pots, at least for screening their overall flavor effect?

M. Gianturco.—Going back to the question posed by Dr. Hornstein concerning the importance or the value of all the components we are finding in various foods. I can see this as a monumental job which needs to be done somehow. I suppose that one could take a wine, de-flavorize it somehow, and add all the components that Professor Webb has reported to be present in wine and find out the possible importance of the various components. The same could be done for other foodstuffs, but this job seems to be a tremendous undertaking. I was wondering whether the statistician, Dr. Calvin, could illuminate us on how statistics might perhaps help in assigning experiments of this type.

L. Calvin.—I think the hardest job here is to define just exactly what is to be done. Once the food researchers and chemists have decided what they wish to have accomplished, it is a matter of sitting down and deciding who can do it best, or who can do it most efficiently. This perhaps is one way. Another way is for every laboratory, every research group, to work by themselves. I think what is wanted is a more organized method of solving these problems. One method, as I would see it, which has been suggested by both of you, is that some group, perhaps IFT or some other organization, would look at the overall problem, make some assignments and priorities, and then ask or work with certain groups to see who would study particular problems. I think the statistical task of drawing these results together does need some looking into, but I think that it is somewhat secondary to assigning priorities and getting the work done.

M. Gianturco.—I am wondering whether our most serious problem would be to get people to agree on what the medium should be for testing these various compounds. Should the base be water, an aqueous solution of carbohydrates, oil, or possibly all of them.

E. A. Day.—On any one specific product it is up to the group working on the product to put it back together. Someway or other you will have to decide where to start, selecting the major components in the mixture and try to get an estimate of the approximate concentrations employed and begin to put these together. I would suggest that you use a medium similar to what you expect to use it in. If it is coffee then I would try to assimilate a medium similar to coffee as the starting material. If it is cheese then we could use cottage cheese as a base. There may be some way of programming this through statistics to select the compounds that are significant statistically.

H. W. Schultz.—I recall several years ago the canning industry was having difficulty with pesticide flavor analysis and it was believed that the problem stemmed from the fact that each laboratory, where flavor testing was being done, was using somewhat different techniques of panel studies. Therefore, the National Canner's Association set up a program in which they examined the panel procedures. I think there were 10, 11, or 12 laboratories that participated in this, and out of it came some conclusions for modifying procedures, which have worked out very well. Maybe we are seeing the symptoms here of a problem; this large number of compounds having been introduced into our flavor literature, and we see it as a conglomerate. Perhaps there is a problem which we will call "the problem" and someone has to sit down and decide what this may be. We need to define "the problem" and I think the discussion between statisticians and the scientists or the chemists would be futile unless they could come to terms as to what they are trying to arrive at; what is "the problem," or the goal?

SUMMARY OF SYMPOSIUM

K. B. Döving.—As a summary I would like to emphasize the areas of olfactory research which are presently productive and offer opportunities for expansion. One subject in the field of olfaction which I find most important is what properties of the odorous molecules determine their threshold and their quality. One way of studying their quality may be to get measurements of their similarity. One way of doing this is the so-called cross-adaptation. Another way is to let people make scalar judgements of the similarity. Amoore, doing this, used five compounds as references, but personally I feel that it is necessary to compare all of them with each other; with 107 odors that makes only 5671 pairs. I have tried to give you a picture of the electrophysiological estimates of similarities.

The next point I wish to discuss is the areas of research which could be productive and contribute significantly to out knowledge, but which presently receive too little attention. First we know very little about the composition of the cell membranes of the olfactory receptors. Very little is known about the structures that are responsible for the sensations at the receptor. They may be lipid membranes and we do know that small differences in the contents of steroids in the lipid membranes change their properties. I think that it is a field which should be emphasized. In the field of olfactory research it would also be advantageous to have a closer working relationship between chemists studying flavors and scientists working on the physiology of flavor. To work out the structures and properties of the odorous molecules and find out what makes them smell differently, we have to rely on the chemists. Another thing the chemists can do, is to select the appropriate odors for experiments which could yield more fruitful results.

W. G. Jennings.—I think intuitively that we are going to find as we get into this, that the flavor of food commodities in a very few cases, may be attributable to 1, 2, or 3 compounds. In the vast majority of cases, we are going to find that it is due to the interaction of a whole host of compounds, and the concentrations of these things become quite critical to the type of flavor that you may develop. There has been all too little attention given to the interactions of these things and the quantitative aspects of the various volatiles that do occur. This brings a chemist to a very dangerous point, because we prepare an essence for gas chromatography, inject it into a chromatograph, and hope we are looking at a spectrum of compounds in the ratios in which they occurred in the original commodity, and this is almost never true. Anytime we resort to a distillation technique we are going to change these ratios, and these ratios are going to be important. Anytime we resort to an extraction technique, the compounds will have different coefficients of distribution among the various phases. All we have to do is change the temperature and we will change the distribution, and not necessarily in the same directions. I think we have to give a great deal of attention to the quantitative aspects of the volatiles in a flavor and then we have to put our own house in order and find some way of trying to relate the things we are looking at on a chromatograph to the ratios in which these occur in the commodity itself.

D. A. Forss.—I would like you to imagine that you are an administrator in Washington with very little scientific knowledge and to try and estimate whether you would go ahead with a particular flavor project, perhaps taking into account the proceedings of this conference. In other words, are we going to get something out of it? I have two themes that I will develop very quickly. One is, it seems to me, that we are trying to make foods more attractive and we can do this by finding out what constitutes flavor, perhaps adding this back synthetically, and also, perhaps learning how flavors are formed and then making the reactions go the way we want them to go. Even so, I feel a little dissatisfied at the present. Are we really getting where we ought to go? I am not answering this question, I am just putting it to you. The other thing is again from an administrator's point of view. As something of a world traveler, I have been to many countries and perhaps in only one or two places in the whole world and even then only to some extent, are they really equipped to do flavor work easily. Perhaps in Holland at Dr. Keppler's laboratory and perhaps in this country at the Albany laboratory they seem to be fairly well equipped for the isolation and identification of flavors. For the sensory evaluation of flavors, I am not so sure and for the study of mechanisms, I am even less certain. What are we going to do about it? Should all the smaller units stop, should we form large units, should the smaller units merely try certain simple types of experiments with perhaps a GC and essentially their nose? I can not answer that but I am deeply disturbed about the present situation and the way a lot of flavor research is being carried out. This is somewhat negative, I know, but perhaps someone else will comment.

E. A. Day.—It might be nice to have a center some place where we could combine the abilities of the physiologists, neurophysiologists, physical chemists, etc., and do something about this. But that was not what I was going to mention. Areas of research which are presently productive and offer opportunities for emphasis and expansion was the first point. This is an area to which I think many of our efforts at Oregon State have been directed. Our objectives have always been in the work that we have done, in what are the compounds, how are they formed and how are they destroyed. If you can answer these three points you are approaching the point where you can control the flavor in a food material. I think we are equipped in many cases to answer these questions. We are finding out what many of the compounds are, in many cases we are proceeding to learn how they are formed, and also how they are destroyed. The next step is to proceed to employ our knowledge in the handling of our food supply. The second point was areas of research which could be more productive and contribute significantly to knowledge, but which are presently receiving too little attention. I would have to reiterate what Dr. Jennings has said on quantitative analysis. I think this is the next step, even though it is going to be very laborious. The flavor panel work will have to be expanded in order to use this information, and new statistical techniques and approaches will be used to simplify the problem. The last point was areas of research which could be advantageous in having a closer working relationship between the chemists and the physiologists. The relationship of structure to odor intensity and also discrimination of odors is a very important area to be explored in such a cooperative effort. There is something peculiar about synergism. Why do two compounds, if you assume they stimulate the receptor and you get an impulse to the brain, why is there a quantitative relationship when you put the two compounds together; it takes less material to get the same effect. I think this is something that Dr. Döving's group could assist us in.

L. Calvin.—I think I have been at an advantage over the rest of you in that I did not know as much when I came about these subjects as you did, so I have been able to learn a lot more. One of the things that interested me very much because of some of the statistical work that is going on in the analysis of chromatographic data, was the comment about the volatile substances and the odors between the peaks. At the present time, the techniques are primarily looking at peaks; and if we also obtain very much information between the peaks, then we are going to have to revise our statistical techniques also. I do not quite know what we are going to do about it. Maybe it is a matter of resolution, I am not sure. If it is, one of the ways to get at this, as suggested by Dr. Teranishi, is to get better resolution by hooking up a computer and essentially getting rid of the measurement error. However, this gets rid of only one type of error. Due to variations in a sample we also need repetition or replication to get rid of another type of error. Replication is sometimes difficult, but I think this is the type of variation that we have to look at. Another point, I think of flavor as something in addition to chemical compounds; primarily the interaction between these compounds and the human beings who are doing the tasting. If flavor is this interaction, then we also have this interaction of product or material and the consumer. I think we need a lot more work in this particular area. I know it is easy to say flavor, meaning these compounds, but these compounds do not mean a thing until they get to the person. It is a little like the old teenage question of what is noise—is it noise if a tree falls down in the forest, or do you have to have somebody there to hear it? I think we need to look at the same things. Mr. Moncrieff has mentioned some of the age effects, and Dr. Webb mentioned wines, and we know that certain wines do go better with particular foods. Why do we have this interaction of these things upon the consumer himself? These are some of the things that I think are going to encourage more teamwork between the physiologists and the chemists and others working in the foods field.

R. W. Moncrieff.—The thing that seems to be most evident from the proceedings of this conference is that the science of flavor has entered a new phase. Within the last few years there has been a push-through, not exactly a breakthrough, which has come rather gradually. What was a science a few years ago which was very short of experimental data is now a science which has a surplus of it. The two new techniques which have been discussed at this conference have given in the case of the gas chromatograph and related instruments, an overwhelming volume of new knowledge about the chemical constituents that are driven off from odorous substances. One point I would like to make is I think as much attention might be given to what is left. Why are we concentrating almost exslusively on what can be distilled away? There are reasons for this, but it would be interesting still to consider what is left of flavor. The other technique is the electron microscope which has given us so many details that the detail exceeds our capacity to assign functions to it. There are two points about these techniques that seem to me to merit more attention than they have received up to now. That is, the people who practice them should make it very clear to the other scientists what the limitations are and what the possible dangers are. I have been told by a man doing electron microscopy and making some remarkable pictures that it is full of pitfalls and one has to be very careful indeed. I think attention ought to be given to the possibility of these artifacts. The odd thing, too, about the gas chromatograms, whether they come from potato or from flour or whatever it is, many of the compounds are very similar. The two new techniques have given us a mass of information and probably it will take us some years to digest it. As far as this conference goes several people have already said "I have learned a lot here." I have asked several people and they say, "Yes, I have learned at lot." And I say, "could you have learned it anywhere else? Could you have learned it from books, could you have gone to libraries?" They say, "No, it would be impossible." If you get 200 people and they all come and learn and enrich their appreciation of the subject, and if you could not do it in any other way, and if at the same time you direct attention to those parts of the science where we do need more information, I do not see how you could do more. You have 200 people who have enriched their knowledge and who could not have done it in any other way. The last note I would like to mention just before I leave, is that there is a lot that we still cannot understand and there are some things that I do not think we shall be able to understand within a reasonable time. The first problem that still completely defeats us is why the arrival of messages in the form of electric pulses to the cortex of the brain should evoke consciousness. The final act, the conversion of the integrated electric messages into sensation is still mysterious. It does not matter whether the messages relate to olfaction, taste, flavor, hearing, vision, or touch—this final act is still a mystery. An act going on through man's conscious life and making his consciousness, and yet completely incomprehensible to him. A century ago the great biologist, Thomas Huxley, in the terminology of his time said to his hearers: "The thoughts to which I am now giving utterance, and your thoughts regarding these, are the expression of molecular changes in that matter of life which is the source of our other vital phenomena." In 1940, nearly a century later, Sherrington more recently put it, referring to Huxley's words:

> The concomitance in time and place between the molecular changes and the thoughts is still all we have correlating the two. Regarded as a paradox, it has become more intriguing. Regarded as a gap in knowledge, more urgent.

A century ago the gap lay between molecules and thoughts. Now it lies between electric pulses and thoughts. A century hence it will lie between something else and thoughts. The terminology will be different, but the gap will be the same.

Index